Looking inside a Louisville Steam Tube Rotary Dryer. The steam tubes line the inner wall of a rotating cylindrical shell which has a horizontal axis and rotates around this axis. The material to be dried enters at one end, is tumbled about as the cylinder rotates, and comes out dry at the other end. A slow current of air travels countercurrent to the material. (By special arrangement with General American Transportation Corporation, Process Equipment Division, Chicago 90, Illinois.)

CHEMICAL PROCESS MACHINERY

Second Edition

by

EMIL RAYMOND RIEGEL, PH.D.

Professor of Chemistry, Emeritus
University of Buffalo
Author of "Industrial Chemistry"

BOOK DIVISION

REINHOLD PUBLISHING CORPORATION

330 West 42nd St., New York 36, N. Y.

Also Publishers of Chemical Engineering Catalog, Chemical Materials Catalog, Materials & Methods—the Magazine of Materials Engineering; Advertising Management for American Chemical Society

1953

DEDICATED TO THE MEMORY OF

FRANCIS MILLS TURNER

VICE PRESIDENT, REINHOLD PUBLISHING CORPORATION,
WHOSE FERTILE MIND CONCEIVED THIS BOOK
AND WHOSE UNFLAGGING INTEREST
HELPED MAKE IT A REALITY

PREFACE TO THE SECOND EDITION

In the present book "Chemical Process Machinery," the organization of the subject matter which had been adopted in the first edition, entitled "Chemical Machinery," remains unchanged. Like its predecessor, this volume is meant to be an exhibit of the devices which are obtainable in the open market, some from stock, others and more generally by casting, assembling or manufacturing from standard designs placed at the disposal of the customer. To any one not familiar with the remarkable resources of machinery and accessories designed, developed, and to a certain degree, perfected for services in the chemical industries, it is a series of show windows, in which the reader is invited to "shop" at his leisure. All the material has been reexamined; new descriptions and items included; obsolete matter has been dropped.

For each group of related devices, a classification in tabular form is offered, a feature which was novel in the first edition, and is continued in this one. The numerical examples have been continued, some of them in altered form, mainly because they permit the spreading of much information in least space, and partly because the earlier ones were well received. Thanks to the prices graciously furnished by many manufacturers the reader can form an idea of the cost of an installation, and decide, for example, whether the expenditure involved is within the range of possibility. The prices are given solely to serve as guides; they are subject to change at any time.

Among the material included for the first time in this edition are the following: two crushers not previously described; a newly designed ball mill; numerous magnetic separators and related devices depending upon permanent magnets rather than upon electromagnets; a new closed belt conveyor which travels like a rope; multispheres for withstanding pressure yet built of relatively thin plate; several developments in chemical pump design and materials of construction; a pitot tube set to work in a proportional feeder; the Lapp Pulsafeeder; tubeaxial and vaneaxial fans more clearly defined and described; the multiclone; the startling P-A cyclonic scrubber and P-A Venturi scrubber; an entirely new treatment of the Mixing of Liquids; the Electro-Matic air filter; the string discharge rotary vacuum drum filter, and the panel type drum suction filter; a whole line of continuously operating centrifuges, as centrifugal filters, separators, and clarifiers, fourteen in all; a self-supporting evaporator, low temperature evaporators, Flat Plate heating surface evaporators; continuous crystallizers which also classify; a turbo-drier with rotating shelves and continuous operation; a new treatment of the fundamentals of distillation and fractionation; novel bubble cap and tray construction; molecular distillation; absorption refrigeration, in which water is the refrigerant and lithium bromide the absorbant; new methods for temperature and other measurements and for automatic control. Drawings and photographs have been reproduced in profusion; in 718 pages of text, there are 597 figures. Tables number over 92.   ·

The author was again fortunate in finding strong support on the part of distinguished specialists in the preparation and shaping of the material for the several chapters. Without this support, the preparation of the book would have not been possible. For their intimate collaboration the author is indebted to the following engineers: to D. J. Van Marle, for two chapters, those on Driers and on Evaporators; to Eugene D. Murphy for contributions to the chapter on the production of vacuum; to Dr. James Y. Oldshue, on Mixing of Liquids; to Bruce W. Ellis, for suggestions and advice on pumps; to Dr. Hal B. Coats, for his searching analysis of the science of distillation, and all the original sketches illustrating the chapter; to Guy Harcourt, for a review of Heating and Cooling, and valuable all-around criticism; and to Albert E. Criqui for his review on Fans. For the chapters 25, 26 and 27, the author was fortunate to enlist the services of Douglas M. Considine, who prepared the text of these chapters as well as almost all the numerous illustrations in them.

At all stages of the work, the author has had the friendly and efficient backing of his editor, G. G. Hawley, and of his staff. To Miss Jeanne Bergquist especially, the technical editor in charge of this book, he hereby expresses his thanks for her patience and skill in handling hundreds of baffling details.

Comments and suggestions from readers will be welcomed at all times.

EMIL RAYMOND RIEGEL.

Westbrook, Connecticut
March 30, 1953

CONTENTS

There are three parts to the foundation of chemical industry: chemical science, engineering, and economics. None can be divorced entirely from the others, and additional fields of knowledge and study must be drawn upon. In the science of plant location, for example, the fields involved are geography, geology, transportation, climatology, housing, and others.

1. INTRODUCTION; CHOICE OF PLANT SITE

The order in which the devices described in this volume are arranged is meant to follow the sequence of events in the chemical plant. From the stock pile or quarry, solid raw materials go to crushers, grinders, and screens, and then by conveyors to the reaction vessels. For liquid raw materials, the storage tank is the starting point, after which pumps, and perhaps proportioning devices, are required. The same is true of gases, which must be propelled, cooled, and washed; occasionally, volatile solvents must be recovered from them within the plant. Materials must be mixed, liquids as well as solids; at other stages, solids must be separated from liquids by filtration or otherwise. Solutions of solids must be evaporated, crystallized and the crystals dried; mixtures of liquids, on the other hand, are usually separated by distillation. Auxiliary equipment, vacuum-producing devices, heat exchangers, and reaction vessels, especially kettles, are required in many of these operations, as well as numerous types of instruments for process measurement and control. Equipment for performing all these varied and specialized functions is discussed in approximately the order indicated.

Not only may the devices described herein be purchased singly from a given manufacturer, but often several units, forming an assembly well fitted for the operation in mind, are obtainable from the same manufacturer. For example, the buyer may purchase the necessary power pump or an accumulator system, with the hydraulic press or presses respectively which he needs. Such a grouping together is advantageous to both buyer and seller; the buyer has less correspondence, less visiting to do, and he looks to a single firm for the proper performance of the devices; the seller, on the other hand, knows more exactly what service may be confidently expected from the several parts of the assembly. This principle is carried so far that one may order a complete plant for a given chemical and leave all designing and constructing to the contracting firm. Thus a manufacturer who uses sulfuric acid but does not otherwise specialize in manufacturing acids may order a sulfuric acid plant, which will be erected on the site he chooses and turned over to him in working order, with trained and instructed operators, all without any attention on the part of the buyer.

There are many other products for the manufacture of which plants

1

may be ordered in a similar fashion; for the erection of the latter the seller assumes all responsibility. One prominent firm offers to install complete plants for the manufacture of industrial alcohol, isopropanol, methanol, and by-product acetic acid from acetate rayon processes, to name only the first four items out of a list of 39; also complete plants for the production of toluene and aromatic extracts, aviation gasoline, and butadiene—three items of a list of 17 petroleum products. It should be mentioned that very often such plants are erected as extensions of existing, already otherwise well equipped installations. Another firm offers to install complete plants for the manufacture of crude dynamite or C. P. grade glycerin, for deodorizing vegetable and other edible oils, or for hydrogenating oils, to mention only three of 15 items. Complete water-treating plants may be erected and handed over in working order to the purchaser. There is at least one firm which will erect from the ground up, anywhere in the world, a plant for the extraction of raw sugar from sugar cane, and undertake the necessary financing as well. There are many firms ready and well equipped to erect complete plants for the distillation of alcohols. Several large equipment manufacturers have long been handling the complete construction of complicated petroleum refining plants.

The main need in chemical engineering equipment, however, continues to be the requirement for single devices for the extension, replacement or modernization of an existing process, to fit specifications written by the plant engineer. Available to the purchaser are the engineering skill, talent, and information of the manufacturer. It is unwise not to take advantage of this knowledge, for it is to be had for the asking. In addition, the independent consulting chemical engineer, who usually specializes in one field, offers the advantage of experience obtained over a number of years of practice.

In the succeeding pages a number of prices are quoted for the convenience of the reader in making preliminary estimates. When judging prices, it is fair enough to consider the amount and kind of material, as well as the fabricating and machining effort involved; but there is another aspect which concerns itself solely with the performance over a reasonably long period, without breakdown, or serious loss of efficiency. In any continuous operation in which a chain of devices is involved, the whole process stops with the failure of a single device. The only way to insure against breakdown is to design properly and adapt exactly to the specified need. To do this requires testing the device, collecting data from plant performance, and the application of good judgment which comes from collective experience. All this is meant by the expression "engineering skill," and a part of the purchase price is in payment for it. Some manufacturers of chemical engineering equipment go so far as to hold that they sell engineering service, rather than the equipment itself.

It might be useful to consider briefly the location of the plants where many of these devices are to be put to work. A sizable literature has developed on this subject.

There are many factors which have a bearing on the choice of location. For any one plant, they rarely point one way; hence they must all be examined, and the factor which outweighs all others becomes the deciding one. Limiting ourselves to peace-time conditions, we must exclude from general consideration all the smaller plants which may be located to equal advantage near almost any town having reasonably good railway facilities, and which are not infrequently located in the home town of the promoters. It may be that the raw materials for such a plant come from widely separated distant points, some of them overseas, and in moderate amounts; similarly, the product may enjoy a national and even an international distribution, so that, except for railway shipping facilities, no one point offers any advantage over any other except with regard to climate. The general considerations apply only to large plants, producing many tons of material per day, valued at a comparatively low figure so that even small savings have a great effect. These general considerations include the availability of raw materials, fuel, power, water for boiler and cooling purposes, labor, and nearness to markets.

Availability of Raw Materials. In the simplest example, the plant is located on the site which yields the raw material, as was done for the manufacture of potassium salts in New Mexico and at Searles Lake in California, and as is generally (but not exclusively) the case in the manufacture of portland cement. Raw materials may be readily available by virtue of cheap ocean transportation, which indicates a location on the sea-coast or easily navigable river; the location of mixed fertilizer plants, of sugar refineries, and of a number of petroleum refineries is due to this factor. The location of the first great bromine-from-sea-water plant in North Carolina provides the raw material, and in addition permits the disposal of the treated water into the Cape Fear River so that it cannot contaminate the incoming water. The location of bromine-bearing brines fixed the site of the original bromine extraction plant in Michigan.

Fuels. Plants requiring a great deal of fuel are located close to the source of fuel, and the materials required are brought from a distance if necessary. The great fuels of the past—wood and charcoal—have given way to soft coal and natural gas. The present iron and steel industry transports the ore to points close to the Pennsylvania-West Virginia coal fields, and brings the fuel but a short distance. Many zinc-distilling plants were located in western Pennsylvania in order to benefit from the natural gas. The glass industry, a large consumer of fuel, is well represented in the same region.

Power. Many chemical industries require power for their crushers and grinders, for plastics mills, centrifugals, and various other machinery. If the requirement is large, it dictates the choice of a location in a region in which cheap power is available, either hydroelectric, or steam-generated. One type of chemical enterprise which requires electrical power to an enormous extent is the electrochemical industry; thus it is not surprising to find such industries clustered about a power-generating center, such as Niagara Falls. For such enterprises, power requirement is the controlling factor, and the raw material is transported to the location selected.

Water. Chemical industries require a great deal of water, mainly for cooling purposes—a requirement they share with the steam-power generating industry. The water is pumped from a river or bay at only the cost of pumping; disposal of the water is to a public or a private sewer. An ideal location is realized in West Virginia, where a plant is located in the bend of a river; water enters the plant from up-stream, performs its mission, and continues as waste water in a straight line to the river, but now down-stream. River water is supplemented by municipal water when possible, in order to obtain a treated water for boiler purposes; when that is not possible, the plants soften their river water for steam requirements. Well water supplementing the river water is of great value for cooling purposes for it is generally cooler (55 or 60°F) throughout the year.

Labor. The chemical industries require a good quality of labor which is skilled in the handling of apparatus, observing controls, and detecting irregularities of operation. This operating labor is supplemented by electricians, pipe fitters, lead burners, masons, and other workers skilled in the trades. It is an advantage to locate the plant where a pool of such labor is available. Should the plant have to be located far from such centers, it is still possible to develop the necessary working force, but it will be an added item in cost and in time.

Nearness to Markets. There is an advantage in locating a number of smaller plants, each in a market center, so that the distance to its periphery is not excessive, rather than building a single plant and shipping long distances. For goods selling between $6 and $30 a ton, the freight involved in a long haul becomes prohibitive, even for bulk shipments, while shipments in small lots over great distances involve more handling and greater expense in packaging. An active acquaintance by the district managers and salesmen with their customers, which becomes possible in smaller plants serving a limited area, is often essential. The heavy chemicals industry is a good example of one with a number of plants located far enough apart for each to serve a distinct region, such as New England, western New York, metropolitan New York, western Pennsylvania, and so on. Some industries originally centered in a single eastern plant have found it essential to erect a second plant on the Pacific coast, and to serve that market from the new plant.

There are several other considerations. One is that the plant should have adequate railway facilities, preferably its own siding, and trackage within the plant area. It is interesting to note, however, that one of the larger pharmaceutical plants in central New York has no railway siding, and that a large plant manufacturing chemical equipment in Buffalo also is without one; all its products must be trucked to the railway. Both of these firms are enjoying a lively business. A chemical manufacturer in Rhode Island is without rail connection, but has water transportation facilities.

More intensely at this time (1952) than ever before, the country has become concerned with water pollution, particularly of streams, rivers, lakes and ponds, by various types of liquid industrial wastes, such as those from paper manufacturing plants. Facilities for waste disposal which will be acceptable must be available, as already suggested for cooling water; the local, state and even the Federal laws and regulations must be explored. Much the same situation obtains with atmospheric pollution by stacks venting acidic gases, which blight neighboring vegetation and impair the health of residents.

A location at tidewater is advantageous, for there solids (cinders, ashes and muds) may be dumped to make new land on which buildings may later be erected; the same purpose is served inland by nearness to a swamp area. With regard to waste disposal, it is important to look ahead and consider the possible growth of residential areas. What seemed to be a satisfactory location on Jamaica Bay became an impossible one as the city of Brooklyn grew, for finally the city forbade an aniline works to discharge its effluent into the bay, which was its only outlet.

The location of a plant may be dictated by the need of a material which is the by-product of another enterprise; the new plant may be located to advantage in close proximity. Thus in western New York, a Dry Ice plant was located across the street from a carbide plant; the latter collected and compressed its waste carbon dioxide and delivered it by pipe line to the Dry Ice plant. In Iowa, a hydrogenation plant was located close to a large railway-car building company so that a by-product, oxygen gas from cells, might be conveniently piped and delivered to the latter. An established plant, such as a smelter, may yield a secondary product which after some years is declared a public nuisance, and must be absorbed and recovered, if possible, in a marketable form. This circumstance fixed the location of a sulfuric acid plant in the middle South, and of another in the Northwest, as adjuncts to the smelters, to give but two examples out of many.

Again, an otherwise disadvantageous location may be retained for its advertising value, as is the case with a plant in Brooklyn. In a Pennsylvania city, a large plant retains its somewhat cramped quarters because it has a contract with a railway company which obligates the latter to provide the former with a tax- and rent-free site, owned by the railway. In another city, there is maintained by a newspaper a complete paper manufacturing plant spread over several floors of a building, with the apparatus piled up instead of spread out, as an insurance against interruption of supply by wars, strikes or riots. There also may be a combination of two first-order qualities, as in a plant situated on navigable waters which also enjoys high advertising value.

Reading References

"Plant location," by Charles W. Cuno, *Ind. Eng. Chem.*, **28**, Insert p. 108–111 (1936).

"Chemical Engineering Economics," with a chapter on plant location, by Chapin Tyler, New York, McGraw-Hill Book Co., 1948.

"Chemical Plant Location, a Symposium," *Chem. Eng. Progress*, **45**, pp. 283 to 322 (1949), containing six articles: "Methods of determining plant location," R. S. Aries and D. F. Othmer; "Relation of water supply to chemical plant location," S. T. Powell and L. G. von Lossberg, "Location factors in heavy chemical plants," H. A. Sommers; "Plant location in agricultural process industries," W. L. Faith; "Factors in the location of the plastics industry," C. O. Hoyer; "Economics of petroleum chemical plant location," Marcus Sittenfield.

"Waste disposal as a factor in plant location," *Chem. Eng. Progress*, **46**, 321 (1950).

In the period following the economic depression of 1932, many young men in the Civilian Conservation Corps learned how to split and break apparently seamless stones with a sledge hammer; many of them became remarkably adept at finding the seam and breaking what seemed to be unbreakable boulders into small pieces. The crushers described below are our mechanical CCC boys.—In Europe, for the maintenance of stone roads, the workman has among other tools a light hammer on a long, slightly flexible wooden handle. With this tool he strikes a 2- or 3-inch stone, his standard supply, in order to obtain smaller fragments with which he may complete the filling of a hole. The swing hammer mill is the mechanical light hammer of the road man.—The grinding mill is the chemist's and pharmacist's mortar and pestle multiplied many times.

2. DEVICES FOR THE DRY REDUCTION IN SIZE OF SOLID MATERIALS

The material from quarry or mine is brought to the "breaker" or "mill" by means of narrow-gauge cars, buggies, or trucks, so that it may be reduced in size. Some materials are reduced to smaller, graded sizes, as for example crushed stone for road building or for concrete, anthracite for domestic use, pebble calcite for pebble lime; other materials must be reduced to a fine powder, e.g., portland cement from clinker, bauxite for making alum, bituminous coal for powdered coal. Reduction in size takes place in steps; a series of devices (at least three) is used when reducing the product from the quarry to a fine powder. The stones as quarried

TABLE 1. DEVICES FOR REDUCING THE SIZE OF SOLID MATERIALS

Primary Crushers	Secondary Crushers	Intermediate Crushers	Fine-grinding Mills or Pulverizers
Gyratory	Crushing rolls	Rod mill	Pebble mill
Jaw	Single roll crusher	(Pebble mill)	Ball mill
Fairmount	Hammer mill		Tube mill
Screw	Ring crusher		Compartment tube mill
	Shredders		Conical ball mill
	Rotary crusher (pot		Conical pebble mill
	crusher)		Ring roll mill
	Squirrel cage disintegrator		Bowl mill
	Gyratory for fine reduction		Pulverizer with grinding balls
	Jaw crusher for fine reduc-		Buhrstone mill
	tion		Mikro pulverizer
			Canary pulverizer
Size of product:			
3 inch	1, ½, ¼ inch	10 or 20 mesh	100, 200, 325 mesh

7

are of assorted sizes, such as would require a steam shovel to handle. The mine cars dump their load into a primary crusher, which may be either of the gyratory or the jaw type; the product from this is stone 3 inches in diameter, which is a popular size. This is delivered to crushing rolls or swing-hammer mills in order to reduce the size to 1 inch, ½ inch, or ¼ inch. This second reduction may also be performed with gyratory or jaw crushers of a construction which makes them suitable for this purpose. The final reduction to a powder is performed in ring roll mills, ball mills, pebble mills, tube mills, buhrstone mills, and other mills of special design.

Devices are judged by the degree of perfection with which they perform their tasks. For the production of ¼-inch stone, with nothing smaller, a device is selected which gives no fines, or more practically, a minimum of fines. On the other hand, if only fines are required, such as would pass through a 200-mesh screen, a device must be chosen which produces a maximum of fines. Closely related to mills are the screens which serve to grade the stones as to size; these are described in the following chapter.

GYRATORY CRUSHERS

The gyratory crusher has a central vertical, cone-shaped element working in a shell resembling an inverted cone, open at the top. The space between the central cone and the shell hopper decreases gradually, the narrowest gap being at the bottom of the crushing space; at this level, the material drops out of the crusher to a short chute leading to a conveyor, which removes it. The material to be crushed enters at the top, which is free, except for the heavy spider which straddles it. In the earlier designs, the crushing head and the inner wall of the shell with their lining had straight lines; the new designs provide concave surfaces for the mantle on the crushing cone, and for the inner wall of the hopper. The latter are referred to simply as "the concaves." The new surfaces are curved for about 30 per cent of their length from the bottom up. The main result is a decrease in choking tendencies, for now, thanks to the concaves, the opening very gradually increases over the last part of the descent so that the stones fall faster in the lower part of the crushing space and thus reduce packing. Also, point-to-point wear is eliminated. As would be expected, the capacity of the crusher fitted with concaves is increased. The concaves, as well as the older straight lining, are made of hardened steel, such as manganese steel, zincked in place.

The central element, which is called the crushing head, does not rotate, practically speaking, although it is free to do so; instead, it gyrates, which means that it has a rolling action, very much like that of a man sitting in a chair and rolling his torso gently and smoothly around so that his shoulders describe a small circle while he remains firmly seated. The crushing head has a vertical shaft, the top of which ends in a universal carried by the spider. The bottom of the shaft rests in the eccentric, a gear-driven member below the crushing space, machined and babbitted to receive the shaft. The bore in this member is eccentric to the axis of the crusher, while the gear-driven member as a whole is exactly centered. As the eccentric is turned, the bottom of the shaft describes a small circle; the shaft does not rotate (see next sentence) because it is easier for it to slip along the well lubricated wall which confines it. To be quite correct it should be said that the crushing head does have a slight rotating motion amounting to about 1 turn in one minute, while the gyrations, and with them the rotations of the eccentric, number 300 to 500 per minute.

FIGURE 1.—Type T Bulldog Gyratory Crusher (largest size) with 60-inch opening. The frame is made of either meehanite or cast steel, in five sections. The crusher is 36 feet, 4 inches over-all height and weighs 950,000 pounds. (Courtesy Traylor Engineering and Manufacturing Co., Allentown, Pa.)

As the crushing head gyrates, it comes closer to the concaves at one spot, while at another spot, 180° away, a maximum gap forms, down which the charge at once slips. At the next half gyration, this gap is reduced; as the space is too narrow to accommodate the material, it is crushed by the pressure. The crushing pressure travels around the concave, reducing in size whatever material is lodged in the crushing space.

Gyratories fall into two main classes: the large and heavy crushers (primary) having a large feed opening, and the special, usually smaller ones, called "fine reduction" crushers.

Primary Gyratory Crushers. The primary gyratory crusher has a heavy main frame of cast iron or cast steel, and crushing surfaces, as already mentioned, of manganese steel or other hardened steel. An example of a primary crusher installation is that in a stone-crushing plant (LeRoy, N. Y.). The gyratory is set in the ground, with its spider rim just below the level of the narrow-gauge railway bed. The cars carry steam-shovel-size rock close to the crusher, and are dumped directly into it. Lumps as large as can be handled by a steam shovel and a variety of somewhat smaller sizes tumble in. The crushing head gyrates, and the product, about 3 inches in size, is brought from below the surface by a belt conveyor. Motor, belt, pulleys and eccentric gears are all below ground and are reached by an inclined walk and steps, for inspection and lubrication. The conveyor carries the discharge to secondary crushers at an elevated point.

Table 2 gives a few figures on the Superior McCully gyratory crusher which indicate sizes, crusher settings (opening at the base of crushing space), and corresponding capacities.

TABLE 2. TECHNICAL DATA ON SUPERIOR McCULLY GYRATORY CRUSHERS (STANDARD CONCAVES) (SELECTED ITEMS)*

Size of Crusher (in)	Two Feed Openings (in)	Finest Setting (in)	Capacity (tons/hr)	Coarsest Setting (in)	Capacity (tons/hr)
13	13 × 45	2½	78	3	106
16	16 × 60	3	120	4	196
30	30 × 98	4	270	5	420
42	42 × 143	5	400	6½	670
60	60 × 196	7	900	10	1530
60 spec.	60 × 195	7	1200	10	1886

* Data supplied by Allis-Chalmers Mfg. Co., Milwaukee, Wis. (1951).

The capacities of the Type T Bulldog gyratory crusher (Traylor) are similar. For example, the 30-inch size has an approximate hourly capacity of 450 tons; the gyrations per minute are 126; the weight of the crusher is 175,000 pounds, and the maximum horsepower required is 225. There are 14 different sizes in the Type T Bulldog series of crushers, each of which may be adjusted to a variety of settings. The largest is shown in Figure 1, with some descriptive figures to which might be added the following: from the foundation to the top of the spider cap, the height is 23 feet, 4 inches; down to the bottom of the spout, 13 feet, making a total of 36 feet, 4 inches; the largest diameter at top of crusher is 21 feet; size of base, 16 feet by 16 feet, 4 inches; height of foundation to provide necessary room for working under the machine, 14 feet, 2 inches. The weight of the crusher is close to one million pounds.

Type TC Bulldog gyratory crushers are similar to Type T; the essential differences are in the main shaft suspension and the countershaft bearing and assembly. That Type TC also represents giant crushers is shown by the weight of the head and shaft (crushing head) of the 60-inch model, which is 180,000 pounds.

Gyratories are suitable for almost any rock or ore which is reasonably hard; softer materials which do not break clean and tend to pack are difficult to handle.

Fine-reduction Gyratory Crusher. Distinct from the large gyratory, which functions as a primary crusher, is the smaller "fine-reduction" gyratory crusher which produces material of ¾₁₆ inch, ¼ inch, and all intermediate sizes up to 1 and 1¼ inches. The feed is material roughly 2 inches in diameter. The reduction crushers are made with concaves against which the crushing head works.

One of the latest models of fine-reduction gyratories is the Hydrocone of the Allis-Chalmers series, in which the shaft is not suspended from the universal, but is carried by oil under pressure. In order to establish

FIGURE 2.—Bottom section of the Superior McCully fine-reduction crusher showing automatic lubrication of eccentric and gearing. Left side shows sectional mantle and concaves; right side shows one-piece mantle and concaves. (Courtesy Allis-Chalmers Mfg. Co., Milwaukee, Wis.)

clearly the great value of this innovation, it should be explained first that in order to change the setting in the older types, it is necessary to empty the crusher, expose the adjusting nut in the universal, turn it to raise or lower the crushing head and then reassemble. In the Hydrocone, the setting is changed quickly, without disturbing the assembly, by a few strokes of a hand-operated or motor-driven hydraulic pump. A second advantage is that tramp iron may be made to drop through the crusher by the use of an accumulator, which lowers the crushing head and then returns it to its initial setting automatically. The Hydrocone fine-reduction crusher, like similar crushers, has a shorter and broader crushing head than the primary gyratory. A number of additional interesting details are shown in Fig. 3. One is the three-piece step bearing, shown about in line with the center of the pinion shaft, on which the slight rotary

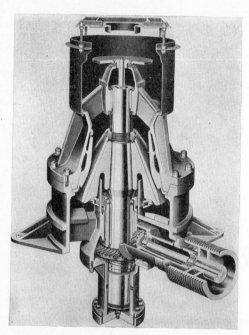

FIGURE 3.—View of a cut-open model of the Hydrocone Type "R" Crusher with wobble plate feeder, a gyratory crusher for fine reduction. The hydraulic relief device is applied at the lowest point of the crusher (instead of the plug shown). (Courtesy Allis-Chalmers Mfg. Co., Milwaukee, Wis.)

FIGURE 4.—The fine-reduction Hydrocone gyratory crusher; note operator's hand on the handle of the hydraulic pump for adjusting the setting. (Courtesy Allis-Chalmers Mfg. Co., Milwaukee, Wis.)

motion of the crushing head takes place. The Hydrocone is made in seven sizes, as shown in Table 3.

The Hydrocone fine-reduction crusher gyrates faster than the Superior McCully crusher; taking average values, it may be said to gyrate about

TABLE 3. CONDENSED CAPACITY TABLE FOR HYDROCONE GYRATORY CRUSHER
(SELECTED ITEMS)*

Close Side Setting and Eccentric Throw (in)	$\frac{3}{16}$	$\frac{1}{4}$	$\frac{1}{2}$	$\frac{3}{4}$	1	$1\frac{1}{4}$	$1\frac{1}{2}$	2	Rpm of Pulley on Pinion Shaft	Gyrations per Minute
				Tons Per Hour						
No. 322	9.5	14	36						1160	425
530		20	51						390	390
636			64	108					350	350
848			83	135	192	237			300	300
1051			90	160	235	305			880	290
1260				200	275	342	462		880	260
1784					440	555	690	1005	695	200

* Data supplied by Allis-Chalmers Mfg. Co., Milwaukee, Wis. (1951).

three times as often per minute. In this faster-gyrating crusher, the size of product is controlled more closely by the close side setting—a striking difference from the slower primary gyratories, in which the size of product is governed by the open side setting.

The Traylor Type TY reduction crusher is a secondary fine crusher which is nonchoking and nonpacking, largely because the head is bell-shaped. As a result, the controlling zone is moved upward; and inasmuch as this zone has the smallest volume of any in the crushing bowl, free discharge at the bottom of the head is assured. Type TY is made in six sizes. This crusher will nip larger lumps of rock than other crushers in its class.

FIGURE 5.—A cutaway drawing of the Symons Standard Type Cone Crusher, showing its construction and working principle. Note the shape of the gyrating element, mantle and head; the threaded arrangement of the bowl in the adjustment ring; the crushing cavity; the large opening available for the discharge of the crushed product; the parallel zone; the coil springs which are just indicated. (Courtesy Nordberg Mfg. Co., Milwaukee, Wis.)

An important member of the fine reduction, secondary gyratory crushers is the *Symons cone crusher*, designed for a finer reduction of the crushed product as well as for greater capacity. It is an outgrowth of two earlier successful developments, the Symons horizontal and vertical disk crushers. It is distinguished by an improved shape of the crushing cavity, a parallel zone between the crushing members to insure uniformity of size, coil spring protection against tramp iron damage, and greater ease in changing the size of the product. This latter change is brought about by turning the bowl in the adjustment ring, which carries it. The bowl is threaded on its outer circumference, and is screwed into a similar set of internal threads of the adjustment ring (see Figure 5).

The bowl may be turned to raise it, producing a coarser product; when it is turned in the opposite direction, the product will be finer in size.

In this crusher, the action of the cone is a combination of high speed and wide travel. It should be pointed out also that when the material reaches the lower portion of the cavity, it travels in and through the "parallel zone," wherein the surfaces of the bowl and of the cone are parallel. It is the parallel zone which insures a uniform product.

The protection against damage caused by tramp iron is in the form of a circle of upright heavy coil springs which for normal operation hold the bowl and adjustment ring down firmly into the frame. When tramp iron enters the cavity, "these springs are compressed with each gyration of the head, allowing the bowl to rise the full movement of the head until the noncrushable material has passed into the discharge." The springs then return to their normal position.

The *Symons short head type* cone crusher supplements the standard type, producing a still greater reduction in size of the product, with a high capacity.

Jaw Crushers

In the jaw crusher, a swinging jaw moves back and forth, working against a stationary surface (the anvil jaw) with which it forms a V-shaped chamber, wide at the top and narrow at the bottom, within which the crushing takes place. The other two walls of the chamber are formed

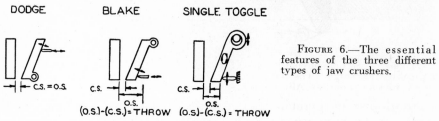

Figure 6.—The essential features of the three different types of jaw crushers.

by the frame. The swinging jaw is suspended at one point, and receives its motion from an eccentric shaft on which it rides at its unsupported end. The construction and operation will be clear from Figure 6. Both jaws are essentially flat, except that many have shallow vertical ribbing; the surface of the movable jaw forms an angle of not quite 30° with the vertical anvil jaw. In a number of designs both jaws lean back from the vertical to form an angle with each other of about the same size. The charge is introduced at the top; as the swinging jaw moves out, the charge slips down; when the jaw moves in, the space is too small, and the material is crushed. On the next outward motion, the crushed material slips down again into a narrower space, and the cycle is repeated. It takes 8 to 10 such slips for the average material to reach the bottom of the chamber, where it is discharged. The width of the discharge is adjustable, and controls the size of the product. At the end of its working stroke, the movable jaw is brought back to its starting position by a spring acting through a tension rod, as indicated in Figure 7.

Both the movable jaw and the anvil jaw are faced with manganese steel; the faces are either straight or "concave," as described under gyratories. Jaw crushers are generally belt-driven, and are fitted with two flywheels besides the pulley.

There are three general types of jaw crushers, the Blake, the Dodge, and the single-toggle or fine-reduction type; these are discussed and illustrated. The large jaw crusher is a primary crusher, and in some services

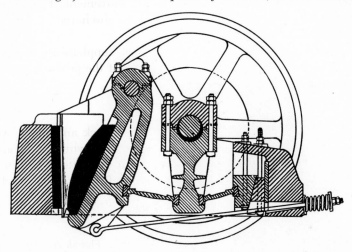

FIGURE 7.—Section through a Blake-type jaw crusher. The swing-jaw plate is of the nonchoking design. The stationary plate is straight. Note the eccentric shaft and the fly wheel. (Courtesy Allis-Chalmers Mfg. Co., Milwaukee, Wis.)

is favored over the gyratory; however, it has a lower capacity and wears faster. It should be noted that the gyratory has an even, uninterrupted gyration, while the jaw crusher has a reciprocal motion. The jaw crusher, on the other hand, has a simpler construction, and a principle of operation which is easily grasped by workmen.

In the Blake type crusher, the swing jaw is suspended from the top, and it is its bottom lip, the point of the jaw, which has the maximum motion. The eccentric acts on the pitman which in turn affects a toggle joint; one toggle plate rests on the frame, while the other imparts motion to the movable joint. Maximum force is exerted when the jaw is at the extreme of travel on its working stroke, which is where this great force is most needed. The discharge opening is adjustable; the size of product in the Allis-Chalmers Blake type crusher, for example, may be 1½, 2, 2½, 3 or 4 inches, with capacities which are less for the smaller size, and greatest for the largest size products, as may be seen from Table 5 (page 18). The crusher has two flywheels, and may be driven by a Texrope multiple V-belt. In one form, marked "A," the jaw plates are straight; in the other, marked "B," the new concave non-choking jaw plates are used. Table 5 also illustrates the jaw motion and the minimum settings.

The Traylor jaw crushers, Types H and HB, Type R and Type S, all have the non-choking plates which embody the principle of the Traylor Bell Head and Curved Concaves, already presented.   The lower end of the swing jaw plate is concave while the opposite lower half of the fixed jaw plate is convex; as a result, there can be no packing or choking at the discharge.

Type S is the strongest and most massive breaker of the jaw type ever built.   It is made in seven sizes, ranging from 36 × 42 inch feed opening

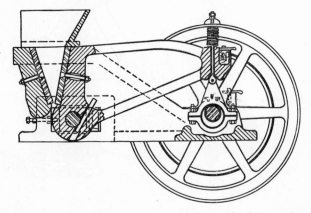

FIGURE 8.—Section through a Dodge-type jaw crusher, with plain stationary jaw plate, and plain swing-jaw plate.   (Courtesy Allis-Chalmers Mfg. Co., Milwaukee, Wis.)

to 60 × 84 inch.   In this largest size, the capacity is between 500 and 1000 tons per hour, depending upon the closed setting.   Type R is made in three sizes; type HB in five, and type H in eleven.   For the latter, the capacity runs from 4 tons per hour to 275, depending upon the size crusher, the setting for discharge opening, and other factors.   The Traylor jaw crushers have the toggle system, with a front and a back toggle; the former rests and works upon the plunger of a safety device which operates, when an obstruction occurs, by arresting the swinging of the jaw.

The Sturtevant cam-and-roll jaw crusher is of the Blake type.   The jaw motion is produced by two small but wide cams on a massive high-carbon steel shaft.   As the cams revolve, they lift a large roll twice in each revolution; this moves the swinging jaw also twice per revolution by means of a short toggle plate and a heavy intermediate member.   The 12 by 26-inch crusher may be adjusted to a minimum setting of 1½ inches, or to a maximum of 5 inches.

In the Dodge type jaw crusher, the swinging jaw is pivoted at the bottom, and the discharge opening has almost no motion, the greatest movement being at its top. It is built in moderate sizes only. The product is more uniform in size than that from the Blake, and its capacity is less for a given size, as indicated in Table 4.

TABLE 4. COMPARISON OF DIFFERENT TYPES OF JAW CRUSHERS*

Dodge	Blake	Single toggle
Small capacity	Large capacity	Large capacity
Uniform sized product	Product size controlled by O.S. setting	Fairly uniform product
Most movement on large rock	Most movement on small rock	Good movement on all rock
Leverage on small pieces	Leverage on large pieces	

C.S. = Closed Sizes; O.S. = Open sizes.
* Adapted from data supplied by Allis-Chalmers Mfg. Co.

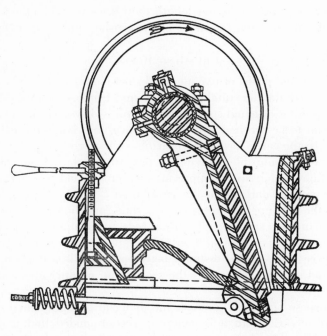

FIGURE 9.—Section through the Denver jaw crusher, of the single-toggle type. The discharge opening is altered by turning the handle shown at middle left. This crusher is a fine-reduction crusher.

The Denver jaw crusher is of the single-toggle type. The movable jaw is pivoted at the top, and when it moves forward, it also moves downward, which tends to increase its capacity. It is made in medium sizes, and as it serves the mining industry chiefly, it is sectionalized so that mule-back transportation is feasible.

Prices of jaw crushers differ not only with size, but also with type and variations in specifications.

TABLE 5. CAPACITIES AND DATA ON BLAKE TYPE JAW CRUSHERS (SELECTED ITEMS)*

Size of Jaw Opening (in)	Capacity in Tons/Hour (1 ton to 20 cu ft Capacity) Open Side Setting (in)							Jaw Motion (in)	Horse Power Req.	Rpm
	1	1½	2	2½	3	4				
10 × 7	7	9	12				A	5/8	7½	300
	8	12	16				B			
20 × 10		15	20	24	31		A	5/8	15	275
		24	32	40	49		B			
30 × 18				38	45	61	A	1 1/16	40	250
			48	60	74	102	B			

A, straight jaw plates; B, nonchoking jaw plates.

* Data supplied by Allis-Chalmers Mfg. Co., Milwaukee, Wisconsin.

It is held by some students of this subject that the shape of the product from the gyratory crusher approximates a cube, whereas that from the jaw crusher may have a greater length than thickness. In the latter, the direction of crushing and the shape of the crusher outlet favor the longer, flattened fragment.

CRUSHING ROLLS

Crushing rolls consist of two identical steel-rimmed rolls mounted with their axes horizontal, on suitable bearings and frame, and made to revolve toward each other at equal speeds. Each roll is driven by its own pulley. The material to be crushed is fed from above, and is discharged beneath the rolls. In the early forms, the bearings of both rolls were fixed so that the rolls were immovable; but in the present standard form, one roll is made movable so that any tramp iron or other unbreakable material may be passed without damage to the equipment. This is accomplished by mounting the bearings of one roll, on a slide, and holding the roll to its work by springs, or springs and tension rods. The diameter of the roll is generally greater than the width of the face; it may be twice as large, even close to three times. The distance between the rolls, called the crusher setting, is adjustable; it controls the size of the product and also the capacity.

The purpose of rolls is to crush the material once and then discharge it. The feed varies, but it is generally recommended that it consist of pieces 2 inches or 2½ inches at the most, because the angle of nip (31°) is such that larger pieces are not readily accepted. The size of the product depends upon the size of the feed, for the maximum crushing ratio of rolls is 4 to 1; thus with 2-inch feed, and a crusher setting of ½ inch, the product will be ½ inch to the extent of 85 per cent. Other sizes, mainly smaller, are produced in different percentages; a chart permitting the estimation of the sizes in the product and the proportion of each is reproduced in Table 6.

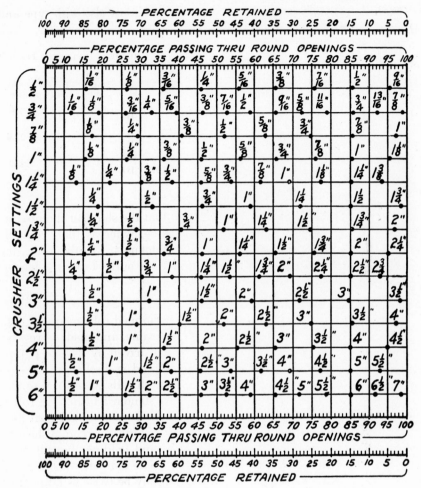

TABLE 6. Roll crusher product chart of size percentages, to show which sizes are produced, and how much of each, for a given crusher setting, in terms of particles passing through round openings of the dimensions written on the chart. (*Courtesy Denver Equipment Co., Denver, Col.*)

Explanation: For maximum efficiency from a roll-type crusher, the opening should be set to produce 15 per cent oversize, which prevents an excess production of fines.

Example: Crusher setting, 1½″, shown on left-hand side of chart. Read percentages in table on the line, which are as follows:

Round Screen Opening (in)	Percentage Through	Percentage Retained
¼	19	81
½	33	67
¾	46	54
1	59	41
1¼	72	28
1½	85	15
1¾	98	2

Crushing rolls are generally used for intermediate crushing; for making granular products with a minimum of fines they are unsurpassed. The capacity is high.   They are made as small as 8 inches in diameter and 5-inch face, with a speed of 150 rpm, and capacity of 2 tons per hour, and as large as 62 inches in diameter and 24-inch face, with a speed of 50 rpm, and capacity of 10 tons per hour (of minus ¾-inch product from 2½-inch feed from a jaw crusher).

FIGURE 10.—Over-all view of the Sturtevant crushing rolls. (Courtesy Sturtevant Mill Co., Boston, Mass.)

In the case of balanced rolls (Sturtevant), both rolls are mounted against heavy springs, so that both are movable; the result is that the crushing shocks are exactly balanced, vibration is a minimum, and the operation smoother.   Some capacity figures for stated feed, with a definite roll setting, are given below.

TABLE 7.   RELATION OF CAPACITY, SIZE OF FEED, ROLL SETTING AND SPEED OF ROLLS
  FOR STURTEVANT BALANCED CRUSHING ROLLS; SCREENING IN CLOSED CIRCUIT
     (AVERAGE ROCK, WHICH CAN BE NIPPED AT SPEEDS NAMED)

Size of Roll Diam. × Face (in)	Feed Cubes (in)	Roll Setting (in)	Speed (rpm)	Capacity (tons/hour)
	1.25	0.61	200	26.6
	1	0.25	212	11.6
16 × 10	0.75	0.2	225	9.8
	0.50	0.125	245	6.67
	0.25	0.065	272	3.86
	2	1	115	56.4
	1.5	0.54	130	34.4
24 × 15	1	0.25	140	17.15
	0.75	0.2	150	14.7
	0.5	0.125	163	10
	3	1.5	59	87
	2.5	1	62	61
36 × 20	2	0.5	70	34.2
	1.5	0.37	78	29.2
	1	0.25	85	20.9

Each Sturtevant balanced crushing roll has a flywheel pulley, and is driven independently; both are driven while the machine is in operation.

The product of the crushing rolls is intermediate between that of fine-reduction crushers and grinding mills. The former are mainly the "f ne-reduction gyratory," special designs of gyratories. One example is the Allis-Chalmers Hydrocone fine-reduction crusher; another is the Traylor-Stearns multi-stage fine-reduction crusher. In addition, there are several fine-reduction jaw crushers. The size of the product from the fine-reduction machine varies with the setting, but in general it may be said that it produces material from ¼ to 1 inch in diameter and larger.

In addition to the standard design of crushing rolls, which provides two rolls, both driven, with smooth surfaces, there are a number of modifications. The roll surface may have horizontal straight-line corruga-

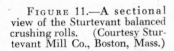
FIGURE 11.—A sectional view of the Sturtevant balanced crushing rolls. (Courtesy Sturtevant Mill Co., Boston, Mass.)

tions; the surface may consist of tooth-like or knife-like projections. A double-roll crusher with teeth, so that it reduces by cutting and picking action, is shown in Figure 12. The rolls are belt-driven, and one roll is mounted on spring bearings so that it moves to pass unbreakable materials. The teeth are in removable segments.

Another double-roll crusher has crusher parts which consist of two cylinders (the rolls) of breaker saws made of special hardened steel and mounted on square shafts.* The teeth of one roll pass between the teeth of the other, effecting a uniform reduction. The product is fine enough to go direct to the attrition mill. The drive is positive; the rolls are geared together with a 2 to 1 differential speed. This is the first crusher so far mentioned in which the crushing rolls have not rotated at the same speed. The saw-tooth crusher, Monarch 10-E.C., is recommended for reducing unshucked and shucked corn ears, meat scrap, cracklings, bone,

* Sprout, Waldron and Co., Inc., Muncy, Pa.

talc rock, shells, etc., to a uniform product. The speed of pulley is 500 rpm; capacity per hour 4 to 5 tons; power 8 to 15 hp. Monarch roller crushers are available two-pair high and three-pair high.

A single-roll crusher with teeth which are set in segments to facilitate replacement is shown in Figure 13.

FIGURE 12.—Double-roll crusher which reduces by cutting or picking action. One roll is mounted on spring bearings to pass foreign material; the teeth segments are renewable. (Courtesy Jeffrey Mfg. Co., Columbus, Ohio.)

FIGURE 13.—A single-roll crusher, used for coal, bone, alum, salt, gypsum, etc.; reduces to as low as 1¼″ or smaller. The tooth segments are renewable. Sizes up to 36 inches × 54 inches. (Courtesy Jeffrey Mfg. Co., Columbus, Ohio.)

The Gruendler swing roll crusher is a single-roll crusher especially adapted for handling mine runs of coal, clay, gypsum, shale and other medium-hard materials, taking the load from the mine cars directly into the hopper.

The Fairmount crusher is a single-roll primary crusher working against a curved anvil plate. It is built with capacities up to 1500 tons per hour.

A new crushing principle is used in the Freeport Crusher,* a *screw*

---

* "Freeport uses new crushing principle," by A. A. Gustafson, AIME Annual Meeting, New York City, 1950.

crusher which is portable, and which has been built only in very large sizes. The Freeport Crusher consists of a steel trough, a strong screw with a 6-inch shaft, and teeth set in the frame forming the outlet for the screw action. The screw has two ribbons. The large one, of 1¼-inch plate, is bent to make a diameter of 30 inches; the smaller one, of ¾-inch plate, has a diameter of 18 inches. As the screw turns (15 rpm), chunks slide down the hopper surmounting the working trough, to the screw flights, whence they are forced against the teeth in the frame and split into smaller fragments. The particular crusher being described takes feed 3 to 4 feet in diameter, and delivers a product 10 to 12 inches in diameter. It has a capacity of 350 tons of sulfur per hour. It may be built in larger and smaller sizes, and with a different screw pitch.

The Bradford breaker is both a crushing device and a separator; it is used in handling coal at the mine or in coke plants. The Bradford breaker is a steel drum set on its sides and rotated; its sides are provided with perforations which allow only 1-inch and 1¾-inch size coal to pass; angle irons parallel to the axis are mounted on its inner sides. The breaker discards pieces of timber and larger pieces of tramp iron through one end; the coal is thrust down and over within the drum until crushed small enough to pass through the openings provided in the side wall.

Swing Hammer Mills

The swing hammer mill contains a number of disks mounted on a shaft and carrying at the periphery small hammers, each of which is free to swing on a pin. The bottom part of the crushing chamber generally has a cage, or grid, through which material can pass; the upper part of the housing carries the feed hopper and the breaker plate. As the material is introduced, it travels slowly over the breaker plate; here the rapidly moving hammers strike the material and shatter it into smaller fragments, which are swept down and around against the grid. Breaking and crushing are brought about not only by the impact of hammer on stone, but also by that of stone upon stone, so that the hammer mill may be said to crush both by impact and by attrition. Particles small enough to pass through the openings are discharged, while the oversize ones are hurled upward again to receive another blow at the breaker plate. This is continued until all the material has left the mill through the grid.

A number of disks, perhaps six, each carrying four hammers, are keyed to the shaft close together, so that the row of hammers fills the width of the chamber. The hammers may be staggered so that no gaps are left between any two rows of hammers. The simpler form is a rectangular length of bar iron, drilled with three holes for the pin so that as the hammers wear, they may be advanced and reset. Another form has a hammer with a broader head which accentuates the momentum of the

swinging hammer as it approaches the breaker plate. The Sturtevant
"Open-Door" swing sledge mill has hammers of the latter type; in addition, the entire front of the mill may be opened like a safe, by throwing
over two latches, and the interior exposed for adjustment, cleaning, removal of unbreakable material, and replacement of parts. The standard
means of operation is by a flat belt, driving a single pulley on one end of

FIGURE 14.—"Miracle" Hammer Crusher
for reducing large pieces of limestone, shale,
slag and cement rock. Steam-shovel size is
reduced to 1, 2, 3, or 4 inches and under in
one operation. (Courtesy Jeffrey Mfg. Co.,
Columbus, Ohio.)

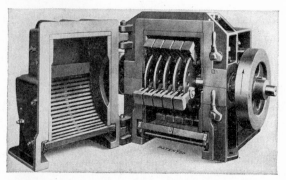

FIGURE 15.—A swing-sledge hammer mill, with the "Open Door" feature, permitting
complete accessibility. Note the grate and the sledge hammers. (Courtesy Sturtevant
Mill Co., Boston, Mass.)

the shaft; but when the material to be crushed is of large size and hard,
a flywheel is installed on the other end of the shaft, to keep the mill from
slowing down. A few capacities for two different materials and two different gratings are shown in Table 8, together with some dimensions and
speeds.

The number of disks carrying hammers is not definite, but varies with
the size of the mill. The Williams "Jumbo" type, for example, has 16
double disks; it is built for large-capacity operations, and crushes up to

250 tons of coal per hour to a size of $1\frac{1}{4}$ inches, or up to 150 tons to a size of $\frac{3}{4}$ inch, or up to 100 tons to a size which passes a $\frac{1}{8}$-inch mesh (85 to 95 per cent). The speed of rotation of the shaft is between 900 and 1200 rpm.

Hammer mills are made in all sizes; some are very large, and some so small that they have but one disk, of small diameter. There is furthermore a variety in design, each one possessing special merit. The Allis-Chalmers Pulverator No. 3 takes medium-hard man-size stone ($12 \times 10 \times 8$ inches) and produces material passing through $\frac{1}{8}$-inch opening grate bars, for example. The Raymond No. 0000 Pulverizer is a hammer-type grinding unit with small capacity, by means of which pitch is pulverized to a fineness of 95 per cent through 100 mesh at the rate of 400 to 800 pounds per hour. Both the Raymond Screen mill and the Raymond Imp mill are of the hammer type.

Ring crushers are similar to hammer mills, differing mainly in that loosely hung rings take the place of hammers.

With slight modifications, the hammer mill becomes a shredder; thus the Jeffrey Type A shredder serves for reducing wood refuse, chips, or bark. Other examples are the Jeffrey-Searby sugar-cane shredder, the bark shredder, screenings grinder, and bale breaker.

TABLE 8. APPROXIMATE CAPACITIES OF HAMMER MILLS WITH VARIOUS MATERIALS AND TWO DIFFERENT GRATES*

	Limestone, $\frac{1}{8}$-inch slots	Limestone, $\frac{1}{4}$-inch slots	Burnt lime, $\frac{1}{4}$-inch slots
		Tons per hour	
0 Swing-sledge	2 to 4	4 to 7	7 to 9
1 Swing-sledge	6 to 10	12 to 15	18 to 20
2 Swing-sledge	12 to 15	20 to 30	60 to 70
00 Hinged-Hammer Pulverizer	1 to 2	2 to 4	4 to 6

APPROXIMATE SCREEN ANALYSIS OF PRODUCT, REDUCING 3-INCH LIMESTONE

Grate Spacing (in)	$\frac{1}{4}$ inch	10 mesh	50 mesh	100 mesh
		Per cent passing through mesh stated		
$\frac{1}{4}$	99.8%	85%	50%	40%
$\frac{1}{8}$		99	70	60

$\frac{1}{8}$-inch slots means that the grating space was $\frac{1}{8}$ in.

DIMENSIONS AND SPEEDS

	Length	Width	Inside Diameter	Inside Width	Feed Opening	Pulley Speed (rpm)	Approx. hp
0 Swing-sledge	4'-3"	4'-1"	24"	10"	13×11"	1200–1500	12
1 Swing-sledge	5'-1"	5'-8"	30"	20"	17×20"	1000–1300	40
2 Swing-sledge	6'	7'	36"	30"	20×30"	1000–1200	75
00 Hinged-Hammer Pulverizer	2'-5"	3'	16"	11"	12×12"	1200–3600	5–20
0-24" Hinged Hammer Pulverizer	3'-7"	5'-8"	24"	24"	$12\frac{1}{2} \times 24$"	1000–1200	15–20

* Data supplied by Sturtevant Mill Co., Boston, Mass.

Rotary Crushers

The rotary crusher, also called a pot crusher, has its crushing head exactly centered in the shell in which it rotates. Its construction is well shown in Figures 16 and 17. The rotary crusher will do many things

FIGURE 16.—A rotary crusher with the additional "Open Door" feature, permitting easy access to crushing space. The size of the product is regulated by turning the hand wheel at lower right. (Courtesy Sturtevant Mill Co., Boston, Mass.)

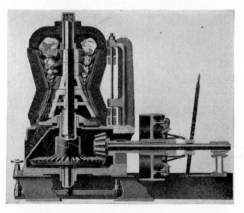

FIGURE 17.—Cross-sectional view of the rotary crusher in action. Note the method of driving. (Courtesy Sturtevant Mill Co., Boston, Mass.)

which the gyratory or jaw crusher does, provided the material is not hard or abrasive; in the chemical industries it gives excellent service at low cost. It is made in a number of sizes, and in each size, the setting is adjustable; the product is 1 inch or less, down to ¼ inch. Additional information is condensed in Table 9.

TABLE 9. STURTEVANT ROTARY FINE CRUSHERS

No.	Hopper opening (in)	Capacity at $\frac{1}{4}$-inch setting (tons/hr)	Speed (rpm)
00	6 × 18	1 to 1½	300
0	9 × 18	1 to 2	250
1	6 × 19	2 to 4	300
1½	10 × 28	5 to 7	200
2	19 × 30	8 to 10	250

The coarsest settings are, for the different crushers in order, ½″, ½″, ¾″, 1″, and 1¼″.

CAGE DISINTEGRATOR

The squirrel-cage disintegrator is also called both a cage disintegrator and a bar disintegrator. It consists of a squirrel cage-like rotating element with a horizontal axis running in one direction, and a second cage, slightly smaller in diameter and fitting inside the first, running in the other direction. The charge is fed to center of the smaller cage, and as it tends to pass out to the periphery, the horizontal bars of the fast-moving cages throw them back and forth until the fragments are small enough to drop through. Both cages may be run from pulleys on the same side, by mounting one on the sleeve, the other on the inner shaft. The same jackshaft furnishes the power, by crossing one belt. The first pulley may drive a double cage, which then fits over the intermediate cage driven in the opposite direction. Some machines have four, five, and more cages. Both large and small cage disintegrators are built.

In the chemical industries, the squirrel-cage disintegrator serves to reduce nitre cake to an assortment of granules which pour easily from a small can. It is used for coal, fertilizers, and many other purposes, and also in conjunction with drying, as exhibited in the flash dryer assembly shown in Figure 351. The reduction in size is by impact and attrition. The bars are round steel or alloy steel. Not only granules, but powders as fine as 325 mesh may be produced; generally, however, the cage disintegrator has a product which is intermediate. For fine reduction, the bars are spaced closer than for coarse reduction, and the output is less for cages of the same diameter.

THE CANARY CRUSHER OR PULVERIZER

Of great interest is a pulverizer which combines centrifugal distribution with impact and attrition. The Canary pulverizer* has three horizontal steel disks or plates, mounted on a vertical shaft. These gradually increase in diameter (in model C, 18¾ inches, 29½ inches, and 40 inches), the largest being at the bottom. Spaced along the circumference of each plate are blocks of chilled manganese steel (the hammers) bolted to the rotor. (See Figure 18.) The space between the hammers is several times the width of the hammer. The face of the hammer is corrugated

* James D. Canary, 3501 Wazee Street, Denver, Colorado.

vertically.   The three plates, with a distributor plate surmounting them, are rotated on the chrome-nickel steel shaft within a housing carrying the breaker rings.   Each level of rotating hammers faces a stationary ring, and the free space between hammer and ring decreases gradually as the particles descend.   The breaker ring is made up of corrugated chilled manganese steel liners held securely in place in the housing.

The feed, entering at the top, first reaches the rotating distributor plate, which makes an even distribution of the material to the first rotor plate.   Here the hammer strikes a blow, throwing the particle to the breaker ring, from which it rebounds, to be struck by the next hammer. After several repetitions, the particles drop to the second rotor, are swept

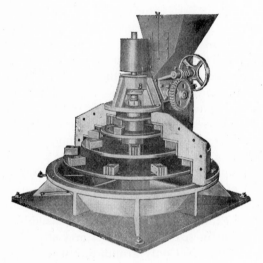

FIGURE 18.—The Canary Pulverizer; capacity between 1 and 15 tons per hour, depending upon fineness desired and other factors. (Courtesy James D. Canary, Denver, Colo.)

to the hammer by centrifugal force, receive a blow and counterblow; finally they reach the third rotor with maximum peripheral speed, where the successive blows and return blows again are administered.   As the particles decrease in size, they are struck ever-increasing blows by the speedier hammers, on their travel downward, swept along by the fan-like action of the rotating element.   At each level, numerous particles collide with one another, each helping to reduce the size of the other, hence pulverizing by attrition.

The finished material collects in the hopper at the base of the pulverizer.   When 1½-inch material is fed to the mill, the finished product may be 10 to 300 mesh.   The capacity is 1 to 15 tons per hour, depending on many factors.   The higher the speed at which the pulverizer is operated, the finer the product.   The speed of the shaft may be varied from 500 to 2340 rpm.   The overall height of Model C is about six feet.

The Canary pulverizer has been successfully applied to finishing crushed and ground synthetic abrasives, removing sharp projections and producing a more blocky grain with a higher bulk density. Hammers, breaker rings and wear plates are made of specially selected hard materials for certain duties.

PEBBLE MILLS AND BALL MILLS

The pebble mill, like the ball mill, is a steel cylinder lying on its side, rotated about its long axis, and containing an appropriate grinding medium. The material is introduced through a manhole in the center of

FIGURE 19.—Style BS pebble or ball mill with Type A roller chain connecting to variable speed motor; jacketed for heating or cooling, with special stuffing boxes for operating mill under pressure or vacuum. Upper left, vacuum or pressure line. The grid for discharging is shown on the floor. (Courtesy Abbé Engineering Co., New York.)

the shell length, after which the opening is closed hermetically by a cover plate. The discharge is by the same opening, after replacing the cover plate by a grate with wide slots, to hold back the balls.

The mill is rotated by means of a girth gear placed at one end of the cylinder, meshing with a pinion direct-connected to an electric motor, or by means of a pinion shaft rotated by pulleys, multiple V-belts, flat belts, or sprockets. In the chemical industries, the mill is sometimes provided with an outside gear, that is, a gear set outside the supporting pedestals, so that the mill proper may be jacketed (Figure 19).

The pebble mill is lined with porcelain or buhrstone shapes, and is half-filled with flint pebbles, or porcelain balls, which constitute the grinding medium.   The pebble mill is therefore well adapted to the grinding and mixing of white or light-colored pigments and paints, of food products, and other materials which must not come into contact with iron or steel. Coming into use as a supplement or improvement over the porcelain balls are high-density synthetic grinding balls.   They are about 40 per cent heavier than porcelain balls and are doing faster and better grinding jobs in many instances.*

A jar mill is an assembly of very small pebble mills (Figure 20).

The essential difference between a pebble mill and a ball mill is the nature of the grinding agent; for this the ball mill has steel balls instead of flint pebbles.   Steel is three times as heavy as flint; hence if balls of equal weight are sought, steel has the advantage, because three times as

FIGURE 20.—A 10-jar mill with motor drive; it may be obtained five tiers high.   Suitable for small production. Each jar is a miniature pebble mill.   (Courtesy Paul O. Abbé, Inc., Little Falls, N. J.)

many of the smaller steel balls can be placed in a mill of given volume as of flint pebbles individually of equal weight.   The grinding efficiency of the mills depends upon the number of contacts between any two balls or pebbles; the more balls, the more contacts will there be, and the more grinding.   As a result, a steel ball mill of given volume grinds, roughly speaking, three times as fast as a pebble mill of the same total volume.

The ball mill is almost always lined; when employed in mining enterprises and destined to work on hard ore, it must be provided with heavy manganese-steel liners to protect the walls; in the chemical industries, on the other hand, with their generally softer materials, a lighter liner of plain-carbon steel or of special alloy steel is generally suitable.   Occasionally, a mill having a shell made of special alloy steel may be left unlined.

The action of the balls and materials gives the interior of the mill a polished surface, which permits a sliding action not beneficial to the grinding operation.   To avoid this, baffles in the form of waves in the inner wall surface, or longitudinal bars, are provided; for example, the Abbé

* Compare "Grindings and Mixings" for November and December, 1951, Paul O. Abbé, Inc.

Wave Type Baffle Bars (Abbé Engineering Co.) are made of heat-treated alloy steel, are beveled at 45°, and are welded to the inside of the cylinder at definite spaces around the circumference to produce a uniform, smooth, rolling and cascading action of the steel balls. The cascading and rolling action make a miniature grinding mill of any pair of balls (or pebbles).

The Speed Change Baffle Bars (Paul O. Abbé, Inc.) shown in Figure 21 also have as their primary purpose the avoidance of slippage along the shell wall, but their effect additionally reduces the grinding time. According to this manufacturer, the grinding balls in the ball mill and the pebbles in the pebble mill should have the same diameter, which should be the smallest possible. Superior results have been obtained in this practice. Other manufacturing engineers prefer a diversity in diameter

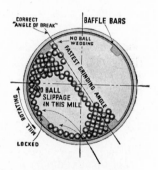

FIGURE 21.—A sketch of the events inside a ball mill which is unlined, but provided with the Paul O. Abbé Baffle Bars. These latter prevent slippage over the surface of the shell, and make for more efficient grinding. (Courtesy Paul O. Abbé, Inc., Little Falls, N. J.)

sizes. In the Denver mills, for example, the balls and pebbles are of several diameters; in the 4-foot by 4-foot Denver ball mill, with a total charge of 5900 pounds of balls, the distribution would be as in Table 10.

TABLE 10.   GRINDING AGENT IN THE 4-FT BY 4-FT DENVER BALL MILL

	For Coarse Grinding			For Fine Grinding		
Diameter of the balls (in)	2	3	4	1½	2	3
Weight (lb)	1900	2000	2000	1900	2000	2000

The operation of the ball or pebble mill will be readily followed with the aid of the preceding illustrations. The material is introduced through the manhole; the cover plate is set in place, sealing the mill tightly. The mill is set in motion and revolved until the required degree of fineness (or of mixing) is achieved, when it is stopped. The cover plate is replaced by a coarse grid, just able to hold back the grinding agent, and the mill is revolved again until all the powder has been discharged on an apron under the mill, which is then ready for the next cycle. The operation is by batch.

The ball mill requires more power to operate, for it is heavier than a pebble mill of equal volume; but its greater output in a given time makes up for this, so that per unit of product the power consumption is no greater.

For any mill, the time of grinding is longer, the finer the product is to be, and this is reflected in the decreased capacities for the finer powders, shown in Table 11.

TABLE 11. DIMENSIONS AND CAPACITIES OF ABBÉ PEBBLE AND BALL MILLS FOR BATCH OPERATION (SELECTED ITEMS)

		Pebble Mills				Ball Mills			
Mill No.	I.D. of Steel Cylinder	Capacity, Dry Grinding (lbs) Porcelain	Buhrstone	Approx. rpm	Price	Capacity, Dry Grinding (lbs)	Rpm	Price	For Jacket on Shell Only, Add to Price
8½A	24 × 24″	104	90	40	$ 918	188	36	$1021	$ 306
8½C	24 × 36″	164	145	40	995	280	36	1105	332
6 A	30 × 36″	273	245	36	1244	440	32	1381	415
5	36 × 42″	440	440	32	1512	740	29	1680	504
4½	42 × 48″	720	720	29	1812	1152	27	1908	604
2 A	60 × 60″	1916	1890	19	3372	2936	17	3372	938
1 A	72 × 72″	3456	3410	16	4787	5076	14	4787	1392
1 C	72 × 120″	5900	5850	16	6327	8460	14	6327	1840

Operating capacity is based on sand at 100 lbs per cu. ft. with 50% charge of pebbles or porcelain balls; ball mills with 33% charge of steel balls. Prices of pebble mills are for porcelain lining; the buhrstone lining is either the same or less. The drives are partly pulleys, partly gears; the smaller sizes (to 5 incl.) are furnished in either, the larger sizes only in gear and pinion. (Data by courtesy of the Abbé Engineering Co.) (The prices are as of November 1951; they are subject to change.)

Pebble mills and ball mills are made in almost all sizes; a few are shown in Table 11 for Abbé mills, with rate of revolution, capacity, and prices for making preliminary estimates. There is a still larger mill with

FIGURE 22.—Abbé pebble mill, No. 3-C, Type B, with "Compack" motor drive, a unit used widely in the chemical industries. Inching device spots and holds the mill in any desired position. Brake is provided. (Courtesy Paul O. Abbé, Inc., Little Falls, N. J.)

a capacity of 13,216 pounds of material for the ball mill, slightly less for the pebble mill. The function of the pebble and ball mill in chemical plants is not only to grind but also to mix, for example, salt (NaCl) with granular nitre cake to feed the Mannheim salt-cake furnace. By placing a jacket around the mill, the temperature may be controlled, and the grinding operation conducted either at room or at elevated temperature. The period of rotation depends upon the size of the feed, the hardness or better, the grindability of the materials, and the fineness desired.

A Paul O. Abbé pebble mill, shown in Figure 22, is a typical mill in the chemical field, both in type and size. It is motor-driven, and geared so that the cylinder makes 26 rpm when grinding dry, 22 rpm when grinding wet. Its diameter is 54 inches and its length 60 inches; if porcelain-lined, the total content of cylinder is 457 gallons; if it is buhrstone-lined, the capacity is 9 gallons less. The operating capacity is about 1500 pounds (dry).

Continuous Grinding Installations

Continuous Ball Mills. The ball mill is adapted to continuous operation by giving it wide, hollow trunnions, and by feeding at one end and discharging at the other. A distinction is made between the center-dis-

Figure 23.—A three compartment Compeb Mill, for Dry Grinding. Note man's figure at far right center. (Courtesy Allis-Chalmers Mfg. Co., Milwaukee 1, Wis.)

charge, overflow type, which requires the pulp level to be carried high enough to permit the discharge, and the grate-discharge type, in which a low pulp level may be carried because the discharge is first through the slots of an inner grate and then by lifter bars to the trunnion (Denver).

Continuous operation is secured also by peripheral discharge, for which a part of the lining is provided with perforations so that the material can discharge freely to screens arranged around the circumference of the mill. The material passing the screens collects in an outside trough from which it is removed by a screw conveyor, the whole being enclosed in a dust-proof housing. The material which fails to pass the screen is returned to the grinding chamber as the mill revolves. A low pulp level is secured, and the mill grinds in a closed circuit. The conical ball mill, described later, also is continuous.

In a compartment mill, the body is lengthened to provide for two or more compartments in which different stages of grinding take place. In the first compartment, the feed of ½ to ¾ inch is reduced to 20 mesh; this is discharged by an end grate to narrow scoops, which deliver it centrally to the second compartment, where the fineness is increased to between 200 and 325 mesh. The Compeb mills (Allis-Chalmers) are of this type, and are especially valuable in portland cement plants.

Figure 24.—Dry Grinding Compeb Mill with Combination Division Head. Interior view, showing first and second stage each with its proper size grinding balls, and also the table feeder and screw driven from mill gudgeon. (Courtesy Allis-Chalmers Mfg. Co., Milwaukee 1, Wis.)

In both continuous and batch operation, the degree of fineness of the product affects the amount produced, either by lengthening the period (batch) or by reducing the amount produced per unit of time. This is well shown in Table 12, in which the capacity of the same mills grinding to different finenesses is listed. The mills shown have continuous feed and continuous discharge.

Tube Mill, Rod Mill. The tube mill is a long cylinder, the length of which is many times the diameter. It may be one continuous chamber having the same diameter throughout. It may be used as either a batch or a continuous mill, with proper modifications in construction. Its function is that of a finishing mill, that is, its total product is of suitable fineness and is ready for shipment without reworking. The tube mill

TABLE 12.   CAPACITIES OF DENVER BALL MILLS
(SELECTED ITEMS*)

Denver Ball Mill Size Dia. × Lgt. (ft)	2-in to 35 mesh	1-in to 48 mesh	½-in to 65 mesh	½-in to 100 mesh	¼-in to 200 mesh	Rpm Mill	To Run	Of Motor
	—Capacity (tons per 24 hrs) Medium-hard Quartz—						—Horsepower—	
3 × 2	15	11	9	6		33	7½	10
3 × 3	20	16	14	9		33	10	15
3 × 4	25	21	19	12	7	33	12	15
3 × 6	35	31	29	18	9	33	17½	20
3 × 9	50	46	44	27	13	33	24	25
4 × 3	42	34	30	22	12	28	17	20
4 × 5	63	55	50	31	16	28	28	30
4 × 10	116	108	103	62	26	28	49	50
5 × 3	77	63	55	40	22	26	34	40
5 × 6	130	116	110	67	33	26	57	60
5 × 12	250	236	224	136	54	26	103	125

* Data supplied by Denver Equipment Co., Denver, Col.

may also be a compartment mill as, for example, Sturtevant 8740, the first section of which is 8 feet in diameter, followed by a second section 7 feet in diameter, with a total length of 40 feet. It may have two, three or four compartments, each compartment being furnished with different sized balls or grinding agents. The tube mill is usually fed with material 20 mesh in size or even finer; it produces material with a fineness of 325 mesh, with or without closed circuiting. For extremely fine work, it is equipped with steel balls 1½ inches or less in diameter.

The Compeb mills (Allis-Chalmers) are compartment tube mills, as already mentioned, and are made in various diameters and in lengths from 15 to 50 feet. An example is the 7 foot diameter by 26 foot mill with two compartments. The first has 5 to 2-inch steel balls, 46 per cent volume; the second has 1¼-inch Concavex balls, 46 per cent volume. The rotation is about 20 rpm, and the capacity in terms of cement clinkers of average grindability is 75.6 barrels per hour. The mill grinds in a closed circuit, with an air separator whose discharge averages 95 per cent through 325 mesh. The Concavex balls have two deep dimples which offer greater contact surface. Cast Concavex balls are made of special white-iron alloy; forged Concavex of carbon steel, which is subsequently hardened.

Rod mills have the outer shape of tube mills, but the grinding agent consists of rods about as long as the interior of the mill. As the mill turns, the rods drop onto lower ones, reducing the charge partly by grinding, partly by impact. The rod mill has the distinction of producing few fines; it is considered by many engineers as a granulator. It may also properly be classed as a medium-fine grinder, giving a product up to 50 or 60 mesh, with a minimum of flour, which again distinguishes it from the tube mill, in which flour is desired.

The Hardinge conical rod mill has two conical pieces as heads which afford spaces for the feed on one end and the product on the other. The rods also do not scrape the end plates, as they might in the standard cylindrical mill, because they align themselves within ten revolutions in the central part of the mill. This rod mill is an excellent grinding device for the reduction of a fairly soft ore from ½ inch maximum pieces to about 20 or 30 mesh, with a minimum of fines.

The ball mill is considered a preliminary grinding machine, the tube mill a finish-grinding machine, and the rod mill an intermediate size grinding machine.

Closed-circuit Grinding. In closed-circuit grinding, the mill discharge is elevated to a screen, a wet or dry classifier, or an air separator, where material of the required fineness is removed and collected, while the oversize is returned at once to the mill (see Figures 25 and 27). The classifier

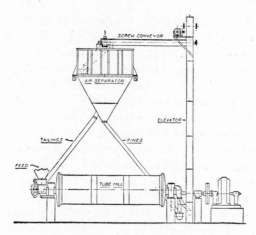

Figure 25.—Closed-circuit grinding unit with tube mill and air separator. (Courtesy Sturtevant Mill Co., Boston, Mass.)

may be wet, for closed grinding is equally applicable to wet-grinding. The portion rejected by the classifier is termed the "circulating load." When grinding in "open circuit," the mill is limited in output by its ability to finish all the feed given it to the required fineness in one passage through.

In a study of a tube mill 26 feet long, it was found that 75 per cent of the grinding was accomplished in the first 4 feet, 85 per cent in the first 6 feet and 91 per cent in the first 8 feet, so that the balance of the mill, or 10 feet, was required to finish 9 per cent of the material fed in. By drawing the pulp at the 8-foot point and removing the 91 per cent with the required mesh, the balance may be returned and ground again to 91 per cent of the whole in 8 feet of length. The balance of the mill may be utilized for an equal tonnage of fresh feed. Actually, it is the circulating load which is increased in closed-circuit grinding; the capacity is almost doubled in some installations, and more than doubled in others.

An important advantage of closed-circuit dry grinding is the cooling effect of the increased circulating load, which passes through the air separator where the moving air cools it. Still another is the reduction of moisture.

Conical Ball Mills; Pebble Mills. The conical ball mill has a central cylindrical part, with a shorter conical head for the feed end, and a longer, more sharply tapered cone for the discharge end; the assembled body lies

FIGURE 26.—The Hardinge conical mill with housing partly removed to show the relation of size of balls, height of drop and effective grinding energy in the different zones. Zone 1, left; Zone 2, middle; Zone 3, right. Note entering feed at left, and product discharge through reverse cone grate at right; also the wedge bar type lining. (Courtesy Hardinge Co., York, Pa.)

on its side, and turns about its long axis, which is made horizontal (see Figure 26). Hollow trunnions permit continuous feed on one side, continuous discharge on the other. The grinding agent is graduated steel or iron balls. As the mill revolves, a classification of balls as to size takes place, the largest ones collecting in the widest part (the cylindrical one), while the medium ones collect in the first part of the cone, as shown in Figure 26. The largest balls drop a long distance, developing considerable energy; the smaller balls drop a shorter distance and develop less energy.

The new feed reaches Zone 1 first, and the greater energy is expended on the larger pieces; the lesser energy in Zone 2 is exerted on medium-sized pieces, while the still smaller energy deep in the cone (Zone 3) is exerted on small particles with excellent efficiency. In a general way, the energy is suited for the work it must perform, and development of excess energy is avoided. As a result, the power requirement is a minimum.

Discharge may be by gravity, or by means of a current of air in dry grinding; with either method, closed-circuit grinding may be adopted.

TABLE 13. ENERGY DISTRIBUTION IN THE VARIOUS ZONES
OF THE HARDINGE CONICAL BALL MILL

Zone 1 (Left in Fig. 26)	Zone 2 (Middle)	Zone 3 (Right)
4-in balls	3-in balls	2-in balls
3-ft drop	2-ft drop	1-ft drop
18-ft-lb energy	8-ft-lb energy	1-ft-lb energy

The conical ball mill is lined with manganese-steel or other hard steel liners. It is offered in 38 sizes, of which 25 are standard. The capacities are shown in Table 14. The conical ball mill, as well as the pebble mill, grinds wet or dry.

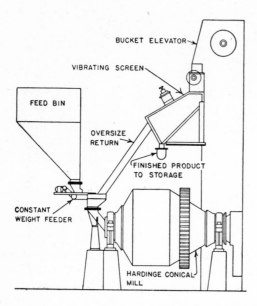

FIGURE 27.—Sketch showing a Hardinge conical mill in closed circuit with vibrating screen. (Courtesy Hardinge Co., York, Pa.)

The shell of the smaller mills is made of cast iron; the 6-foot diameter mill is standard in either cast iron or steel plate; the larger mills are made of steel plate.

For every conical ball mill (Hardinge), there is a pebble mill of equal size, but the lining is different; it consists of Belgian Silex or domestic silica blocks 2½ and 4 inches thick, set in neat cement. Porcelain linings are furnished when even the slight impurities which silica might introduce must be avoided. Some further information on conical pebble mills is included in Table 14.

TABLE 14.   HARDINGE CONICAL MILLS, WITH CONTINUOUS OPERATION (SELECTED ITEMS)

BALL MILLS

Size	Weight of Mill	Lining	Weight of Balls Maximum (lbs)	Rpm*	Motor (max. hp)	Capacity (tons per 24 hrs) 1½-in to 10 mesh	½-in to 100 mesh	¼-in to 98% −325 mesh
3′ × 24″	3,050	2,400	2,400	39.8	10	32	12	4
5′ × 22″	10,200	8,000	8,300	30.4	40	140	49	19
6′ × 36″	17,100	11,700	17,500	27.7	75	282	97	38
8′ × 48″	29,000	23,000	43,500	23.8	200	820	274	108
10′ × 66″	50,600	35,000	83,500	21.2	450	1,900	632	249

PEBBLE MILLS

Size	Weight of Mill	Lining	Weight of Balls Maximum (lbs)	Rpm*	Motor (max. hp)	Capacity (tons per 24 hrs) 1½-in to 10 mesh	½-in to 100 mesh	¼-in to 98% −325 mesh
3′ × 24″	3,000	1,300	700	40.4	5	15	5.5	2.1
5′ × 22″	9,600	4,000	2,300	31.2	15	54	19	7.5
6′ × 36″	16,500	6,500	4,800	28.2	30	117	42	17
8′ × 48″	19,400	12,300	12,700	24.1	75	326	117	45
10′ × 66″	35,900	16,800	25,500	21.4	150	675	242	95

* Maximum. For weights of balls and pebbles, the minimum is about 20% less. The capacities given are for wet-grinding of material of average grindability; dry-grinding capacities are 80 to 90% of wet-grinding capacities. Normal operating ball or pebble charges for mill operating with air classifiers are 5 to 10% below minimum weight. Data supplied by the Hardinge Co., York, Pennsylvania.

The mill is driven by means of a girth gear, which may be a cast-iron, cast-tooth gear, a cast-iron or cast-steel cut-tooth gear, or a cast-steel herringbone gear, with pinion to match. The latter is driven by any one of six methods.

The *Hardinge Tricone mill*, of very recent development, is a ball or pebble mill with continuous operation. It consists of two conical heads (which may also be rounded or convex in shape), a short cylindrical section, and a longer conical barrel with a taper of approximately 7°. The Tricone mill (Figure 28) preserves the approximate shape and volume of the cylindrical mill, but retains all the operating advantages of the Hardinge Conical mill, with greater capacity per unit of diameter. It is designed for both wet and dry grinding, and is available in two main sizes, each with modifications, so that there are 11 from which to select.

Ring Roll Mill. The ring roll mill is a pulverizing device, reducing materials from 1 to 1½-inch feed to any mesh from 20 to 200. It contains a steel ring against the inner, finished face of which two or more rollers press. The ring may be rotated while the rollers are held against it by springs; or the rollers may be rotated, when the centrifugal force is the source of the necessary pressure. The mill may have gravity discharge and operate in a closed-grinding circuit, or it may deliver its product to a current of air traversing the mill housing. Furthermore, the mill may be horizontal, with a horizontal driving shaft, or vertical, with a vertical driving shaft.

In the Sturtevant ring roll mill (No. 1½ and 2), a steel anvil-ring, 45 and 44 inches in diameter, is mounted in a head which is revolved by a

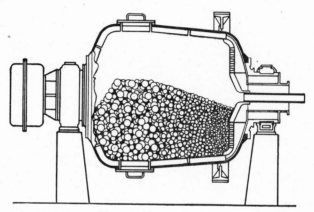

FIGURE 28.—Assembly and sectional view of Tricone Ball Mill showing balls and discharge grate. (Courtesy Hardinge Co., York, Pa.)

FIGURE 29.—The Sturtevant ring-roll mill for fine grinding, with horizontal shaft. Two of the three rolls, working on the anvil-ring, are shown. The mill is operated in closed circuit with an air separator. (Courtesy Sturtevant Mill Co., Boston, Mass.)

horizontal shaft. Against the inner face of the revolving ring the rolls, 16 and 18 inches in diameter, are equally and elastically pressed by springs. The revolving ring causes the rollers to revolve about their axes. The material to be ground (up to 1½ inches) is fed to the anvil-face of the rotating ring and held there by centrifugal force; it is crushed by being drawn under the rolls. Rocks are crushed down on other rocks between ring and roll, producing a maximum of fines. The pressure between roll and ring is very great, and is adjustable (from the outside of mill) to values from 20,000 to 60,000 pounds. The smaller mill, No. 0, has only one roll; its output is more moderate, its first cost much lower. All three mills are best operated in closed circuit. Capacities, dimensions and speeds are shown in Tables 15 and 16.

TABLE 15. CAPACITIES OF NO. 1½ STURTEVANT RING ROLL MILL ON VARIOUS MATE-RIALS AT DIFFERENT MESHES

Barytes, 8 to 10 tons/hr to 40 mesh	Gannister, 10 to 12 tons/hr to 14 mesh
Coal, 5 to 6 tons/hr to 40 mesh	Iron borings, 8 to 10 tons/hr to 20 mesh
Coke (96 hour) 3½ to 4 tons/hr to 20 mesh	Limestone, 8 to 12 tons/hr to 20 mesh
	Limestone, 3 to 4 tons/hr to 85%—200 mesh
Fire clay, 8 to 11 tons/hr	Manganese, 2 to 4 tons/hr to 80 mesh
Florida pebble, 7 t. to 85%—60 mesh	Marble, 3 to 4 tons/hr to 95%—100 mesh
Florida pebble, 3 t. to 95%—100 mesh	Oyster shells, 4 to 5 tons/hr to 60 mesh

The No. 2 mill has 50 per cent larger capacities.

The No. 0 capacity is approximately 35 per cent of the figures for No. 1½ in this table.

Size of feed: 1″ to 1½″.

TABLE 16. DIMENSIONS AND SPEEDS FOR STURTEVANT RING ROLL MILLS

Size	Ring Diam. × Face	Rolls Diam. × Face	Ring Speed (rpm)	Horsepower
No. 0	24″ × 7″	14″ × 7″	125	8 to 15
No. 1½	45″ × 8″	16″ × 10½″	64	40 to 50
No. 2	44″ × 14″	18″ × 14″	70	75

In the *Raymond Bowl Mill,* which pulverizes coal for direct-firing of rotary kilns, grinding takes place in a revolving bowl with an inner grinding ring, turning on a vertical shaft at approximately 1200 feet per minute. Two or three stationary grinding rolls (the number depending on the size of the machine) are pre-loaded by adjustable spring pressure, and are set with surfaces parallel with and close to, yet clear of, the ring. A strong flow of air is pulled through the mill by an exhauster while the mill is in operation; the resulting coal-air mixture enters the classifier located above the grinding chamber. The outlet from the classifier is connected by piping to the exhauster inlet. The entire mill assembly is suitably enclosed for dust-free operation.

The mill is fed by means of an internal rotary feeder which discharges into the revolving bowl. The taper of the grinding ring is such that the coal is retarded a sufficient time to be nipped between the rolls and ring. The ground coal is thrown against a series of deflectors and the coarse particles return to the bowl, whereas the fine and medium particles are carried into the classifier by the airflow. (See Figures 30 and 31.)

In the classifier, the coal enters the inner cone and is deflected into a

FIGURE 30.—The Raymond bowl mill producing pulverized coal mixed with air for the direct firing of a rotary kiln. Hot air from the discharge apron enters the mill body just below the bowl, picks up the dust, travels through the classifier, is pulled into the fan and delivered through the burner pipe to the kiln. (Courtesy Raymond Pulverizer Division, Combustion Engineering-Superheater, Inc., Chicago 22, Ill.)

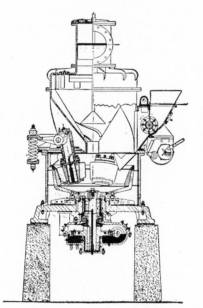

FIGURE 31.—Vertical cross section of the Raymond bowl mill showing the grinding rolls and the pressure spring which holds it against the grinding ring. At middle right, note the feed hopper and feeder roll. (Courtesy Raymond Pulverizer Division, Combustion Engineering-Superheater, Inc., Chicago 22, Ill.)

circular path by a series of adjustable vanes, set at an angle to separate the finished coal from the oversize by a vortex action. The oversize particles flow down the inner cone wall and return to the mill for regrinding. The fine coal is carried from the classifier outlet to the fan (exhauster) inlet; the fan finally blows the coal-air mixture into the kiln through the burner pipe.

The air drawn into the mill by the action of the exhauster enters the mill housing around the bowl as preheated air for simultaneous drying and grinding. The pulverized coal-air mixture is maintained at 165–175°F for maximum drying and grinding efficiency. An additional design feature of the mill is an automatic rejector of foreign material such as tramp iron or pyrites.

Power efficiency in grinding and pulverizing operations is remarkably low. Though it varies in the several devices, which differ in the total dead weight which must be revolved or moved, industrial crushing in general requires about 100 times as much energy as theoretically necessary.* Grinding in closed circuit is a step forward, for it removes the fines almost at once, so that no energy is wasted in acting upon them further.

Reading References

"Ball, rod and tube mills," by William H. Withington, *Ind. Eng. Chem.*, **30**, 897 (1938).

"Multiple use of pebble and ball mills," by E. M. Underwood, *Ind. Eng. Chem.*, **30**, 905 (1938).

"Pulverizers with air separation and air drying," by W. A. Koven, *Ind. Eng. Chem.*, **30**, 909 (1938).

"Developments in grinding," by Lincoln T. Work, *Ind. Eng. Chem.*, **30**, 130 (1938).

"A review of certain unit processes in the reduction of materials," by J. C. Farrant, *Trans. Inst. Chem. Eng.* (London), **18**, 56 (1940).

"Crushing and grinding appliances—the connection between type and purpose," by Prof. B. W. Holman, *Trans. Inst. Chem. Eng.*, **12**, 186 (1934).

"A view of grinding fundamentals," by W. L. Maxson, *Chem. Met. Eng.*, **45**, 226 (1938); "Grinding in closed circuit," by H. W. Hitzrot, *Ibid.*, 234; "Size reduction by impact," by J. T. Fowler, and "Size distribution in crushing," *Ibid.*, 243, and subsequent articles in the same volume.

"Modern machines for dry size reduction in fine size range," by C. E. Berry, *Ind. Eng. Chem.*, **38**, 672 (1946).

"Crushing and grinding," by W. F. Carey, *Trans. Inst. Chem. Eng. (London)*, **12**, 179 (1934).

"Energy-new surface relationship in crushing," by J. N. S. Kwong, J. T. Adams, Jr., J. F. Johnson, and Edgar L. Piret, Part 1, *Chem. Eng. Progress*, **45**, 508 (1949); Part 2, ib., p. 655; Part 3, by J. F. Johnson, J. Axelson, and Edgar L. Piret, ib., p. 708 (1949).

"Crushing and grinding, review of unit operation," by Lincoln T. Work, *Ind. Eng. Chem.*, **42**, 26 (1950); an annual feature.

* "Crushing and Grinding," by W. F. Carey, *Trans. Inst. Chem. Eng. (London)*, **12**, 179 (1934).

Breaking larger pieces into smaller ones is only part of a task; there remains the separation of sizes in groups having designated limits. Many chemical materials will not function unless the particles have a certain size; others will function, but not at the faster rate desired. Linked to the separation on the basis of size is that based on separation of kinds, and in this work electromagnetic and electrostatic separators are taking the lead.

3. SCREENING AND GRADING EQUIPMENT

Separation of the various sizes of grains and lumps in a solid material of uniform composition is performed on a large scale by means of automatic screens and grizzlies; the latter serve for the coarser separations, and the former for medium, coarse, and fine sizes. The screens, which may be either revolving or flat, are supplemented by air separators, in which a steady air current traveling a definite distance sorts the fine particles from coarser ones, taking the place of the woven wire or other screen cloth in the screener. The separation may be not only as to size, but also as to composition, when a nonhomogeneous material, such as a crushed rock, is treated. This is an important distinction; the "separator," which sorts in kinds as well as in sizes, goes a step further than screening, which separates into· size only. The separator accomplishes its purpose by bringing into play events which depend upon the specific gravity, the magnetic susceptibility, or the electrical conductivity of the component parts. Affinity for an added chemical becomes the basis of another separation as to kind, namely, the one performed in the flotation cell. Sorting in respect to sizes is called grading as well as screening, and the device may be known as a grader, or screener, as well as a screen.

The grizzly may consist of a number of steel bars laid parallel to one another, with regular spacings of, let us say, 3 inches between them, with suitable side panels. Such an assembly may be set at an angle high enough to permit the oversize material to roll down over the bars, while the smaller lumps drop between. There are variations in grizzlies; all of them, however, pass large particles, or rather small lumps, while still larger ones are the oversize. Next in size of spacing come screens with wide meshes ("coarse screens"), which have openings ranging from 4 inches to ¼ inch; such coarse screens may even overlap the grizzlies. Fine screens follow the coarse ones, with an increasing number of meshes to the inch, up to 325.

Screens

The "mesh" in a screen is designated in several ways. When it is specified by a number, the number indicates how many square openings

44

there are to the linear inch; thus 100 mesh means a wire cloth with 100 square openings to the linear inch. A fraction of screened material designated as "through 10 mesh" might also be labeled "minus 10 mesh," or "—10 mesh;" such a sample would have passed through a 10-mesh sieve, but would still contain a variety of sizes, from those larger ones which just passed through the sieve down to very fine ones. Its lack of assortment is reflected in the term "unsized." Another fraction labeled "on 100 mesh" or "plus 100 mesh," which is the same as "+100 mesh," consists of material lying on top of a 100-mesh screen and unable to pass through; it too may contain a variety of sizes and is therefore "unsized." On the other hand, the sizes of the particles in a sample marked "—10 +20 mesh" would lie within narrower limits, for all of them passed a 10-mesh screen, and failed to pass through the 20-mesh one; such material would be "sized."

The Bureau of Standards has pointed out that stating that a sieve has a certain "mesh" without giving other data is meaningless because it does not give information regarding the important dimensions in the sieve, namely, the clear opening. The size of the clear opening is smaller than the fraction of the inch suggested in the "mesh designation" by the diameter of the wire; precision is attained by listing the diameter of the wire after the mesh designation, thus "200 mesh 0.0021 inch wire" would mean a clear opening of 0.0029 inch. Standards have been set by the Bureau, and the manufacturers of commercial sieves have succeeded in bringing their product into line with the corresponding specification of the Bureau.

The Tyler standard screen scale provides a ratio between the widths of

TABLE 17. THE TYLER STANDARD SCREEN SCALE*, WITH CORRESPONDING DESIGNATION AND VALUES FROM THE UNITED STATES STANDARD SIEVE SCALE
(SELECTED ITEMS, SQUARE OPENINGS)

Mesh	Diam. of Wire (in)	Width of Clear Opening (in)	Designation (microns)	Corresponding U. S. Standard	Clear Opening (in)	Opening (mm)
4	0.065	0.185	4760	(No. 4)	0.187	4.76
6	.036	.131	3360	(No. 6)	.132	3.36
8	.032	.093	2380	(No. 8)	.0937	2.38
10	.035	.065	1680	(No. 12)	.0661	1.68
14	.025	.046	1190	(No. 16)	.0469	1.19
20	.0172	.0328	840	(No. 20)	.0331	0.84
28	.0125	.0232	590	(No. 30)	.0232	.59
35	.0122	.0164	420	(No. 40)	.0165	.42
48	.0092	.0116	297	(No. 50)	.0117	.297
65	.0072	.0082	210	(No. 70)	.0083	.21
100	.0042	.0058	149	(No. 100)	.0059	.149
150	.0026	.0041	105	(No. 140)	.0041	.105
200	.0021	.0029	74	(No. 200)	.0029	.074
270	.0016	.0021	53	(No. 270)	.0021	.053
400	.001	.0015	37	(No. 400)	.0015	.037

* W. S. Tyler Company, Cleveland. The widths of the openings increase in the ratio of the square root of 2.

the clear openings of adjacent screens of 1.414, (i.e., $\sqrt{2}$) so that while the width of each screen opening is 1.414 times the clear opening in the previous sieve, the area is double. Large-scale screen cloths for commercial screens are made on the same basis. An advantage of this series is that skipping one size gives a ratio for the widths of the clear openings of 2 to 1; skipping two sizes gives a ratio of 3 to 1 (approximately), and skipping three sizes gives a ratio of 4 to 1.

The scale given in Table 17 is for the fine series; there is a table for the coarse series having a maximum clear opening of 4 inches. There is also a standard table for round-holed plate screens.

Complete sieve analyses are made with 18 screen sizes graduated from 0.0029-inch (200 mesh) to 1.05-inch opening; the results are plotted in order to study the size distribution, and to compare it with a normal curve. Size analyses are made for other reasons also.

The wire used for screen cloth may be bronze, steel, stainless steel, copper, nickel, or "Monel." A number of different weaves are offered.

Silk bolting cloth, an important screening medium, is generally designated by the number of meshes to the inch.

TABLE 18. A CLASSIFICATION OF SCREENS

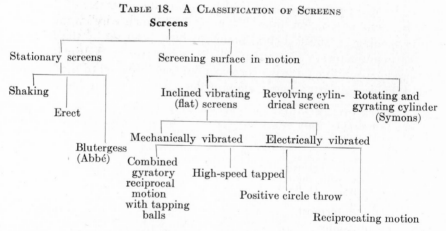

Screens with Automatic Operation

Revolving Screens. Revolving screens are horizontal or nearly horizontal cylindrical screens which receive the mixed sizes of crystals or other material at one end, permit the portion with the proper particle size to pass through, and discharge the tailings or oversize material at the other end. The screening medium may be a perforated plate, with round or slot-shaped openings, or it may be a woven metal wire cloth. When the revolving cylinder has perforations of one size only, the material is divided into two portions—the screened portion, and the oversize. When the revolving cylinder has perforations of two or three sizes (or more), the material is fed first to the end having the smallest opening, let us say ⅛ inch; the unpassed portion travels to the center part, with ¼-inch openings, where particles of that size pass through the screen to a chute below; the part still remaining reaches the third size perforations, ½-inch for example, where the particles able to pass through are screened away. There remain only the oversize particles, which are discharged over the far edge. Another arrangement for obtaining several sizes is to use a nest of cylinders, with the largest openings in the innermost one, and the

FIGURE 32.—A 72-inch diameter by 28 foot over-all length rotary cooler screen in which are located two 6-inch long screen sections, each double jacketed. The inner section of screen cloth has 0.305 by 1.475 inch openings. The outer jacket screen cloth has 0.178 by 0.728 inch openings. Only the fine product passing through the small openings of the outer jacket is desired. The material coasting between the inner and outer sections of screen cloth is continuously returned to the inside cylinder from which it discharges along with the normal tailings. Housing removed. For cooling, see Figure 33. (Courtesy C. O. Bartlett and Snow Co., Cleveland 5, Ohio.)

smallest in the outermost. As many sizes will be separated as there are screen sizes, plus one.

One type of revolving screen is built so that the inner surface is free from any obstruction; the material can flow along without piling up on any structural members, for these are placed on the outer side. The drive is by means of a spur-girt gear secured to the dead plate at the feed end of the screen. The screen as a whole is carried on two riding rings, and the speed of rotation is rather slow. In another design, intended for lighter service, the screens, or rolled wire cloth or perforated rolls, are mounted on a series of interior spiders, carried by a cold-rolled steel central shaft running through the entire length of the screen. The shaft is driven by bevel gears.

Revolving screens are generally rather large, such as from 6 to 16 or 18 feet in length, and from 36 to 72 inches in diameter, although there are rotary screens as short as 4 feet, and as small as 18 inches in diameter. A large rotary cooler screen is shown in Figure 32 with the housing removed, and in Figure 33, with the housing in place. The captions will furnish a complete description. Figure 33a shows a rotary screen with

FIGURE 33.—The double-jacketed rotary cooler screen shown with its housing; Figure 32 shows it without the housing. The cool air inlet ports are located at the base of the housing, just over the hopper which directs the screened and cooled product to the belt conveyor below the floor. Capacity 200 tons per hour of foundry shakeout sand. (Courtesy C. O. Bartlett and Snow Co., Cleveland 5, Ohio.)

two sizes of openings, the smaller ones meeting the feed first, the larger ones next. The tailings form the third size.

Another interesting screen is one which has a diameter of 8 feet, 10 inches; a screening length of 8 feet, 1 inch; and an over-all length of 10 feet, 3 inches. It is equipped with $\frac{3}{8}$-inch steel plate having $\frac{5}{8} \times 1\frac{1}{4}$-inch staggered perforations, and revolves at the rate of 10 rpm. It is set on a slope of about $1\frac{1}{2}$ inches in 12 inches, downward toward the tailings discharge end, and handles, for example, 1500 tons of coke weighing 29 pounds per cubic foot in a period of 22 hours. The fines pass through the screen and are collected in a hopper below; the tailings are discharged at the end of the screen cylinder. It is to be noted that the interior of this screen is entirely free of obstructions.

Another screen, called style N, illustrates the internal spider construction; it is 36 inches in diameter, has a screen length of 7 feet, 9 inches and an over-all length of 9 feet, 3 inches. It is set on a slope of about ¼ inch per foot, is covered with wire cloth having 5-mesh 0.092-inch wire, and revolves at 2 rpm. When handling sand weighing about 100 pounds per

FIGURE 33a.—A rotary cylindrical screen, with first smaller, then larger openings, in action. The screenings from each size openings go to different bins. Note spray of water to keep down the coal dust. (Courtesy Link-Belt Co., Chicago, Ill.)

cubic foot, the screen, run as indicated, has a capacity of about 30 tons per hour.

Revolving hexagonal screens give greater agitation of the material and for that reason are sometimes preferred for screening fine materials. The cloth may be of woven wire or silk; the latter is mounted on wooden frames instead of metal ones. There are also tapered hexagonal screens.

Flat Screens. The simplest type of flat screen, or flat angle screen, consists of a single deck, which is flat, a frame with side panels or a box with suitable outlets and feed mechanism. The deck may be covered, so that the whole assembly is enclosed (closed model); or it may be uncovered (open model). The closed model has a feed inlet; in the open model, the feed is directly to the upper end of the screening surface, or deck. The flat deck is inclined; in some models the inclination is slight. The screens receive a rapid motion, in any one of several ways. The purposes of the motion are (1) to keep the openings from clogging, in which case the operation of the screen would come to an end, and (2) to move the material still on the screen toward the discharge spout. The motion may be induced by tapping, or by rapid shaking in the horizontal or slightly inclined plane, perhaps by differential shaking consisting of a slow forward stroke and a rapid backward stroke. Or it may be brought about by an eccentric shaft carrying the screen assembly and giving it a "full circle throw" motion; by rapid shaking of the screen frame; by electrical vibration imparted to the cloth itself or to the frame; or in other ways.*

FIGURE 34.—Open type of Day RoBall Gyrating screen with two screening surfaces and with end discharge; cog belt drive. (By permission.)

Flat Screens with Gyratory Motion and Tapping Balls. In the single-deck screens with combined gyratory and reciprocal motion, the rectangular flat deck is slightly inclined from the horizontal. Its upper end is fastened to the eccentric driving head turned by a vertical shaft, which in turn is driven by a worm gear from the motor shaft (in one of the standard machines taken as an example), while its lower end has a slide-type bearing and executes a reciprocal motion.

The gyrating motion in the upper end brings about a stratification of the material, the finer particles below, the coarser ones on top; it also forces the particles against the screen surface. The reciprocal motion at the lower end helps convey the material. The screen deck has two layers, an upper wire or silk cloth, and a lower coarse-mesh wire; between the

* The difficulty about inclined vibrating screens of high inclination is that they are not critical as to sizes, due to the variability in the size of the opening, and the approach of the material to the opening. Therefore, for close sizing, in which the tolerances are very limited, one of the so-called flat angle screens is used. Where critical grading is not required, the inclined vibrating screen has a great advantage in its high capacity, and is then very satisfactory.

two a number of rubber balls are placed, in small compartments formed by cross strips and rods. As the deck moves, the balls are in constant motion; on rebounding from the retaining coarse wire screen they strike the upper cloth and shake loose any particles tending to "blind" it. In the single-deck machine, the operation produces two parts: the sieved portion, the "throughs," which leave by a tubular passage in the front end of the pan, and the oversize, the "tails," which may also leave by a tubular opening in the pan. Instead of these outlets, a screen may have end discharge (see Figure 34). The feed is at the upper end of the screen in the closed models, through one or two tubular or other inlets; in the open models it is directly onto the screening surface. The feed is continuous, and so also is the discharge of both "throughs" and "tails"; the operation is automatic.

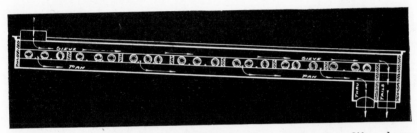

FIGURE 35.—A cross-sectional view of the one-sieve Unique Gyro-Sifter shown in Figure 37, but without the mechanism for motion. Note the path of the feed over the screen, the outlet in the pan for the "throughs," and a second outlet for the "tails." (Courtesy Robinson Mfg. Co., Muncy, Pa.)

In the two-deck screens, the lower screen generally has a finer mesh than the upper, and three separations occur. A three-deck machine with the screens of gradually finer mesh delivers four separations. But one manufacturer, at least, offers these devices in two fundamentally different styles. The Gyro-Sifter* of Style A having, for example, two sieves, makes only two separations, because the two screens have the same mesh; both receive feed directly, and both deliver the same "throughs" and "tails." The attribute of Style A is its greater capacity. The Gyro-Sifters of Style B, on the other hand, have the usual sequence of screens, each deck with a closer mesh than the one above it; the separations are here kept apart, and are equal to the number of screens, plus one. The Gyro-Sifters are made in 44 standard sizes and models, mainly closed models which are entirely dust-proof.

An additional example of this type of screen is the RoBall stabilized Gyrating Screen,† made with one, two, three or four decks and in a num-

* The Robinson Manufacturing Company, Muncy, Pennsylvania.
† The J. H. Day Company, Cincinnati, Ohio.

ber of screen dimensions; thus the two-deck machine is made in five sizes, ranging from the smallest, 20 inches wide and 48 inches long, to the largest, which is 60 inches wide and 120 inches long. There are in all 15 different machines of the standard types.

The drive for the flat screens with combined gyratory and reciprocal motion is by direct motor, cog-belt, pulley or other standard means. The motion varies, in one well known series, from a 2-inch diameter at 322 rpm to a 3½-inch diameter at 214 rpm, depending upon the size of the

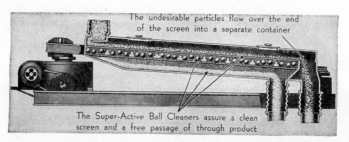

FIGURE 36.—Working principle of the Day RoBall Gyrating screen, illustrating the path of the separations, and the action of the tapping balls. (By permission.)

FIGURE 37.—A standard model of the Unique Gyro-Sifter, with one sieve, motor driven, and example of the flat screen with combined gyratory and reciprocating motion. (Courtesy Robinson Mfg. Co., Muncy, Pa.)

screen. In another series (RoBall), for the smallest size, 20 × 48 inches, the eccentricity of the motion is 1 inch, and the reciprocating travel of the tail twice that; the speed is 320 rpm. For all other sizes in the same series, the diameter of the motion is 1¼ inches, the reciprocating motion twice that, and the speed 275 rpm. The oscillations per minute are equal in number to the revolutions per minute.

The screen's cloths may vary widely in the mesh, for example, from 2 to 250 mesh. Screens with mesh numbers between 2 and 50, with openings from 1.446 inches to 0.0145 inch, are available in brass, copper, bronze, stainless steel and special alloys. Silk bolting cloth No. 0000 with

0.0537-inch opening is the first of 26 numbers with gradually decreasing openings, the finest being No. 25 with 0.0025-inch opening.

Cooler with Gyratory and Reciprocating Motion. A vibrating cooler has been developed, which in the specific example chosen, the RoBall Cooler, is a converted gyrating and reciprocating screen. The screen frame is removed, and stainless steel top and bottom pans provided with

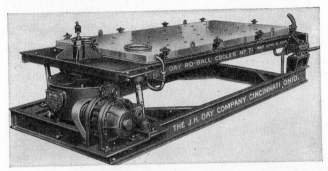

FIGURE 38.—A vibrating cooler, with combined gyratory and reciprocating motion, with stainless-steel pan and cover, both water-jacketed for the rapid cooling or conditioning of powders. The capacity is high. (Courtesy J. H. Day Co., Cincinnati, Ohio.)

FIGURE 39.—A powder sifter with rubber bearings and rubber-sealed driving rod, especially adapted to handling explosive or abrasive substances. Feed is at upper right, screenings leave through spout at near left, tails through spout just visible at far left. (Courtesy J. H. Day Co., Cincinnati, Ohio.)

cooling jackets are mounted on the same mechanism. Either cold water or brine may be circulated through the jackets. It is intended for cooling powders, as for example in the manufacture of plastics. The feed and discharge are continuous. The capacity is high, as may be seen from the following example: using cold well water in the cooling jackets, the temperature of a "plastic" product in powder form was cooled from 150°F (54.4°C) to 75°F (23.9°C) at the rate of 1800 pounds per hour, in a cooler 40½ × 90 inches. The cooling is indirect, by contact with the cold walls, and by radiation from the powder to the cold top or bottom. It will readily be seen that, by using a colder liquid, a more rapid cooling and a greater capacity could be obtained. By using liquids maintained at certain constant temperatures, this device becomes a conditioner, and should be extremely valuable. The eccentricity and the rate of vibration are the same as those for the RoBall screens.

Flat Screen with Reciprocating Motion. A flat screen with straight reciprocating motion of special interest is the "Rubber-bearing Powder Sifter." The construction in general is similar to that of the RoBall Gyratory and Reciprocal Motion screen, but there is no eccentric motion. Instead the screen frame with its housing is pushed back and forth by means of a connecting rod driven from an eccentric within the dust-tight

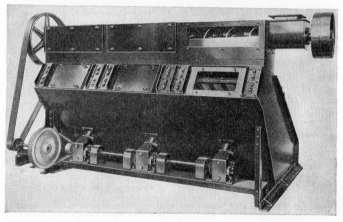

FIGURE 40.—The Sturtevant Moto-Vibro Screen, a mechanically vibrated screen; a rear view showing the vibrators at the bottom. One cover is removed to show conveyor feed screw and adjustable feed board. (Courtesy Sturtevant Mill Co., Boston, Mass.)

drive housing, as shown in Figure 39. The construction features render this sifter especially interesting to manufacturers of abrasive and explosive materials; no friction contacts are exposed, and the point of entrance of the connecting rod into the drive box is sealed by means of a molded corrugated rubber sleeve.

Inclined Flat Screen with Frame Mechanically Vibrated: the Moto-Vibro. Among the vibrating screens wherein the vibration is developed mechanically and applied to the frame, is the Sturtevant Moto-Vibro inclined screen, the successor of the earlier Newaygo screen. The screen frames are set at a considerable inclination, and the motion is applied to the frame, not to the delicate cloth. Also, the upper part of the screen, which receives the feed, has the greater vibration and amplitude, the motion diminishing in amplitude to only an intense buzz at the bottom, where there is less work to do. The vibration is applied two-thirds of the way up the frame on a 6-foot frame, for example, while the lower end of the frame is allowed to move but slightly; this brings about the desired differential vibration. The vibrator has an eccentric shaft with a total throw of $\frac{1}{16}$ inch, making 1800 rpm, producing vibrations small in amplitude but of stinging intensity. The feed is by screw conveyor, or simply by a chute; the screenings and tailings are collected separately below the floor or platform. The screens are dustless, as each unit is enclosed in a welded steel case.

The capacity varies with the mesh; it is smaller with the finer meshes, which is true of all screening devices. The Moto-Vibro is recommended for products 40 mesh and coarser. The Single Unit Moto-Vibro with one screening surface has the following capacity, in terms of a single product:

        10 tons per hour through 6 mesh
        6 tons per hour through 20 mesh
        3 tons per hour through 50 mesh
        1 ton per hour through 80 mesh

The capacity by weight depends also upon the weight per volume of the material. Although the Standard Single Unit machine has but one screening surface, it may be equipped with two or with three surfaces, one above another in the same housing and separated by spacing blocks which transmit the motion applied to the lowest frame. In a Two Unit machine, two single units are set up side by side, in a larger housing; the Three Unit machine has three single units set up side by side. For estimating purposes, the following figures will be convenient: the Single Unit machine with spout feed is $1365 (with conveyor feed $1895). The Two Unit machine is about $850 more, and the Three Unit machine costs $800 more than the Two Unit. The figures given are all for single screening surface machines; for each added screen frame, there is an additional cost of $175 (October, 1951).

Exolon Multi-form Grader. In the Exolon Multi-form Grader, another example of the flat screen with the frame mechanically vibrated, the whole inner structure is shaken by a rapid back-and-forth motion, supplied by the Ajax-Shaler Shaker, in which two weights rotate in opposite directions.

The Multi-form Grader is made with a single deck, or with any number of decks, between 1 and 12 or more. In Figure 41, a four-deck Exolon machine is shown. It consists of an outside, stationary steel structure, and of an inner steel structure to which the decks, spouts, and shaking mechanism are attached. The inner structure is either suspended from the outer structure by strips of steel spring, or mounted on the base by upright spring steel supports, as in the model illustrated. The entire inner structure with its attached parts vibrates, including the vibrator itself.   The vibrator is driven through a V-belt by a motor resting on the outer structure.   The material of construction is steel, except for the screen frames, which are of wood.

Each deck carries a wooden frame, on which is tacked the screening agent proper, which in this device is silk bolting cloth of various meshes. The top deck might be 20 mesh, and the next three, in order, 40, 64, and 100.   At each screen the oversize, or tailings, roll to a collector ending in a spout delivering to an outside receptacle; the fines, which have passed through the bolting cloth, reach the surface of the next screen, there to be divided again into the part which is oversize, and the part which passes

FIGURE 41.—Rear view of a four-deck Exolon Multi-form Grader, showing the shaking mechanism. Four delivery spouts run to the left; the collecting troughs of the first and third face the observer. The fifth spout delivers downward and is just visible in bottom center, with the fourth spout plainly shown. (Courtesy Exolon Co., Inc., Tonawanda, N. Y.)

through.   Five fractions will be obtained on this four-deck grader, and they would be designated as +20, +40, +64, +100, and −100, arranged in the order of decreasing size.   The capacity is 5000 pounds of head feed per hour.

A line of graders with suitable screens is offered which covers the whole range between 4 mesh and 250 mesh, and high capacities, with separations into as many fractions as there are decks, plus one.

Standard equipment includes gravity feed or, if recommended by the manufacturer, electrically vibrated feed, shaking mechanism and motor, and extra frames; thus the four-deck grader is supplied with 8 frames. No bolting cloth is supplied, except that one frame is covered with its cloth, properly applied, to serve as a guide.   The four-deck open model, with gravity or electrically vibrated feed hopper, is $1684; the five-deck model is $1884. The corresponding closed models are $150 to $200 more (November, 1951, f.o.b. Tonawanda, N. Y.).

The shaking mechanism* merits a moment's attention. It contains in a strong housing two equal weights mounted on shafts which are geared together in such a way that the shafts rotate at the same speed but in opposite directions. Twice in each revolution the weights pull in the same direction, and twice they oppose and neutralize each other. The result is that over each revolution, the two weights move once in one direction,

FIGURE 42.—View of a four-deck Exolon Multi-form Grader showing four spouts delivering to the front, with the fifth one in bottom center. The shaking mechanism is just visible between the second and third decks. Note the flat spring steel suspension to right and left of shaker. (Courtesy Exolon Co., Inc., Tonawanda, N. Y.)

then sharply in the opposite direction. The housing moves with the weights, and since the housing is rigidly attached to the inner steel structure, the screens undergo the same rapid vibratory motion. Not the least remarkable feature of the shaker is that its throw may be varied to suit different grading requirements by adjusting the revolving weights.

Inclined Screen with Gyrating Body Balanced on Eccentric Shaft. The flat inclined screen with gyrating body is a high-speed mechanical screen with the vibrating mechanism located at the center of gravity of the gyrating body. As the eccentric shaft rotates, the screen frames with the screening surfaces and their load, receive the eccentric motion and gyrate

* The Ajax-Shaler Shaker, manufactured by the Ajax Flexible Coupling Company, Westfield, N. Y. Made in six sizes.

in a full-circle throw.   An example of this kind of screen is the Selectro*
(Figure 43), one of whose features is that its stroke may be adjusted
quickly, without dismantling and without special tools.   The adjustment
is between 0 and ⅜ inches.   The screen is operated at any angle, and the
tilt may be changed, even while the screen is being operated, to fit the
stroke intensity and obtain best separation.   Too much throw may cause
product degradation, and it will definitely cause "mesh hopping," that is,
jumping over too many meshes before it again hits the screen surface;
too little throw results in poor separation, but the right throw brings about
perfect separation, with maximum tonnage.

The Selectro is obtainable with one, two or more decks, in open as well
as in closed ones, and among the latter the "Fumetite" has its joints so well
sealed that it could be operated under water without damage to the
mechanism.   For the screening surface may be used perforated plate,

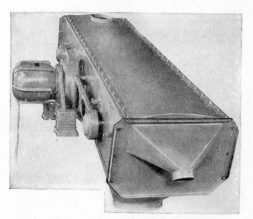

FIGURE 43.—A direct motor-driven
one-deck Fumetite Selectro, a fully
enclosed vibrating screen; the gyrations are due to the eccentric shaft
on which the live portion of the device, the screen and screen frame,
are mounted. The feed is at top
rear; the fines leave by the outlet in
the pan, the tailings through the
front spout. Corrosive fumes, and
abrasive or explosive dusts incidental
to the screening operation are confined within the Fumetite and so
made harmless. (Courtesy Productive Equipment Corp., Chicago, Ill.)

woven wire cloth, a special music wire cloth with openings from ⅜ inch
down to 12 mesh, and silk bolting cloth, to suit.   The Selectro is bedded in
rubber, and is driven by direct motor, V-belt, or other standard means.
For the food industry, where it is very successful in processing ketchup,
soups, fruit juices and other foods, and for the chemical industries, the
parts of the live frame which come into contact with the product are
fabricated of stainless steel, "Monel," nickel, aluminum, or other alloys.

The Gyroset is a somewhat simpler vibrating screen with all the features of the Selectro except the adjustable tilt; it is generally suspended by
cables, although it may just as well be mounted on a base.   The Gyroset
is somewhat lower in cost, as will be seen from the figures in Table 19.

The Ty-Rock and the Tyler-Niagara are two additional examples of
this kind of screen.   The Ty-Rock has rubber mountings at the sides of
the vibrating body, which permit the shaft to find its own natural center

* Productive Equipment Corporation, Chicago, Illinois.

TABLE 19. VIBRATING INCLINED SCREEN WITH GYRATING BODY: COSTS AS OF NOVEMBER (1951)*

	Selectro		Gyroset			
			Suspended		Base-mounted	
	Open	Enclosed	Open	Enclosed	Open	Enclosed
Two deck, 2 ft × 5 ft	$1210	$1460	$ 930	$1125	$1130	$1325
Two deck, 3 ft × 8 ft	1930	2360	1580	2000	1830	2250

* Productive Equipment Corp., Chicago 12, Illinois.

of vibration and prevent the transmission of any vibration to the base frame. The Ty-Rock (Figure 45) is recommended for low angle operation. In the handling of coarse material especially the Tyler-Niagara has immense capacity (Figure 44).

FIGURE 44.—A two-surface Type 300 Tyler-Niagara screen, with the eccentric shaft mounted at the center of gravity of the gyrating body. The motion is high speed and full-circle throw. (By permission.)

Inclined Screens Electrically Vibrated: The Hum-mer. In the electrically vibrated screen, the vibration is produced by an electrical vibrator consisting of coil and magnet, armature and armature post, striking block and wearing plate, and is applied, at least in many of the models, to the screen cloth directly. To take a specific example, the Hum-mer Type 38* is the model used the most in the chemical process industries for screening wet or dry material. It is equipped very generally with fine screening, and is selected where extreme accuracy is important. A

* The W. S. Tyler Company, Cleveland 14, Ohio.

special kind of screen stretch permits the use of the finest cloth over a heavy backing wire. Type 38 is built in 2, 3 or 4-foot widths, and 4, 5, or 6 feet long with a continuous screening surface. It is also built in step tandem. Furthermore, Type 38 is available in multiple-surface units (2 and 3) (Figure 46).

Type 38 Hum-mer is especially efficient for wet screening. It has specially designed feeders, and a dewatering device which overcomes capillary attraction and prevents the solutions from sheeting down the underside of the screening surface.

FIGURE 45.—An action view of an 18 inch × 6 foot, one and one-half deck Ty-Rocket screen, screening coatings which are 65 per cent solids; it is a circle-throw screen especially designed to handle heavy solutions containing up to 70 per cent solids. (Courtesy The W. S. Tyler Co., Cleveland 14, Ohio.)

In the Jeffrey-Traylor FB gravity screen, which is electrically vibrated, the vibrators surround the screen sash, while in the Conveyanscreens made by the same firm, the vibrator is mounted above the screen sash, out of the way of the material. The FB gravity screen is recommended for the coarser materials, the Conveyanscreen for the finer ones. The screens are supplied in single or multi-decked styles and in sizes from 2 to 40 square feet surface.

Among the many other sifters which have been developed for special duties may be mentioned the device in which the sifter box is supported, or suspended from the ceiling, by flexible rods, and is given a rapid motion which causes the box to vibrate. As example, the Gyro-Whip Sifter*

* Richmond Manufacturing Co., Lockport, New York.

might serve, in which the sifter box, supported by flexible rods, whips in motion with a quick circular throw and just a slight up and down movement. The sifter has two main parts: the base and the sifter box. The base is cast iron, and supports the eccentric drive for the sifter box. The latter contains the sieves or sieve frames which are nested one above the other. The sieves may number 10 or more. One box may give two or more separations by changes in the internal construction. The sieves are bolting cloth or metal wire cloth. The Gyro-Whip Sifter is used in flour mills, in feed mills, and for any material which requires sifting, including abrasives. The sifter is made in five series and 18 models.

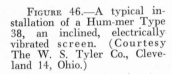

FIGURE 46.—A typical installation of a Hum-mer Type 38, an inclined, electrically vibrated screen. (Courtesy The W. S. Tyler Co., Cleveland 14, Ohio.)

The "heavy-duty, low-head gyratory sifter" of Allis-Chalmers is similarly a box supported on flexible rods, and containing six horizontal sieves, a total of 30 square feet of cloth area. Running at 300 rpm, one low-head, heavy-duty sifter rebolted 125 barrels of flour per hour on a sieve sifter cloth with 6XX silk (74 meshes to the linear inch).

In the *Blutergess high-speed turbine*, which has recently been designated as the Abbé Turbo Sifter,* a different principle is applied. There is no shaking, no vibrating, no suction. The material is thrown by a central turbine against the cloth. The motor is $1\frac{1}{2}$ horsepower; the surface of the stationary screen is only $6\frac{2}{3}$ square feet; yet the capacity

* Abbé Engineering Co., 50 Church St., New York.

is high.   With a speed of 740 rpm and a 110-mesh screen, 550 pounds of precipitated sulfur are screened per hour.   With 1400 rpm and a 60-mesh screen, 2000 pounds of aluminum stearate are delivered through the screen per hour.

The *Symons V-Screen** is probably the latest development in the art of screening.   It also has a screening surface in the form of a cylinder, which is set upright, with its axis vertical, but in this case the *cylinder* is simultaneously *rotated and gyrated*.   The screening surface is a wire cloth held in place between an inner and an outer cage with vertical rods, the cages themselves forming vertical cylinders; or the screening surface may be a Bee-Zee (Bixby-Zimmer) screen surface (made up of round or

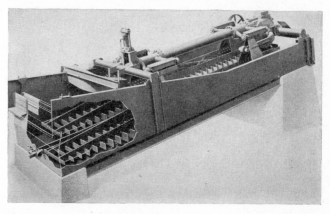

FIGURE 47.—Cutaway view of a Dorr Classifier. Feed is introduced through a curved launder near the top of the tank, and water carrying the finer solids overflows the wooden weir visible on the extreme left.   The heavier settling solids are carried up the inclined deck by two rakes, extending the whole of the tank, and operating with alternated reciprocating movements.   An electric motor, not shown, actuates the mechanism through the drive pulley partly visible at the upper end of the tank.

triangular bars) in the form of a cylinder.   In either form, the cylinder is rotated rapidly, and at the same time gyrated, as for example 14 times per revolution.   The gyration produces an inward deflection of the material being screened, freeing the holes of the screening surface.   "The timing is such that the material contacts the drum and is deflected inward once each gyration."

The material to be screened is fed to a rotating cupped plate with radial vanes set in the upper part of the drum.   It is thrown against the inner surface of the drum; the fines pass through the screen, and thence to an annular collector; the oversize fails to pass, after repeated contacts, and drops into a central hopper.   The capacity of the V-Screen is high; the force which projects the fines through the mesh openings is approxi-mately five times gravity.   In dimensions, one machine is 8 feet high,

* Nordberg Mfg. Co., Milwaukee 7, Wis.

including the collecting hoppers. The main eccentric shaft operates at 1000 rpm.

Hydraulic and Mechanical Classifiers. To these groups belong numerous important devices in which solids of different sizes or different specific gravities are separated from each other by utilizing their differential rate of settling in water. A well known example is the Dorr Classifier (Figure 47), in which the suspension to be classified is fed continuously into a rectangular trough with an inclined bottom. The heavier particles are raked upward along this bottom by a set of mechanically actuated reciprocating rakes and fall out by gravity from its upper end, while most of the water overflows the tank from the opposite end, carrying the lighter particles.

AIR SEPARATORS

The Sturtevant Air Separator. The Sturtevant Air Separator* represents an unusual, not to say unique device for the separation from coarser material of various sizes of powder ranging from 40 to 400 microns. The limits of size for a given separation of the fines are narrow; furthermore, the limits can be varied over a considerable range by means of major and minor adjustments, called control adjustment. The amount of material handled may be very small, or it may be as much as 800 tons per hour. As a definite example: A 16-foot diameter separator takes 800 tons of mixed sizes of material per hour, and separates from it 40 tons of fines per hour. The fines tested 95 per cent through 200 mesh. Another example: With a somewhat smaller feed in the same separator, but using a material richer in fines, there were separated and delivered 60 tons of fines per hour, and the test was 90 per cent through a 200-mesh sieve. When a still finer product is wanted, the same separator will take a similar feed, and separate from it and deliver the finer material, although in smaller tonnage; thus, a separator fed with 800 tons per hour delivers 20 tons of fines per hour, which test 98 per cent through a 325-mesh sieve. Still another example: A 10-foot diameter separator delivers 3 tons of powdered cement which meet the specifications, namely 99.99 per cent passed through a 325-mesh sieve.

The Sturtevant Air Separator consists of (1) an outer chamber in which a circular part surmounts a conical part; (2) a similarly shaped inner chamber, smaller in dimensions; (3) a distributing plate and two fans rotating with the plate as a single mechanical element; (4) a baffled opening in the inner cone for the return of air; (5) two delivery pipes, one for the fines, one for the tailings; and (6) means for feed, and for driving the distributing plate and fan assemblies.

It has merit for its performance in separating and delivering fines of

---

* Sturtevant Mill Co., Boston, Mass.

the sizes stated, within the narrow limits indicated, and with vast tonnage of feed. It has additional merit, however, when used in connection with a grinding mill, whose product is constantly discharged at a higher rate than without such connection, then separated in the air separator. After removal of fines having the desired test of particle size, the tailings or coarse portions are returned to the mill, there to be ground to the desired fineness. As the circuit is a closed one, this kind of grinding has become known as "closed-circuit grinding." Another way of describing the same combination of separator and mill would be to say that the separator frees the mill of the fines, which otherwise cushion the coarser particles and retard their reduction in size. Great economies result: the capacity of the mill is increased, sometimes two- and three-fold; the power consumption per ton of product is greatly reduced, the repair and upkeep of the mill are smaller, per ton of product; without supplementary operation, the product is graded within the proper limits and ready for shipment.

The construction is illustrated in Figure 48. The upper fan, also called the top fan, travels a short distance above the "valves"—flat plates adjustable from the outside, and forming together an iris-like opening, which may be altered to enlarge or diminish the top opening of the inner casing. The lower fan, or rejector fan, travels snug under the "valves." The material to be classified enters by the chute and passage around the central shaft, and drops onto the rapidly revolving distributing plate which whirls it off in a thin stream resembling a curtain of powder. Through this curtain, the upper fan pulls air, which carries solid particles small enough in size to be entrained; they rise, are fanned by the upper fan into the wider outer casing, and travel down the wall of the latter. The rejector fan also acts on the curtain of powder, but in the opposite direction; by its centrifugal and batting action, it forces the heavier particles against the wall of the inner casing. They are prevented from rising through the opening of the inner casing not only because they are too heavy to respond to the upward current induced by the upper fan, but because the rejector fan (which in revolving leaves no opening between its blades and the "valves") whirls the heavier particles outward and downward, to the wall of the inner casing, along which they travel, finally reaching the outlet pipe at the base of the cone. The air which carries the fines upward into the outer chamber returns to the inner chamber through stationary air-vanes set in the inner cone. There it travels upward, sweeping through the separating chamber, where once more the selective entrainment, reinforced by the action of the rejector fan, takes place; the air may be said to circulate.

From the inner cone, the coarser particles, or tailings, are removed and returned to the mill; from the outer cone, the desired fines are carried by an outlet pipe to storage bins or bagging machines. As has been indi-

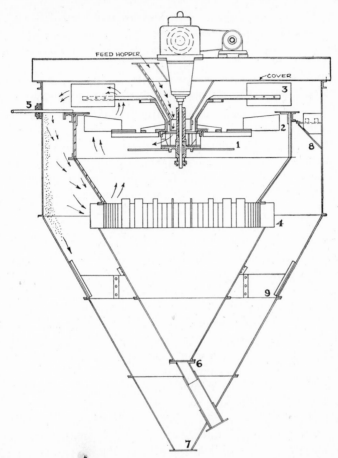

FIGURE 48.—A simplified vertical cross section of the Sturtevant Air Separator; the horizontal cross section is circular. 1, Distributing plate. 2, Rejector fan. 3, Upper fan. The distributing plate and the two fans revolve together. The path of the feed to the distributing plate is shown by single arrows. 4, Air vanes between which the return air enters the inner cone and chamber; the twin arrows show the circulation of the air. 5, Adjustable valve; the valves overlap and form an iris around the top opening of the inner chamber. 6, Outlet for the tailings. 7, Outlet for the fines. 8, Inner drum bracket. 9, Brace for the inner cone. Feed hopper liner, intake cone liner, inside drum and drum cone liner, and other liners, not shown. (Courtesy Sturtevant Mill Co., Boston, Mass.)

cated, the fineness of the product is controllable, first by the adjustment of the "valves," which permits an enlargement or a contraction of the opening at the top of the inner chamber, and secondly, by increasing the number of blades in the rejector fan. For extreme fineness, as many as 48 are used; the number may be decreased to as low as 6, and in some installations to none at all. The most efficient operation is obtained by making the top opening as large as possible, and then increasing the number of rejector blades to as many as may be required for the rejection of undesired (large) particles. The entire plate and fan assembly may be raised or lowered by the manipulation of set screws in the jack at the base of the shaft.

It will be of interest to point out that the mechanical air separator may be used for the separation of materials differing in specific gravity, and of particles differing in shape; for example, flake mica and cubical feldspar; iron ore and shale.

The Sturtevant Air Separator is built in nine sizes, ranging from 3 feet to 16 feet in diameter; the horsepower required to drive the distributing plate and fan assemblies varies from 2 to 5 for the 3-foot size, to 60 to 75 for the 16-foot size. A motor is mounted on top of the separator; the shaft is driven through a bevel gear. In the smallest size the shaft, and hence the distributing plate, revolves at the rate of 750 rpm; in the largest, the shaft and fans rotate at the rate of 245 rpm. The prices run from $2170 for the former, to $14,275 for the latter (October, 1951).

Air Float Separators. The Air Float Separator, also called the Dry Table,* resembles the wet oscillating table in that it too has an oscillating deck inclined longitudinally and laterally, and equipped with riffles. The place of the water on the wet table is taken by compressed air, admitted through the deck itself, which is porous. The deck cover is of metal or other cloth, and surmounts an air chest which receives its air from a built-in fan, direct motor-driven. The fine-ground material is fed to the left rear of the deck, where it meets the flow of air, which renders the whole mass fluid. The lighter particles are forced upward and ride over the heavier ones; they are able to travel over the riffles and ultimately reach the side of the deck (toward the observer), with a further sorting along the side, the lightest ones dropping over the nearer part, the slightly heavier ones over the farther part of the side. The heavier particles ride close to the cloth behind the riffles and ultimately reach the top end of the deck (to the right of the observer), where they drop clean, free from admixtures, into a hopper. By means of cutting fingers, any number of separations, as far as the hoppers allow, can be made.

The separator is a unit, with built-in fan, motor, hoppers and baffles. The porous deck oscillates on toggles set at approximately 17° off vertical. The forward movement of the deck moves the heavy material slightly uphill; the light material, which is suspended, flows backward and downhill by gravity. The stroke varies in the various models and sizes from $\frac{1}{4}$ inch to $\frac{3}{8}$ inch, and the oscillations per minute are between 380 and 470.

For certain duties, the deck is also supplied without riffles, in which case it is known as a blank deck.

* Sutton. Steele and Steele, Inc., Dallas, Texas.

The separation depends upon the difference in specific gravity of the constituents; as a heavy particle falls faster in air than in water, separation on the Air Float is more rapid than on the water table. The decks differ in size; in B series, the deck is 78 inches long, 48 inches wide; in C series, 87 inches long, 54 inches wide.

Magnetic Separators and Other Magnetic Equipment

Magnetic separators remove certain substances from physical mixtures because of the difference in the response of these substances to the magnetic flux. The separation of bits of iron, such as nails, bolts, washers, nuts, broken hinges, wire, tobacco tins, from glass (foreign cullets), for example, is simple, for the difference in response is *great;* the iron, which is the most magnetically susceptible substance known, responds to even a feeble magnetic flux, while glass is unaffected. The bits of iron which have been described are called collectively "tramp iron." A kindred material which finds its way into finely divided, originally iron-free material, is iron of abrasion, the removal of which is somewhat more complex, yet still comparatively easy. There are, however, separations performed today which depend upon a *slight* difference in magnetic susceptibility, hence upon a slight difference in response—separations which would not have been thought possible twenty years ago. They are accomplished in large part on machines having rotating parts, special designs and extremely high flux.

To the magnetic equipment depending upon *electromagnetism,* which was first in development, there has been added in last few years equipment which depends upon *permanent magnetism.* A good part of magnetic equipment is now employing permanent magnets, made almost exclusively of "Alnico"; a number of applications of the electromagnet remain, however, especially for larger sizes (drum separators over 18 inches in diameter). Permanent magnet installations offer the immense advantage of simplicity; they do not have to be served with electric current, and their magnetic life is unlimited.

Returning for a moment to electromagnetism, it may be observed that a piece of iron or steel around which a coil of wire is wound immediately becomes a magnet, with north and south poles, when a direct current is passed through the coil. The polarity of the magnet depends entirely upon the direction of the current flow. The electromagnetic pulley, and all electromagnetic separators and other electromagnetic equipment, with the exception of the induced-roll type, are merely elaborations of this fundamental principle.

Magnetic Plate. The plate magnet is the simplest of the magnetic devices used to separate iron from other materials which are themselves generally nonmagnetic. It consists, for example, of a steel pole plate to

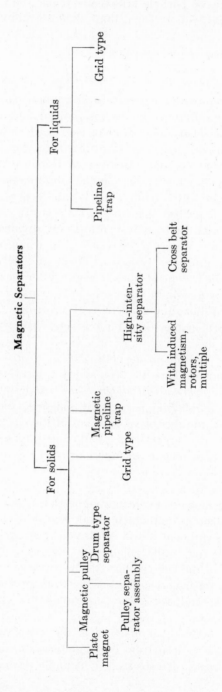

which one or more permanent magnets are attached. The plate magnet is set with its steel pole face in the bottom wall of a chute, allowing the body of the magnet to project outside the wall. As the material to be cleaned of tramp iron flows past the pole plate, its non-magnetizable portion flows on, while any iron object, small and large nails, broken washers, bolts, and the like, are held fast to the plate. The plate magnet is mounted flush with the inner wall, so that it does not obstruct the material flowing by. It may be mounted in chutes, hoppers and feed tables. It may be provided with a hinge, so that it can be swung open, cleaned of adhering iron debris, and then returned to its place. It is made in a number of sizes and models, with a choice of magnetic power (there are 16 sizes, 6 models, for Eriez magnetic plate separators).

The plate magnet frequently serves for suspended application above a slowly moving conveyor belt.

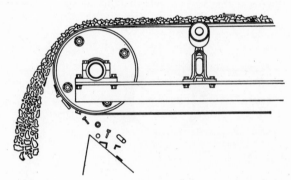

FIGURE 49.—A magnetic pulley, equipped with permanent magnets, installed as the head pulley in a belt conveyor, functions as shown. (Courtesy Dings Magnetic Separator Co., Milwaukee 46, Wis.)

The plate magnet is the workhorse among magnetic devices; it is selected whenever one of the special types which follow are not demanded.

Magnetic Pulleys. The magnetic pulley is the best-known and simplest devices for magnetic separations, although not technically a "separator." It is the simplest because a separate installation is not required: the magnetic pulley generally takes the place of the head or drive pulley of any belt conveyor. As the material handled passes the head pulley, the unaffected portion is dumped at the turn, while the attracted portion is held against the belt and pulley, traveling on the underside of the belt. Just beyond the last contact point of belt and pulley, the magnetically held material drops off into a separate receptacle (see Figure 49).

Magnetic pulleys in the popular sizes, from 8 to 30 inches in diameter through five intermediate sizes, are *nonelectric, permanent magnet-equipped* devices. The magnets are "Alnico," which may be further specified as, for example, "Alnico" V (Stearns). The magnets are first cast, and since the product is extremely critical with respect to design

(Eriez) (Figure 50), its shape and dimensions must be planned with care. The casting is then energized so as to produce maximum magnetic strength. In the magnetic pulley, the magnets are set under the entire surface, so that every square inch of the pulley surface is in the magnetic field. The depth of the field beyond the surface, as well as the strength, is a major consideration. A number of permanent magnets are assembled for the various sized pulleys; thus for the 8-inch diameter size, eight, and in the 30-inch diameter size, twelve poles. Larger pulleys, up to 48 inches in diameter, with permanent magnet assemblies are available (there are 24 poles in the 48-inch Perma Pulley). Nevertheless, pulleys larger than 30 inches in diameter have not infrequently been considered special applications, and have been constructed as electromagnetic devices, as all magnetic pulleys were not many years ago.

The electromagnetic pulley consists essentially of a hollow steel casting with recesses in which coils of magnet wire (soft copper) are wound

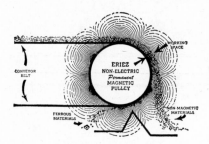

FIGURE 50.—A representation of the deep magnetic field on the outer face of a nonelectric, permanent-magnet-equipped magnetic pulley. The field runs horizontally across the face of the pulley. (Courtesy Eriez Manufacturing Co., Erie, Pa.)

in layers. The ends of the coil or coils are connected by wires passed through the hollow shaft to slip rings, so that a direct current of a selected amperage and with voltage of 110 or 120, generally, may be applied; when it is, the steel becomes a magnet.

Going a step further into the details, it should be mentioned that in a three-recess casting, the coil in the second recess receives its current in a direction opposite to that in the first and third coils. The windings are protected by cover plates, of bronze or stainless steel, both nonmagnetic. The pulley may have several sections, which have serrated edges which do not quite meet, so that openings are left in the pulley surface (Figure 51). In the pulleys with solid castings, openings are provided and so placed that air is forced in and out by the action of the belt. The object is to provide a constant stream of cool air to the interior and to eject the spent, heated air. The development of magnetism by applying electric current to coils of wire produces heat; the cooler the pulley remains, the greater the flux developed. Pulleys of medium and large diameters have horizontal inner openings connected with the radial openings in order to increase ventilation and heat removal. There is no heat development in the magnetic pulleys or drums equipped with permanent magnets.

An electromagnetic pulley is considerably heavier than an ordinary cast-iron pulley; furthermore, one end of the shaft must be hollow to admit the wires running to the collector rings or slip rings. For these two reasons, the shaft diameters of standard electromagnetic pulleys are larger.

The specific function of the magnetic pulley as a remover of iron should be determined before selecting its size and magnetic strength; separation of iron may be for the protection of crushers, pulverizers and grinders, for the reclamation of iron and steel, or for purification. There is no interference on the part of the belt to the development of the magnetic lines of

FIGURE 51.—The cut-away Dings electromagnetic pulley, showing the details of construction. At extreme left, polished bronze collector rings, contactors, and collector ring housing; next, end ring, then first casting with winding and cover, completed. Beyond the serrations, second casting with heavy bronze coil cover not quite in place. The third casting has its wire winding, but no cover; the fourth casting is bare except for the mica insulation. The end ring at extreme right completes the pulley. (Especially prepared for this chapter by the Dings Magnetic Separator Co., Milwaukee, Wis.)

force. The usual statement is that there is no substance known which insulates magnetism, though it is also true that magnetism may be directed or deflected.

The capacity of magnetic pulleys has increased in recent years. A large pulley, code 4848 Stearns electromagnetic pulley, 48 inches in diameter, for a 48-inch belt, 32 rpm, has a rated capacity of approximately 1000 tons per hour for normal tramp iron removal from coal (Figure 52).

For each diameter pulley, there are available a number of widths, to accommodate different belts; the 18-inch diameter pulley, for example, is made in ten widths, running from 12 to 48 inches. The approximate speed is 40 rpm. The 12-inch diameter Dings Perma Pulley, 12 inches wide, was listed at $480 in 1951; the 48-inch diameter and 60-inch wide pulley costs $10,241 (1951).

Magnetic Pulley Type Separator. The magnetic pulley serves not only when set as the head pulley of a belt conveyor, but it may be mounted by itself with a small conveyor belt, and become a complete separator, which is even portable in some models. There are two pulleys, usually set about 10 diameters apart; one is the tail pulley, the other the drive end and at the same time the magnetic pulley. The belt runs from the former to the latter, along a horizontal or inclined plane. The separator is fed from a conveyor belt above, or in other ways. The magnetic pulley separator may have nonelectric permanent magnets for its source of magnetism, or it may have electromagnetic equipment.

FIGURE 52.—The largest known electromagnetic pulley, 60 inches in diameter. (Courtesy Stearns Magnetic, Inc., Milwaukee 46, Wis.)

Drum Type Separator. By far the most important type of magnetic separator is the drum type. It consists of a drum within which a magnet or magnet assembly is held in a fixed position. The drum shell revolves. As the material to be treated reaches it, it is carried into the magnetic field; the nonmagnetic portion drops off at the turn of the drum, but the iron is held fast against the shell and is carried past a divider, until outside the magnetic field, when it is dropped off to be collected in a separate bin (see Figure 53). The drum type separator is generally attached to a spout, and may be fully enclosed, automatic, and of all metal construction. It is in the spout drum separator that the permanent magnet has found its most general and most successful application, displacing the earlier electromagnetic installations.

The magnet assembly runs the whole width of the drum and covers one-half of the periphery; the right half of the drum from a vertical plane through the center receives the flux, while the left half receives none.

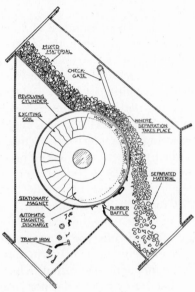

FIGURE 53.—Sketch showing the working principle of a Type LP spout separator, which permits the automatic, rapid, and continuous separation of tramp iron as the material leaves the bin. It is an application of the drum-type separator. The several parts are marked on the drawing, as they would be chosen for an electromagnetic drum; in the permanent magnet drum, permanent magnets occupy the same space as the electromagnet did in the earlier models. (Courtesy Stearns Magnetic, Inc., Milwaukee, Wis.)

It will be noted that no conveyor belt is needed, and that the drum separator may be used where there is no conveyor system. This is a great advantage, as the material flows directly down the chute onto the revolving

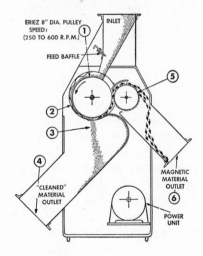

FIGURE 54.—Working principle of the Eriez micromagnetic separator. The contaminated powder is fed onto rapidly revolving magnetic cylinder 1. It is torn apart and combed by a series of concentrated magnetic fields. A shroud, 2, containing a number of rubber baffles reintroduces the powder repeatedly into the face of the cylinder. Centrifugal force throws the nonmagnetic powder off at point 3. Iron powder adheres to the magnetic cylinder until it reaches a point, 5, adjacent to a moving induction roll, where it is removed. As the surface of the induced roll moves away from the magnetic cylinder, it loses its magnetism and the iron drops into the discharge chute 6. (Courtesy Eriez Manufacturing Co., Erie, Pa.)

drum, and the separated portions flow away by gravity.

Among the many modifications there is a twin type "DH" magnetic drum assembly, in which two drums function; the drums rotate with the flow of material and pick out the magnetic portion. There is also a twin drum construction in which the rotation of the drums is counter to the flow of the descending materials, with favorable results in the proper applications.

There are a number of "agitating" magnetic separators, one of the drum type, in which the material is scoured and torn apart so that all magnetic particles come under the influence of the field. In the Type "M" Stearns magnetic separator, a number of short, rectangular magnets with alternating polarity field bring about a zigzag motion which turns over the material. The high agitation releases the entrained impurities. In the Type "AM" Stearns magnetic separator, advantage is taken of the pulsating characteristics of the alternating current (AC current) when applied to electromagnets to produce a cleansing action; in this separator, the material is left free from magnetic lines of force due to residual magnetism, which is very desirable in many problems.

Cross Belt Type Separator. While it was thought ten years ago that the cross belt magnetic separator would be superseded and replaced by the induced roll type of magnetic separator, it now appears that through improvements in its construction the cross-belt type retains a definite rôle in the magnetic separation field.*

The cross-belt separator uses the lift principle: the magnetically susceptible impurity jumps upward to the cross belt from the conveyor belt, and is carried out beyond the edges of the latter, there to be dropped. In the specific form described and illustrated in Figure 55, the separator consists of three endless belts, a feeder, two stationary horseshoe electromagnets, and auxiliary parts. The magnets have a special construction: the upper pole is wedge-shaped, so that there is a concentration of flux there; the lower pole is flat, and its field becomes comparatively ineffective. The material from the feed roller flows to the main belt in a uniform, thin layer, and the belt with its load travels, at a rather slow rate, through the first gap. The attached particles jump toward the upper pole, but strike the under side of the small cross belt, often called the take-off belt, traveling through the pole gap, and above the feed belt, at a right angle to it. The cross belt, which also travels at a slow rate, carries the attracted particles out of the magnetic field, where they drop off by gravity into a receiver. In one design the pole nose is extended past the feed belt and flattened there, which permits a gradual (instead of sudden) reduction of the magnetic field, and this assists the removal. After passing the first gap, the feed reaches the second, where the process is repeated and a further quantity of magnetically susceptible material is pulled out of the

* The modern cross-belt magnetic separators are the newer forms of separators embodying the Rowand-Wetherill principle.

feed and discharged separately by the second cross belt. The magnetic force in the two gaps is the same; the first pair of poles do most of the work, the second pair merely supplementing the first. The nonmagnetic (essentially) residual material is carried by the feed belt to the turn, where it drops to the tailings bin.

The size of the material should be between ¼ inch and 50 mesh; it may be finer than 150 mesh if highly magnetic. The gap distance is adjustable (between ⅛ inch and 1 inch), and the speed of the several belts may be varied. The take-off belts are much narrower than the conveyor belt on which they work, but travel faster; if the conveyor belt approximates 100 feet per minute, the take-off belt travels about 200 feet per minute. The

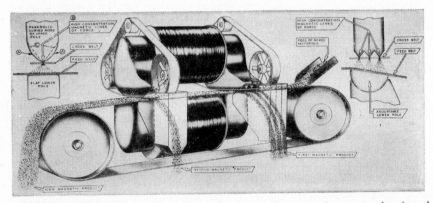

FIGURE 55.—The Stearns Cross Belt Type "R" Magnetic Separator, showing the recent improvements. It is an electromagnetic device. The angle of the lower flat pole face is adjustable. The three legends in the lower part of the picture read, left to right: nonmagnetic product, second magnetic product, first magnetic product.

maximum to be removed on any one cross belt should never exceed 10 per cent of the head feed.

The two horseshoe electromagnetic separators which have been described are of the simple construction; in the multiple separators, the magnets number four, six, or more. The feed travels through the several gaps in succession. By giving the magnets an increasing flux, the cross belts will carry out materials of increasingly weaker magnetic susceptibility. For example, in the treatment of monazite sand, magnetite is first removed by the weakest magnet; then ilmenite by the second magnet, of medium strength; finally monazite by the third magnet, of high strength, leaving the valueless sand to be discharged by the feed belt. A number of other similar separations are accomplished daily on this device.

The illustration of the Stearns Cross-Belt Type R Magnetic Separator (Figure 55) shows one of the recent improvements. It consists of the incorporation of multiple points at each magnetic field, coupled with the variation in strength in these multiple points by means of variation in the angle of a lower flat pole face. The lower pole is adjustable, so that its angle may be set at will; it is set as indicated in the smaller sketch at the upper right in the illustration. As the air gap for the three points becomes smaller from left to right, the strength of the field becomes correspondingly greater. This is in addition to the greater concentration of magnetic lines at the points due to their shape.

In the Dings new cross-belt magnetic separator (Wetherill Type E), a new pole piece construction provides three separate pole noses on each cross-belt unit. Any number of cross belts may be provided with this separator, depending on the number of products concentrated and on the volume to be handled. The separator operates on the electromagnetic principle rather than on permanent magnets, because the magnetizing force may be as high as 40,000 gilberts, which cannot be equalled with a permanent magnet.*

High-Intensity Magnetic Separators, with Induction Rolls. A comparatively recent development is the high-intenstiy magnetic separator, distinguished by the high flux densities employed; thanks to these, it is possible to effect the separation of weakly magnetic materials. The material to be separated is fed onto a swiftly revolving roll, or rotor, at a point where the material is wholly supported by the rotor, and is then revolved through an intensely effective magnetic field. The magnetizable particles adhere to the magnetized edges in the rotor face and are retained on its surface a moment longer than the nonmagnetizable or less magnetizable particles. As the rotor revolves, its imparts to both kinds of particles a centrifugal force which whirls them off along different angles; the nonmagnetizable particles are whirled away first and farthest (compare Figure 56). By placing a knife edge between the falling trajectories the magnetizable portion is cut away from the non- or less-magnetizable ones. The separation is carried further by allowing the magnetizable portion to fall on a second roller, with higher intensity, giving again a division into the more magnetic particles and the less magnetic or nonmagnetic ones. This rotor may be followed by one or several more, with gradually increasing flux densities.

The rolls or rotors are constructed in very special ways, two of which will be described. The rotor may be made up of alternate aluminum and iron disks, about ⅛ inch thick; the disks are pressed together with jam nuts, the surface turned smooth on a lathe, and polished. The purpose of this lamination is to produce a number of sharp edges in the steel; when it is magnetized by induction, there will be a convergence of lines of force

* For a closer study of the many other types of magnetic separators, consult Bulletin number 9, Minnesota School of Mines, University of Minnesota.

TABLE 20. RELATIVE MAGNETIC ATTRACTIVE FORCE OF VARIOUS MINERALS ON THE BASIS OF 100 AS THE VALUE FOR IRON*

Material	Attractive Force	Material	Attractive Force
Iron	100.	Apatite	.21
Magnetite	40.18	Willemite	.21
Franklinite	35.38	Tetrahedrite	.21
Ilmenite	24.70	Talc	.15
Pyrrhotite	6.69	Arsenopyrite	.15
Siderite	1.82	Magnesite	.15
Hematite	1.32	Chalcopyrite	.14
Zircon	1.01	Gypsum	.12
Limonite	.84	Fluorite	.11
Corundum	.83	Zincite	.10
Pyrolusite	.71	Celestite	.10
Manganite	.52	Cinnabar	.10
Calamine	.51	Chalcocite	.09
Garnet	.40	Cuprite	.08
Quartz	.37	Smithsonite	.07
Rutile	.37	Orthoclase	.05
Cerussite	.30	Stibnite	.05
Cerargyrite	.28	Cyrolite	.05
Argentite	.27	Enargite	.05
Orpiment	.24	Senarmontite	.05
Pyrite	.23	Galena	.04
Sphalerite	.23	Niccolite	.04
Molybdenite	.23	Calcite	.03
Dolomite	.22	Witherite	.02
Bornite	.22		

* "Magnetic concentration of iron ore," by Edward Davis, Bulletin No. 9, page 26, Minnesota School of Mines, University of Minnesota, 1921. For another table, compare Arthur F. Taggart, "The Handbook of Mineral Dressing," Chapter 13, New York, Wiley and Sons, 1945.

to the edge. Aluminum, like copper, is essentially nonmagnetic. The other method of construction is to build the rotor of thin steel disks (to avoid eddy currents), to press these together on the shaft, turn them down to a smooth surface on a lathe, and then to cut a screw thread in the surface. The screw has straight sides, and has about 7 turns to the inch. The screw thread is then filled with copper, the surface once more turned down on a lathe, and polished. In this way a large number of steel edges is again created, resting against the wall of the inert copper.

The first construction—alternate aluminum and steel disks—is less expensive, but does not permit development of the highest intensity. The second construction—that of laminated steel—produces a more permeable rotor, and for that reason does bring about the highest intensity. In the Exolon Induction Separator, "single 30" model, shown in Figures 56, 57, and 58, the upper rotor has the first construction; the second and third have laminated steel, the screw thread being filled with copper, in order to develop there the highest intensity. The rate of rotation may be 100 rpm, although it varies between 50 and 350 rpm. The three rotors are 30 inches long; the first one is 4 inches in diameter, the second and third 5 inches. Each rotor is highly magnetized by induction and revolves in a magnetic field. The electromagnet for the second and third rotor is horseshoe-shaped (really, a horseshoe with the bend drawn out), and the main

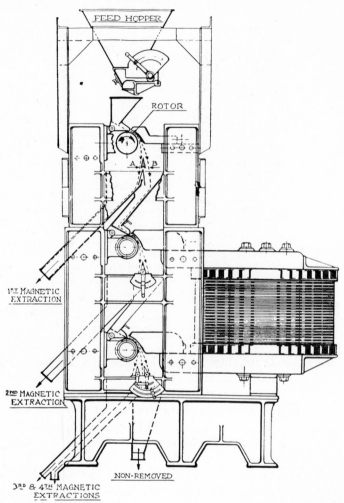

FIGURE 56.—Diagrammatic sketch showing the operation of a "single 30" Exolon Induction Separator. *A*, the readily magnetized material; *B*, the portion of the material which has remained unaffected when passing over the first rotor. Note that the trajectory of *B* is farther from the rotor than that of *A*. (Courtesy Exolon Co., Tonawanda, N. Y.)

strength of the field is applied there; an upright branch, called the auxiliary pole, brings a comparatively weak field to the first rotor. On the other side of the rotor a steel or iron yoke, or keeper, presents a face with curvature to match that of the rotor; it is with the help of the yoke that the path for the magnetic flux is completed. The air gap between yoke and rotor is adjustable. The strength of the flux is for example as follows:

First rotor.......................... 5,000 maxwells per square inch
Second rotor........................ 80,000 maxwells " " "
Third rotor......................... 85,000 maxwells " " "

FIGURE 57.—The Exolon Induction Separator, a high-intensity magnetic separator, model "single 30," three pass. The knife edge dividers are well shown; also the special shape and position of the pole-nose over the second and third rotor. Electric motor drive through adjustable speed reducer. (Courtesy Exolon Co., Tonawanda, N. Y.)

The material meets gradually increasing flux densities, so that there is improvement in separation as it travels down. The strong field is able to affect particles small in size and low in susceptibility.

The efficiency of the high-intensity magnetic separator with induction rolls depends not only on flux density, but also on field configuration, which means essentially the relation between grain size and thickness of lamination. The size (width) of the iron disk is chosen to match the size of the particle to be worked on and retained.

The efficiency may be interfered with by the converging lines of force over the inert metal, which tend to pull the magnetic particle upward and away from the surface of the rotor; this is avoided in the Exolon by placing the pole piece over the top center of each rotor so that the magnetic flux is concentrated at the "twelve o'clock" position, and by the shape and curvature of the pole piece. The possibility that weakly magnetic materials will fail to respond to the magnetic force is thus greatly reduced, and purity of the concentrates produced on this device correspondingly increased.

The mode of operation is as follows. The material is ground to 20 mesh or finer, and fed from the hopper through a feedroll or other feeder to the first rotor, where readily magnetizable particles are diverted by the knife edge divider and collected separately (*A* in Figure 56), forming the

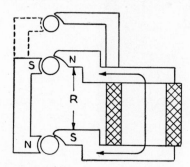

FIGURE 58.—Schematic drawing of the high-intensity magnetic separator showing the relation of the electromagnet to the rotors.

first magnetic extraction. The unaffected material (*B* in the same figure) is fed to the top of the next rotor which has a far stronger flux, as stated above; the weakly magnetized particles are now affected and pulled close to the rotor, so that they fall to one side of the knife edge divider (second magnetic extraction). The unaffected portion drops to the third rotor which has a still higher flux density; particles which are still lower in magnetic susceptibility are pulled in to drop over the innermost edge of a first knife (third magnetic extraction), while the totally unaffected or inert parts roll off by themselves (nonremoved), and a middle portion between these two is collected by itself (fourth magnetic extraction). A separation into five parts is thus possible. As a rule, the second rotor does most of the work.

The Exolon separator removes ilmenite from beach sand; mica from feldspar; ilmenite and mica from apatite. One of its early duties, which it discharged successfully, was the production of a super-refractory material by almost complete removal of iron oxides.

The model "single 30" is supplemented by a "double 30", with three 'otors on each side. The capacity of the "single 30" Exolon is 4000 pounds head feed per hour, variations depending upon the materials; hat of the "double 30" may be as high as 8000 pounds per hour head eed. The "single 30" was priced $8,743 in 1951; the double machine at he same period was $13,522.

The Stearns Type K Separator is a corresponding device, with high :apacity and improvement in separation over previous models. It is made n various sizes.

Since the expression "high intensity" has been used several times, it night be well to compare the intensity of the field in the several devices liscussed, as they are usually constructed. It is not enough to know how nany watts are applied to an electromagnetic device, for the magnetomo- :ive force depends not only upon the ampere turns (NI), but also upon the type of path provided for the flux. In general, the magnetic pulley levelops a flux density of 1000 or 1500 maxwells per square inch; but in the high-intensity magnetic separator with induction rolls, the flux density leveloped is not far from 100,000 maxwells per square inch. The term "high-intensity" magnetic separators for the latter devices would there- fore seem to be justified.

ELECTROMAGNETIC SEPARATORS FOR LIQUIDS

FerroFilter. An example of an electromagnetic separator for liquids is the FerroFilter, which consists of a set of magnetized screens enclosed in a casing through which the liquid flows. The screens present strongly magnetized edges to the material passing through, retaining any suspended magnetic particles, even those as small as one micron. The liquid travels through a stack of flat annular pieces which are the screens; each one is built up of ribbon steel and offers many triangular openings. The screens are surrounded by a magnet coil receiving direct current, usually at 110 to 120 volts, which induces the magnetism. A spider casting is pro- vided above and below the stack of screens, so that the path of the lines of force includes the spiders, cover, outer wall, and base piece of the hous- ing around the magnet coil. The magnetizable impurities, chiefly specks of iron and steel, accumulate on the screens and are periodically removed by demagnetizing and then flushing the filter.

There are three types of FerroFilters. One of them, the pipeline type, is shown in Figure 59. The other two types, the underfeed type and the gravity type, serve certain specific purposes. Each is available in four sizes, running in maximum capacities from 20 to 200 gallons per minute, and in pipe sizes from 1 to 3 inches. The prices for the pipeline type begin at $250 for the smallest and run up to $950; the underfeed and the gravity types, for corresponding capacities, are either the same or a little lower in price (November 7, 1951).

For process work the metal parts in contact with the liquid are usually made of stainless steel or aluminum; when stainless steel is used for the screens instead of steel, it is of the ferritic, or magnetizable, type. The filters intended for lubricating-oil service are made of steel throughout.

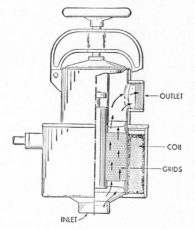

FIGURE 59.—A partial cross section and outside view of the FerroFilter of the pipeline type, for the removal of iron contaminations from liquids and slurries. The liquid travels upward through the grids which are strongly magnetized by a direct current coil surrounding them. The grids retain the iron. (Courtesy S. G. Frantz Co., Trenton 6, N. J.)

In addition to the electrically energized models, which require a line connection, there are permanent-magnet FerroFilters. In these, two strong permanent magnets are situated one above, the other below, a stack of soft steel grids. The two magnets magnetize the grids. There is con-

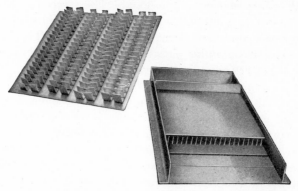

FIGURE 60.—The Eriez Ferrous Cleaner is a nonelectric magnetic separator for the removal of iron from liquids. The liquid is forced to pass 124 magnetic grid fingers, against which the iron is removed. It may also be used for slips, slurries, and dry powders. Upper left, the 124 grid fingers exposed; lower right, the assembled Ferrous Cleaner with grid in place. (Courtesy Eriez Manufacturing Co., Erie, Pa.)

centration of magnetic lines at any sharp edge, and as there are many such edges in the stack of grids, iron impurities are readily retained by the filter. These FerroFilters are made in six sizes, up to 3-inch IPS. The capacities are as high as 90 gallons per minute. No electrical connection is required. For cleaning purposes, the grids are removed from the filter; as a result, they are demagnetized. The metallic impurities are easily removed by washing in water or kerosene. The permanent magnet FerroFilters range in price from $20 for the ⅜-inch IPS size, to $375 for the 3-inch size. The latter size may be furnished with flange as well as pipe connections.

Eriez Ferrous Cleaner. This magnetic separator (Figure 60) is designed primarily for the cleaning of liquids, but it may also serve for powders, slips, and slurries. It is nonelectric. It contains 124 grid fingers of magnetizable steel which become magnetic by induction; the required magnetic force is provided by two rows of magnetic castings (Alnico) located under the surface. Particles of contamination (iron) cling to the fingers as they would to any magnet, and are thus removed from the flowing liquid. From time to time the machine is taken apart for cleaning; the grid fingers are thus demagnetized, and the adherent impurities are flushed away.

Stearns Magnetic Screen Filter Separator. This separator, unlike the preceding one, is electromagnetic. The fluid material is filtered through a highly magnetized screening element of more than double the area of earlier designs. Several modifications, each in several sizes, are available.

ELECTROSTATIC SEPARATOR

The electrostatic separator is intended for the separation of dry materials having different electrical susceptibilities, mainly different electrical conductivities. A number of machines have been developed over the course of years, and improvements devised, resulting in the present machines of superior reliability. After the stationary charged bar of the original device was replaced by the rotating charged collector, two methods, selected among others, were prominent. In the first method of separation, the conductors in the mixture of particles are repelled by the rotor, while the nonconductors of the same mixture remain practically uncharged. As the rotor revolves, the good conductors leave first; the nonconductors cling longer and are carried past the dividing partition. In the second method, the conductors are allowed to remain electrically inert, while the nonconductors are heavily charged, and a constant difference of electrical potential is maintained between them and the rotating electrode, so that they remain adhering to it, and in fact have to be brushed off mechanically. The Electro-Float separator* is a modern device in which these two opposite methods have been combined, and in which a number of advances have been incorporated. Its construction and operation will be described with the aid of Figure 61.

The current is usually taken from rectifying vacuum tubes, which

* Sutton, Steele and Steele, Inc., Engineers and Manufacturers, Dallas, Texas.

yield a high-tension unidirectional, although rapidly pulsating, current
it has been found that this current performs as well as the original direc
current from electrostatic generators. This is a major improvement
The Electro-Float proper consists of feed hopper, heated shaker pan (to
remove all traces of moisture), the insulating curtain and the gas tube
electrode, the rotating metal cylinder, adjustable dividing partitions, discharge spouts, cleaner brush, and electrical connection as shown. The
conducting particles are shown in solid black; the nonconductors are
drawn in outline. As the particles leave the shaker pan and pass under

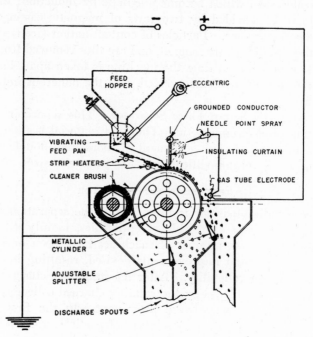

FIGURE 61.—The Electro-Float Separator, an electrostatic separator of advanced design.
(Courtesy Sutton, Steele and Steele, Dallas, Texas.)

the insulating curtain, they are met by a spray discharge from the needle-
point electrodes. The nonconductors are charged and remain so for a
time; the conductors are also charged, but lose the charge at once by contact with the rotor, which is grounded. The conductors are therefore
now inert. As the material continues, it advances toward the gas electrode which attracts the conductors, deflecting them sufficiently to drop
beyond a splitter. The nonconductors are slower in losing their charge;
a portion drops off over the next segment of the revolution. Another portion, the least conductive, clings to the rotor and leaves it only on being
brushed off.

When the high-tension current is passed through the gas electrode, whose contents are under low pressure, static charges are released which collect on the outer surface of the tube. If the current flows in one direction, these static charges have one polarity; if the current flows in the other direction, the opposite polarity is developed. The purpose of the gas electrode is to make a clean separation with a single pass. The electrode attracts and pulls away the conductors at the very moment the rotor holds the nonconductors. There must be no moisture on the outside of the gas electrode, and, as already mentioned, the materials must be dry.

The 12-inch-wide roll Laboratory Model is priced at $1,650. The 48-inch-wide roll sections are sold at $3,500 per roll; they are designed to stack one upon the other, and as many as four roll sections can be used in one Separator. The prices are f.o.b. Dallas, and without rectifier (1951).

Reading References

"Electrostatic separations of solids," by Foster Fraas and Oliver C. Ralston, *Ind. Eng. Chem.*, **32**, 600 (1940).

"Electrostatic Solid Separations," by Henry M. Sutton and G. W. Jarman, *Chem. Met. Eng.*, **45**, 277 (1938).

"Screens in the process industries," by Albert E. Reed, *Ind. Eng. Chem.*, **30**, 1369 (1938).

A bibliography of articles on Theory and Laws of Crushing has been compiled by the W. S. Tyler Co., Cleveland, Ohio.

Pertinent Patents

U. S. Patent 1,692,590, on method of and apparatus for magnetic separation.

U. S. Patent 2,078,513, magnetic separator and concentrator.

U. S. Patent 2,074,085, magnetic separator, Samuel G. Frantz.

U. S. Patent 2,226,503, on a multideck screen, Dell Mack Ramsey.

U. S. Patent 2,155,587, rotary sifting and separating devices, Ramsey and Johnson, 1936.

U. S. Patent 2,156,483, structural and operation details of a cyclone separator.

U. S. Patent 2,156,125, wet magnetic separation of feebly magnetic materials, Clarence Q. Payne.

U. S. Patent 2,201,628, filtering or screening apparatus suitable for use with oils, syrups, paints, and other materials.

The study of the unit operation designated as "materials handling," with respect to solids, is not new, but the intensive application of its results in factories of all kinds is a comparatively recent development. It is a study which logically leads to labor-saving devices. The assembly line in the automobile factory and the airplane construction plant is perhaps its highest expression today; by means of a slow-moving conveyor, the engine, chassis, wing, or body, as the case may be, comes to the operator, who can stand still and devote his energies to the building step entrusted to him. A moment later, the completed piece moves away of itself. Smaller assembly lines such as that for the lead storage battery are less spectacular, but equally effective in avoiding nonproductive motions, thus permitting lower production costs, which in turn lead to wider distribution.

4. HANDLING BULK MATERIALS—CONVEYING AND ELEVATING EQUIPMENT FOR SOLIDS

In handling bulk materials, conveying and elevating equipment is foremost; a table of classification for such equipment is shown on page 87. It will be noted that the first distinction to be made is between equipment which is fixed in position, such as conveyors and bucket elevators, and equipment which is movable, such as industrial trucks. The first group may be subdivided into mechanical and pneumatic conveyors; related to the pneumatic conveyor, but really in a class by itself, is the Fuller-Kinyon pump.

It is interesting to note that any one of the mechanical conveyors is also an elevator, with the single exception of the belt conveyor, the most important member of the whole list; even the screw conveyor becomes an elevator when provided with a closed casing. It should perhaps be added that any conveyor may be inclined and made to travel upward at an angle from the horizontal, and this applies particularly to the belt conveyor. The term "elevator" as used here means elevation along the vertical. Only one device, at the other end of the list, is an elevator, and not a conveyor, or at best, an inefficient one, and that is the bucket elevator.

Belt Conveyors. The horizontal belt conveyor consists of an endless belt stretched out in a slender loop over the drive or head pulley and the tail pulley. The belt carries material from near the tail pulley to the head pulley, where it turns, dumping the material it carries, and returns face down to the tail pulley, where it turns again and is in position to repeat the cycle. With the single-head pulley, unassisted by additional members, the belt is said to have "plain drive." The belt may lie flat

TABLE 21. CLASSIFICATION OF CONVEYORS AND ELEVATORS

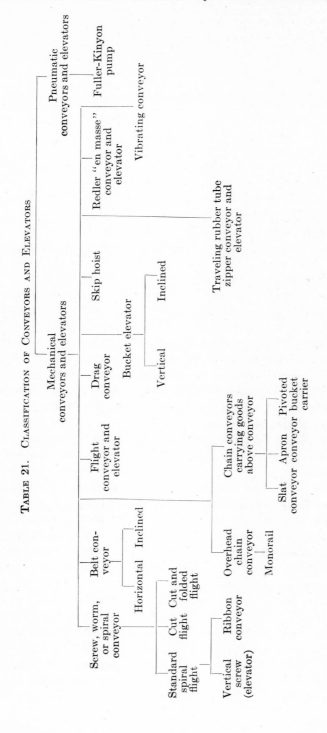

throughout its trip, in which case the members supporting it between the pulleys are flat rollers; or it may be "troughed." The troughed belt is supported by carriers in groups of three, which take the place of the single flat roller for the flat belt; the central carrier is horizontal; the outer ones are inclined at an angle of 20° (generally) to the axis of the central one, so that the belt running on them takes the shape of a shallow trough. On reaching the head pulley, the belt resumes a flat position, so that over its return trip to the tail pulley, it may be supported by flat rollers. The belt is shaped into a trough because the troughed belt has a capacity twice as great as the same belt left flat. A narrow conveyor belt may be troughed by means of only two carriers, both inclined toward each other at an angle of 20°. The belt is loaded from an overhead chute, the load falling between two carriers and not directly on one. At that spot, skirtboards and sealing strips may be provided to prevent spilling.

Troughed conveyors serve for bulk goods of all kinds. The flat conveyor has many uses also; it is particularly well suited for the handling of packaged goods.

Conveyor belt may be short, as in many automatic packaging machines; it may be of medium length, e.g., 50 or 100 feet; or it may be over 1000 feet long. It is made up of shorter lengths, connected together by vulcanization. The normal operating speed generally recommended for a belt 12 inches wide is 200 feet per minute; it gradually increases for wider belts, to reach 450 feet per minute for belts 54 to 60 inches wide. It is usually most economical to operate the narrowest conveyor at the highest speed at which good loading conditions and freedom from damage to the material can be assured. For ordinary large-scale operation, belts 12 inches wide and over are employed, but belts as narrow as 2 inches are widely used; the narrower belts not infrequently are integral parts of automatic machines.

The belt is made of a variety of materials. There are leather belts, solid woven white cotton beltings, oiled and stitched canvas belting, and reinforced rubber belting, which usually consists of four or six plies of duck coated with gum rubber, covered on both sides with black rubber and the whole vulcanized to produce one single body. There are also metallic beltings made of woven wire, with various types of weaves, and with or without plate-retaining selvage. The metallic conveyor belts serve as cooling conveyors for any hot material or objects, such as machine blown bottles.

Returning now to the nonmetallic belts, carriers for troughed belts are spaced 4 to 5 feet apart for smaller widths (12 to 18 inches) and light materials, and 3 or 3½ feet apart for heavier, wider belts (36 to 60) carrying heavy material. The return rollers are spaced farther apart, as for example 10 feet.

Next to the plain drive is the "snubbed drive," in which a snub pulley is placed just beyond the drive pulley; it serves to hold the belt against the face of the driving pulley, so that the arc of contact is increased from 180° to 220°.   It is well when using a snub pulley to provide for constant cleaning of the belt when the materials handled require it.   This is

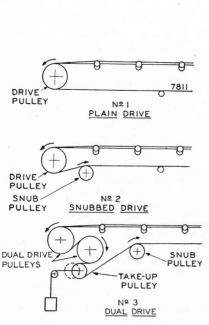

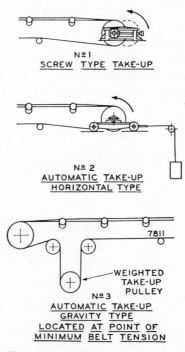

FIGURE 62.—Three kinds of drive for belt conveyors: plain drive, snub drive, and dual drive. The three belts shown have end discharge. The drive pulley is also known as the head pulley. (From "Belt-Conveyor Design," Stephens-Adamson Mfg. Co., Aurora, Ill.)

FIGURE 63.—Three types of "take-ups" for adjusting the tension on the conveyor belt to the desired value. The screw type take-up requires occasional adjustment by the operator; the other two types are automatic. The first two types are applied to the end or tail pulley; the third type is preferably placed directly back of the drive pulley. (From "Conveyor Belt Design," Stephens-Adamson Mfg. Co., Aurora, Ill.)

usually accomplished by means of a spring type belt wiper, or other standard means.   The dual drive pulleys provide, at the drive end, an arc of belt contact of 420° to 480°; they are placed side by side, the second just a little lower than the first, so that the belt describes a letter *S*.   The dual drive is used for longer conveyors and those carrying materials to a considerable height.   A snub pulley is usually used with the dual drive. Covering the drive pulley with a lagging of 4-ply rubber belt will increase the driving capacity for the same rubber belt (as the lagging) from 3 to 10 per cent.

The proper tension on the belt, which insures among other things proper traction, is maintained by means of an automatic type of take-up consisting of pulley with a movable carriage, or by a screw type which is adjustable by hand; the latter is applied to the tail pulley, while the former is placed close to the drive pulley, acting on the belt as it begins its return trip (Figure 63).

Inclined Belt Conveyors. The belt conveyor will carry its load up a slope, provided the slope does not exceed the angle just beyond which the material begins to slide and roll on the belt. The maximum angle of incline for a belt conveyor handling various materials is given in Table 22. The inclined belt conveyor is an elevator, using the term in the

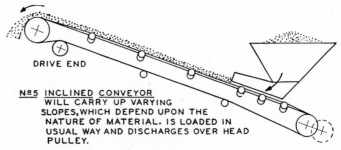

DRIVE END

N⁰5 INCLINED CONVEYOR
WILL CARRY UP VARYING
SLOPES, WHICH DEPEND UPON THE
NATURE OF MATERIAL. IS LOADED IN
USUAL WAY AND DISCHARGES OVER HEAD
PULLEY.

FIGURE 64.—An inclined belt conveyor, exhibiting at the same time loading point, loading hopper, end discharge, and snub pulley. (From the collection of the Stephens-Adamson Mfg. Co., Aurora, Ill.)

TABLE 22. MAXIMUM ANGLE FOR BELT CONVEYORS WHEN HANDLING THE MATERIALS SPECIFIED (SELECTED ITEMS)*

Material Handled	Maximum Angle of Incline
Dry silica sand	15°
Free-flowing materials, such as washed gravel, fine-sized coal, grain	18°
Sized lump materials (stone, lump coal, ore)	22°
Granular materials (sand, crushed coke, glass batch, salt, crushed ore)	22°
Powdered materials (lime, cement, sulfur, chemicals)	23°
Tempered molding sand	24°
Wood chips	27°

* Data supplied by Stephens-Adamson Mfg. Co.

broader sense; by taking the distance great enough, the belt will reach the desired elevation. The same belt may run first along the horizontal, then follow an incline upward and discharge; it may on the other hand first rise up the incline, and then follow a horizontal path for a given distance. Any one of a number of combinations may be selected. The belt conveyor may also travel an incline downward, in order to lower materials gently down slopes. Under certain circumstances it may be of advantage to use two conveyors, a horizontal one discharging onto an inclined belt, instead of a single horizontal-inclined conveyor.

The capacity of belt conveyors will vary with the width of the belt, its speed, the weight per cubic foot of the material carried, and the state of subdivision, as indicated in Table 23.

TABLE 23.   CAPACITIES OF TROUGHED BELT CONVEYORS CARRYING SAND, GRAVEL, STONE WEIGHING 100 POUNDS PER CUBIC FOOT, AND OTHER MATERIALS OF APPROXIMATELY THE SAME WEIGHT
(SELECTED ITEMS)*

Width (in)	Belt Speed (ft/min)									Maximum Size of Lumps	
										If Uniform (in)	If Mixed with Fines (in)
	100	150	200	250	300	350	400	500	600		
12	23	35	46	58	69					2	4
18	53	80	110	135	160	190	215			4	6
30	160	235	315	395	470	550	630	790		6	10
48	440	655	875	1095	1310	1530	1750	2190	2630	10	16
60	720	1080	1440	1800	2160	2520	2880			12	24

* Data supplied by Stephens-Adamson Mfg. Co.
The tonnage for materials of other weights will be very close to the proportionate figure.

The capacities in Table 23 are computed by the Goodyear revised formula, in terms of the width of the belt, W, in inches, the speed of the belt, S, in feet per minute, and the weight of a cubic foot of the material, M. The capacity, T, is in tons (2000 pounds) per hour.

$$T = \frac{(W + 180) \times W^2 \times S \times M}{12,000,000}$$

Tables are available (see footnote to Table 23) for finding the horsepower required for driving the empty conveyor, the additional horsepower for conveying the material horizontally, and also the horsepower required to elevate or lower materials.

A single example will suffice to show the usefulness of the tables.   315 tons an hour of material weighing 100 pounds per cubic foot are to be moved horizontally a little less than 200 feet.   The belt selected will be 30 inches wide, and will be run at a speed of 200 feet per minute (from Table 23).   The power required will be as follows:

To drive empty conveyor, 30 inches wide, 200 feet per minute, for each 100 feet per minute belt speed 1.0 hp.. 2.0 hp
To convey material 200 feet distance...................................... 3.35
To elevate... 0
                                                                          _____
                                                          Total....... 5.35 hp

(Add 5 per cent for drive losses.)

Loading and Discharging.   The belt may be loaded from the spout under the bin, as already said, but it is recommended that a feeder be installed.   There are many types of feeders; a convenient one for this purpose is the type which is a short conveyor itself. Whichever the style, the feeder regulates the amount fed to the belt, avoiding both over- and underloading.

In end discharge, the material leaves the belt as the latter turns over the drive pulley. It may be necessary, however, to discharge the belt at an intermediate point, and perhaps to vary the point of discharge from day to day, or even hourly. The discharge is then by tripper. This consists of a frame bearing two pulleys and chutes, and is set on wheels which run on a small track. The belt rises to the upper pulley, and turns on it to pass around the second pulley which is set back from the first and under it (see Figure 65). As the belt turns, it unloads into the chutes, which

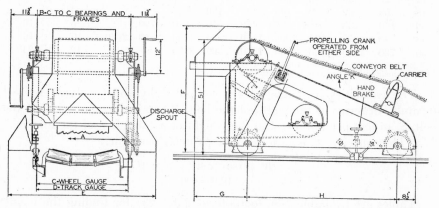

Figure 65.—A hand-propelled tripper, for unloading the belt conveyor at intermediate points instead of at the end. The cross section at the left shows among other things the troughed belt lying on the carriers, and the discharge spouts which straddle the belt. The drawing on the right is a side elevation of the tripper and shows the turning of the belt over the several pulleys of the tripper. The tripper is moved at will, so that the discharge is over any one bin or dissolving tank selected. (Courtesy Stephens-Adamson Mfg. Co., Aurora, Ill.)

straddle the belt. Upon leaving the tripper, the empty belt resumes its journey. In a simple form, the tripper is moved to the proper position by turning a hand crank. There are many other forms of trippers, among others an electrically operated one.

The head, or drive, pulley may be at the same time a magnetic pulley, so that a purification of the material by the removal of tramp iron is accomplished with no extra movement. The iron objects in the feed are retained against the belt at the end discharge; the material dumped is free from such iron. A short distance further, the pulley is passed, and the iron objects drop off into a receptacle. A separate short conveyor placed just above but close to the moving mass, the tail pulley of which is the magnetic one, is another device for the removal of tramp iron; the tail pulley pulls the iron upward, loads it on the belt, and removes it by discharging it at the head pulley.   The iron-free material continues its travel on the main belt.

Chain Conveyors.   Chain conveyors fall into two general classes: those which carry goods on their upper side, and overhead conveyors from which the goods are suspended.   Conveyors of the first class may be fitted with wooden aprons, steel aprons, slats, or other supporting members, on which the goods to be carried are particularly well accommodated. One such conveyor carries pivoted buckets which travel right side up no matter whether the chain travels, up, down, or laterally in either direc-

FIGURE 66.—A conveyor for the continuous casting of silver pigs.   (Courtesy Link-Belt Co., Chicago, Ill.)

tion; at a designated point, a tripper turns the bucket over to deliver the load to a waiting chute.   At another point further on, the bucket passes under a chute or feeder, to receive its load.   The pivoted bucket conveyor has been placed in many early automatic coal-handling installations in powerhouses.

The overhead chain conveyor is an endless chain carried by Y-shaped members fitted with small wheels which run on the flange of the overhead I-beam.   The chain is fitted with hooks or other means of suspension, and on these the work is hung.   The overhead chain serves many process industries, in some of which it performs one or several of the essential steps in the process.   To cite an example, vitrified enamel is applied to steel as the pieces travel suspended from overhead; they are spray-dried, sprayed again, dried again, heated in a furnace to the sintering point of the enamel, and then cooled, all without being handled by anyone.

Screw Conveyors. Screw conveyors consist essentially of a trough fitted lengthwise with a spiral mounted on a shaft; as the shaft revolves, the spiral turns and pushes the material along the trough, generally from one end to the other. The feed is from an overhead spout, and the discharge is provided by an opening in the bottom of the trough, usually fitted with a delivery spout. The shaft is driven by belt, gear, or any other standard drive, and is supported by bearings at the end of the trough, with intermediate bearings if it is very long.

The screw in the horizontal screw conveyor may be right-handed or left-handed, and each may turn clockwise or counterclockwise. Turning clockwise, the right-handed screw will move the material in one direction, the left-handed screw in the opposite one; turning counterclockwise, the motion will be just opposite. In these four instances, the feed is at one end of the conveyor, the discharge at the other. There is a screw conveyor which distributes the material both ways from a central feed point; half of the conveyor spiral is of left-hand construction, the other half right-hand, so that with a single direction of rotation, the conveyor carries the material in both directions, to two delivery points, for example, at either end of the trough. The same right and left conveyor serves when there are two feed points (at the extremities, for example) and one discharge point (center).

Inclined screw conveyors are slanted both upward and downward, generally at an angle not over 20°, for duties which require that the material be elevated, or lowered more gently than it would be with a chute or at an angle so slight that it would not move of itself.

The screw conveyor with a vertical screw becomes an elevator, and as such has a number of points in its favor.

The standard spiral steel conveyor is the solid spiral used very generally; in its simplest form it is called the sectional-flight conveyor, because it is made up of sections each equal to one turn. The sections are riveted together, and the spiral thus formed is secured to the shaft by steel lugs. The standard spiral is obtainable in standard sections 8 to 12 feet long depending upon the diameter; the required full length is obtained by joining a number of sections. In the standard-pitch conveyor used on ordinary longitudinal and inclined conveyors, the pitch of the flight is approximately equal to its diameter; this gives a means of estimating the number of turns per standard length. The standard pitch is the one most generally used, but there are a number of variations. In the long-pitch conveyor, the spiral has fewer turns per standard length; in the short-pitch screw, it has, on the contrary, more turns, perhaps twice as many, per standard length. There is also a variable-pitch screw. By retaining the standard pitch, the conveyor may have two flights side by side, in which case it is known as a double-flight standard-pitch conveyor; and there are still others.

The sectional-flight conveyor continues in general favor for various reasons, among which is the ease in which it can be repaired by the renewal of a single flight. However, an improved spiral has been intro-

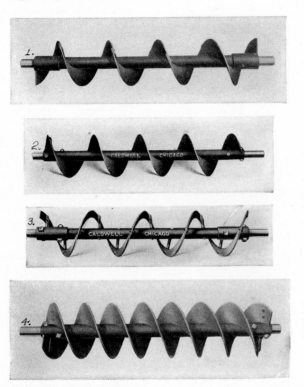

FIGURE 67.—Several styles of flights for screw conveyors. *1*, sectional flight conveyor; *2*, helicoid spiral; *3*, single-ribbon conveyor, standard pitch; *4*, double-flight helicoid conveyor, with standard pitch. (Courtesy Link-Belt Co., Chicago, Ill.)

duced, with great success. This is the helicoid spiral, which has the same dimensions and turns as the sectional-flight spiral, but is formed of a single continuous strip of steel which presents a smooth surface to the material. It should also be stated that the helicoid flight is tapered in cross section; it is about twice as thick at the base as at the outer edge, and this makes for strength. The thickness of the flight in the sectional-flight spiral is uniform.

The helicoid conveyor is available also in stainless steel, mounted on a stainless steel shaft, for corrosion and heat resistance.

The conveyor may also be cast or gray iron, steel, or alloys. The continuous-flight cast-iron conveyor serves, for example, for moving ashes or clinkers; it is capable of resisting high temperatures, and is used in underfeed screw stokers.

The complete conveyor consists of the spiral or screw; the trough or box (generally of steel); cast-iron box ends with the bearing for the screw shaft, and with a foot on which the conveyor rests; and of pulley, bevel gear, or other means of driving. Within the box the screw is carried by cast-iron hangers resting on the trough and equipped with babbitted bearings. The box may be made of wood as well as of steel. As to the steel box, it may be open, or it may have a cover plate, which furthermore may

FIGURE 68.—A screw conveyor in a dust seal trough and cover. (Courtesy Link-Belt Co., Chicago, Ill.)

be equipped with clamps so that it may be closed, to make the conveyor dust-tight.

Wherever possible, especially on long conveyors, it is recommended that the drive be located at the discharge end of the conveyor, causing the screw to pull the material toward the drive. It may be of interest also to call attention to a second kind of trough, the flared trough, used generally with ribbon conveyors. The ribbon spiral steel conveyor has a ribbon spiral carried by short rods inserted in the central pipe, so that there is an open space around the pipe; it is used for handling sticky materials, such as molasses, hot tar, asphalt, and similar substances.

The spiral revolves in the trough. The inside width of the latter is generally 1 inch greater than the diameter of the screw, while the depth of the trough exceeds the diameter by 2 inches in smaller sizes, to 4 inches in the larger sizes (20 inches diameter). The material handled by the

conveyor may cover all the area of the screw, or less; curves are available*
giving values for 12½, 25, 31, 38, and 45 per cent; also for 100 per cent,
which applies to screw feeders. The capacities listed in Table 24 are for
material covering one-third the area of the screw.

TABLE 24. SPIRAL STEEL CONVEYOR WITH SECTIONAL FLIGHTS
(SELECTED ITEMS)*

Conveyor Diameter (in)	I.D. of Pipe (in)	Standard Length (ft)	Maximum Speed (rpm)	Capacity (cu ft per hr)	Bushels Per Hour
4	1	8	200	72	58
6	1½	10	180	243	195
9	1½, 2	10	170	910	728
10	1½, 2	10	165	1205	965
12	2, 2½, 3	12	165	2180	1745
14	2½, 3	12	160	2935	2305
16	3	12	160	5110	4100
18	3	12	150	7600	6080

* Data supplied by Robinson Mfg. Co., Muncy, Pa.

The main function of the screw conveyor is to move material horizontally from one point to another; it may have one of several auxiliary
functions. A wetting conveyor, for example, has cut-flight spirals, which
may have in addition small mixing paddles. Water is sprayed in and

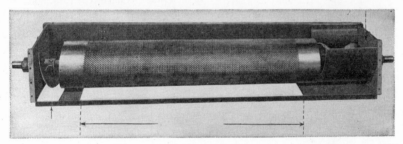

FIGURE 69.—A rotary screen screw and vane feeder. (Courtesy Link-Belt Co., Chicago,
Ill.)

mixed with the substance, as in tempering wheat before grinding. The
cut-flight spiral with mixing paddle is used for thorough mixing of the
materials. The cut and folded flight spiral steel conveyor also serves for
thorough mixing, at the same time retarding travel; it permits cooling and
drying light substances. The screw conveyor may be equipped with a
lining of perforated steel (or other metal), so that it may function as a
dewaterer as well as a conveyor. Assume that the material to be conveyed contains much free water; as it is moved along by the screw, water
escapes through the perforations. Screw washers are conveyors with one
or two spirals side by side in a trough, to which water is admitted freely

* Link-Belt Company, Chicago, Ill.

as the sand, for example, is moved along. There is an overflow over which low specific gravity materials are carried away, leaving comparatively pure sand.

Vertical-screw Conveyors. The space required by the vertical-screw conveyor is less than for any other type, for it has but a single leg; no return casing or space for the empty conveyor is required. A specially rolled, carefully balanced helicoidal flight, mounted on straightened steel

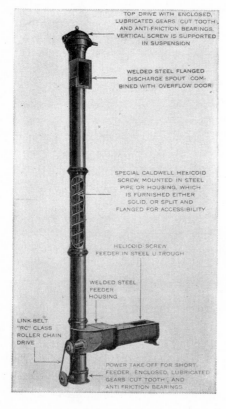

FIGURE 70.—Type "A" medium duty Rotor Lift, a vertical helicoid screw. (Courtesy Link-Belt Co., Chicago, Ill.)

pipe, is suspended from a top thrust bearing; it rotates in a round, smooth tube with a small clearance. The feed is by means of a hopper at the base, for free-flowing materials, or by a screw conveyor for sluggish materials. The discharge is at the top. The vertical-screw conveyor is light and compact, and is therefore adapted to temporary or portable installations.

One manufacturer* offers a "medium-duty rotor lift," with top drive and split flanged housings, and also a "heavy-duty rotor lift," with bottom drive and solid tubular housing. The first serves for cereals, cottonseed,

* Link-Belt Co., Chicago, Ill.

and light granular products; the second for such materials as cement and lime. Both are made in three sizes, namely, with screw diameters of 6, 9, and 12 inches. Another manufacturer* has, among others, a special unit of the motor-driven kind which has a reversing switch so that the spiral can be driven backward and any residue in the tube quickly lowered to the bottom. This same unit is fitted with clean-out doors over its entire length. For application in the food industries, or in others if advisable, the unit is made of stainless steel, "Monel" metal, or of iron with galvanized or tinned surfaces. The model is made in four sizes, 4½, 6, 8, and 10 inches in screw diameter. The speed of rotation is 350 rpm for the small size, and decreases as the diameter increases; for the large one, the speed is 125 to 200 rpm. Capacities are from 100 to 600 cubic feet per hour. The maximum lift recommended is 16 to 20 feet.

For vertical-screw conveyors in general, the maximum practical lift is 50 feet, and their capacities are as high as 50 to 60 tons per hour.

Drag Conveyors. The drag conveyor is a chain conveyor, usually with a single strand of chain, of special construction in that the links are large. The chain travels slowly in a trough, and the head of each link pushes the material along. The chain returns empty to the starting point. The trough may be of steel, usually with flared sides; it may also be made of concrete, generally with straight sides. The drag conveyor is largely used for conveying sawdust.

Flight Conveyors. In the flight conveyor, the horizontal chain carries short vertical projections called flights. It is these which push the material along in the steel trough, usually traveling at a good rate, such as 150 feet per minute. The vertical flights are attached to a single- or double-strand chain; they ride on the bottom of the trough, causing wear. In an effort to counteract wear, the flights, usually of malleable iron, are made with a thickened scraping edge; or they may be reversible. A further, still more important improvement is the use of small rollers at each link; these run on the edges of the trough, thus avoiding dragging on the bottom. The material conveyed is usually discharged through openings provided with gates in the bottom of the trough, so that the material can be accumulated at numerous points in succession.

The flight conveyor gives good service when operated horizontally, but its special value lies in conveying materials on inclines between 20° and 45° to the horizontal, angles which the belt conveyor cannot negotiate. The flight conveyor is suitable for either lumpy or small material.

Flight conveyors give a wide variety of services. A light chain with its flights is used, for example, in a concrete or bricked trough; it moves rapidly and not only pushes, but kicks the hot pebbles of lime just discharged from a rotary kiln to the bottom of a bucket elevator, which lifts

* Robinson Mfg. Co., Muncy, Pa.

it to the cooler. It may also become a splendid elevator, by running it vertically in a casing similar to that of the bucket elevator. The chain runs close to the steel plate of the casing, so that the shallow flights are held tight against it; an apron on the chain helps lock whatever material has entered, and as the chain rises, this material is conveyed to a discharge chute. Such a device is used to move the irregular and rather large segments of shredded rubber tires in the reclaimed rubber industry.

FIGURE 71.—A system of horizontal screw conveyors and vertical Rotor Lifts, distributing to four storage bins. (Courtesy Link-Belt Co., Chicago, Ill.)

Bucket Elevators. The bucket elevator is the best known and probably the most widely used device for vertical lifts. It consists of a number of buckets fastened to an endless belt or chain which runs over an upper driving pulley, and a lower idling pulley for belt, or corresponding sprocket wheels for the chain. Near the bottom, the buckets are filled, and then travel upward with their load; on turning over the head pulley. the bucket tips and the load slips out and reaches a discharge chute placed in the right position to receive it. The empty buckets continue downward, face down. After turning on the idling pulley or tail pulley, they refill and start up again. The endless belt or chain is enclosed, usually but not always, by a vertical chamber, rectangular in cross section, of steel, wood, or other material. The casing is wide enough to give ample clearances; the area of the casing is several times that of the buckets, as shown in Table 25.

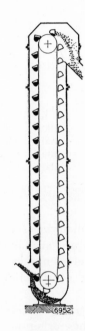

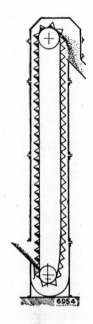

FIGURE 72.—The spaced-bucket elevator is shown at left; the continuous-bucket elevator at right. Note the bucket digging through the material in the boot of the elevator at left, and note also the richer discharge from elevator at right. (Courtesy Stephens-Adamson Mfg. Co., Aurora, Ill.)

For chain elevators with the same bucket size, the speed is about the same, a little lower for small buckets, a little larger for large ones. The other data are the same, except that the pitch diameters of the corresponding sprocket wheels are given, with a choice of several diameters. The width of the belt is generally one to two inches greater than the bucket.

As already indicated, the buckets may be mounted on a belt or chain.

TABLE 25. BELT ELEVATOR DATA (SELECTED ITEMS)*

Bucket Size (in)	Speed of Belt (ft/min)	Rotation of Head Pulley (rpm)	Pulley Diameter (in) Head	Foot	Size of Casing Intermediate Sections (in)
5 × 3½″	225	57.3	15	12	30½ × 10
6 × 4	225	47.7	18	14	36½ × 11
8 × 5	225	43	20	16	39½ × 13
10 × 6	258	41	24	18	48½ × 15
14 × 7	258	41	24	18	48½ × 19
16 × 8	298	38	30	24	56½ × 22

* Data supplied by C. O. Bartlett and Snow Co., Cleveland, Ohio.

TABLE 26. DIMENSIONS AND CAPACITY OF A VERTICAL SPACED-BUCKET ELEVATOR (SELECTED ITEMS)*

Size of Bucket (in)	Bucket Spacing (in)	Maximum Height (ft)	Sprocket Head	Diameter T.U.	Speed (ft/min)	Material 75% Under	Size up to 10%	Lbs/ cu ft	Tons/ hour
7 × 4½ × 5	16	50	21.77	20.50	250	1″	2″	100	15
10 × 6 × 6¼	16	40	22.92	20.40	250	1½″	3″	50	13
10 × 6 × 6¼	16	80	20.30	17.80	250	1½″	3″	100	26
16 × 8 × 8½	18	40	30.76	25.07	300	2″	4″	50	68
16 × 8 × 8½	18	80	28.87	23.18	287	2″	4″	100	136

* Data supplied by Stephens-Adamson Mfg. Co.
Notes: For other weight per cubic foot materials, approximately proportional capacities. T.U. means take-up bearing, at the base of the vertical elevator. The width of the casing runs from 42½″ for the smallest elevator, to 54½″ for the largest one in the table.

TABLE 27. DIMENSIONS AND CAPACITIES OF A VERTICAL CONTINUOUS-BUCKET ELEVATOR (SELECTED ITEMS)*

Size of Bucket (in)	Bucket Spacing (in)	Maximum Height (ft)	Sprocket Head	Diameter T.U.	Speed (ft/min)	Material 75% Under	Size up to 10%	Lbs/ cu ft	Tons/ hour
8 × 5½ × 7¾	8	50	22.92	20.40	137	1″	2″	100	26
9 × 6 × 8¾	9	50	22.58	20.71	145	1¼″	2½″	100	45
12 × 7 × 11¾	12	80	28.86	21.30	142	1½″	3″	100	68
16 × 8 × 11¾	12	80	28.86	23.18	171	2″	4	100	152

* Data supplied by Stephens-Adamson Mfg. Co.
Notes: For other weight per cubic foot materials, approximately proportional capacities. T.U. means take-up bearing, at the base of the vertical elevator. The width of the casing runs from 42½″ for the smallest elevator, to 54½″ for the largest one in the table.

The belt is recommended for the handling of very abrasive materials such as sand, glass, and the like. The chain-mounted buckets are available for a variety of services, including the handling of mildly and even highly abrasive materials, the chain being of suitable strength and construction for each application.

A distinction is made between spaced buckets and continuous buckets. In the spaced-bucket elevator, the buckets are 16 to 18 inches, or similar distances, apart. The feed is from a hopper in the bottom or "boot" section; the buckets may be filled directly, or, more generally, the boot may first be filled and the buckets allowed to dig through the material. The continuous-bucket elevator has its buckets closer together, perhaps 8 to 12 inches apart, or similar distances depending upon the size of the bucket; the feed is at the bottom, directly to the buckets. The spaced-bucket elevator belt travels faster than the continuous one; the elevator is lower in first cost, and the horsepower is less. In distinguishing between spaced and continuous bucket elevators, the emphasis has been placed on the construction feature. Some manufacturers place the emphasis on the kind of discharge and rate the elevators accordingly, so that one speaks of the continuous-discharge bucket elevator, in which the discharge is unbroken, since the buckets are close together, in contrast with the usual, slightly pulsating discharge of the spaced-bucket elevator.

A further distinction is made between the centrifugal-discharge bucket elevator and the special or "Perfect" discharge bucket elevator. The centrifugal discharge is the usual one, caused by the tipping of the bucket as it turns unassisted over the head pulley. In the "Perfect" discharge the descending chain meets a special pulley which snubs the chain and keeps it in contact with the sprocket wheel or pulley over a greater angle; as a result of the "snubbing" the bucket is upended, and a clean discharge is secured, even with fluffy, powdery, or sticky materials. It is for the handling of such materials that the special or "Perfect" discharge is intended.

There is finally a "Super Capacity" bucket elevator, in which the buckets are built out at the back; it is a variation of the continuous-discharge bucket elevator, or continuous-bucket elevator.

The bucket elevator may be driven by belt, direct motor, gears, or chain; usually the head pulley is the driving pulley. A take-up arrangement is generally provided in the boot section, with which any excessive

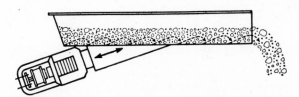

Figure 73.—Vibrating feeder, illustrating the Traylor principle of feeding and conveying by means of vibrations. The feeder operates upward, downward, or on the horizontal. (Courtesy Jeffrey Mfg. Co., Columbus, Ohio.)

slack in the belt or chain may be taken up. Should the boot section be inaccessible or hard to get at, the head pulley frames may be provided with the "take-up," and the boot section with fixed bearings.

Bucket elevators may be used on an incline instead of the vertical, generally without casing.

Vibrating Feeders. A vibrating feeder is a kind of conveyor, generally for short distances, such as a few feet. The vibrating feeder (see Figure 73) operates uphill, downhill, or along the horizontal. Its short, metal, rigid trough receives vibrations, consisting of rapid back and forth strokes. On the forward stroke, the material in the trough is thrown forward; the trough itself is pulled back while this forward movement of the material is taking place.

Vibrating Conveyors. The vibrating conveyor operates on the same principle as the vibrating feeder, except that it conveys materials over longer distances which may be as great as 100 feet. The rate of travel of the material may be 60 feet, or as great as 100 feet, per minute.

A vibrating conveyor is made up of standard lengths of a shallow steel trough or pan with a special length to reach the exact distance desired.

The shallow trough is attached to pairs of coil springs and rocker arms; a belt-driven eccentric drive shaft gives a forward motion, against the tension of the coil springs, which is followed by the return motion in which springs and eccentric reinforce each other. In the "Natural Frequency Vibrating Conveyors," the rate of vibration furnished by the eccentric is matched by the natural balance frequency of the coil springs, with a resultant saving in power.*   In an extension of the same conveyor but with "balanced vibration," a balance frame is provided in addition to the base frame. The balance frame is carried by the rocker arms, at their lower

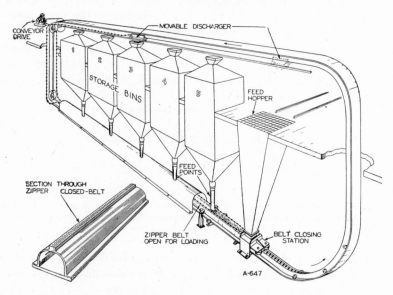

FIGURE 74.—A "Zipper" closed belt conveyor-elevator installation, showing feed hopper, belt closing, movable discharge over storage bins. At lower left, a section through the Zipper closed belt. (Courtesy Stephens-Adamson Mfg. Co., Aurora, Ill.)

end; the coil springs run from the trough to the balance frame, so that conveyor and balance frame vibrate in opposite directions. The base frame and the floor thus remain essentially vibrationless.

The vibrating conveyor moves bulk materials horizontally and up inclines to 10°; it serves also to convey packaged materials.

Closed Belt Conveyors. An example of a closed belt conveyor (Figure 74) is the "Zipper," in which a rubber belt carrying flexible side walls equipped at their upper end with zipper teeth may be closed and opened by mechanism. The closed zipper belt travels on pulleys in any direction, horizontally, on inclines, or vertically. It may be discharged at the end of a horizontal or gently inclined run, at the turn over the head pulley;

* Stephens-Adamson Mfg. Co., Aurora, Illinois.

at the top of an elevating run; or on a horizontal run by a fixed or moving belt discharger.

The standard 4-inch Zipper belt can be run at speeds ranging up to 200 feet per minute. It handles bulk material up to a lump size of 2-inches. The amount of material is so proportioned that it completely fills the conveyor when the latter is closed; it then becomes practically a moving pipeline for bulk materials. The power requirements are favorable.

Conveying-Elevating by "En Masse" Action. In the conveyors and

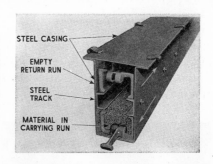

FIGURE 75.—Section through the horizontal Redler conveyor, showing the U-type skeleton flights moving the material in the carrying run, and returning empty in the upper part of the casing. The skeleton flights are linked to form an endless belt. (Courtesy Stephens-Adamson Mfg. Co., Aurora, Ill.)

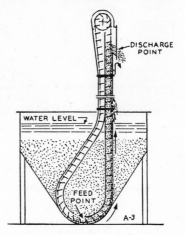

FIGURE 76.—A vertical Redler conveyor, the "double-loop boot elevator" with side discharge, showing the general disposition common to all the vertical Redlers, and in addition its service as a processing machine. (Courtesy Stephens-Adamson Mfg. Co., Aurora, Ill.)

elevators studied up to this point, the material is carried by the bucket, belt, or disk, or is pushed along by the positive action of the screw, drag link, or other member. In the Redler conveyor the action is partly indirect; skeleton flights move the material in a solid column, yet cover but a fraction of the cross section.

The Redler conveyor-elevator consists of skeleton flights connected by a central or side arm to form an endless chain with flexible joints. The chain travels in a dust-tight casing. In the standard model, the skeleton flights are U-shaped, and there is a generous clearance between flight and casing wall; yet the material within the carrying run is moved along in a solid column. The impulse communicated directly to the particles in contact with the advancing skeleton flights is spread in all forward directions; the preceding flight promotes the movement by impelling its load forward, while the flight in the rear also contributes by sending its load forward. The continual flow of additional material into the casing from the feed point causes the material farther on in the carrying run to move along at a constant speed. The "en masse" movement is successfully applied to pulverized, granular, small lump, or flaky material.

In the standard form, the carrying and return runs are in a single casing with a divider plate which may, but need not be, continuous. The horizontal conveyor is the simplest form, with the loading and discharge points at the head and tail end respectively; but these may be placed at any intermediate points. The horizontal path may be replaced by a horizontal-inclined path, or by a loop boot design. Still other types are the

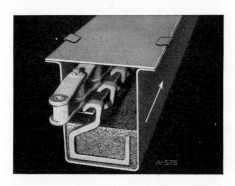

FIGURE 77.—Section through a horizontal closed-circuit Redler conveyor, showing one type of side-pull flights, which permit the conveying of material without bringing it in contact with the chain. There are several modifications of side-pull design, avoiding contamination. (Courtesy Stephens-Adamson Mfg. Co., Aurora, Ill.)

Z-type conveyor-elevator, the vertical closed-circuit elevators with U-flights, and several more. For lifting a fragile material from a low point to an elevated bin, an elevator with its casing open within the bin (for the rising leg only) is available. The "elevator with open casing" avoids dropping the material; instead it is discharged gently at the top of the pile, the discharge point rising as the top is raised.

In the horizontal closed-circuit Redler conveyors, with multiple feed and discharge if desired, provision is made to prevent contamination. One of the several types of side-pull flights is selected, which permits placing the driving part of the chain in a separate compartment from the one carrying the conveyed material; both compartments (Figure 77) are within the usual rectangular casing. There is also a model in which the chain is in a compartment separate from that housing the carrying run. For a long vertical elevation, the tubular type elevator with carrying and return runs in separate casings is more economical.

The Redler conveys through the whole of the casing area in the carrying run, so that it requires less space for a given tonnage handled than the bucket elevator or belt conveyor (one-fourth that of the bucket elevator).

The horizontal, inclined, and vertical conveyor-elevators of the standard type, with rectangular casing and U-type skeleton flights are made in ten sizes; for the smallest, the carrying compartment would be 3 inches high and 3½ inches wide; in the largest, 15 inches high and 23 inches wide.

The capacity depends upon the weight per cubic foot of the material handled, and upon the speed of the conveyor, for a selected size. The charts in Figure 80 will permit the solving of a number of problems. The power required for operating the conveyors and elevators may be de-

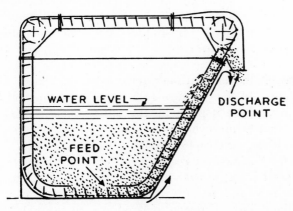

FIGURE 78.—Elevation sketch of a vertical closed-circuit Redler elevator, which has the function of a dewaterer as a secondary one. As the elevating run rises above the level of the slurry, the water escapes through suitable openings, so that the material discharged is considerably lower in water content.

termined by using formulas and factors for a list of thirty materials, available in the reference below.* Among the materials handled are dry navy beans, pulverized bicarbonate of soda, portland cement, shredded coconut, ground coffee, corn flakes, fuller's earth, lump or pebble lime, dry granulated salt, dry sawdust, lump starch, dry granulated sugar, wheat, wood chips, and coal.

Other conveyors which embody the "en masse" flow principle include Bulk-Flo (Link-Belt) and Mass-Flo (Jeffrey).

Pneumatic Conveyors. In the pneumatic conveyor, the solid materials in powder, pulverized, or granular form, or hulls such as cottonseed hulls, are carried through the pipe or duct from receiving to delivery point by a current of air. A distinction is made between the suction (or vacuum) system, and the pressure system, in which a medium or low pressure is used. In the suction system an exhauster pulls the requisite volume of

* Stephens-Adamson Mfg. Co., Aurora, Ill.

air through the pipe; this system should be used when the material is to be picked up at several points to be conveyed to one destination point. In the pressure system a medium- or low-pressure blower supplies the air; the pressure system is generally preferred when the material is to be conveyed from one receiving point to several delivery stations. These rules are not adhered to absolutely; there are systems with one receiving and one delivery point which operate with suction, for instance, in unloading a boxcar of bulk soda ash. In either system, the material occupies about 12 per cent of the pipe area, and air 88 per cent.*

The pneumatic conveyor consists essentially of metal pipes or ducts; a blower or an exhauster; a receiver, such as a cyclone collector which may be surmounted by a bag filter; a feeder; and discharging devices. In the suction system the exhauster pulls air in succession through the receiver or collector, the bag filter if any, and the pipe system including the flexible hose and nozzle, hand-governed. A mixture of air and material flows along the ducts, reaching the collector where the material drops to the base of the cone, while the air continues to the exhauster which discharges it to the atmosphere. In the pressure system, the air from the blower passes below a feeder, where it picks up the solids and continues, now laden, through the duct to the cyclone or other collector, where the solids accumulate while the air escapes through the central pipe.

The pneumatic conveyor requires little space, it saves labor costs, and has the further advantage over mechanical conveyors in that it costs less to install. Still another feature is that the duct may be carried through a building without inconvenience, or under a street. The air stream is enclosed in the ducts, so that there is no formation and escape of dust.

In addition to the uses already suggested, the pneumatic conveyor handles brewer's grain, coal slag, ashes, rock wool, bagasse, peat, fertilizer, clay, malt, corn, starch, and many other materials. It not only unloads railway cars, but loads them; similarly it loads and unloads barges and boats.

Fuller-Kinyon Pump. The Fuller-Kinyon pump is shown in Figure 79. The screw feeds the cement powder, for example, into the aeration chamber, where the air jets deliver a stream of compressed air. This unites with the powder to form a fluid mass which travels, for example, 600 feet laterally and then 95 feet vertically to the top of the storage silos.

Skip Hoist. The skip hoist consists of a rectangular bucket, usually of large capacity, running on vertical or inclined tracks, and a hoisting cable attached to a suitable power source. The general model is the counterweighted two-bucket type, in which the descending empty bucket balances the weight of the ascending bucket, so that the hoisting engine has only the weight of the conveyed material to lift. There are single-

* Brady Conveyors Corp., Chicago, Ill.

bucket models; and both single- and two-bucket types may be provided with automatic operation. The skip hoist is well adapted to high lifts, and is reliable. It is operated at low as well as at high speeds. A balanced skip hoist, as used in a coal mine, attains a velocity of 50 feet per second in portions of its travel.

Choice of Conveyors. The belt conveyor requires less power and less maintenance than any other type of conveyor, its operation is uncomplicated and in full view, and it conveys on moderate inclines as well as along the horizontal. Its first cost is not excessive. The life of the conveyor is comparatively long; as a rule several belts are installed before the conveyor as a whole requires renewal of other parts. For these several good reasons the belt conveyor is widely used.

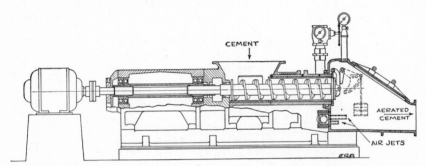

Figure 79.—Sketch of the Fuller-Kinyon pump for conveying portland cement.

The screw conveyor is inexpensive, requires but little room, and little head room. It is used for the lighter classes of services, including the handling filter cake from continuous filters.

Flight conveyors extend the services of the belt conveyor, for they serve for inclinations higher than 20° with the horizontal, which is the limit for the belt conveyor, and as high as 45°.

For vertical lifts, the bucket elevator or the vertical screw conveyor is used.

Other conveyors serve specific duties; each one performs some one service better than any other. The special virtue of each has been stated under the separate headings.

Numerical Examples and Problems

Capacity charts of Redler conveyor-elevators, as examples of charts for such equipment, are shown in Figure 80.

The three charts presented are used in series. The material to be handled is first established and expressed in pounds per minute or tons per hour.

The first chart, the weight chart, is now consulted. The performance of the conveyor depends upon the volume of material, so that the weight must be transformed into a volume value. A number of cross lines representing materials weighing from 5

FIGURE 80.—Capacity charts for Redler conveyor-elevators. The method of using the charts is illustrated in "Numerical Example" No. 1.

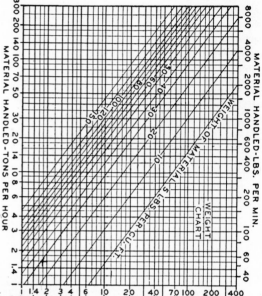

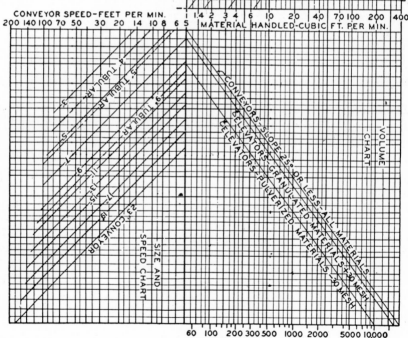

to 150 pounds to the cubic foot are shown, which permit the transformation of the pounds into the volume in cubic feet.

The second chart is the volume chart, leading to the third one, the size and speed chart. The volume chart offers a choice of the three differing services: the horizontal conveyor and the horizontal-inclined conveyor for slopes not exceeding 25° and for all materials, the elevator handling granulated material of 30 mesh and over, and finally the elevator handling pulverized material of 30 mesh and smaller. For a given number of cubic feet per minute to be handled, the conveyor will require the least speed, the elevator for granulated material the next least, and the elevator for pulverized material the highest speed; for example, 40, 55, and 80 respectively for 11 cubic feet per minute.

The vertical line dropped from a point in the conveyor line on the volume chart to the third chart, cuts a number of diagonal lines, each representing a size, so that a choice may be made. The intersection of the vertical line with the selected size of conveyor line is extended horizontally to the left, where the speed of the conveyor in feet per minute is ascertained. It will be noted that the smaller sizes require higher speeds, and it may be the better practice to select a larger size, run at a lower speed.

Problem 1. The use of the charts will be illustrated by means of a problem, namely that of finding the size and speed of this type of elevator which will handle 17 tons of coal per hour. Enter the weight chart at 17 tons per hour, or at its equivalent 575 pounds per minute, and move up to the diagonal line representing the volume weight of the coal, namely 50 pounds per cubic foot. From the intersection, move horizontally to read the volume, namely 12 cubic feet per minute. By running across on this chart, a value in bushels per hour may be read.

On the volume chart, follow the 12 cubic feet per minute horizontal line to the second diagonal line, representing elevators for granulated material 30 mesh and over, which permits the dropping of a vertical line from the intersection, to the third chart, taking the diagonal marked "7 inch" size as the proper one. A horizontal from this intersection run to the left gives a reading of 55 feet per minute for the running speed on the elevator. The same vertical strikes the 9-inch diagonal size line, giving a reading of the speed as 35 feet per minute, and the 5-inch size line, to be run at a speed of 90 feet per minute.

Answer: Select the 7-inch elevator and run it at 55 feet per minute.

Problem 2. 20 tons per hour of wood chips, weighing 20 pounds to the cubic foot, are to be conveyed along the horizontal. Find the size and speed of the Redler conveyor best suited.

Answer: The 15-inch conveyor, traveling at the speed of 39 feet per minute.

Reading References

"Mechanical power transmission in process industries," by William Staniar and John H. Perry, *Chem. Met. Eng.*, **41**, 624 (1934).

"Mechanical power transmission," *Chem. Met. Eng.*, **47**, 482 (1940).

"Belt conveyors, industry's bulk handling giant," by L. O. Millard, *Am. Soc. Mech. Engrs.*, Nov. 28, 1951, Atlantic City meeting, paper 51-A-150.

The tank for storage is the silent, indispensable servant of the manufacturer; in it he accumulates the product until the desired volume is reached and the shipping containers are ready; from it he draws the acid in the quantities called for by his formula. It is in tanks that the raw material for many industries is dissolved, ready for the process. Next to piping, fittings, and pumps, tanks are the most common type of equipment in the chemical and allied industries.

5. TANKS

In many industries reserve stocks of raw materials are accumulated against a disturbance in regular deliveries, or because shipment is periodical and in large volumes. Solid raw materials are made into convenient stock-piles, for example: coal, sulfur from Texas and Louisiana, phosphate pebbles from Florida, a boat-load of bauxite from France, limestone from Michigan, and hematite from Minnesota. For materials which are liquid, storage tanks take the place of the stock-pile, for example: petroleum crude oil, vegetable oils, molasses, solvents, benzene, toluene, crude distillates from hardwood, and acids. Tanks are used not only for primary, but for intermediate storage; an intermediate product is nearly always accumulated in quantities sufficient to permit several days' run, thus providing a certain amount of slack. The product of the plant, if it is liquid, is collected in tanks.

However, tanks are used for many other purposes beside storage; if they serve in one of the steps in the manufacturing process, they are designated collectively as process tanks. Thus there are dissolving tanks, blending tanks, and treating tanks. Not infrequently, reactions are carried out in tanks. Many other devices listed under different names include a tank as the essential part, as for example, many thickeners, settlers, clarifiers, and fermenters. Tanks of special shapes and construction serve for the transportation of liquids by both land and water.

STATIONARY TANKS

Wooden Tanks. Wood as the construction material for tanks is highly prized in the chemical and allied industries, because it is not attacked by a number of solutions, such as dilute hydrochloric acid, lactic acid, acetic acid, and salt solutions, which do attack steel. Hence wooden tanks are found in bone-dissolving plants preceding the preparation of glue, in sauerkraut factories, in vinegar plants, and in the numerous chemical works which require a solution of salt (NaCl). Many other factories, such as tanneries, breweries, vinegar works, and paper mills, find wooden tanks suitable, if not indispensable. Wooden tanks are well adapted for water storage; they are made in a number of shapes, and in all sizes. A partial list of shapes would be: open-top cylindrical tank (upright cylinder), closed-top cylindrical tank, open-top oval tank, closed-top oval tank, rectangular tank, open- and closed-compartment tank, and half-round tank. Cylindrical tanks 48 feet in diameter and 38 feet high have been constructed, while a tank with a diameter of 60 feet is not beyond reason. The horizontal wooden pipe which serves as a penstock in many of the smaller waterpower installations is 8 or 10 feet in diameter and may be several miles long.

FIGURE 81.—Unlined wooden tank for acid storage and storage of liquids with dehydrating properties; the hoops are kept away from the staves by means of wooden blocks. (Courtesy Hauser-Stander Tank Co., Cincinnati, Ohio.)

The cylindrical tank is constructed of vertical staves held together by round iron rods with threaded ends so that they can be taken up by means of draw lugs. Low-carbon steel rods are used whenever allowable, but "Monel," stainless steel, and other nonrusting alloys are employed when necessary to insure acid- or corrosion-resistance. The modern wooden tank has staves which are so well jointed that the tank is usually watertight when new; should there be a drop leak, the wood swells in a short time, and the leak stops.

Rectangular tanks generally reinforced with steel tie rods are built in many sizes, and as large as desired. Other useful forms are the wooden sink, the wooden stationary suction filter, and the multi-sided tumbling barrel.

The staves may be of any thickness, 1½, 2, 2½, 3, and up to 8 inches as the service requires.   The 1½-inch thickness would be selected for a tank in which there is to be no agitation and no abrasion.   Tanks which are to hold brine or other solutions which, like brine, tend to draw water from the wood, are in a special class and have a very special construction.   The materials available for general tank construction, to quote the exact words of one construction firm, include "Florida Tidewater Red Cypress, Old Growth Yellow Douglas Fir, Dense Unbled Florida Long Leaf Yellow Pine, Medium Textured Appalachian White Oak, Hard White Maple, California Redwood, and Virginia White Cedar."   In addition to the resistivity to dilute acids and to salt solutions, other properties which distinguish wooden tanks are low heat conductivity (so that the contents are relatively cool in summer and warm in winter), and freedom from rusting.

When a tank is to hold solutions difficult to retain because of corrosive or dehydrating properties and must moreover be unlined, the construction illustrated in Figure 81 is of great value.   Small blocks are used behind the hoops, so that the latter are kept away from the staves proper and hence out of reach of a possible leak or spillage; besides, the use of blocks makes practically the entire hoop accessible for painting.   Corrosion- and rust-resistance are secured without the use of expensive corrosion-resisting metals.

It is interesting to note that the "run-down tanks" in at least one of our large synthetic rubber plants are of wood.   In these tanks a number of batches of GR-S emulsion, for example, are blended preparatory to the coagulation step.

The usefulness of wooden tanks is greatly extended by providing them with linings of various materials, especially lead and rubber.   A rectangular wooden tank lined with soft lead makes an excellent storage and dipping tank for sulfuric acid of medium strength.   Closed-compartment wooden tanks lined with lead serve for the adjustment to strength and subsequent storage of aqua ammonia.

Rubber-lined wooden tanks are used to store hydrochloric acid in a number of steel plants.   Two types of lining for wooden tanks are applied: unvulcanized crude rubber in $\frac{3}{16}$-inch thickness, and vulcanized rubber in the same thickness.   The cover of the tank may also be rubber-lined, or it may be treated with acid-resisting asphalt only.   Outlets of hard rubber, rubber-lined steel, "Duriron," or special tinned bronze are available.

Steel Tanks.   The great majority of tanks for storage and general use are made of steel; the explanation is that steel tanks are strong, comparatively light, and relatively indestructible.   As a general rule there is, in normal times, an advantage in cost.   Only when steel is not suitable because the stored liquid would attack it, is recourse had to other construction materials.

The simplest steel tank is the open-top tank of vertical cylinder shape such as that used for water storage; it is made in all sizes, as large as 185 feet in diameter by 25 feet in height, 200 feet in diameter by 34 in height, or even 292 feet in diameter by 1 foot in height. Shell thicknesses vary, and may be as great as $1\frac{1}{2}$ inches.

The modern method of construction is by welding. The sides are welded to the base plate which extends somewhat beyond the diameter of the tank, and a weld is made on both inner and outer surfaces. The curved sections for the cylinder are similarly welded together. An angle iron is welded for strength to the upper edge of the open tank. In the chemical industries, tanks used for storage in the open are of the closed type; that is, they have a cover welded to the upper edge. In tanks up to 70 or more feet in diameter, the roof, if so ordered, may be made self-supporting. However, in tanks between 20 and 50 feet in diameter, the

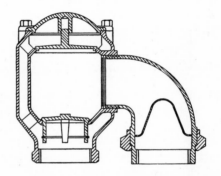

FIGURE 82.—A breather valve suitable for gasoline storage tanks. Connection to vapor space of the storage tank is at bottom left; bottom right leads to atmosphere. The valve operates at 2 ounces pressure and 1 ounce vacuum. A strainer over air inlet stops air-borne dirt. (Courtesy Ellis Vacuum and Pressure Valve, Standard Oil Co. of N. Y.)

roof is often supported by a central column and radial rafters; and beyond 50 feet in diameter, the roof commonly is supported on a central column and, in addition, on one or more circles of columns and connecting girders, with radial rafters on the girders and central column. The open tank remains important in the chemical industries, because tanks set indoors may be left uncovered under ordinary circumstances.

Piping and valves for filling and draining tank are provided, as well as a manhole nozzle and cover for the closed tanks.

Tanks built at grade are of the flat-bottom type, while outdoor elevated tanks may be either flat-bottom, supported by a suitable grillage of beams, or of the suspended-bottom type, in which the bottom is suspended from the sides. The suspended bottom may be hemispherical, hemiellipsoidal, conispherical, or conical. The outdoor flat-bottom tank built at grade may rest on a foundation of sand, or on both sand and a curbing of concrete slightly larger than the tank diameter. Indoor process tanks are generally flat-bottom.

An example of outdoor tanks, which are closed tanks with flat bottoms, resting on a foundation of gravel, is that of a "bulk plant" for petroleum products. The cover is flat, except for the largest tank, in which it is slightly conical. The shape is that of an upright cylinder. The several tanks are as follows:

No.	Diameter (ft)	Height (ft)	Liquid Stored	Capacity (gal)
1	60	40	Gasoline	850,702
2	25	35	Kerosine	129,310
3	25	35	Fuel oil	129,310
5	25	30	Gasoline	110,198
6	10	26	Ethyl gas	15,276

Closed tanks generally carry a vent. If they contain a volatile liquid such as gasoline, they must be vented by a two-way valve, so that the vapors which form during the heat of the day may escape, preventing a rise in pressure, and during the night, when a reduction in pressure develops, air may be able to enter.

FIGURE 83.—One of two tanks for the storage of gasoline, each being 100 feet in diameter and 40 feet in height, with a capacity of 55,000 barrels; they are built by the Chicago Bridge and Iron Co., Chicago, Ill. The tanks are equipped with Wiggins pontoon roofs to prevent evaporation loss.

There are other ways to avoid the losses resulting from the diurnal fluctuation in temperature. For the storage of gasoline and other volatile petroleum products, there is in fairly wide use a steel tank with a pontoon roof instead of a fixed, slightly conical roof. The pontoon roof fits the tank with a small clearance, and has enough buoyancy to float on the surface of the liquid gasoline; it rises and falls with it. At no time is there any vapor space which might undergo expansion or contraction. The clearance between the roof and the side walls of the tank is closed by means of thin metal shoes which rub on the tank shell and extend into the gasoline; a practically impervious and chemically inert flexible seal connects

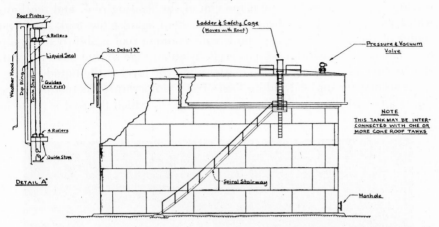

FIGURE 84.—The Graver tank with expansion roof for the storage of volatile liquids. (Courtesy Graver Tank and Mfg. Co., East Chicago, Ind.)

FIGURE 85.—Two 4,000-barrel spheres, 35 feet, 3 inches in diameter, for the storage of butane, built by the Chicago Bridge and Iron Co., Chicago, Ill. The pressure is 100 pounds.

the tops of the metal shoes and the rim of the floating roof, and mechanical devices support the shoes and press them against the tank shell and center of the roof.   A storage tank with pontoon roof is shown in Figure 83.   It will be noted that the passerelle is on a hinge so that observers can step to the roof conveniently no matter what the level of the liquid is.

A second means of avoiding losses from temperature fluctuation is the use of a Graver tank with an expansion roof, in which the roof is made in

FIGURE 86.—A Hortonsphere 30 feet, 3 inches in diameter built by the Chicago Bridge and Iron Co., Chicago, Ill., for the storage of anhydrous ammonia.   It has a working pressure of 50 pounds.

the form of a bell fitting in a liquid seal.   The roof lifts when the vapors expand, and falls when they contract; there need be no loss to the atmosphere.   The lift is 5 foot, or 10 foot, in the two standard constructions.   A pressure-and-vacuum valve is provided as a safety device.   A ladder reaching the top of tank is made long enough to be always within reach of the fixed platform at the side of the tank.   The Graver conservation system is extended by connecting several cone-roof tanks to one with the expansion roof, or to a special gas reservoir with uniform operation pressure.

The third way to avoid breathing losses of volatile liquids is to install tanks of sufficient strength to withstand the maximum pressure developed, and to store under pressure. A number of different shapes other than the upright cylinder have been developed. The full spherical shape is used, for example, for the storage of butane (see Figure 85), and is capable of withstanding safely a pressure of 100 pounds per square inch. The sphere is used for the storage of anhydrous ammonia, as shown in Figure 86; the horizontal cylinder, however, is also used widely for this purpose. The

FIGURE 87.—A 38-foot, 6-inch diameter sphere built by the Chicago Bridge and Iron Co., Chicago, Ill., for the storage of nitrogen.

full sphere is used for storage of nitrogen gas under pressure (see Figure 87).

For the storage of natural gasoline, a suitable closed storage vessel is the welded Hortonspheroid, shown in Figure 90. Two hemispheroids (Figure 91) are also suitable for pressure storage of various gasolines and, like the hemispheroids and spheroids, have distinctly pleasing lines. There is also an ellipsoidal pressure tank which is made with large capacity. Cylindrical tanks with outward dished roofs serve for medium pressures and for low-pressure; certain motor gasolines may be stored in 3-pound pressure tanks of this type.

FIGURE 88.—An elevated suspended bottom acid storage tank, for the storage of sulfuric acid, with an ordinary railroad tank car in the foreground for comparison. The tank is made of steel plates, riveted. (Courtesy Pittsburgh-Des Moines Steel Co., Pittsburgh, Pa.)

FIGURE 89.—Insulated naphthalene storage tank with heating coils in which steam is circulated to keep the naphthalene in the molten state, ready for drawing off. (Courtesy Pittsburgh-Des Moines Steel Co., Pittsburgh, Pa.)

A closed tank with hemiellipsoidal suspended bottom serving for the storage of sulfuric acid is shown in Figure 88.

The storage tank for naphthalene shown in Figure 89 is a closed upright cylindrical tank fitted with steam coils. The arrangement of the coils is as follows: A few inches above the bottom, coils are laid at close

FIGURE 90.—A 100,000-barrel welded Hortonspheroid of the noded type, 141.5 feet in diameter, 40 feet in height, for the storage of natural gasoline with 26 pounds Reid vapor pressure. (Courtesy Chicago Bridge and Iron Co., Chicago, Ill.)

FIGURE 91.—Two Hemispheroids 48 feet in diameter and 48 feet high, for the storage of gasoline, built by the Chicago Bridge and Iron Co., Chicago, Ill. In right rear, three fuel oil storage tanks with rigid conical roofs. Note the concrete retaining walls.

spacing over the whole of the floor, so that by turning on the steam, the operator can thaw out the entire area of the tank just over the bottom. Circular coils are spaced around the sides of the tank, one for each of the valves shown in the figure, covering the entire shell well. When steam is turned into these coils, the whole mass drops down as the portion near the sides melts, and comes within the range of the bottom coil. The roof of the tank is made self-supporting, to avoid inner members which might hold blocks of solid, while the outside of the tank is covered with insulation.

Horizontal Tanks. Horizontal storage steel tanks are cylindrical in shape but lie on their side, with the axis therefore horizontal, and belong to the closed-tank group. Examples of thickness of plate and capacity are given in Table 28.

TABLE 28. HORIZONTAL STORAGE TANKS OF STEEL (SELECTED ITEMS ONLY)*

Diameter (in)	Length (in)	Thickness (in) Shell	Thickness (in) Heads	Capacity (gal)	Weight (lbs)
24	5' 0	$\frac{9}{64}$	$\frac{9}{64}$	115	275
36	5' 0	$\frac{3}{16}$	$\frac{3}{16}$	260	565
48	11' 0	$\frac{3}{16}$	$\frac{3}{16}$	1,000	1,400
48	22' 0	$\frac{3}{16}$	$\frac{3}{16}$	2,000	2,555
60	6' 0	$\frac{3}{16}$	$\frac{1}{4}$	880	1,505
60	24' 0	$\frac{5}{16}$	$\frac{3}{8}$	3,520	6,300
72	30' 0	$\frac{5}{16}$	$\frac{3}{8}$	6,345	6,015
84	36' 0	$\frac{3}{8}$	$\frac{3}{8}$	10,360	15,150
120	42' 0	$\frac{1}{4}$	$\frac{3}{8}$	25,000	18,600
120	42' 0	$\frac{3}{8}$	$\frac{3}{8}$	25,000	26,460

For each diameter, several shell thicknesses are offered.
* Data supplied by Lancaster Iron Works, Lancaster, Pa.

FIGURE 92.—A steel Multisphere with capacity of 2,500 barrels, and able to withstand 150 psi. (Courtesy Chicago Bridge and Iron Co., Chicago, Ill.) (For size comparison, note the figures of the operators on the ground.)

The tanks listed in Table 28 are made of Class A open-hearth steel plates, riveted, and all seams and rivets are welded. The heads are made in a single piece, which is flat; hence they are referred to as "one-piece flat heads." Every tank is tested under an air pressure of 5 to 10 pounds before shipment, and receives one coat of paint. It is recommended that the length of a tank be not more than five times its diameter.

Standard pressure tanks are made in three thicknesses of shell, the lightest to withstand 25 to 30 pounds pressure and the intermediate to resist 85 pounds pressure with a safety factor of 4; the heaviest are built on order. Tanks 48-inches in diameter have one head convex and one head backed in; all tanks 60-inches in diameter and larger have both heads convex.

Some additional information on tanks for certain purposes will be found in Chapters 21 and 24.

Multisphere. For a gas volume and gas pressure which would require prohibitive thickness in a single sphere, a *Multisphere*, made of thin plates, may be substituted for the same duty. The Multisphere is a new development (1951); it is a cellular structure, much like a honeycomb. It con-

FIGURE 93.—A Multisphere built to serve as a propane tank. (Courtesy Chicago Bridge and Iron Co., Chicago, Ill.)

sists of a shell made of plates pressed (or dished) to spherical segments, and internal plate diaphragms welded to each other and to the shell, so arranged that the spherical segments of the shell and the diaphragms are in biaxial tension when the shell is under internal pressure.* Holes in the diaphragms balance the pressure in the cells (or compartments) and pro-

* The outer edge of each diaphragm is welded to two adjoining shell segments so that the components of the stresses in the segments parallel to the diaphragm are resisted by the diaphragm, and the components perpendicular to the diaphragm are in equilibrium. The thickness of each shell segment varies with the product of the internal pressure and radius of curvature. Therefore for any given pressure, the radius of each shell segment can be chosen so that a specified maximum shell thickness will not be exceeded or so that the optimum thickness for fabrication and welding will be used. The choice of curvature in no way limits the volume of the vessel, since as many spherical segments and internal diaphragms may be used as are necessary to provide the required capacity. (Private communication from Mr. H. C. Boardman, Research Director, Chicago Bridge and Iron Company.)

vide access to them. Hence it is practical to build vessels of the Multisphere type, which will resist high pressures, using relatively thin steel plates, instead of the very thick plates which would be required for the standard sphere.

The Multisphere is built of easily rolled shapes, while for the internal diaphragms, flat pieces only are required. By judicious choice of radius of curvature, a high-strength and relatively hard-to-weld steel may be employed instead of plain carbon steel, with resulting savings. The Multi-

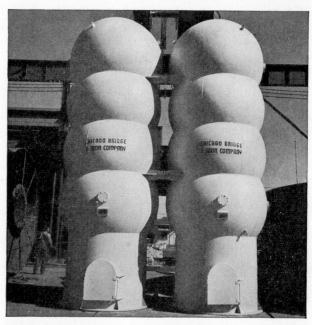

FIGURE 94.—Two Multispheres to hold nitrogen gas under pressure. (Courtesy Chicago Bridge and Iron Co., Chicago, Ill.)   (For size comparison, note the figure of a man, at left.)

sphere can be built in unlimited size, and its shape can be modified to fit it into a given space in barges, ships, and ground areas.

A *Multicylinder* consists of cylindrical shell segments and internal diaphragms, and ends which may be partial Multispheres (see Figure 95). Multispheres and Multicylinders are suitable for storing either liquid or gas in large quantities, at high pressures.

Lined Steel Tanks.   The usefulness of the horizontal steel tank as well as of any other steel tank is extended enormously by linings of various kinds, such as glass, vitreous enamel, rubber, lead, stainless steel, nickel, and others.

Horizontal steel tanks lined with glass, or "glass coated," are of value for the storage of liquids which would become discolored in a bare steel tank; they are valuable, furthermore, in the chemical industries for the storage of chemicals which attack steel. Many pieces of equipment other than tanks are glass coated, including condensers, absorption columns, receivers, pipe, fittings, and even glass-lined flush valves, as well as reaction vessels and distillation and mixing units, so that complete processing assemblies are available in the total absence of metal. Many pieces of glass-lined equipment will be found described elsewhere, with a number of illustrations.

The manufacture of glass-lined equipment has been described in the literature.* A number of grades of glass are used for lining equipment; those employed by one manufacturer† are mainly three. The most

FIGURE 95.—A Multicylinder built to serve as a propane tank. (Courtesy Chicago Bridge and Iron Co., Chicago, Ill.)

highly resisting glass (first class) is resistant to all acids at all concentrations and temperatures, with the exception of hydrofluoric acid and commercial phosphoric acid containing fluorides as impurities; it is the type of lining used generally for the chemical process industries. All such equipment, in addition, is electrically spark-tested for glass coating coverage before it leaves the factory (Pfaudler). In the second class are similar highly resistant glasses which are subjected to less rigid electrical testing, and which are suited to all organic acids and some concentrations of nitric, sulfuric and hydrochloric acids in the cold. In the third category are the glass linings suitable for milder service, such as the handling of milk, carbonated beverages, fruit juices, wines, whiskeys, and beer. Recently developed is a new glass with similar acid resistance but also with improved resistance to alkalies. Use of this glass permits extending the versatility

* "Glass-lined Chemical Equipment," by A. I. Andrews, *Trans. Am. Inst. Chem. Eng.*, **35**, 473 (1939).

† The Pfaudler Co., 3, Rochester, N. Y.

of glass-lined equipment to include neutralizations and other mild or short term alkaline conditions.

Glass-lined equipment is used widely by manufacturers of chlorinated organic products. Biological products and synthetic pharmaceuticals are processed very generally in glass-lined equipment.

As a result of developments in recent years, excellent field repairs to glass-lined equipment can readily be made by the installation of tantalum plugs. In certain environments where tantalum is not suitable (high SO₂ for example), gold is used successfully.

Defects or damaged spots on enamelware are corrected by the application of a gold patch.* Both cast iron and sheet steel are enameled.

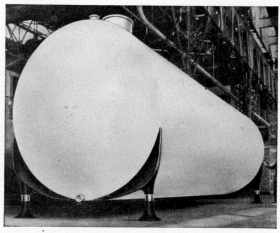

FIGURE 96.—Large mixing and storage steel tank, horizontal type, 12 feet in diameter and 45 feet long, lined with glass. Capacity 35,000 gallons. (Courtesy The Pfaudler Co., Rochester 3, N. Y.)

Steel tanks may be lined with rubber, and essentially the same types of rubber lining previously listed for wooden tanks may be used. The linings are generally made no heavier than the service requires, and the rubber may be unvulcanized, partly vulcanized, or fully vulcanized. For heavy-duty work, superior linings have been developed. The Vulcalock (Goodrich) linings are five: Acidseal MA, Amorite, Superflexite, Acidseal E, and Triflex. For tanks and tank cars, Acidseal and Triflex are generally selected. Triflex is recommended for the heaviest service. It is a 3-ply acid-proof rubber lining (U. S. Patent 1,919,366) in which a layer of true hard rubber is cushioned between two plies of resilient soft rubber, vulcanized together to form an integral lining structure which is bonded to the steel with an adhesion exceeding 500 pounds per square inch. The

* "Glass-lined Chemical Equipment," by A. I. Andrews, *Trans. Am. Inst. Chem. Eng.*, **35**, 473 (1939).

soft inner ply is built up of first coatings of rubber cement, followed by thin sheets of rubber laid one on another; the outer ply is assembled in a similar way. Inasmuch as rubber expands more than steel, the rubber layers are so laid that they overlap, so that the hard rubber of one section can move past that of another within the soft envelope.* As a result of this construction, the Triflex linings have the chemical resistance of hard rubber with the desirable expansion and contraction properties of soft rubber. The thickness of Triflex lining for large tanks and for car tanks is generally $\frac{3}{16}$-inch over-all.

For certain services, the rubber-lined tank may in turn be protected by a brick sheathing.

Linings of lead are the oldest kind of linings for steel tanks, and are still highly prized. For this purpose, sheet lead is manufactured in several grades: chemical lead, which is practically pure lead, free from bismuth, containing about 0.06 per cent of copper; tellurium lead which contains less than 0.1 per cent of tellurium and possesses superior corrosion resistance, as well as the property of work-hardening;† antimonial lead; and crawl-proof lead, a reinforced chemical lead. Antimonial lead is "hard" lead; it contains between 4 and 10 per cent antimony, 6 per cent being the average figure; it is twice as strong as chemical lead, harder, stiffer, and more resistant to mechanical blows. It must be remembered, however, that antimony lowers the melting point of lead from 620 to 477°F. Tellurium-antimonial lead combines the desirable properties of tellurium lead and of antimonial lead.

The buckling and crawling of chemical lead sheets made into linings has been overcome by reinforcing the sheet of chemical lead with antimonial-lead bars. The method is to place the bars or rods in the lead like the steel rods in reinforced concrete. Lead so reinforced is called crawl-proof sheet lead.

When a large tank, let us say a round one, is being lined with sheet lead, the sheet may be laid against the wall and held in place by a steel strap set upright and bolted to the tank. The sheets are "burned" to each other to form a continuous wall of lead, and the strap is then covered with sheet lead burned onto the sheet lead lining. Lead is still "burned" by a hydrogen-oxygen flame.

In another type of construction, the lead lining in a sulfuric-acid concentrator, for example, is protected by a heavy layer of acid-proof bricks laid in acid-proof cement.

In the majority of lead-lined vessels, the lead linings are not bonded to the steel, but are merely laid against it; for these vessels, lining with

---

* "The Pickling Tank of Tomorrow," by J. R. Hoover, *Metals and Alloys*, p. 100, (May, 1934).

† U. S. Patent, 2,060,534.

lead really means constructing a duplicate vessel just fitting within the steel one and supported by it. There is available, however, steel equipment with bonded lead lining, including any form of fabricated apparatus as well as lead-lined steel pipe. Such apparatus is built of sheet steel which is provided with a bonded lead lining, by welding the steel into the desired shape and then puddling lead over the welded area. Bonded lead-lined steel equipment is of special importance in the chemical industries.

Concrete tanks which are comparatively shallow, and are lined with chemical lead, are used as storage tanks for battery acid in wet-battery building plants.

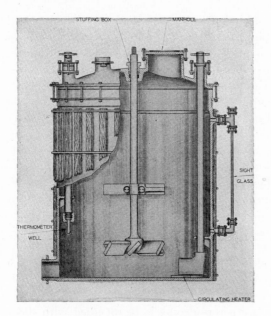

FIGURE 97.—A Haveg tank with turbine agitator made of "Haveg." (Courtesy Haveg Corp., Newark, Del.)

"Haveg" Tanks. Tanks made of "Haveg" resist the action of any acid and of many salt solutions. There are several compositions under the general name of "Haveg" which serve various special purposes. "Haveg 41" is a composition containing phenolformaldehyde resin and an acid-digested asbestos fiber. It is tough, strong, and resists blows; it is unaffected by sustained temperature as high as 265°F (130°C). "Haveg 43" is a composition containing phenolformaldehyde resin and graphite. There are several other formulas. Pipes, fittings, and valves are also made of "Haveg," as well as stirrers, bubble-cap towers, and numerous other special shapes. "Haveg 41" (standard) and "Haveg 43" are not recommended for use with alkaline solutions, but "Haveg 60" is alkali-resistant and may be so used. "Haveg 60" is based on a furfuryl alcohol resin and asbestos fibers; it resists the action of many organic solvents.

"Haveg" cylindrical tanks are molded in a single piece without seams or joints, in standard sizes with a maximum of 10 feet in diameter and 12 feet in depth.

TANKS FOR TRANSPORTATION

Tanks permanently mounted on railway cars serve for bulk shipments of raw and finished materials in the chemical industries. The tanks are generally made of steel plates which may be riveted or welded, and the capacities range from 4,000 to 11,500 gallons for ordinary service. Car tanks are always constructed to conform to specifications issued by the Interstate Commerce Commission.* The tank is generally a single container in the form of a horizontal cylinder, surmounted by a dome, and provided with a small sump under the dome. The latter has a number of pipe connections: one for filling, one for applying air pressure, and one which dips into the sump for unloading. It carries also a manhole and cover, and a safety valve. Unloading may be done by pumping as well as by syphoning or blowing. A car-unloading unit in which a pump is used is illustrated on page 154. Tank-car tanks are also provided in multiple-compartment construction, permitting different types of commodities to be transported at the same time in the same car, or permitting definitely separate shipments of the same commodity to be unloaded at different points along the line of transit. Not only liquids but liquefied gases are transported in tank cars with heavy tanks designed to withstand definite pressures and insulated to maintain a definite temperature.

Liquid chlorine is transported in steel, either in the single-container tank or in series of smaller holders each one of 1-ton capacity and mounted permanently on the car.

Liquids which attack steel are transported in lined tanks. Hydrochloric acid (35 per cent), for example, is now generally shipped in steel lined with Triflex or other approved rubber lining, with complete success and certainty of nonattack. Lead lining, and, increasingly, clad steels (stainless steel clad, nickel clad, and other alloy clad steels) and other forms of metal linings are in use. There are, furthermore, a number of linings which consist of various heavy paints or enamels applied in multiple coats, some baked on the interior of the tank and some air-cured. Glass-lined tanks are freely used for the transportation of delicate materials. One model has two glass-lined tanks set inside an insulating housing with a cab in the center of the car which encloses tank outlets and inlets, valves, motor drives, and other accessories. Total capacities are 6000 or 8000 gallons.

A number of commodities solidify at comparatively moderate tem-

* Interstate Commerce Commission, Bureau of Explosives (Pamphlet No. 9), 30 Vesey Street, New York. Welded steel tanks to be mounted on cars follow specification 106A500 in thickness of plate, method of welding and heat treating, and all other details; riveted steel tanks follow specification 103, riveted alloy steel 103C.

peratures, so that they must be loaded and unloaded hot. For such service, cars are generally provided with coils in which steam or hot oil may be circulated. Sodium metal is transported in bulk in steel car-tanks with complete success.* The capacity of the tank is about 80,000 pounds of sodium. The air in the tank is replaced by nitrogen; then the liquid

FIGURE 98.—Modern welded tank car for handling ethylene dibromide, built of wide plates of 10 per cent Lukens Nickel-Clad steel by General American Transportation Corp., Sharon, Pa. (Photograph courtesy Lukens Steel Co.)

FIGURE 98a.—A tank with outer housing cut open to show the two glass-lined tanks, each heavily insulated, and the central cab in which the tank outlets, inlets, valves, and motors are conveniently collected. (Courtesy Pfaudler Co., Rochester, N. Y.)

sodium is fed in and solidified by circulating cold oil through steel coils welded to the outside surface of the shell. About 16 hours are required for filling the tank and solidifying the sodium. In this state the metal is shipped to its destination, where it is melted by circulating hot oil through the coils, requiring a period of about 13 hours for complete liquefaction. The tank is unloaded by syphon, started by applying compressed nitrogen.

* P. J. Carlisle, *Trans. Am. Inst. Chem. Eng.*, **31**, 318 (1935).

Another way to handle chemicals which solidify easily is to add an antifreeze; an example is oleum, to which anhydrous nitric acid may be added in moderate amounts to prevent freezing.

Horizontal wooden tanks, lined and unlined, are mounted on railway cars for bulk transportation.

Tanks for trucks are made of all the materials which are used for railway car tanks, with the addition of aluminum for milk transportation. Road oils which would thicken in transport are kept liquid by flames of oil under the shell. At the other end of the temperature scale, liquid oxygen is transported in truck tanks which are double-walled; the space between the shells is filled with diatomaceous earth and evacuated, producing a most satisfactory insulation.

Some comments on tanks for high-pressure work are included in Chapter 24, which deals with high-pressure equipment.

Valves

Close to the subject of tanks is that of piping, fittings, and valves. Cast iron, wrought iron, and steel piping, with flanged ends as well as with screwed ends, are used for general purposes in the chemical industries; each of these materials has its special merits. They serve all industries, in households, apartment houses, and institutions, as well as in mills and factories; hence their treatment is not a special concern in a book devoted specifically to chemical process machinery. Similarly the vast subject of valves of all types and sizes, made of ordinary materials, must be left to the books, handbooks, and catalogues which specialize in that subject. Only the special materials and designs which specifically serve the chemical industries will be considered in this chapter.

Piping and fittings of wrought iron, cast iron, steel, copper, brass, and other standard metals are supplemented by others made of special materials and combinations of materials, for example, lead pipe, which resists corrosion, although itself structurally weak; and lead-lined steel pipe, which combines the corrosion resistance of lead with the strength of steel. It is important in lead-lined pipes and fittings that the lead be well bonded to the steel (or iron). This may be done by first coating the steel pipe on its inner surface with a thin layer of lead, formed by immersing the cleaned and fluxed iron pipe in a tank of molten lead which contains 4 per cent of tin; the steel is now leadized. Later, molten lead is poured in around a mica mandril, with the pipe held at an angle of 50°, and the right temperature maintained by means of gas flames. The molten lead fuses with the leadized steel, producing an inseparable lead lining after cooling.[*] Minimum thickness of the lining is $3/16$-inch.

Also available are rubber-lined piping (compare rubber lining of tanks

* Lead Lined Iron Pipe Company, Wakefield, Mass.

in this chapter), piping of Pyrex glass, of chemical stoneware, of porcelain, of "Duriron," and others.

· Valves and cocks made of special materials or in special design for service in the chemical industries include lead-lined (iron) flanged globe valves, lead-lined (Wakefield Amalgamated) flanged gate valves, and lead-lined "Y" or free flow (Chemtrade) flanged acid valves. A few valves of special construction and design are shown in Figures 99–104.

A flush-type outlet valve, mounted on the bottom of a kettle or tank and designed to present no obstruction to the arms of an agitator, is shown

FIGURE 99.—A corrosion pattern globe valve with jacket for heating medium, generally steam, with flanged ends. The jacketed valve is made also in gate, swing check, and horizontal lift check valve. (Courtesy Wm. Powell Co., Cincinnati, Ohio.)

FIGURE 100.—Sectional view of globe valve with vulcanized composition disk screwed ends, Union bonnet. The valve is made of any selected alloy, and the disk may be of the same material. (Courtesy Wm. Powell Co., Cincinnati, Ohio.)

in Figure 106, while the same type valve mounted on a kettle and operated from an upper platform may be seen in Figure 450. A globe valve with yoke construction, and one with vulcanized composition disk illustrate the globe principle; the valve is so connected that the fluid under pressure strikes the base of the disk. Y-valves present least obstruction to the flow of liquid. One made of "Duriron" is shown in Figure 102. The same valve is made of "Durichlor," and of both materials; seven sizes from ¾ inch to 6 inches, with split flange connections, are available. A gate valve of special design is shown in Figure 103, and in Figure 104, an angle valve which is also a needle valve. A jacketed check valve which permits the main-

FIGURE 101.—A corrosion-resistant flanged end globe valve, with outside screw stem and bolted yoke. Left, outside view; right, sectional view. It is made in any one of 16 different corrosion-resisting alloys. (Courtesy Wm. Powell Co., Cincinnati, Ohio.)

FIGURE 102.—A Y plug valve made of Duriron. (Courtesy Duriron Co., Dayton, Ohio.)

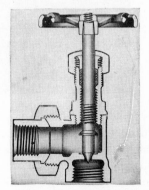

FIGURE 103. (left).—A gate valve of special design. (Courtesy Crane Co., Chicago, Ill.)

FIGURE 104. (right).—A needle valve, representing also the angle valve. (Courtesy Crane Co., Chicago, Ill.)

taining of an elevated temperature is illustrated in Figure 105; an all-porcelain flush valve in Figure 106. Valves are made of most of the special corrosion-resisting alloy steels, and some firms devote an entire department to this work.

FIGURE 105.—Sectional view of a steam-jacketed horizontal lift check valve. The jacket will accept any suitable heating agent. It is available in 18-8S alloy and eight other corrosion-resistant alloys and metal. (Courtesy Wm. Powell Co., Cincinnati 22, Ohio.)

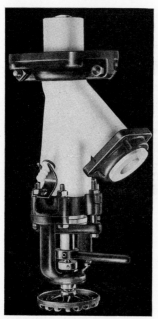

FIGURE 106.—An all-porcelain flush valve for tank bottom outlet. Poppet rises to drain. (Courtesy Lapp Insulator Co., Le Roy, N. Y.)

Flush valves, Y valves, angle valves, and plug cocks, built of a pure nonporous porcelain, white in color, iron free, resistant to all acids except hydrofluoric and to most alkali solutions, are manufactured in constantly increasing number. Porcelain valves in an aluminum casing make up a new line of armored porcelain valves. Square cut porcelain piping in many sizes is much in favor, with flanges externally attached to close the joints. Flanged piping is available, with auxiliary iron flanges. A porcelain centrifugal pipe of similar merit is made in several sizes (Lapp).

A diaphragm valve is shown, open and closed, in Figure 107. It provides a streamlined flow passage to the liquid, and a positive shut-off; it also prevents contamination of the liquid being pumped (Figure 108). The diaphragm valve shown is nonclogging, and requires no stem packing. When the valve is open, the liquid (or slurry or emulsion) travels easily through a nonclogging double convex opening passage. When closing the valve, the diaphragm seats tightly under closing pressure on the weir, which runs at right angle to the direction of flow.

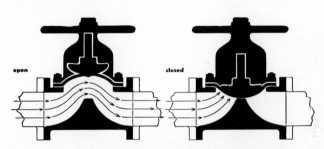

FIGURE 107.—A diaphragm valve with streamline flow passage and positive shut-off. (Courtesy Hills-McCanna Co., Chicago 18, Ill.)

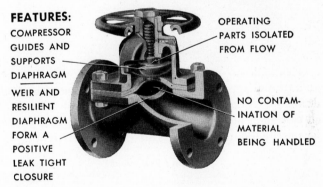

FEATURES:

COMPRESSOR GUIDES AND SUPPORTS DIAPHRAGM

WEIR AND RESILIENT DIAPHRAGM FORM A POSITIVE LEAK TIGHT CLOSURE

OPERATING PARTS ISOLATED FROM FLOW

NO CONTAM-INATION OF MATERIAL BEING HANDLED

FIGURE 108.—The Hills-McCanna diaphragm valve, with parts indicated in the picture.

Figure 109 shows an acid-resistant pipeline valve, made of cast iron lined with glass, to represent a line of seven styles of valves, each made in a number of sizes, and all lined with glass (for types of glass, see page 125. The body connector in the valve shown can be assembled for either straight line or right angle mounting.

The lubricated plug valve in general use in chemical plants (acid plants, alkali plants, wet cement plants, petroleum refineries) is made in an almost infinite number of styles, sizes, and materials. One example is the "Sealdport," a plug valve in which passages are provided in the valve body for the introduction of, for instance, a plastic lubricant, and for its distribution under pressure to ducts on the face of the plug, both vertical and horizontal.* At the base of the plug, which is tapered, the lubricant reaches a chamber in which it can exert an upward pressure and overcome a tight seat. Foreign matter cannot enter the valve, and leakage channels cannot develop, while in addition the lubrication prevents the freezing of the plug in its seat. Materials used include "Mercoloy," a nickel bronze alloy; "Merco" bronze, a copper-tin-lead bronze (18-10-2 bronze); aluminum, as a 5 per cent silicon alloy; and pure nickel, in addition to the well-

FIGURE 109.—A pipeline valve, lined with acid-resistant glass. The valve can be assembled for either straight-line (as shown) or right-angle mounting. (Courtesy of Pfaudler Co., Rochester 3, N. Y.)

known standard and special metals and alloys. The "Merchrome" valve has a hard metal coating on its entire interior surface. Small plug valves are wrench operated, larger ones are worm or spur gear operated, others are cylinder operated, and still others are operated by motor.

Reading References

ON TANKS

"The Book of Tanks," Issue No. 80, The Hauser-Stander Tank Co., Cincinnati, O., 100 pages, with index, 1951.

"Handbook, Welded Steel Plate Construction, Design Data, General Information," by the Buffalo Tank Corporation, Buffalo, N. Y., 288 pages, with index.

"Conservation of Gasoline," Tech. Bull. C-100, Graver Tank and Manufacturing Co., East Chicago, Indiana, 1940, with tables and graphs on expansion of vapors.

"Glass-lined Steel Equipment," by P. S. Barnes, *Ind. Eng. Chem.*, 29, 378 (1937).

"Glass-lined Chemical Equipment," by A. I. Andrews, *Trans. Am. Inst. Chem. Eng.*, 35, 473 (1939).

"Rubber-lined Equipment, Fundamental Principles of Design," by J. R. Hoover and H. C. Klein, *Ind. Eng. Chem.*, 29, 394, (1937).

"Koroseal As an Engineering Material," by Frank K. Schoenfeld, *Trans. Am. Inst. Chem. Eng.*, 35, 477 (1939).

* Nordstrom Lubricated Valves, Rockwell Manufacturing Co., Pittsburgh 8, Pa.

"Field-welded Storage Tanks," Chapter 50, p. 1146–1156, Welding Handbook, Third Edition, The American Welding Society, New York, N. Y., 1950.

"The Application of Welding to Large Steel Tanks," by H. C. Boardman, *Welding J.*, March 1939.

"Field-welded Pressure and Variable Volume Storage Tanks," by F. L. Plummer, *Welding J.*, January 1945.

ON PIPING AND FITTINGS

"Mechanical Engineers' Handbook," by Lionel S. Marks, New York, McGraw-Hill Book Co.

"How to Break Piping Bottlenecks," by G. W. Hauck, *Petroleum Refiner*, **22**, 71 (1934); reprinted in *Chem. Eng. News*, **21**, 756 (1943).

"Pipe and Fittings," by the Editorial Staff, *Chem. Met. Eng.*, **44**, 265 (1937).

Every municipality has a public water-distribution system, and almost every municipality has a pumping station equipped with pumps that may be huge, delivering in some cases, 75,000 gallons per minute; the pumps are required to put the water under pressure. A few fortunate cities receive their water under a sufficient head by virtue of its elevation; in these, city pumping stations are unknown. Such cities are Los Angeles and New York.

6. DEVICES FOR PROPELLING AND ELEVATING LIQUIDS: PUMPS, BLOWCASES, EJECTORS*

Devices for propelling and elevating liquids fall into three main classes, of unequal importance: pumps, which are devices with mechanical parts; blow-cases; and ejectors. In addition, devices primarily serving other purposes may be pressed into service, perhaps a very imperfect service, as for example a screw conveyor for solids.

The most important class of devices for propelling and elevating liquids, i.e., pumps, may be further divided into centrifugal, reciprocating, and rotary, as well as special pumps which do not fit clearly into the first three classes, or which partake of the characteristics of two classes. Such a classification is based on the type of mechanical motion of the moving element of the pump, and each group has subgroups which continue the same consideration. Pumps may be grouped together on other bases, for example, on the method of driving the moving element, or on the service the pump performs, such as proportioning, acid-propelling, slurry pumping, and others. The division in this chapter is according to the mechanical motion of the pumping element.

PUMPS

Centrifugal Pumps. There are four main classes of pumps which come under the general heading of centrifugal pumps: the volute pump, in which the impeller discharges into a volute, a spiral-shaped passage with

Centrifugal pumps

Volute pump	Diffuser type pump	Peripheral flow type ("turbine type")	Propeller pump

Mixed flow type

* With suggestions and advice from Mr. B. W. Ellis, Chief Engineer, Buffalo Pumps, Inc., North Tonawanda, N. Y.

138

TABLE 29. CLASSIFICATION OF DEVICES FOR PROPELLING AND ELEVATING LIQUIDS

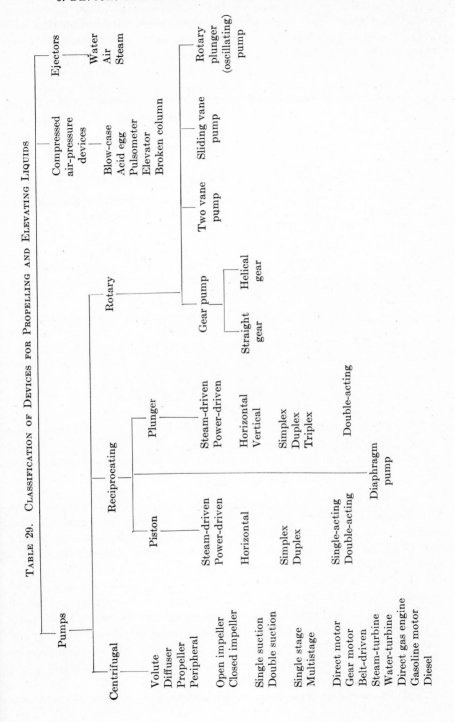

gradually increasing cross section; the pump with diffusers, in which the propeller discharges into fixed diffusers, and these in turn to a water passage which may be circular or spiral-shaped; the propeller pump, which has a propeller-type rotor; and the peripheral pump. In the volute pump, and in the pump with diffusers, the flow of the liquid is centrifugal. In the propeller pump, the flow of the feed water (or other liquid) is axial, parallel to the shaft, and the water leaves at the opposite side through a coaxial conduit, and with the same directional flow; the propeller pump is said to have "axial flow." There is a third kind of flow, mixed flow, which partakes of the centrifugal and of the axial characteristics.

The propeller pump is used for low heads, under 40 feet, and large capacities, over 300 gpm, as in sewage disposal, storm-water disposal, and irrigation service. The mixed-flow pump is for similar duties.

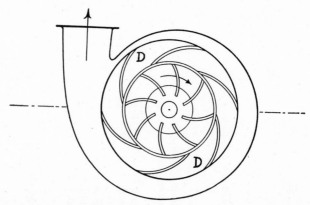

FIGURE 110.—Working principle of a centrifugal pump with diffusers, mounted in a fixed, nonrotating but removable section marked D. It will be noted that by reversing the flow a water turbine would be obtained.

The centrifugal pump with diffusers has an annular member between impeller and casing to hold them. The diffusers offer the liquid a widening path from the impeller chamber to the casing; it is here that the kinetic energy of the flowing liquid is changed into a pressure head. The volute pump changes the kinetic energy of the flow imparted by the rotating impeller into pressure in the volute, whose shape offers the same ever-widening channel to the flow. The volute pump is essentially as efficient as the diffuser type. Furthermore, it is cheaper and there are fewer parts to be replaced because of wear. It is used almost exclusively in chemical and allied plants. The diffuser pump is chosen only when certain definite characteristics are desired—characteristics in which the chemical plant operator is generally not interested.

The two-or-more stage deep-well pump with a rotating element is a

good example of a centrifugal pump with diffusers.   The shaft carries two
or more impellers, each surmounted by stationary vanes, the diffuser
vanes, which are part of the steel casing.   One of these "vertical turbine
pumps" as they are called, is the Layne pump,* which raises water from
strata as deep as 2500 feet.   The centrifugal pump with diffusers need not
be vertical; many of its models are horizontal.

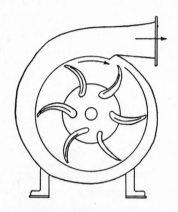
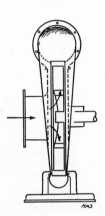

Figure 111.—The principle of the centrifugal single suction pump, volute type.
Left, front view with part of casing removed to show the six-bladed, open impeller;
right, side view showing entry of feed.

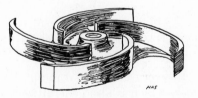

Figure 112.—Impellers for centrifugal pumps.   Left, enclosed or shrouded impeller;
right, open impeller.   The enclosed impeller shown has two vanes and is a trash-type
impeller.   The open impeller shown has four vanes.   In the more recent design for
trash-type, the impeller is wider, and Francis-type inlet vanes are used because of their
relatively large inlet widths.

The impeller in the centrifugal pump may be an "open impeller,"
which has its vanes cast free on both sides; it may be a "semi-enclosed impeller," which has its vanes free on one side and enclosed on the other by a
shroud forming part of the casting; or it may be an "enclosed propeller,"
fully enclosed, the vanes lying between two disks, all in a single casting.
In the latter type of impeller, the liquid travels between the disks.   The
"enclosed impeller" is also termed the "hooded impeller" and the
"shrouded impeller."   Figures 111 and 112 will make the meaning of these
terms clearer.

* Layne and Bowler Inc., Memphis, Tenn.

The open impeller is usually less efficient hydraulically; and, what is even more important, its efficiency drops off more rapidly with wear than does that of the enclosed impeller.

An impeller may have two or more vanes, depending on the size of the pump and the service for which it is designed. A clear liquid pump impeller will usually have six or eight, or even more in the large sizes, whereas a wood-pulp pump impeller will be wider and will have fewer vanes, to permit easier passage of the suspension. A sewage or sludge pump impeller will usually have only two or three vanes, and will be wide in proportion. In spite of the required non-clog construction, the pump efficiency remains high.

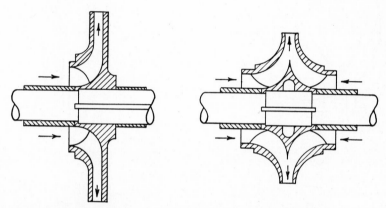

FIGURE 113.—Impellers for centrifugal pumps, showing single-suction type at left and double-suction type at right.

In every centrifugal pump, the liquid enters at the center of the impeller, which is also generally the center of the pump, and is delivered at the circumference of the casing or volute.

A centrifugal pump with one impeller is a "single-stage" pump. The discharge from such a pump may be fed to the suction side of a second pump of the same size, design, and speed; the second pump now receives its water or other liquid at a considerable pressure, which it preserves, and to which it adds the pressure energy which it develops. The head at the discharge piece of the second pump will now be twice as high. Such an arrangement is embodied in the "two-stage" pump. Similarly, there are four-stage pumps, and pumps with a still greater number of stages. The delivery at each stage becomes the feed of the next one; the pressure imparted by the several impellers is cumulative. All pumps beyond the "single-stage" are termed collectively "multi-stage."*

* In an emergency, the plant engineer might set up a multi-stage pump by connecting several pumps of the same size and speed in series.

A distinction must also be made between single-suction and double-suction pumps. In the former, the impeller receives the entering liquid on one side only. For double suction, the suction inlet chamber of the pump is divided so as to feed equal quantities of liquid to both sides of the impeller. The double-suction impeller has vanes on both sides of a central web; and two streams are united only just before leaving the outer edge of the vanes (see Figure 113).

The capacity of any centrifugal pump depends upon the size and design of the pump, on the rotating speed of the impeller, on the absolute pressure of the suction supply, on the discharge pressure, and on the characteristics of the liquid handled. With a given pump in a specific service, changing the impeller diameter changes the head or discharge pressure, and also the power required. Within certain limitations of the pump, a change in impeller diameter with constant speed will give approximate changes as follows: (1) capacity, directly as the diameters; (2) total head, directly as the square of the diameters; (3) power, directly as the diameters cubed. The design of the pump includes the shape, height, and number of impeller vanes, the size and shape of the suction inlet and of the volute, and the type of close-running clearances. As to the last, the clearance between the impeller and the wearing ring is important. In its simple form, the wearing ring clearance line is a straight line; in the order of increasing resistance to "leakage" (slippage), it may form a right angle, or a labyrinth. The normal clearance on the diameter when the pump is new should be about 0.015 inch; on a well-designed pump, that clearance can be re-obtained by adjustment to compensate for wear, or, to the same end, new wearing rings can be installed on the rotating and stationary parts.

Increasing the speed of rotation with the diameter constant results in higher capacities and higher heads. For example, the following are the capacities for the maximum heads attainable with the same pump run at different speeds:

Comparison of the Effect of Various Speeds
1½ Inch CL Enclosed-impeller, Single-stage Centrifugal Pump

Rpm	1150	1450	1750	2900	3500
Capacity (gpm)	40	80	80	150	125
Maximum head (ft)	30	45	65	160	250
Horsepower of motor	¾	1½	3	10	15

On the other hand, a lesser head permits a higher capacity at a definite speed, for a given pump:

The Increase in Capacity with Diminishing Head
2 Inch CS Enclosed Impeller Pump at 2900 rpm

Capacity (gpm)	70	100	125	200	225	250	275
Head (ft)	130	120	110	100	90	80	70
Horsepower of motor	5	5	5	7½	7½	10	10

A few examples of open-impeller, cast-iron centrifugal pumps are given in Table 30.

The size of the pump for the performance of a certain duty is related to its speed. Leaving out of account the special considerations of the

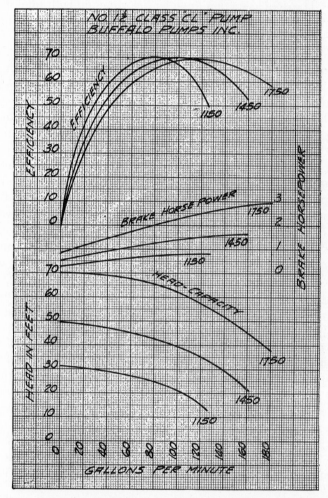

FIGURE 114.—Curves for head-capacity, efficiency, and horsepower for three rates of rotation of an open impeller in a centrifugal pump, to show the great effect of speed on capacity and head. The numbers 1750, 1450, and 1150 are the rates of rotation per minute (rpm).

chemical pump, it may be said that it is desirable to select a smaller pump, that is, smaller diameter casing and impeller, and to operate it at a higher speed. The smaller pump will be less expensive, and the power for operation will probably be no greater; in fact, it may be less, because the disk friction loss, which depends upon the diameter of the impeller, will be less in the smaller pump. The tendency is to improve the efficiency of the pump by reducing the diameter of the impeller, and this will be the result provided the design is properly made.

TABLE 30. TYPE CF SINGLE-STAGE VOLUMETRIC CENTRIFUGAL PUMPS, OPEN IMPELLERS WITH BASE PLATE AND COUPLING. MATERIAL: CAST IRON, WITH BRONZE FITTINGS

Size Discharge Opening (in)	Speed	Motor (hp)	Capacity (gpm)	Pressure (ft)
1	1750	1	40	40
2½	1750	7½	200	80
4	1750	30	850	100

When there is no corrosion problem, ball-bearing construction is often preferred over sleeve bearings for the pump with the higher speed. One manufacturer, for example, installs full ball-bearings for all speeds over 1750 rpm (except for very high ones), whereas pumps rotating at speeds below 1750 rpm may have bronze or babbitted sleeve bearings, with ring-oil lubrication. Very high speeds, such as 4000 and 5000 rpm, are reached in steam turbine-driven pumps; for these, babbitted sleeve bearings with pressure oil lubrication are in wide use, and are usually preferred, although ball-bearings are not excluded. In chemical works, the lower speeds, 1750 rpm or less, are generally preferred, because it was held, formerly more than now, that higher speeds would accentuate corrosion. With the development of special metals, this possible danger has become less.

Definitions. The most important guide in the selection of a pump today is specific speed. The explanation of this term will be preceded by a few essential definitions.

The *capacity* of a centrifugal pump depends, among other factors, upon the relation of the level of the entering liquid to the level of the pump.

When the suction-liquid level is above the pump's center line it is called a *static suction head,* and is equal to the difference in elevation between the suction liquid level and the pump's center line. A *static suction lift* exists when the suction-liquid level is below the pump's center line. The total suction head is the static suction head measured to the pump's center line, minus friction losses for the capacity pumped, minus entrance losses at the beginning of the suction line, plus any pressure existing on the suction supply.

The *static discharge head* is the difference in elevation between the pump's center line and the discharge liquid level (see Figure 115).

Friction head is the equivalent head expressed in feet of liquid pumped, necessary to overcome friction losses caused by liquid flow through the piping, including all fittings.

Velocity head is related to the velocity of a liquid at any given point in its flow line, expressed in feet head of the liquid. If the liquid is mov-

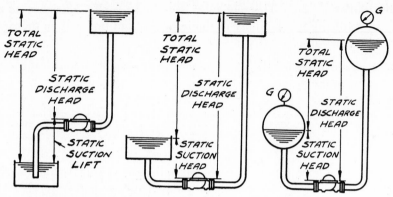

FIGURE 115.—Sketches illustrating static suction lift (left), static suction head (middle), and static suction head for a system at a pressure other than atmospheric.

ing at a given speed, the velocity head is equivalent to the distance the liquid would have to fall in a vacuum to attain that velocity.

$$\text{Velocity head in feet of liquid pumped} = \frac{(\text{liquid's velocity in ft/second})^2}{64.4}$$

The *discharge head* of a pump is measured at the discharge nozzle, and can be expressed in absolute or gauge pressure readings, or in feet head. It is the sum of the static discharge head, friction head for the capacity considered, the exit losses at end of the discharge line, and the terminal head or pressure expressed in feet of liquid being pumped. Discharge head is always measured from the pump's center line.

Total head is the discharge head plus suction lift, if suction lift exists, or discharge head minus suction head if suction head exists, or discharge head only if zero suction lift or zero suction head exists. It is a measure of work done by the pump on the liquid, minus all friction losses in the pump from its suction to discharge nozzle.

1 pound pressure = 2.31 feet of water, or other liquid with specific gravity 1.00
1 pound pressure = (2.31 ÷ specific gravity) feet

The *efficiency* of a pump is the ratio of the liquid horsepower to the brake horsepower.

$$\text{Per cent pump efficiency} = \frac{\text{liquid horsepower}}{\text{brake horsepower}} \times 100$$

$$\text{The liquid horsepower} = \frac{\text{gallons per minute} \times \text{total head} \times \text{specific gravity}}{3960}$$

or, $$\text{The liquid horsepower} = \frac{\text{gallons per minute} \times \text{total head in psi} \times 2.31}{3960}$$

The limit of the suction lift of a centrifugal pump is 27 feet of water, more or less, but the economically accepted standard is 22 feet. The suction lift will depend, however, upon the design and the capacity of the pump; for a given standard pump, a greater capacity will be accompanied by a lower suction lift.   The pressure of the atmosphere is equivalent to a column of water 33.93 feet high, at 60°F.   The actual lift falls short of that because, aside from limitations of pump design, the vapor pressure of the water, gases dissolved in it and released as the pressure drops, and leaks, act counter to the atmospheric lifting power.

Specific Speed.   Specific speed of an impeller has become more and more important particularly as it applies to the classification of pumps and also to the allowable suction lift.   The expression for specific speed, N_s, is:

$$N_s = \frac{\text{gallons per minute} \times \text{rpm}}{H^{3/4}}$$

in which H is the total head on the pump, or the total pump head.   The specific speed of an impeller is the revolutions per minute at which a geometrically similar impeller would run if it were of such size as to discharge one gallon per minute against a head of one foot of water.   The specific speed of an impeller is an index to its type.   Impellers for high heads usually have low specific speeds; impellers for low heads usually have high specific speeds.   "Centrifugal pumps with radial vanes will have specific speed values ranging from about 500 to 3000.   Pumps with Francis vanes involving combined radial and axial flow at inlet and radial flow only at discharge, will have specific speeds ranging between 1000 and 4000; mixed flow impellers will have specific speeds ranging from about 4000 to 7900, and propeller pumps will have specific speeds greater than 8000."[*]   Charts published by the Hydraulic Institute are available[†] for determining the upper limit of specific speed in respect to capacity, speed of rotation, and suction lift or suction head which may be applied with assurance of freedom from cavitation (see further).   This information combined with the manufacturer's experience permits him to select the proper pump.

When pumping requirements are variable, it may be more economical to install several small pumps instead of a single large one.   When the demand drops, one or more pumps can be shut down, allowing the remaining pumps to operate at peak efficiency.   *Units* operated *in parallel* give multiple capacity against a common head [for "system head curve" and "head capacity curve," see reference below[‡]].

If two *pumps* are operated *in series*, the combined head for any flow is equal to the sum of the individual heads.

[*] From a private communication from Mr. Bruce W. Ellis, Chief Engineer, Buffalo Pumps, Inc., North Tonawanda, N. Y.

[†] "Standards of Hydraulic Institute, 1948," 90 West Street, New York 6, N. Y., pp. 14, 15, and 16.   For many of the expressions and definitions cited in this chapter see the "Centrifugal Pump Section," in the same volume.

[‡] "Centrifugal Pump Application Manual, Buffalo Pumps, Inc., pp. 17 and 18.

Cavitation is caused by operating a pump with excessive suction lift as far as cold liquids are concerned, and with insufficient positive suction head, as far as hot liquids are concerned. If the pressure inside the pump drops below the pressure corresponding to the vapor pressure of the liquid the latter will vaporize and form cavities of vapor. The vapor bubbles are carried along with the stream until a region of higher pressure is reached when they collapse (or "implode") with a tremendous shock to the adjacent walls. The phenomenon is called cavitation. It causes mechanical destruction apparent as pitting or explosion.*

In the pumping of hot water, it is necessary to have a net positive suction head. For pumping liquid at lower temperature, the required net positive suction head may be less, and may even be a suction lift.†

Effect of Specific Gravity. In order to explain the effect of specific gravity on the capacity of the pump, it should be stated first that the total head developed by a centrifugal pump at a given speed is constant, no matter what the specific gravity of the liquid may be. For example, when petroleum naphtha (specific gravity 0.8) or sulfuric acid (specific gravity of nearly 2) is pumped, the head developed and the height of the sustained column in both cases will be the same as for water. However, the load recorded by a pressure gauge at the base of the column (at the outlet of the pump) will differ; it will be least for the petroleum naphtha, greater for water, and greatest for the sulfuric acid. There is no violation of the law of energy conversion, for the power input will be least for pumping the light naphtha, greater for pumping the water, and greatest for pumping the sulfuric acid. The power is measured by calculating the brake horsepower.

$$\text{Head in feet of water} = \frac{\text{pounds per square inch} \times 2.31}{\text{specific gravity}} = \frac{\text{inches of Hg} \times 1.133}{\text{specific gravity}}$$

A centrifugal pump can safely handle liquids with viscosities as high as 600 SSU (Saybolt Seconds Universal), but a special procedure must be followed in the head estimate, pump selection, and motor selection.‡

Priming. When a centrifugal pump and the suction pipe are full of water (or other liquid), so that an unbroken stream of liquid is assured, the pump will function as it is. When the pump proper is empty, however, it must first be filled with water by some outside means before it will begin to operate: i.e., it must be "primed."

Priming is performed by pulling away the air in the casing by means of a vacuum pump, some other source of vacuum, or by means of a steam, air or water jet ejector, operated just long enough to fill the suction pump and pump casing. Of late, the self-priming centrifugal pump has come

* *Ibid.*, p. 23.
† *Ibid.*, p. 25.
‡ *Ibid.*, pp. 19 and 20.

into prominence; it has a reservoir in the discharge line above the level of the pump which remains filled when the operation is interrupted. When it is time to start the pump again, the liquid in the reservoir is admitted to the pump which works in a mixture of air and liquid; run-backs are provided so that the air is gradually eliminated and the pump is left filled with "solid" liquid, ready to function.

By locating the pump below the level of the source of liquid, it may be filled by gravity; the pump is then said to be "flooded." The higher point or points of the casing must be adequately vented of all air and gas so that the pump can be started. By so locating the pump, all the

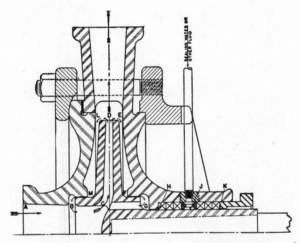

Figure 116.—Cross section through a chemical centrifugal pump to show the water-seal cage in the stuffing box. *J*, the seal cage. The pressures at various points are such that there is little tendency for the sealing liquid to enter the pump, or for the liquor or slurry to enter the stuffing box. Pressures in terms of discharge pressure: at *L*, *D*, and *E*, 100; at *H*, 11; at *J*, 30; at *K*, 0. Entry of liquid at left; impeller shaft at right. (Courtesy Worthington Corp., Harrison, N. J.)

difficulties of priming are avoided; thus this is done wherever possible, especially in chemical plants where such an arrangement is easily made.

In another method to facilitate priming, a closed chamber may be provided on the suction side of the pump, in which a volume of liquid sufficient to prime the pump is trapped when the pump is stopped. The chamber must be so proportioned that it retains a volume somewhat in excess of the volume of the suction line; with such a volume, priming will be achieved. As the pump is being primed, it pulls out liquid and air, so that very shortly the chamber is entirely filled with liquid, and ready to serve after the next shut-down.

In addition to the means for priming indicated here, there are "self-priming" pumps in the narrowest sense; one such is discussed in the next division. There are, furthermore, pumps which return a percentage of their flow for priming; such pumps are not truly self-priming.

Self-priming Pump with Special Construction. The LaBour horizontal centrifugal pump, Type DPL, is a truly self-priming pump, in that the pump itself, unaided by auxiliary devices, or even fore-tanks and reservoirs, performs that function. The self-priming pump DPL consists of the pump proper, of the trap on the suction side, and of the separator on the discharge side. The pump chamber is connected to the separator by two passages accurately shaped, dimensioned, and placed to deliver air

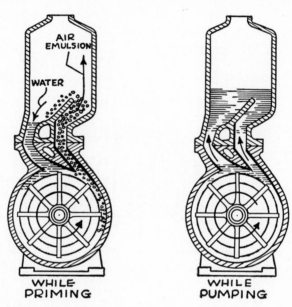

FIGURE 117.—The self-priming principle in the LaBour centrifugal pump type DPL and others. Left, cross section of the pump while in the act of priming; right, the same pump a few moments later, while pumping. The trap, which is not shown, stands just in front of the impeller. The separator may be set at the same level instead of above as here.

emulsified in water (or other liquid) to the separator through one throat, and to return the solid water to the pump chamber through the second throat. The air escapes from the separator through the discharge pipe. The suction pipe is gradually freed of its air until very shortly only liquid rises in it, and the pump is primed. As soon as this has happened, the pump delivers the liquid through both throats to the discharge system. There is no relation between the volume of the suction line and the volume of liquid retained in the separator.

The self-priming pump of Allis-Chalmers relies on a priming chamber in the discharge line in front and just above the pump casing; a by-pass runs from the chamber to the suction side of the pump.   Air or vapor is ejected until a valve operating automatically closes the by-pass; the latter opens again should air leak in or vapor develop in the suction line or in the pump.

Stuffing-box Problems and Remedies.   A source of difficulty with pumps handling chemicals is the likelihood of leakage at the stuffing box. Some chemicals such as gasoline and naphthas rob the packing of their softening agents, and the hard packing then cuts the shaft.   Other liquids attack and crumble the packing.   In many plants, leakage is collected in a special receiver and returned periodically to storage.   One way to prevent or reduce leakage is to use a deep stuffing box.   Another is to place a lantern ring or seal cage in the stuffing box, and to connect a sealing fluid to the seal cage (Figure 116) under constant pressure.   An external

FIGURE 118.—Single-stage centrifugal pump, direct-motor driven, with water-sealed stuffing box. The chamber is filled with water and seals the stuffing box against air leakage. Note the sturdy bearing and bearing stand. The pump proper may be made of iron, steel, bronze, stainless steel, "Monel," or other special metals. (Courtesy Taber Pump Co., Buffalo, N. Y.)

source of water, grease, oil, or other liquid is preferable to the earlier practice of returning some of the liquid from the discharge.   Cold water should be used as the sealing liquid whenever possible; with water, a steady drip of 30 drops a minute from the gland is permitted.

A centrifugal pump which must draw liquid from a vessel under reduced pressure, such as from an "effect" in a multiple-effect evaporator, suffers greatly from air leaks through the stuffing box.   The difficulty vanishes by installing a pump having a large, water-filled chamber surrounding the stuffing box (Figure 118); the sealing water prevents the entry of false air, and permits the pump to exert its full suction on the liquid in the evaporator.

There are solutions which are pumped warm, and whose dissolved solids readily carbonize under the influence of frictional heat, producing a grit which brings about leaks in the stuffing box; this is true, for example, of a sugar solution.   The remedy is to place a cooling jacket around the stuffing box and gland; the circulating cold water removes the heat of friction.

An entirely different solution to stuffing-box troubles which has met with great success is offered by the vertical submerged pump, in which a long shaft (5 or 6 feet) separates the pump casing from the stuffing box. If the liquid is not under pressure, and the stuffing box is placed above the level of the liquid fed in, the packing will not be attacked. There are many modifications of the vertical centrifugal pump. It may be set in the storage tank itself, or it may be beside it, and fed through a line outside the vessel; by returning the flow to a far point in the vessel, one would have an excellent circulating pump for mixing corrosive liquids. With slight modification, the vertical pump is a sump pump.

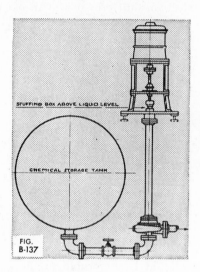

FIGURE 119.—Assembly showing application of vertical centrifugal pump with the pump so placed that the stuffing box cannot leak. (Courtesy Taber Pump Co., Buffalo, N. Y.)

Mechanical seals for sealing stuffing boxes, replacing the conventional packing held in place by a gland, are rapidly coming into favor. In mechanical seals, the shaft packing rotates with the shaft, and the only rubbing surface is between parts of the seal itself, thus eliminating shaft and shaft sleeve scoring. In the Dura Seal, to give an example, the gland holds the removable gland insert, which is stationary, while the seal ring is part of the rotating assembly. The seal ring is held against the gland insert by the action of coil springs. It is the contact formed by the seal ring and the gland insert which provides the prime function of the Dura Seal.* The only rubbing surface is between the gland insert and the seal ring.

The John Crane Bellows-Type Shaft seal† has the flexible rubber

* Crane Packing Company, Chicago 13, Illinois.

† Durametallic Corporation, Kalamazoo, Michigan.

bellows and a low friction sealing washer, both of which rotate with the shaft. The washer mates against a stationary floating seat and forms the seal.

The mechanical seal may be used singly, or, for certain applications such as pumping high-temperature liquids, in a double seal assembly. It has given good service not only in avoiding wear and scoring of shafts, but, in the form of special "balanced design" (Crane), for example, in fulfilling requirements for which the conventional compression packing would have been inadequate.

All services do not require the mechanical seal; for many of them, the compression packing may be more applicable.

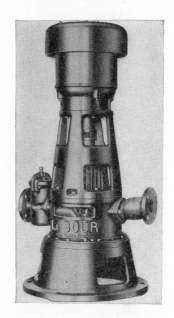

FIGURE 120.—The LaBour centrifugal vertical pump, type "G," a self-priming pump without a stuffing box nor mechanical seal; coupling connected to motor. (Courtesy LaBour Co., Inc., Elkhart, Ind.)

Self-priming Pump without Stuffing Box. A recent development of importance to the chemical industries is that of the self-priming, packingless, multithroat, vertical, single-stage, open impeller centrifugal pump, so designed that the stuffing box is eliminated (type "G" LaBour pump). The self-priming principle with the double throat described earlier is applied, except that normally two sets of throats are used, and pump, trap, and separator are combined in one compact casing. A self-priming pump should accomplish its priming in a short time; the rate of air removal from a suction line of the same inside diameter as the pump suction opening should be $\frac{1}{2}$ to 1 linear foot per second. The type "G" pump has produced speeds as high as $4\frac{1}{2}$ linear feet per second.

Type "G" pump has but one running part, the impeller with its integral hydraulic seal. The drive shaft enters the pump on the suction side, and the seal is thus required to work only against atmospheric pressure, with maximum pressure differential of 14.7 pounds per square inch. The seal is never subjected to, and is, moreover, unaffected by, discharge pressures.

The seal in type "G" is dynamic only; it is created by the operation of the pump, so that there is no seal when the pump is at rest. It follows that no part of the suction line may be above the pump inlet; on the contrary, it is intended to operate with less than atmospheric pressure on the

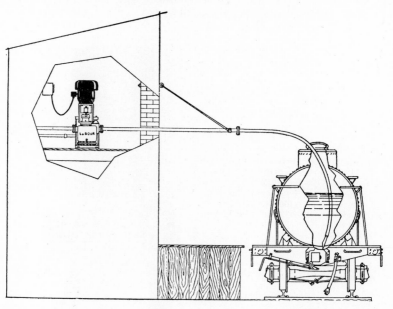

FIGURE 121.—A tank-car unloading unit with the LaBour Type R vertical self-priming pump drawing the content of tank into its pumping chamber by virtue of the reliable vacuum produced on its suction side. (Courtesy LaBour Co., Inc., Elkhart, Ind.)

suction. The seal is part of the impeller, and the process liquid forms the sealing liquid. The force set up by the whirling of the hydraulic seal liquid is used to counterbalance the atmospheric pressure and seal the shaft. The self-sealing arrangement has been accomplished without resorting to close clearances; there is at least $\frac{1}{32}$ inch designed clearance between rotating and stationary parts. The impeller, shaft, and drive shaft are suspended and free running; efficiencies as high as 70 per cent have been obtained.

Any one given seal assembly can operate only over a limited speed range (viz, 2850 to 3600 rpm, or, 1450 to 1800 rpm), since the effective specific gravity of the sealing liquid must be held within set limits. Special impeller blading is therefore incorporated, so as to maintain the air-handling activity vital to a self-priming pump, while varying the performance over the wide range demanded by the industries.

The materials of construction employed in the type "G" vertical LaBour pumps are R-55 (basically 23 per cent Cr, 52 per cent Ni); Elcomet K (basically 20 per cent Cr, 26 per cent Ni); 149 alloy steel (basically 14 per cent Cr, 9 per cent Ni); 304 or 316 stainless steel; and special electric furnace cast iron which has fine texture and is very low in carbon. This cast iron is suitable for handling caustic, 60 to 66°Bé sulfuric acid, and oleum, as well as for general hydraulic service.

The sizes available at the present time, and prices for cast iron construction, are given in Table 31; alloys cost more, up to three times as much depending primarily upon the nickel content.

TABLE 31. SIZES AND SPECIFICATIONS OF TYPE "G" LABOUR VERTICAL CENTRIFUGAL PUMPS*

Size	Suction Diameter	Discharge Diameter	Range† Gpm	Range† Ft Th	Present Price‡ (cast iron)
10	2	2	10–175	115–40	$ 538.00
11	2	2	10–150	50–20	$ 553.00
12	2½	2½	10–200	160–60	$ 600.00
14	2½	2½	15–200	75–25	$ 648.00
20	4	3	25–400	90–30	$ 739.00
30	5	4	30–700	100–20	$1004.00

* Courtesy of The LaBour Company, Inc., Elkhart, Ind.
† At 60 cycle speeds. Ft Th means feet total head.
‡ As of December 10, 1951, subject to change without notice.

Close-coupled Pumps. A special form of the centrifugal pump is the close-coupled pump; it has the advantage of requiring less space. A comparison follows:

Pump Size Suction (in)	Standard Motor-driven Centrifugal Pump, Example of Length (in)	Close-coupled Pump, Example of Length (in)
1½	58	28¼
3	78	35

The standard centrifugal pump is the horizontal type, generally motor-driven, with a long bearing box. Only when lack of space prohibits the installation of the standard pump is the "close-coupled" centrifugal pump recommended. There is, furthermore, a limitation to the usefulness of the close-coupled pump, because it requires special electric motors; in case of motor failure, shut-down periods are excessive unless the precaution has been taken to carry spare motors.

The Electrifugal (Allis-Chalmers) is a close-coupled centrifugal pump which has a unit-cast frame for perfect and permanent alignment. Motor and pump have a single shaft; there are no adapters or joints between the two. It is made for capacities of 10 to 500 gpm, at heads of as high as 220 feet.

FIGURE 122.—A close-coupled, single-suction centrifugal pump. (Courtesy Buffalo Pumps, Inc., North Tonawanda, N. Y.)

FIGURE 123.—A two-stage, close-coupled steam turbine-driven centrifugal pump, with capacities up to 500 gpm for heads lower than 500 feet, and for capacities lower than 500 gpm for 500 feet head. Cast-iron casings, bronze impellers, bronze fitted. (Courtesy SS unit of Allis-Chalmers Mfg. Co., Centrifugal Pump Division, Norwood Works, Cincinnati, Ohio.)

Hot Charge Pump. A centrifugal pump for hot charge service in refineries is the four-stage "barrel pump" recommended for high pressures and high temperatures. The rotor assembly is built for quick withdrawal onto a portable assembly truck, when necessary; no piping or driving connections are disturbed. The rotor functions within the assembly; it is surrounded by diffusers, which are stationary, but removable with the "barrel" for inspection. The pump handles changes in temperature from 400 to 900°F; commonly, the temperature is 800°F. The capacities run from 100 to 1500 gallons per minute, while the differential pressures may vary between 700 and 2000 pounds per square inch.

Chemical Centrifugal Pumps. Centrifugal pumps for chemical processes are generally made of the corrosion-resisting special alloys, although the plain cast iron pump still finds applications. A standard material for general use, second to cast iron, is bronze, a metal which in many installa-

FIGURE 124.—A single-stage volute centrifugal pump, type CG-3, a chemical pump made of "Worthite," special chrome-nickel-iron alloy, with ball bearings. Motor driven. (Courtesy Worthington Corp., Harrison, N. J.)

tions has insured low wear and long life. Cast-iron pumps with steel impellers resist abrasion fairly well; cast-iron pumps with bronze impellers are not uncommon. High silicon iron, with 14 to 16 per cent silicon, resists corrosion and abrasion extremely well; it has a certain degree of brittleness, and is extremely hard, so that true surface must be produced by grinding. Another interesting alloy with high corrosion resistance, which is not brittle, is "Hastelloy" C. Best known are the pumps made of the chromium-nickel-iron alloys, classified in various ways, one of which is shown in Table 32. In addition to the specific designations, the following are used, for simplicity: Standard and Bronze Fitted SF; All Iron AI; All Bronze AB; types 4, 5, 6, and 7 (in the table) AA.

There is also obtainable a table of "Cast Products of Corrosion-resisting Alloys" which gives the standards of the Alloy Casting Institute (1949), and a table for wrought stainless steels giving the designations and standards set up by the American Iron and Steel Institute (1949).*

* A convenient pocket-size folder may be obtained from the Worthington Corporation, Chemical Section, Harrison, N. J.

TABLE 32. SPECIAL MATERIALS FOR THE MANUFACTURE OF CENTRIFUGAL, RECIPROCATING, AND ROTARY PUMPS*

Type No.	Designation	Carbon	Chromium	Nickel	Molybdenum	
1	AISI 410	.15 max.	11.5–13.5			Free machining type is 416
	ACI CA14	.14 max.	11. –14.	1.0 max.		
2	AISI 442	.35 max.	18. –23.			
	ACI CB30	.30 max.	18. –23.	2.0 max.		
3	AISI 446	.35 max.	23. –27.			
	ACI CC35	.35 max.	27. –30.	3.0 max.		
4	AISI 304	.08 max.	18. –20.	8.–10.		Free machining type is 303
	ACI CF7	.07 max.	18. –20.	8.–10.		Free machining type is CF7Se
5	AISI 316	.10 max.	16. –18.	10.–14.	1.75–2.5	
	ACI CF7M	.07 max.	18. –20.	8.–10.	1.5 –3.5	
6		.07 max.	15. –28.	22.–36.	1.5 –4.0	Optional elements Cu, W, Si, Mn Ti, Cb
7	A series of nonferrous alloys, of less than 20 % iron, containing nickel, chromium, or molybdenum, or both, in major amounts, and copper, tungsten, silicon, and manganese in lesser percentages.					
8	High silicon iron, 14.25 % silicon minimum.					
9	Austenitic cast iron; total nickel, chromium, copper contents: 22 % minimum.					
10	"Monel" metal					
11	Lead					
12	Nonmetallic					
13	Nickel					
14	Steel					

* Standards of Hydraulic Institute, Data Section, p. 15 (1948). The figures in the third, fourth, fifth, and sixth columns are percentages.

Probably 90 per cent of all sulfuric acid is now propelled by pumps made of chrome-nickel-molybdenum-copper alloys which would fall under the Hydraulic Institute classification Nos. 6 and 7. The commercial alloys designated by trade names which correspond to these two classes are "Worthite," "Durimet 20," "Stainless 20," "Labour R-55," and others.

Nitric acid is handled in high chrome-steel pumps; formaldehyde solutions in aluminum pumps. Centrifugal pumps are furthermore made of "Monel," or aluminum bronze; in short, of any metal which can be cast and machined or ground.

Rubber-lined iron pumps, hard rubber pumps, and stoneware pumps have proved useful. Pumps made of plastics are appearing on the market; a glass pump will be mentioned later in the chapter.

Table 33 presents examples of chemical pumps of special alloy. The efficiencies for the pumps vary from 35 per cent for the smallest size to 83 per cent for the larger sizes. Standard Worthite centrifugal pumps are available in sizes larger than those given, to as large as 20,000-gpm capacity and heads up to 550 feet. Worthite contains 20 per cent Cr; 24 per cent Ni; 3 per cent Mo; 3.25 per cent Si; 1.75 per cent Cu; 0.60 per cent Mn; maximum of 0.07 per cent carbon; and 47.33 per cent Fe.

FIGURE 125.—A diagonally-split, high-consistency centrifugal pump, with a screw-booster in the inlet. Single-stage, single-suction, with standard bearing stand. (Courtesy Buffalo Pumps, Inc., North Tonawanda, N. Y.)

FIGURE 126.—A rubber-lined, direct motor-driven centrifugal pump, with vertically split housing, and with split bearing stand. Single-suction at right; single-stage; discharge at upper flange. (Courtesy Buffalo Pumps, Inc., North Tonawanda, N. Y.)

Among other pumps available for use in the chemical industries are those with "split" casings. One diagonally split, and two vertically split casings are shown in Figures 125, 126, and 127.

The centrifugal Durcopumps are manufactured of the special iron

TABLE 33. CHEMICAL PUMPS, WORTHITE, OPEN-IMPELLER, TYPE CG, FOR MOTOR DRIVE, WITH BASE PLATE AND COUPLING, BUT WITHOUT MOTOR*
January 2, 1952, Prices Subject to Change

Discharge (in)	Speed (rpm)	Capacity and Head	Price
¾	3500	10 gpm at 100-ft head	
		32 " " 72-ft "	$ 200
1½	1750	20 gpm at 70-ft head	
		100 " " 52-ft "	316
1½	3500	20 gpm at 208-ft head	
		140 " " 174-ft "	384
3 (CG-1)	1750	100 gpm at 86-ft head	
		400 " " 60-ft "	665
3 (CG-3)	1750	100 gpm at 150-ft head	
		500 " " 120-ft "	890
4 (CG-3)	1750	1000 gpm at 110-ft head	1060
6 (CGV)	1750	1800 gpm at 78-ft head	1440
8	1150	2500 gpm at 88-ft head	3690
10	1150	5000 gpm at 95-ft head	4420

* Courtesy of Worthington Corporation, Harrison, N. J.

alloys, high in silicon, "Duriron," and "Durichlor," in many sizes. One example of these pumps of special metal is shown in Figure 128. The two alloys named are hard, and must be machined by grinding. The pumps are also made, however, in machinable alloys; in all, there is a choice of eleven metals or alloys, including cast steel and cast iron.

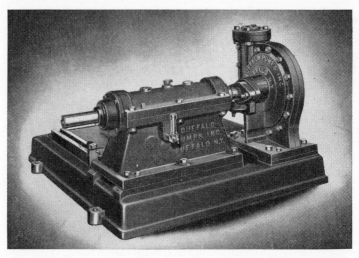

FIGURE 127.—A lead acid pump with vertically split casing. Note the long bearing. (Courtesy Buffalo Pumps, Inc., North Tonawanda, N. Y.)

The Glass Centrifugal Pump. Of special interest to chemical manufacturers is the all-glass centrifugal pump, in which a balanced glass rotor with glass vanes works in a glass housing, so that the material pumped

TABLE 34. CAPACITIES OF CENTRIFUGAL DURCOPUMPS, OPEN IMPELLER
(WITHOUT MOTOR)*

Size Discharge Opening (in)	Speed (rpm)	Readings from a Capacity-Head Curve	Price
1 × 1	1750	20 gal at 22-ft head	$ 200
1½ × 1½	1750	60 " " 38-ft "	270
2 × 2	1750	150 " " 98-ft "	477
4 × 3	1750	400 " " 70-ft "	520
6 × 6	1750	1400 " " 93-ft "	1539

* The Duriron Company, Inc., Dayton 1, Ohio.   Prices as of January 1952, subject to change without notice.

touches no metals.   The glass pump proper consists of the body, the head through which the shaft passes, and the rotor; the glass body is surrounded and protected by a cast-iron bracket and cover-plate housing.   The glass body fits against the head with a flat ground-glass joint, held tightly closed by springs mounted on the metal housing.   Should the pressure become

FIGURE 128.   A Durcopump, with its pump end of "Duriron." (Courtesy Duriron Co., Dayton 1, Ohio.)

dangerously high, the spring pressure would be overcome and the joint would open, avoiding possible rupture of the body.   The stuffing box consists of a novel mechanical and acid-proof seal, especially reliable because the pressure on it is decreased by back blades mounted on the shaft side of the impeller.

The Nash glass pump made of "Pyrex" glass, with 2-inch suction and 1½-inch discharge openings has a capacity at 1760 rpm of 6000 gallons per hour against a 65-foot head (measured as water).   The smaller pump, with 1-inch suction and ¾-inch discharge, will give, for example, 17.5 gallons per minute against a head of 35 feet.

The "Pyrex" glass used has high resistance to most chemicals; it is also shock-resisting, and heat-resisting. The material pumped may be as cold as brine-cooled liquids, or as hot as 150°F (65°C).

The Lapp *chemical porcelain centrifugal pump* has a porcelain body, porcelain impeller. The body is fully enclosed within a cast-iron armor; the impeller shaft has a running seal instead of the conventional stuffing box.

Designation of Pump Size: Pressure Limits: Types of Drives. The size of a pump is generally designated by the size of the pipe connections at suction and discharge. It would be better to designate the pump by a statement of the capacity under the head developed; quantity specifications mean nothing unless the head against which the quantity is to be discharged is also known. The same pump may be provided with two or three different pipe connections, to suit the specifications, while the pump itself is the same. The method generally followed is to provide the largest pipe connection likely to be needed in the operation of a given pump, and this is the connection for the highest capacity at the lowest head. The same pump casing, with the same impeller running at different speeds, or with modified impellers running at different speeds, will deliver lower volumes at higher heads, and a small pipe connection would be correct. The designation by the size of the pipe connection is simple, and probably will remain in use for many years; while it so remains, the buyer should always examine the head capacity curves for the several designs of impellers and for various speeds in order to know the true performance of the pump.

Centrifugal pumps are made in all sizes, ranging from as large as 75,000-gpm capacity, such as are found in municipal plants for low lifts, to 5-gpm pumps and smaller. The pressures developed in the early centrifugals were low; but they have been increased constantly by better design. A regular two-stage centrifugal pump normally would deliver water under a pressure of 250 pounds per square inch, and a four-stage pump, at a pressure of 500 pounds (more or less, depending upon size and speed). It used to be the rule that boiler-feed pumps, which must overcome boiler pressure, were plunger pumps; to-day, they are being replaced quite rapidly by centrifugal pumps, especially for capacities of about 25 gpm or greater. The maximum head developed by centrifugal pumps, with the exception of unusual installations for display, is 1000 to 1200 pounds. As to temperature, centrifugal pumps move liquids at high temperatures, up to 1000°F [537.8°C], without difficulty, providing they are properly designed for such service.

Although centrifugal pumps are generally direct-connected to the driving motor, there are other methods in use. The pump may have a flat-belt drive, or a V-belt drive; it may be direct-connected to a steam turbine, a gas engine, a gasoline engine, or a Diesel. There are also pumps which are driven directly by water wheels.

Rotary Pumps. Rotary pumps have a rotating element with auxiliary parts of various characters. In the gear pump, two gears mesh and rotate toward each other; ·in the spacings running up on the wall of the casing, liquid is trapped and carried upward toward the discharge. In the sliding vane pump, the rotating element is eccentric to the casing; it has four flat vanes free to slide in and out of the rotating element.* There is formed between two adjacent vanes and the casing a pocket which is large when nearing the inlet port; the material entering the space is carried

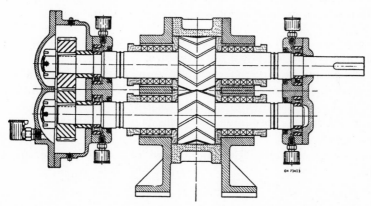

Figure 129.—Section through a double helical gear pump. One shaft is driven, while the other meshes with the first and receives its motion through the gears. The two gear wheels rotate toward each other. (Courtesy Worthington Corp., Harrison, N. J.)

farther in a gradually diminishing pocket as it nears the outlet port. Finally, the space is reduced to almost nothing, and the material is all discharged to the outlet port. The rotary plunger pump, the two-lobe pump of the Roots-Connersville type, and the swinging-bucket pump each has its characteristics and special adaptation.

The main duty of rotary pumps is to handle liquids too viscous for centrifugal pumps. They have one common defect: one metal surface rubs against another, causing wear. If the material to be pumped has lubricating properties, the defect vanishes. It is for that reason that vegetable oils, melted fats and fatty acids, and similar materials present a field for successful application for rotary pumps. Molasses and glue are pumped by means of rotary pumps, which may be steam-jacketed for pumping materials which are solids or semi-solids when cold, but which melt easily.

* A device with sliding vanes is illustrated in Chapter 19.

In the original gear pump, the gears have straight faces. Each gear is mounted on a shaft; one gear shaft is driven, and drives the second gear through the enmeshment in the pump space. Of the several modifications of this simpler design, one is the double helical gear pump, made in seven types: steam-jacketed pumps for low-melting solids, chemical pumps for special materials, and others. For small capacities and low pressures, pumps illustrated in Table 35 are examples:

TABLE 35. DOUBLE HELICAL GEAR ROTARY PUMP, TYPE GA (WORTHINGTON)*

Size (in)	At 1750 RPM			At 1150 RPM			At 850 RPM		
	Capacity (gpm)	BHP at 50 lb	100 lb	Capacity (gpm)	BHP at 50 lb	100 lb	Capacity gpm	BHP at 50 lb	100 lb
½	4.0	0.29	0.43	2.4	0.18	0.27	1.6	0.13	0.19
1	25.0	1.7	2.6	15.5	1.0	1.6	11.0	0.7	1.2
1½	51.0	3.9	5.6	32.0	2.3	3.5	22.0	1.5	2.5

* Three intermediate sizes left out. The ratings above are for thin liquids, having viscosities up to 400 SSU (Seconds Saybolt Universal).

The standard unit of iron construction, without motor, costs from $19 for the smaller size to $44 for the large size.

Chemical pumps are made of cast iron, bronze, nickel, nickel-iron, stainless steel, aluminum, high chrome-iron, or any other special material. The roller bearings are externally lubricated. Capacities are as high as 750 gpm; the liquids may have viscosities as high as 500,000 SSU (110,000 centipoises).

Table 36 gives examples of pumps used for large capacities and higher pressures.

TABLE 36. DOUBLE HELICAL GEAR PUMP WITH INTERNAL ROLLER BEARINGS, TYPE GR (WORTHINGTON)*

Size (in)	Speed (rpm)	Displacement Gpm at Max. Speed	Maximum Pressure (psi)	Price (1951)
1½	1450	48	500	$ 119
3	950	162	500	390
6	540	885	500	1485
12	375	3100	500	7560

* Cast-iron casing, steel shaft, steel roller bearings, Wompco gears. When pumping thin liquids, the actual capacity will be less than displacement. At reduced speeds, the pumps listed in the table will handle liquids with viscosities up to 500,000 SSU.

For pumping liquids between 100 and 1000 SSU, the pump, run at constant speed, will have a greater capacity for the 1000 SSU liquid, because the thinner liquids (low SSU) have a greater slip. On the other hand, for liquids with viscosities greater than 1000 SSU, the pump speed has to be reduced, because the flow is slow, which also results in reduced capacities. Thus the effect of viscosity is a double one.

The gear pump, it will be noted, has no valves, and requires none for unidirectional service. When the pump must be reversed periodically, the gear pump is provided with two inlet and two outlet valves, which then make possible the reversal.

The two lobe-type rotary pump, exemplified in the Connersville, may be considered a gear pump with two gear teeth. The principle of operation is illustrated in Chapter 8, Figure 167.

The rotary plunger pump, which might be called a pump with an oscillating round piston, may be classed here. An important representative is the Kinney rotating plunger pump for liquids,* which operates on the same principle as the Kinney vacuum pump, illustrated in Chapter 19, although it differs in important details of construction. The Kinney pump is especially valuable when pumping conditions require the moving of viscous liquids or mixtures of viscous liquids and entrained gas, and for operations requiring a calibrated output where the consistently high volumetric efficiency permits its use as combined pump and meter. There are at least two vacuum pumps and one compressor which employ this principle.

FIGURE 130.—A section through the Kinney rotating plunger pump for liquids, showing the plunger starting downward, the suction port closed, the discharge port in slide starting to open.

The sliding-vane pumps are run at comparatively low speeds, such as 300 rpm for light liquids, and 150 rpm for thicker ones. The ratings are established for the speeds of 250 to 300 rpm and hold good for light liquids of low viscosities. For higher viscosities there are two ways to adapt the pump. Its speed may be reduced and the horsepower of the motor increased; or the same speed may be retained, and a special rotating element with half the displacement of the standard one inserted. The velocity of the liquid in conveying pipes will limit the capacity of the pump; for corn sugar syrup and for molasses, a velocity of between 0.5 to 1 foot per second, depending upon the temperature which affects the viscosity considerably, is recommended.

In addition to the preceding, single-vane pumps with unusually large spaces are available for pumping liquids containing trash.

In the bucket rotary pump, the rotor carries three (or four) swinging buckets which run the width of the face of the rotor. The latter is eccen-

* Kinney Manufacturing Co., Boston, Mass.

tric; as it revolves, the buckets are swung against the casing, and carry the liquid to the outlet port. The buckets are easily replaced when worn.

It may be of special interest to point out that the rotary pumps are suitable not only for viscous liquids, but also for very volatile liquids, such as ethyl acetate and carbon bisulfide.

Power Pumps. Power pumps are reciprocating pumps which are driven by an external source of power such as an electric motor, steam turbine, steam engine, gasoline engine, or any other type of prime mover. There are two main classifications of power pump types, horizontal and vertical, each of which may be of the piston or the plunger type. Power

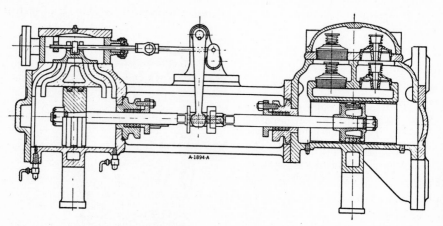

FIGURE 131.—A longitudinal vertical cross section of a horizontal duplex direct-steam piston pump, with disk-type valves and with renewable liners in the liquid cylinder. The steam and liquid cylinders are double-acting. Only one steam cylinder (at left) and only one of the twin liquid cylinders (at right) are visible. Worthington Type VC, for general service, for liquid at pressures up to 350 psi. (Courtesy Worthington Corp., Harrison, N. J.)

pumps are positive displacement pumping units suitable for many types of applications and covering a wide range of service conditions when handling liquids of every description.

Reciprocating pumps, as already stated, may be either piston or plunger pumps, in either of which the pumping element has a back-and-forth motion. A *piston pump* is double-acting, filling and discharging alternately on each side of the piston. There are usually four or more valves, a suction and discharge set of valves on each side; their function will be clear from Figure 131. The pump may be direct steam-driven, in which case it has a double-acting driving steam cylinder. A solid shaft, or as in the newer constructions, a divided shaft, connects steam piston to water piston, which move as one. The pump may be driven by power, by a belt, or by gears. Direct-acting steam pumps are either horizontal or vertical in the piston pattern, but only horizontal in the plunger design. Power-driven piston pumps are horizontal, but power driven plunger pumps may be either horizontal or vertical. The medium-pressure triplex, for example, is generally vertical. The valves are generally disks, provided with guides; a spring set over the disk helps it seat, with a gentle pressure.

The direct steam-driven piston pump possesses the advantage of latitude; should it become necessary to develop an extra head on the discharge, in order to deliver unexpectedly at a more distant or more elevated point, it is only necessary to open the steam valve a little wider. This advantage is denied to centrifugal pumps. The piston pump is the proper device for pumping water which contains much air. It serves also for special services, for which the cylinder proper may be equipped with a lining, which is occasionally replaced; for pumping hot oil at 500 pounds pressure, for example, a nickel steel lining is used. The steam-driven, simplex, double-acting piston pump is excellent for pumping such liquids as anhydrous ammonia or others which tend to gasify, because it cannot "short-stroke." And further, the direct-steam piston pump is much used wherever a motor would be objectionable because of the explosion hazard.

Pumps with one liquid end cylinder are simplex. Pumps are also duplex, which means that there are two steam cylinders and two liquid cylinders side by side, working in parallel. To avoid disturbing the cover plate in order to reach the valves, the latter may be set in an individual casting, allowing each valve to be examined and changed independently; such a pump is said to have pot valves.

The standard piston pump delivers the liquid under a maximum pressure of 250 to 350 pounds. With special construction of a high-grade cast iron, the pressure may be as high as 500 pounds; if it is made of cast steel, the maximum is 750 to 1000 pounds. Beyond that, the piston pump is not recommended. At such higher pressures, it is the plunger pump which finds popular use.

In the *plunger pump*, the cylinder is divided into two parts by a central wall; in each part a plunger works, on only one of its ends. The simplest pump is double-acting only because it has two plungers, connected by two outside rods. The plungers move together, and as one plunger withdraws from its cylinder chamber, which then fills with liquid, the other enters its filled chamber and forces out the liquid. Each cylinder and plunger has its complete set of valves. The plungers are generally outside-packed. Plunger pumps are made for all services requiring medium pressures and moderate volumes; their best field, however, is for high pressures. For the highest pressures, such as are required for high-pressure hydraulic service, a plunger pump with small-diameter plungers, steam-driven by a much larger steam piston, is standard. If the pump is machined for two plungers in one line, it is a simplex pump; if machined for four plungers, a duplex. The duplex pump is also made of two blocks set side by side, in the larger sizes. The capacity is small, as indicated in Table 37 by the smallest and largest of the eleven sizes in which one

TABLE 37. WORTHINGTON HORIZONTAL SIMPLEX STEAM PLUNGER PUMP, WITH OUTSIDE-PACKED PLUNGER AND FORGED-STEEL LIQUID CYLINDER

Sizes (in)	Gallons Displaced per Min.	Piston Speed per Min. (ft)	Maximum Working Pressure* (psi)
5¼ × 1 × 7	2.5	64	4000
14 × 3 × 12	28	80	2400

* Designs for higher pressures up to 10,000 pounds are available.

such pump is made. The figures in the first column are in the order of steam piston diameter, plunger diameter, stroke.

Power-driven plunger pumps for all pressures are available; for oil-field water flooding, a power pump furnishes water at pressures as high as 11,300 psi, at the rate of 8 gpm, or 8900 psi at the rate of 15.6 gpm (two items out of a list of 46).

FIGURE 132.—A horizontal simplex direct-steam plunger pump with outside-packed plungers and forged-steel liquid cylinder for high-pressure hydraulic service. The maximum working pressure for the liquid end is 5,000 psi. (Courtesy Worthington Corp., Harrison, N. J.)

The plunger pump may be simplex, or duplex with the plungers side by side, working from the same crankshaft; the pump may also be triplex, with horizontal plungers, or, as in the far more familiar example, with vertical plungers, each one single-acting, and driven from one crankshaft. The crankshaft carries the large gear, which is driven by a pinion gear on the pulley shaft, for the belt-driven, single-reduction type. The triplex pump is rather slow, 50 to 75 rpm, three times as many plunger strokes as the simplex. The capacities for the larger sizes vary from 200 to 1200 gpm at pressures ranging from 100 to 300 pounds in the different sizes, and for the smaller sizes 2 to 9 gpm at 250 pounds. The valves are rubber disk valves with bronze seats, or of special material; ball valves are used for viscous liquids and suspensions. The vertical triplex power pump may be driven by a tight belt, a V-belt, or a multi V-belt; in unusual installations, by a water wheel; in oil fields by power derived from gasoline motors or a Diesel.

The slow-moving, large-volume plunger pumps have, at times, been selected in a chemical industry over all other types for the pumping of liquids which tend to foam.

In the standard vertical, triplex, power plunger pumps, the plungers are at the bottom. A new pump has been developed, mainly for high-pressure hydraulic service, with the liquid cylinders at the top. With a 25-hp motor, the smallest of eight sizes, $\frac{5}{8} \times 4$ inches, 250 rpm, displaces 3.98 gpm at a pressure of 9800 pounds. The other sizes have larger capacities at lesser pressures. Reciprocating pumps do not require priming.

Diaphragm Pump. The diaphragm pump is a reciprocating pump; its piston may move vertically or horizontally. The duty of the diaphragm pump is to keep the liquid or suspension fed to the pump separate from the pumping element, in order to avoid corrosion or abrasion. Fifty years ago, diaphragm pumps played a more prominent part in the handling of chemicals than they do now, for since then a vast number of corrosion-resisting alloys have been developed. These alloys are at the same time abrasion-resistant to different degrees, so that the newer pumps have been successfully applied to the pumping of many suspensions of abrasives.

The early diaphragm pump contained a flexible sheet, let us say horizontal, which was held in place by circular flanges, forming a wall between the two chambers. In the lower chamber, the piston worked in a sealed liquid, distending the flexible sheet (upper surface convex), or permitting it to return to normal or to be sucked in (upper surface concave). The liquid to be pumped entered the upper chamber through the inlet valve on the suction stroke, and left through the outlet valve on the pressure stroke. It never reached the piston. The feed was by gravity.

An improved form of the diaphragm pump, indispensable today in certain specific services, will serve to illustrate the modern diaphragm pump. The Shriver duplex piston diaphragm pump has two pistons, each single-acting, with one horizontal axis. Each piston is composite, consisting of five concentric rings which support the diaphragm at every point. There is a rubber or other diaphragm over each set of rings; the diaphragm is the face of the piston. The center of the diaphragm is pierced to fit around a stud to which a drawback disk is securely attached; on withdrawal of the piston, the diaphragm follows because the disk pulls it in. The five rings receive an unequal motion from the central cams; the innermost receives the longest throw; the outermost, the shortest. On the pressure stroke, the diaphragm is flexed outward, forming a convex surface; at the same moment the other diaphragm is flexed inward, forming a concave surface. On the suction stroke, in the first cylinder, the diaphragm is drawn into the concave shape, following the supporting rings which are drawn back by the tie-rods linking them to the corresponding parts of the second piston; at the same moment the second cylinder performs its pressure stroke. The same cams and cam bearings actuate the two pistons; the cam shaft is mounted between the pistons, whose liquid ends face away from the center. The motor runs the cam shaft through gears; the cams run in oil.

At every position of the stroke, every point of the diaphragm is supported, and this explains the high pressures developed, namely 100 psi or more. The pump has a suction lift of 18 feet.

The pump may be driven by any driving mechanism. Sizes, capacities, and prices are shown in Table 38.

TABLE 38.   SHRIVER DUPLEX PISTON DIAPHRAGM PUMP WITH CAST-IRON LIQUID ENDS*

Pump Size†	Capacity	Strokes per Min.	Horsepower at 100 psi	Motor Speed (rpm)	Inlet (inches)	Outlet (inches)	Approximate Price (1951)
00	1–1½	55	⅙	1725	¾	¾	$ 245
1A	18	66	2	1725	1½	1½	810
2A	45	66	5	1725	2	2	1095
3A	100	66–72	10	1725	3	3	1950

* Cast-iron construction, with gear and bed plate, but without motor.
† Selected from a table of eight sizes.

The pump is available with bronze, aluminum, stainless steel, or any other of the special alloys; furthermore, the liquid ends may be lined with soft or hard rubber, or neoprene; or the metal may be electroplated.

General Comments. Centrifugal pumps are the most widely used pumps today. They have displaced to a considerable extent other types of pumps, particularly the piston and plunger pumps of large sizes. There are several reasons for this: the centrifugal pumps are more compact, hence occupy less space, require less metal, give a uniform discharge (free from piston stroke pulsation), are lower in first cost for medium and large sizes, are more efficient (efficiency here is gallons per horsepower for equal head), operate without valves, and are noiseless. The popularity of centrifugal pumps has been advanced by the improvements and modifications made in their construction, but improvements have also been made in every other type of pump. Moreover, there are services which the centrifugal pump cannot give; each of the other types of pump has certain qualities which make it superior for a certain duty to any other type. Thus the centrifugal pump run by a motor is limited in a given installation to a maximum head and maximum capacity; but, in contrast, the direct steam-driven piston pump may be made to deliver its indicated volume at any additional pressure, within reason, by merely turning on more steam. The rotary pump handles thick liquids. Extreme high pressures, such as 10,000 psi, are provided by steam- or power-driven plunger pumps. Other special adaptations have already been indicated.

The pump selected will better fulfill the expectations of the operator-pur-chaser if he fully describes to the consulting engineer specialist or the pump manufacturer the service he desires.

Compressed-air Devices

Compressed air serves to move liquid by the displacement method, and by the broken-column air lift.

Displacement Method. In the displacement method, the liquid is fed by gravity, generally to a closed vessel, until the latter is filled. A com-pressed-air line brings air under pressure to the top of the vessel, so that the entering air acts on the surface of the liquid and forces it out by an external or internal pipe. When the vessel is empty, the air is shut off, the pressure relieved through the delivery line, and the feed allowed to enter again. Such a vessel is a blow case. It may be either small or

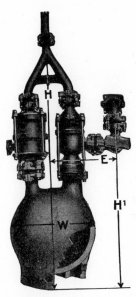

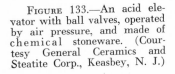

Figure 133.—An acid ele-vator with ball valves, operated by air pressure, and made of chemical stoneware. (Cour-tesy General Ceramics and Steatite Corp., Keasbey, N. J.)

large, and is generally of steel, or lead-lined steel. The pressure applied is usually moderate, and is limited by the strength of the vessel. For in-termittent operation, at infrequent intervals, hand manipulation of the valves is satisfactory, especially for large blow cases. In the chamber process for sulfuric acid the practice in former years was to transport the product to the delivery point in the plant by means of a large closed vessel, shaped somewhat like an egg and therefore known as an acid egg. Such vessels, holding several thousand gallons, could be left to deliver their con-tent over a period of an hour without any attention. For constant opera-tion, the blow case may be made automatic. The Kestner elevator, for example, is equipped with inlet and outlet valves and a float; as the float rises, it finally opens the compressed-air valve which lifts the liquid. As the float sinks, it reaches the air shut-off valve, the air pressure is released through the delivery line, and the vessel fills again. An automatic blow case of this type has a small capacity, such as 10 to 30 gallons. The cycles number perhaps 10 per hour. For elevating to great heights, such as 100 feet, a body of steel, perhaps lined with hard rubber or lead, may be used. For more moderate elevations, requiring a pressure of perhaps 15 or 20 pounds, stoneware vessels with stoneware ball valves are used. For the elevation of concentrated nitric acid, such elevators serve very well, usually with hand manipulation. The hard rubber-lined steel vessels with automatic operation serve for the propulsion and elevation of concentrated hydrochloric acids. A montejus is such an automatic displacement elevator.

Blow-cases handle slurries as well as clear liquids; after some time the solids may fill part of the case and reduce its capacity. A periodic

FIGURE 134.—Type A vertical acid egg for lifting and transferring acids and other liquids. (Courtesy Bethlehem Foundry and Machine Co., Bethlehem, Pa.)

cleaning restores the original capacity. Filter presses may best be served by a blow-case; a single blow-case may fill it, or a second and third one may be applied, using the same vessel or its twin in a two blow-case installation.

The Bethlehem type A vertical acid egg (Figure 134), is made in five sizes with capacities ranging from $7\frac{1}{2}$ cubic feet, or 50 gallons, to 66 cubic feet, or 495 gallons. Type C, an elongated egg lying on its side, is also made in five sizes, with the largest 123 cubic feet, or 922 gallons; it is 4 feet in diameter and 11 feet 9 inches long. Blow-cases are made of steel as well as of cast iron, of welded steel lined with homogeneous lead, or of other material.

For general acid handling, blow-cases have lost ground to chemical pumps. There are special problems, however, in which the displacement method is superior to others, or is the only possible way to transport or elevate the material. Instead of air, an inert gas such as nitrogen may be the compressed gas; or again, carbon dioxide, for organic liquids which are flammable and perhaps have to be handled hot. For example, molten sodium is transported through pipelines by the compressed nitrogen displacement method.   In continued successful use also is the transformation of an evaporator into a blow-case, as follows: at the end of a batch evaporation, the concentrated liquor in the vessel is elevated and delivered, for example, to stationary crystallizers, by shutting off all lines except the delivery line and turning on the compressed air, which enters over the surface of the liquid.   The hot liquor is forced out by displacement.

A blow-case which may safely be subjected to a pressure of 25 pounds, which any ordinary light-weight, soft-steel tank would permit, is capable of elevating acid of specific gravity 1.8354 (66°Bé) just over 30 feet [(2.31 ÷ 1.8354) × 25 = 31.8].

Broken Column Air Lift.   One form of the broken-column air lift consists of a U-tube with legs of unequal lengths.   The tube is placed in a pit, for example, and receives in one leg liquid to be moved from a tank on the first floor; into the other leg, the rising and longer leg, a slow stream of

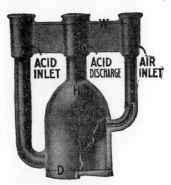

FIGURE 135.—A three-neck pulsometer bottle made of chemical stoneware for elevating acids. (Courtesy General Ceramics and Steatite Corp., Keasbey, N. J.)

compressed air (or other gas) is introduced just beyond the turn.   The air bubbles mix with the liquid and divide it into a series of slugs which are readily driven up by the air pressure.   The shorter, fully liquid column helps balance the longer, broken column, which is discharged at a higher level.   There are many modifications of this device.   A moderate air pressure is sufficient, except that it must be greater than the pressure in the pipe at the point of entry.

Another form of broken-column air lift makes use of the pulsometer, a three-neck bottle-like vessel, made of chemical ware, with one neck entering at the top, one part way down, and the third very close to the bottom. Through the latter, liquid enters under a 12-foot head, to give a definite example; the second side inlet admits compressed air (75 pounds), and the broken column rises noiselessly 29 feet through the vertical tube set in the top outlet.   The pulsometer vessel in this installation is 6¾ inches in diameter for the body, and 16 inches in over-all height (see Figure 135, and compare Figure 196).

Tungstone Air-pressure Pump.   An interesting and valuable pump without moving parts which makes use of the displacement method is the Tungstone Patent Air-pressure pump,* designed primarily for pumping corrosive, sticky, or gritty liquids. The Tungstone pump has two units, each consisting of a central chamber, inlet and outlet compartments with poppet (or ball) valves, the control valve, and a compressed-air line which acts also as a relief line. The pump is placed below or at the level of the liquid, for the feed must be by gravity. The pump has no suction.

At the beginning of the cycle, the air line is connected to the atmosphere. The inlet valve admits the liquor until the central chamber is filled. The control valve now admits compressed air (30 pounds or less); the contents of the central chamber are forced out through the discharge valve (see Figure 136). The air pressure is released again, and the cycle is complete; then the unit starts on another one. The second unit is so timed that it delivers liquor while the first one is filling so that the flow of the discharge is uniform.

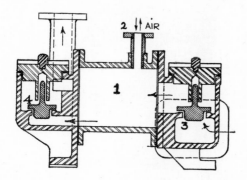

FIGURE 136.—Section through one of the two identical units which make up a Tungstone acid pump. *1*, cylindrical chamber, with *2*, compressed air inlet; *3*, liquor inlet valve, lifted by the head on the feed, while the pressure in line *2* is released; *4*, liquor outlet valve. Line *2* bears a control valve which alternately admits compressed air and releases the pressure. When *1* is filling, the corresponding chamber in the other unit is emptying.

The control valve is the heart of the pump; it consists of two double-faced valves, each controlling one pump chamber. A rocker arm operated by a cam causes each valve to connect its chamber alternately with the compressed-air supply and the atmosphere. The period of the cycle is such that the chambers do not empty completely, so that no air is wasted through the valve openings.

The normal speed is 22 movements per minute, provided the entering liquor is under a head of at least 3 feet 6 inches. The capacities for the several sizes range from 200 to 9000 gallons per hour. The smallest pump is 1 foot 1 inch long by not quite 6 inches in height, made of ebonite. A large one, of rubber-lined cast-iron, is 5 feet 2 inches long, not quite 2 feet high, and 3 feet 1 inch wide. The Tungstone pumps are made of ebonite, rubber-lined cast-iron, nickel cast-iron, stainless steel, acid bronze, antimonial lead, chemical lead, and aluminum. It is now made also of

* Tungstone Products, Ltd., Market Harborough, England.

"Pyrex" borosilicate glass, in two sizes only, 300 gallons per hour capacity and 800 to 1000 gallons per hour capacity.

The Tungstone may be immersed in the liquid to be pumped and will function perfectly. The working agent need not be air, but may be an inert gas or a refinery gas; for hot liquids such as creosote oil, it may be steam. In the latter operation a comparison was made between the Tungstone and the duplex-steam pump, both working on oil at 500°F and pumping 20,000 gallons per hour. The Tungstone pump used 5.6 pounds of steam per minute, the duplex steam pump 50 per cent more.

Each pump consists not only of the twin units and control valve with cam and rocker arm, but also of a small electric motor to operate the cam. An air motor may be substituted for the electric one, in plants in which explosions might occur.

The Tungstone pump handles a variety of liquids, including molten sulfur; it is, moreover, recommended for pumping slurries to filter presses.

WATER-, AIR-, OR STEAM-DRIVEN EJECTORS AND EDUCTORS

In the steam *ejector*, described briefly in Chapter 10, the steam entrains whatever liquid or gaseous substance surrounds the steam nozzle; if that substance is water, the ejector imparts to the previously quiescent water a velocity which suffices to drive it some distance horizontally, or a lesser distance vertically against gravity. The content of a pit may thus be raised to the first floor, or a higher floor. Instead of steam, air or water may be used. If water is used, the device becomes an *eductor*, which is otherwise defined as a liquid jet for pumping and mixing liquids. In the eductor, then, a stream of high velocity water fed to the eductor tube will bring about the entrainment of the water surrounding the tube. The steam ejector will heat the water it entrains, as well as drive it forward or upward. The "steam jet ejector," especially intended for the production and maintenance of vacuum, is designed to entrain vapors or gases, and is fully described and illustrated in Chapter 19.

Numerical Examples and Problems

Example 1. Refer to Figure 137. Find the total head required if a pump is to deliver 300 gpm of water at a pressure of 25 psi at a point 50 feet above the pump centerline. Unit takes suction from a point 10 feet below the center line of the pump. Suction piping consists of 10 feet of 4-inch pipe plus one 90° long-radius elbow, and the discharge piping consists of 60 feet of 3-inch pipe plus one 90° long-radius elbow plus one 3-inch check valve plus one 3-inch gate valve.

Solution:

SUCTION PIPING LOSSES

1–4 inch—90° L.R. Elbow equivalent to 7 feet of straight pipe
Total equivalent length of 4-inch pipe = 10 feet + 7 feet = 17 feet
Loss = 17/100 × 9.3 feet (loss per 100 feet) = 1.6 feet

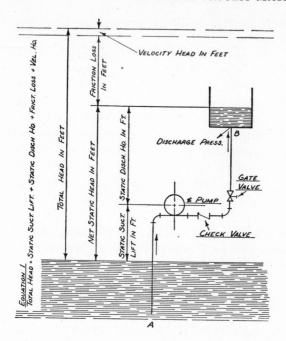

FIGURE 137.—Sketch illustrating the pumping problem involving a suction lift.

DISCHARGE PIPING LOSSES

1–3 inch—90° L.R. Elbow equivalent to   5.3 feet of straight pipe
1–3 inch—Gate valve   equivalent to   1.7 feet of straight pipe
1–3 inch—Check valve   equivalent to 16.0 feet of straight pipe

                                            23.0 feet

Loss varies with type of valve.

Total equivalent length of 3-inch pipe = 60 feet + 23 feet = 83 feet

Loss = $^{83}/_{100}$ × 38 feet (loss per 100 feet) = 31.6 feet

Total friction losses = 1.6 + 31.6	= 33.20
Static suction lift	= 10.00
Static discharge head	= 50.00
Disch. Press. at B = 25 psi, 25 × 2.31 feet	= 57.70
Velocity head	= 2.88
Total head in feet	= 153.78

Add 10 per cent of friction losses.

Total head for pump selection = 153.78 + 3.32 = 157.10 feet

Example 2. Refer to Figure 138. Find the total head required if a pump is to deliver 100 gpm of water at a point 30 feet above the center line of the pump. Unit takes suction from a tank with water level 6 feet above the center line of the pump. Suction piping consists of 20 feet of 2½-inch pipe, and discharge piping consists of 50 feet of 2-inch pipe plus one 90° standard elbow, plus one 2-inch check valve plus one 2-inch gate valve.

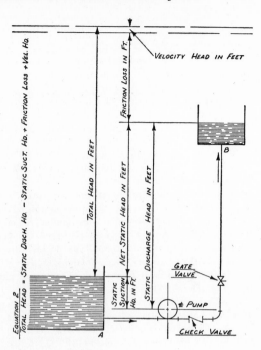

FIGURE 138.—Sketch illustrating the pumping problem involving a suction head.

Solution:

SUCTION PIPING LOSSES

Entrance loss is very low and can be neglected.
20 feet of 2½-inch pipe
Loss $= {}^{20}\!/_{100} \times 12.0$ feet (loss per 100 feet) $= 2.4$ feet

DISCHARGE PIPING LOSSES

1–2 inch—90° Std. Elbow equivalent to 5.5 feet of straight pipe
1–2 inch—Gate valve equivalent to 1.2 feet of straight pipe
1–2 inch—Check valve equivalent to 11.0 feet of straight pipe

$$\overline{17.7}\ \text{feet}$$

Loss varies with type of valve.
Total equivalent length of 2-inch pipe $= 50$ feet $+ 17.7$ feet $= 67.7$ feet
Loss $= 67.7/100 \times 35.8$ feet (loss per 100 feet) $= 24.3$ feet

Total friction losses in feet $= 2.4 + 24.3$	$= 26.70$
Static discharge head in feet	$= 30.00$
Velocity head	$= 1.62$
	$\overline{58.32}$
Suction head in feet	$= -6.00$
Total head in feet	$= \overline{52.32}$

Add 10 per cent of friction losses.
Total head for pump selection $= 52.32 + 2.67 = 54.99$ feet

Note: The sketches and the two examples are taken from the instruction book, Buffalo Pumps, Inc., Buffalo, N. Y.

Reading References

"Power Pumping," a treatise on pumps in the form of a series of illustrated essays entitled: "What is head on a pump? Rotary pumps; centrifugal pumps; reciprocating pumps; deep well pumps; pump operation; boiler-feed pumps; pump priming; pump drives," by F. A. Annett, *Power*, 315–330 (June, 1938).

"Selection of pumps for chemical service," by Ward E. Pratt, *Ind. Eng. Chem.*, 39, 408 (1939).

"Centrifugal pumps for the process industries," by H. E. LaBour, *Ind. Eng. Chem.*, 30, 1105–1109 (1938).

"Packing the centrifugal pump," by F. C. Thorn, *Ind. Eng. Chem.*, 31, 929 (1938).

"Pumps in the chemical industry," by W. W. Mellen and A. P. Smith, *Trans. Am. Inst. Chem. Eng.*, 38, 831 (1942).

"Costs of process equipment and accessories," by H. Bliss, *Trans. Am. Inst. Chem. Eng.*, 38, 763 (1942); section on liquid pumps, p. 784.

"Pumps" (types, selection, installation, operation and maintenance), by F. A. Kristal and F. A. Annett, McGraw-Hill Book Co., New York, 1940.

"Priming centrifugal pumps," by H. B. Hummer, Sales News, Norwood Works (Pumps), Allis-Chalmers Co., Cincinnati, O., July 1951.

"Practical approach to packing of chemical pumps," by Stanley L. Lopata, *Chem. Met. Eng.*, Dec. 1944, p. 104.

"Self-priming Centrifugal Pumps, Their Performance and Testing," a Handbook, by Harry E. LaBour, The LaBour Company, Elkhart, Ind., 1950.

"The Corrosion Handbook," edited by Herbert H. Uhlig, Electro-Chemical Society, New York, John Wiley and Son, 1948.

*The automatic multiple weighing and filling machines for small pack-
ges deliver their cartons or bags, filled, to a folding, labeling, and sealing
nachine which closes and finishes the package so that it is ready for dis-
ribution. A study of the patent literature proves that these developments
re largely the work of American inventors. The continued and extended
pplication of accurately timed, coordinated motions which with gravity
ffects make up the automatic machine is the special province of the me-
hanical engineer.*

7. WEIGHING AND PROPORTIONING SOLIDS AND LIQUIDS

Solids are weighed for a number of purposes. In the chemical industries a product is weighed in bulk in order to judge the continued good performance of a process; raw materials and products are weighed to establish
their relation, which must remain fixed if the process is to function properly. It should be added here that in the heavy-chemical industry, products are made into stock piles, which are measured rather than weighed,
multiplying the number of cubic feet by a factor determined for the mate-

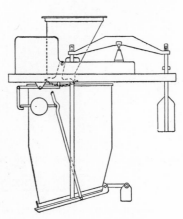

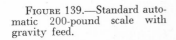

FIGURE 139.—Standard automatic 200-pound scale with
gravity feed.

rial; weights are established only as the goods leave the plant, in railway
cars, for example. The factor between raw materials and product always
involves a certain amount of measured weight. Solids of certain kinds,
such as coffee and sugar, are weighed and packaged ready to distribute to
consumers. Liquids are generally measured: quiescent liquids in tanks
by liquid-level gauges, flowing liquids by meters. However, liquids in
chemical factories are also weighed, in weigh tanks, i.e., tanks suspended
from the beam of a balance. After weighing, the liquid is run into the re-

action vessel. Liquids in small lots are generally measured, for distribution to consumers.

When weighing operations are repeated over and over, without alteration, the automatic scale is employed, and it has become almost indispensable. Not only is it a labor-saving device, but it is considered more uniform and more reliable than hand work.

Automatic batching or proportioning of solids involves the weighing of predetermined amounts of several different solids on scales, and dumping

FIGURE 140.—A 100-pound heavy-duty automatic scale. Note the main weight suspended at right, the positioning weight reading OZ, and to its left, the counterpoise for supply gate. The dump gate with its counterpoise is not visible. (Courtesy Consolidated Packaging Machinery Corp., Buffalo, N. Y.)

them into a mixer, to form the batch of raw materials for a furnace charge, for example. Complicated batch formulas may be filled by machinery in astoundingly short periods of time, with remote control and signal devices which indicate the progress and state of operation, besides safety devices which interrupt when any one part fails to function. An example will be described later on.

The proportioning of liquids is performed by accurate pumping. A number of clever devices, including the Pulsafeeder and the H-O-H Feeder, which employs the pitot tube effect, supplement pumps and meter mechanisms.

Automatic Scales. Automatic weighings are performed on scales, the first weigh-beam movement being used to control the second, and so on. When packages are to be filled, the materials are measured either by the number of turns of an auger, or by the alternate filling and emptying of a small chamber equipped with opening and closing valves which are also called cut-off slides. A machine may deliver a measured amount into a container, which is then automatically positioned under the outlet, or

FIGURE 141.—A unit-type automatic scale, with gravity action supplemented by cam action. (Courtesy Consolidated Packaging Machinery Corp., Buffalo, N. Y.)

"dribble." In this case the machine is functioning as a scale. A machine that performs only the measuring function is called a "powder filler."

It should be explained at this point that many automatic weighings are performed with the aid of two supply gates, the bulk gate which opens wide and admits most of the material rapidly, and the dribble gate which admits the final few grams or fractions of ounces at a slow rate. When there is only one gate, a similar effect is achieved by moving the gate to an almost shut position, called the dribble position, which allows but a slight flow of the material.

Five automatic scales which differ in conception and in adaptation will illustrate the classes to which they belong.

(1) The 100-pound, heavy-duty scale shown in Figure 140 weighs six or eight batches a minute, delivering them to a filling hopper underneath, without any attention from the operator. The principle of this scale is the control of its action entirely by the stream of material, hence by gravity. The supply hopper has a supply gate and a gravity feeder if the material is free-flowing, or a screw- or drum-feeder, if it is not free-flowing. The weigh-beam carries the receiver with a hinged and counterpoised dump gate as its bottom, and also the main weight. A system of levers connects the weigh-beam, supply gate, and dump gate. The supply gate feeds wide open for bulk weight, but soon swings to the dribble position and then to the cut-off position. The weigh-beam swings sharply and trips the gate shut; the dump gate opens by an impulse communicated by the levers from the supply gate. As soon as the receiver is empty, the dump gate swings shut by the counterpoise action, and the lever system opens the supply gate, while in the meantime the weigh-beam has swung back to its original position. There are many minor mechanical features which are properly the subject of patents, and which contribute materially to the success of a particular scale.

This type of scale can also be dumped manually. The automatic mechanism is thrown out of action by a simple adjustment. Thus the scale will weigh a full charge and remain idle until the operator trips the dump gate. The material in the hopper may be dropped into a bag or a barrel, which must be placed in position by hand; for that reason, this scale may be called semi-automatic.

(2) The second automatic scale (Figure 141) is a unit-type scale in which several scales, here four, are operated to dump in succession into a single filling hopper. The scale has a supply hopper which feeds through chutes into the scale buckets. There are four weigh-beams, and the filling of the bucket and shutting of the supply valve take place by gravity, that is, by the action of the weigh-beam, but the dump gates are opened by cam action. Thus the dumping of the scale buckets is not responsive to the movement of the scale beam.

The four buckets are filled in rotation; when one is filling, another is dumping, while the other two are in intermediate stages. The net result is that a continuous stream of material issues from the filling hopper. The unit-type scale avoids loss of time while the single scale is being filled. Also the scales may be used to form unit charges of a complete load. Thus each scale may be adapted to weigh five pounds to form in this instance a twenty-pound load.

(3) Figure 142 shows a six-head scale which fills and weighs its weigh buckets by gravity, and is adapted to filling through single filling spouts, each charge remaining separate and reaching a separate container. It has

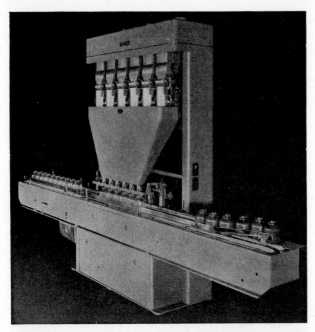

FIGURE 142.—A six-head scale, designed especially as a coffee net weigher.   (Courtesy Consolidated Packaging Machinery Corp., Buffalo, N. Y.)

FIGURE 143.—The flip-flop type scale with a power feeder, a barrel feeder. The scale is set up on a working bench. (Courtesy Consolidated Packaging Machinery Corp., Buffalo, N. Y.)

a timed action, and the time relation is between the positioning of the six containers and the dumping of the scales. Each scale bucket has a weigh-beam; the supply gate is shut off by its movement. The dump gate opens by cam action. The six-head scale fills and moves packages at the rate of 40, 60, or 100 a minute, depending upon the nature and flowing properties of the material.

FIGURE 144.—A duplex net weigher type of powder filler. (Courtesy Consolidated Packaging Machinery Corp., Buffalo, N. Y.)

(4) The flip-flop type scale has a scale bucket with two compartments; a deflector plate swings from left to right to open one compartment, close the second, and direct the feed stream into the first compartment. Each compartment has a dump gate, and each forms a separate weigh bucket. After the weight is received, the weigh-beam rises to normal position, and this action causes the flip-flop gate to swing to the opposite position. This scale is used for small loads; its purpose is to do more weighing per unit of time.

(5) The net weigher type of powder filler illustrates the machines which combine measured filling with gross weighing. Figure 144 shows

a duplex net weigher.   Feed augers working in the delivery spout of the supply bin deliver a measured amount of material; this is forced through the feed spouts into the scale bucket which weighs it.   The weight is not corrected by any auxiliary mechanism; it is correct within the prescribed tolerances.   The two buckets deliver to the same filling hopper.

Powder Fillers.   A powder filler is a filling machine which *measures* the material placed in the container, as contrasted to machines which *weigh.*   Figure 145 shows a powder filler especially designed to handle

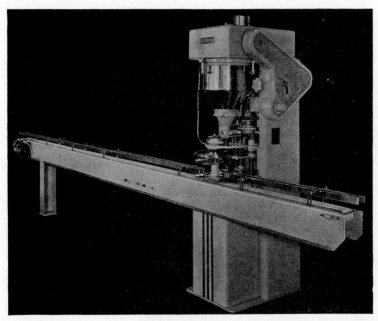

Figure 145.—A powder filler designed for beauty as well as efficiency, single unit, with screw feed; latest model.   (Courtesy Consolidated Packaging Machinery Corp., Buffalo, N. Y.)

small charges.   The material is measured by the number of rotations of the feed auger working in the supply hopper; the machine has but one auger, and one charge at a time is delivered.   The containers are positioned by an indexing star wheel.   The machine shown in this figure is used for weighing out a number of grams of a powder to which other ingredients are added later, on other machines.

A tandem-type powder filler, shown in Figure 146, fills two rows of containers simultaneously.   There are two supply hoppers and two augers on each side.   The first (and largest) auger delivers bulk, and this is a timed filling action, electrically controlled; after receiving the bulk, the container passes to a weigh platform, under the second auger.   A dribble of powder is fed in until the scale tips, when electrical connections throw out a clutch in the feed auger drive to stop it. This powder filler, like No. 5, represents a combination of measuring and weighing principles. It is a net weight powder filling machine used for non-free-flowing materials such as sulfur and flour. The charge is weighed and discharged into the filling hopper and from there into a container. The augers uniformly and positively feed the scale bucket. In this instance they are employed as measuring elements since the charge is determined entirely by the weigh beam.

FIGURE 146.—A tandem-type powder filler which fills two rows of containers simultaneously. The near supply hopper feeds by weight; the far one, to the right, feeds bulk, by measuring. (Courtesy Consolidated Packaging Machinery Corp., Buffalo, N. Y.)

Automatic Proportioning with Remote Control. A number of scales similar to the 100-pound automatic scale which has been described may be combined in order to deliver a batch of several different ingredients. A proposal for an installation for the proportioning of solids on a somewhat elaborate scale will be offered now, by means of which five different materials are furnished from gravity scales in rapid succession to a collecting conveyor belt which delivers its charge to a mixer.

The several scales required would be as follows:

2   500-pound scales, gravity type, trolley-mounted, for weighing approximately 450 pounds of sand at the rate of approximately 5 drafts a minute.

1   50–200-pound scale equipped with twin-screw feeder and trolley-mounted, for weighing 184 or 188 pounds of soda ash at the rate of three drafts a minute; 1½ hp motor and reduction drive.

1   50–200-pound scale, duplicate of the foregoing, for weighing 165 or 176 pounds of lime at the rate of two drafts a minute.

1   50–200-pound scale, equipped with drum feeder and trolley-mounted for weighing 100 to 200 pounds of flint cullet at rate of three drafts per minute; 1½ hp motor and reduction drive. Hard metal surfaces will be added to gate and other contact surfaces.

1   25–50-pound gravity scale, suspended type, for weighing 28 or 42½ pounds of feldspar at rate of three drafts per minute.

1   25–50-pound gravity scale, as above, for weighing 27 or 28 pounds of barytes at rate of one draft in two minutes.

1   Automatic release mechanism interlocked with above to provide introduction of decolorizing agent to batch as per specifications. The release of this chemical will send impulses to control board exactly as is the case with scale unit. This decolorizing release mechanism will be located near discharge end of main conveyor and near to control panel to be convenient for operator to perform this function.

In addition to the scales there are required twelve spouting connections between bin and scale intake; 18-inch conveyors, 12-inch conveyors; electrical interlocking apparatus, which includes a complete electrical control equipment; a main conveyor 30 inches wide and 127 feet long, fully enclosed; magnetic head pulley, electrically interlocked.

Automatic Scale Control and Electrical Interlocking Apparatus. Scales are controlled by a start button on a panel which is pressed by the operator. On the upper right-hand portion of the panel is a series of lights which indicate the progress of the scale cycle. A red light flashes as each scale dump is made. Progress of this light will indicate the speed of scale operation and its status at any moment. Progress of the red light stops when the cycle for that scale is complete. Maximum tentative requirements in number of scale drafts for each material are as follows: sand, 5 drafts; soda ash, 4; lime, 4; cullet, 4; feldspar, 4; barytes, 3; decolorizer, 1 draft. If less than the above number of red lights flash, indicating incomplete delivery, the white light will not flash and the mixing cycle will be stopped. On the control panel is a green light which will flash when the mixer has been positioned to receive delivery from the scale. This will indicate when the operator may start the next scale cycle, which he does by pressing the start button. This light circuit will be interlocked with the scale start button, so that it cannot be started until the green light is showing. It is believed that these light and button arrangements will give complete control and indication of scale performance.

On each scale there will be a solenoid to start operation of the scale. When the solenoid circuit is closed, the scale will begin to deliver drafts of material; when the solenoid is released, the scale will stop. This circuit is closed manually by the operator by a button on the control panel, and the circuit is held closed for the solenoid to control the scale function by automatic switches described below.

When all scale step switches have reached the desired number of dumps, the interlock circuit for swinging mixer is completed, and a blue light will flash before the operator; the control circuit for the mixer will be closed, enabling the operator to swing mixer manually or automatically from receiving to mixing position. When the mixer has completed the job and returned to the position for receiving the next batch, and the signal light has flashed on the board, the limit switch will close, enabling the operator at the scale control panel to start the next scale cycle.

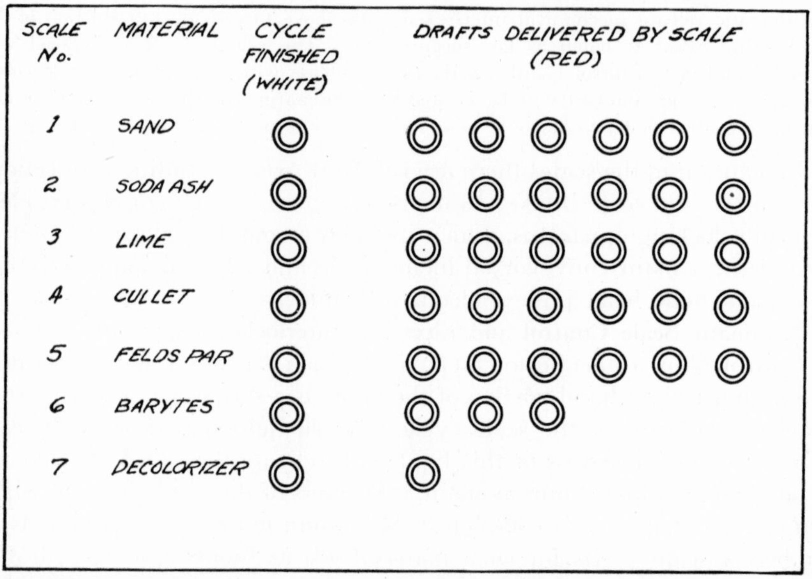

SCALE No.	MATERIAL	CYCLE FINISHED (WHITE)	DRAFTS DELIVERED BY SCALE (RED)					
1	SAND	◎	◎	◎	◎	◎	◎	◎
2	SODA ASH	◎	◎	◎	◎	◎	◎	◉
3	LIME	◎	◉	◎	◎	◎	◎	◎
4	CULLET	◎	◎	◎	◎	◎	◎	◎
5	FELDSPAR	◎	◎	◎	◎	◎	◎	◎
6	BARYTES	◎	◎	◎	◎			
7	DECOLORIZER	◎	◎					

FIGURE 147.—An indicator panel for scale cycle. One red light flashes on and stays on for each draft and each of the seven materials, until the complete mixer cycle is finished, when a blue light (not shown) will appear. A green light (not shown) persists, showing that the mixer is in receiving position and that the scale cycle may be started by depressing starter button (not shown). Interlocks not shown. Except for depressing the start button by hand, the weighing, dumping, and conveying of the proper number of drafts from each of the seven materials to the mixer is automatic. The time required is one minute.

To summarize the performance of the automatic-scale control equipment with electrical interlocking apparatus:

(1) Red lights show progress of scale cycle.

(2) White light shows completion of each scale cycle.

(3) Green light shows that the mixer is ready to receive the next charge, and the scale cycle may be initiated by the operator by pressing the start button on the control panel.

(4) Interlock is provided to prevent the mixer being turned from receiving to mixing position until each scale unit has made its allotted delivery to conveyor belt.

(5) Interlock on control button is provided so that next scale cycle cannot be started until after previous one has been completed, the batch thus delivered carried through the mixer, and the empty mixer returned to receive the next batch.

(6) Interlock will be provided on the start button so that the scale cycle cannot be started until the mixer has been turned to the proper position.

A counter will show the batches delivered in any desired total arrangement, as specified.

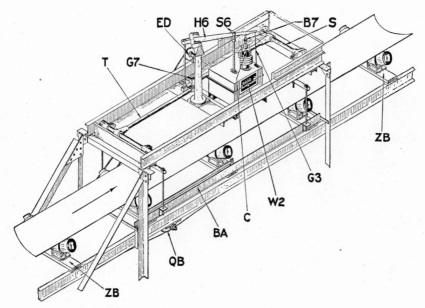

FIGURE 148.—The Weightometer with casing removed and three idlers suspended.
(Courtesy Merrick Scale Mfg. Co., Passaic, N. J.)

An example of another, simpler installation of batching equipment with automatic control, for solids, would be an installation of six standard, automatic, 100-pound scales (as shown in Figure 140) in the batching of graded rice. The objective is to proportion, on a percentage basis, different kinds of rice preliminary to bagging it. The scales overhang, one after the other, a common belt conveyor, which leads to the bagging machine. The entire operation is automatic.

Weightometer. The Merrick Weightometer combines the principles of a platform scale and a mechanical integrator; it continuously records the weight of material on a moving belt conveyor, which may be horizontal or inclined. A certain number of idlers under the belt, usually three, with the material it bears, is supported on a frame which is suspended by rods from a pair of scale levers T and S, which in turn are suspended by a link to the short end of the weigh-beam $H6$ (Figure 148). The weight of material on the suspended section is instantaneously counterbalanced by a cylindrical steel float, C, suspended from the long end of the beam in a pot of mercury. The upward movement of the float is proportional to the net weight of material. The pulley QB, in contact with the return conveyor belt, operates the integrator and totalizer. The totalized weight of material is shown by a master totalizing counter $W2$.

Weightometers differ is size, and are designated by the width of the belt they serve; they are priced from $2900 to $4000 depending on belt width (as of January 4, 1952). The price range covers belts from 10 inches up to 48 inches in width.

FIGURE 149.—A Schaffer Poidometer weighing and feeding alum at a filtration plant. The alum enters the hopper from the chute and overhead bin; the discharge is to the right, to a vertical chute. (Courtesy Schaffer Poidometer Co., Pittsburgh, Pa.)

The Feedoweight is a weighing machine which feeds and weighs by means of a special powered feed regulator. The prices are similar to those for the Weightometer.

Poidometer. The Poidometer is a feeder-weigher-conveyor which feeds material by weight in a steady, uniform stream and weighs and registers the total amount of material it handles. The weight is controlled by a scale beam operating a regulating gate in the hopper. The essential parts of the Poidometer are a short belt which bears on a weighing roller; a scale beam with adjustable weights; a yoke; a hopper with a regulating gate; driving pulley; and motor. The material enters the hopper by a chute from an overhead bin; the hopper feeds it through the space provided by the regulating gate to the short belt, which weighs it and delivers it to a chute or conveyor. An excess of material flowing on the conveyor belt depresses the weighing roller, which elevates the yoke and scale beam and lowers the regulating gate, thereby reducing the flow of material, while a deficiency of material on the belt permits the weighing roller to rise, the yoke and scale beam to decline; this raises the gate and increases the flow of material. The machine maintains an even and constant flow at the "weight per foot of belt" set by the scale beam weights. The Poidometer is built in seven sizes; the smallest size, with a 6-inch belt, has a capacity which may be varied from 1 to 100 pounds per minute. The largest, with a 48-inch belt, has a capacity of between 30 and 10,000 pounds per minute.

Automatic Liquid Scales. For the accurate bulk weighing of liquids, the Richardson Automatic Electric Mechanical Liquid Weigher,* an open type double tank liquid scale, may be used. It consists among other parts of two alternately operating weighing tanks, two automatically operated feed valves, two discharge valves, operating parts, two sets of scale levers, indicators, and motor and electrical control.

Each of the twin circular weighing tanks is carried on its own set of levers and each lever system terminates in a conventional graduated scale beam with hanger weights for the full capacity of the scale. The weighing tanks are filled and discharged respectively through inlet and outlet valves operated by a system of cams mounted on a horizontal shaft which is motor driven. Completion of a weighing in one tank starts the motor which starts the cam shaft, which in turn opens the discharge valve of the filled scale and opens the second inlet valve, allowing the second weighing to be made. While the second tank fills, the first one is in the process of emptying. At each cycle, each tank weighs automatically a preset quantity of liquid, and each such weighing is registered and totalized on an automatic counter. The unit capacity of one model Automatic Double Tank Scale is 3,000 pounds; the hourly capacity is 120 to 250 tons. In a cane sugar house, the Automatic Double Tank Juice scales would be positioned to weigh hot juice from the clarifiers, delivering to the evaporator supply tank.

PROPORTIONING OF LIQUIDS

The proportioning of liquids means, in the simplest case, the feed of a chosen volume of liquid A into such a volume of liquid B that a definite ratio persists. With the flow of B steady, all that is needed is a steady flow of A. But proportioning in the exact sense must provide for a variation in the added liquid A for every variation in the main flow, so that the ratio selected will be maintained no matter what the flow of B is. There must be a control of the volume of liquid A by the flow of liquid B. This is brought about in a variety of ways.

Generally, it will be a small volume of A which is fed into a large volume of B; thus, A may be a solution of an acid, an alkali, a boiler-water compound, or a sterilizing solution, injected into a larger volume of water. Both volumes A and B are in motion when they meet. There may be a

* Richardson Scale Company, 19 Rector Street, New York 6, N. Y.

greater number of liquids.   However, in addition, proportioning may be performed for more nearly equal quantities.

A definite ratio between two liquids may be maintained by mounting two plunger pumps, for example, on a single shaft; the stroke may be the same; the volumes will depend upon the bores of the cylinders.   If the bores are the same, the two liquid ends will deliver identical volumes, and these may be allowed to mix in the delivery line.   The bore of A may be made such that its area is one-tenth that of B; the ratio of A to B will then stand at 1:10.

Proportioning devices fall into two classes: those which are concerned with the addition or injection of very small amounts of a liquid into a second liquid, the added substance being present in quantities under 10,000 ppm (parts per million); and those which provide proportions of added substance well over 1 per cent, or well over 10,000 ppm.   The two classes

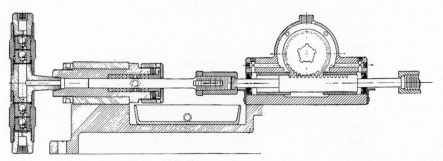

Figure 150.—Sketch showing the construction of "U" type proportioning pump.
(Courtesy Hills-McCanna Co., Chicago 18, Ill.)

do not compete with each other.   The same device may bridge the two classes.   It might be said that the H-O-H Feeder and the Pulsafeeder fall into the first class, and proportioning pumps and meter-controlled control valves into the second.

Proportioning Pumps.   A proportioning pump with single plunger, outside packed, and with outside check valves, is the Hills-McCanna* type "U" chemical proportioning pump, a unit of small capacity equipped with either mechanical, electric, or hydraulic drive.   A second type is type "K" which is a hydraulic drive unit of larger capacity.   Both types are precision instruments designed to meter the required volume accurately with manual, electrical, or pneumatic controls; both speed and stroke are adjustable, separately or in combination.

The construction of the "U" type pump is illustrated in Figure 150. The plunger is horizontal and the stroke adjustable from 0 to 1.25 inches. Plungers are $\frac{5}{16}$ inch, $\frac{7}{16}$ inch, $\frac{3}{4}$ inch and $1\frac{1}{4}$ inches in diameter,

* Hills-McCanna Co., 2449 W. Nelson Street, Chicago 18, Illinois.

with ¼- or ⅓-horsepower motor drive through gears at speeds of 30, 40, 50, and 70 strokes per minute.   At full stroke, capacities range from 1.60 to 24 gph per feed (1-, 2-, 3-, or 4-feed assemblies are available).   Pressures range from 125 to 5000 psi.   The stroke adjustment is by means of a stop nut on the plunger shaft, or if desired, the pump can be equipped with a micrometer screw adjustment that permits adjusting the stroke while the pump is in operation by means of a knurled knob.   The check valves are external.

The "K" type pumps utilize a hydraulic drive (which operates in oil) and are available in two sizes.   The "K-2" offers a maximum stroke of 2 inches and is powered by a ¾-horsepower gear-head motor, while the "K-3" has a maximum stroke of 3 inches and is powered by a 3-horsepower gear-head motor.   The plunger sizes range from ⅜ to 5 inches in diameter.   The speeds may be varied from 0 to 65 strokes per minute. The capacities per feed (one or two feeds) range from 0.5 to 1200 gph. Special liquid ends permit operation of the pump at pressures up to 35,000 psi.   Manual stroke adjustment is by means of a knurled knob; adjustment may be made while the pump is in operation.   Type "K" design is adaptable to pneumatic or electronic speed and stroke controls.

Pitot Tube as Proportioning Device.   The most ingenious installation for proportioning a small amount of one liquid into a main line liquid is that of a pitot tube as the source of the driving force or pumping effect, as embodied in the H-O-H Feeders.*   The pitot tube is of the divided type, the original form; one opening faces upstream and may be called the impact tube; the other opening faces downstream and may be called the discharge tube.   Placed in the center of the flowing stream of water in a pipe, a quantity of water proportional to the velocity head of the stream would be forced into the impact tube and an equivalent volume of chemical solution would be discharged from the downstream tube.   In the H-O-H Feeders, it is this quantity of water which is made to drive ahead of it an equivalent (or lesser) volume of a solution; the latter discharges into the main stream in the pipe.

The H-O-H "Model B" Feeder is the most popular model and is of simple design, as shown in Figure 151.   Two compartments, A the red oil compartment and B the reagent compartment, compose the main body. In operation, compartment A is filled with red oil and compartment B with the reagent.   As the fluid flows through the main line, a proportionate quantity rises in the impact tube into compartment A, where it underlies the red oil and displaces an equivalent amount of it through the needle valve control and an internal pipe in B to the base of the sight glass.   Red oil discharged here rises up through the reagent in the sight glass, one drop at a time.   This arrangement provides sight indication of the rate of feed

* D. W. Haering & Co., Inc., P. O. Box 6037, San Antonio, Texas.

by drops and makes it possible for the operator to determine at a glance whether the Feeder is functioning properly. After the oil rises in the gauge glass, it enters compartment *B* and overlies the reagent, displacing an equivalent amount of reagent out through the discharge tube into the main stream flow. The oil has been aptly called the "fluid piston."

The position of the indicator needle valve on the oil line from compartment *A* insures a permanent setting. Nothing but oil enters this valve and consequently it cannot corrode or become clogged.

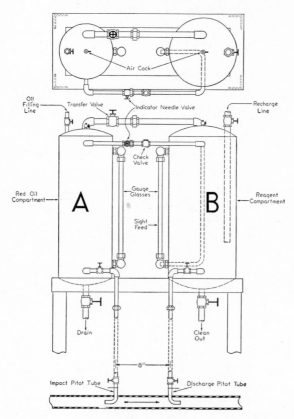

FIGURE 151.—Line drawing showing the essential parts of the H-O-H Feeder, with the divided pitot tube in the pipeline providing the motive force. *A*, the oil compartment; *B*, solution compartment; other parts and functions are indicated. The red oil in *A* is called the fluid piston. Reg. U. S. Pat. Off. (Courtesy D. W. Haering and Co., San Antonio, Texas.)

Compartment *B* is 25 per cent larger than compartment *A* in order to prevent any possibility of oil being discharged into the main fluid line. If all the oil is transferred to compartment *B* and the machine is left in operation without recharging, fluid from the main line will flow through the needle valve control and being heavier than oil will stay on the bottom of compartment *B*, diluting the reagent until eventually the machine will merely be by-passing the main fluid. In one test, an H-O-H "Model B" Feeder was left in this position for six months without any loss of red oil.

When the gauge glass on compartment *A* is filled with the main fluid, the unit should be recharged. The drain on compartment A is opened and reagent is allowed to flow into compartment B. A transfer line between the tops of the two compartments is provided for the recharging operation and when the transfer valve is opened the oil flows back into compartment A. When the gauge glass on compartment A is filled with oil, the valves are closed and the machine returned to operation. The needle valve control is not touched during this operation and does not need to be reset. Recharging time is less than five minutes and a size unit usually is employed which does not require recharging more often than once a day and sometimes once a week.

The divided pitot tube is installed on the main pipeline with the impact and discharge tubes at 8-inch centers and the tube openings in the center of main-line flow. The velocity of the main-line fluid across the pitot tubes should be at least 1.5 feet per second in order to overcome frictional losses through the Feeder and to provide sensitive operation. If sufficient velocity is not present, the pipe should be reduced in diameter at this point, or an orifice may be installed between the pitot tubes. With slight modification in installation the H-O-H "Model B" Feeder may be used to introduce a liquid reagent into saturated steam.

It should be noted that as the velocity of the main liquid and therefore the impact pressure increases, the rate of feed increases proportionately; conversely, the rate of feed is decreased with a decrease in main-line flow. The Feeder is therefore an accurate proportioning device particularly suitable where fluctuating flow rates are encountered. The dimension of the pitot tube sets the maximum volume of main-line fluid which may be displaced, and of that, the needle valve determines the fraction which will actually be displaced.

The H-O-H "Model B" Feeder is made in a number of sizes; compartment B has a capacity of 5 gallons, or it may be chosen in 10-, 20-, 30- and 50-gallon sizes. Standard units are designed for operation at pressures less than 150 pounds per square inch gauge, but units may also be obtained which are constructed under A.S.M.E. codes for higher pressures. The H-O-H "Model B" Feeders in the 5-, 10-, 20-, 30- and 50-gallon sizes for operation at less than 150 pounds pressure are available at $165, $245, $365, $490, and $595 respectively, F.O.B. San Antonio, Texas, or Chicago, Illinois, net. Prices on units designed for higher pressure and constructed under A.S.M.E. codes are available from the manufacturer upon request. All prices are as of January 1952.

The H-O-H Feeders may also be used as samplers. The main-line fluid which displaces the red oil in compartment A is a composite sample of the material which has flowed through the main line since the first drop of red oil was displaced into compartment B. A portion of it may be drawn off at any time from the bottom drain valve of the A tank.

Numerous variations of the H-O-H "Model B" Feeders are available for special operations and applications, and all employ the simple principle of the "Haering Fluid Piston" and divided pitot tube.   The H-O-H "Model E" Feeder is a popular model with rubber-lined tanks and fittings designed for proportioning corrosive liquids such as hypochlorite solutions.

Pulsafeeder.   The Lapp Pulsafeeder* is a combination piston-diaphragm proportioning pump; it may also be described as a variable output metering diaphragm pump.   A piston reciprocates within an accurately sized cylinder, pushing out and pulling in an accurate volume of oil (or other approved liquid); the oil body in turn moves the diaphragm correspondingly.   On its other side, the diaphragm working in the

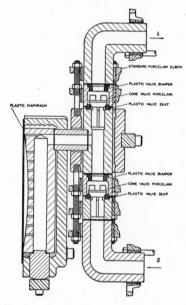

FIGURE 152.—Design detail for Lapp chemical porcelain pumping head for the Pulsafeeder. The liquid is discharged at *1*, as the diaphragm flexes inward; it is sucked in at *2* as the diaphragm flexes outward. The hydraulic piston drive in a closed cylinder, the handwheel for adjustment of stroke, and the vacuum and pressure compensating valves are not shown; they extend to the left of the diaphragm. (Lapp Insulator Co., Le Roy, N. Y.)

chemical end of the pump, in conjunction with the check valve cylinder, alternately draws in a measured volume of liquid (or reagent solution) from the supply tank, and feeds it through the discharge check valve into the line to the reactor (or other designated vessel).   The chemical reaches only the head plate cavity on the one side of the diaphragm, and the check valve cylinder; the rest of the pump, piston, cylinder, gears, eccentric, all work submerged in oil, and require no protection from the action of the chemical.   The volume displaced is adjustable, even during operation, by varying the length of the stroke of the piston.   In the standard Lapp Pulsafeeder, the adjustment is done manually; in the Auto-Pneumatic Pulsafeeder, it is done automatically.

An air cylinder mounted on the Pulsafeeder responds to instrument air

* Lapp Insulator Company, Inc., Le Roy, N. Y.

pressure changes and establishes a concurrent pumping rate, thus producing the Auto-Pneumatic Pulsafeeder. Its air cylinder takes air pressure from the control instruments and translates it into pump output.

In either model, an electric motor drives the piston through a worm gear reduction. The diaphragm is made from any one of a wide variety of materials: any type of rubber or plastics, stainless steels, or other metal alloys. There is no stuffing box. The chemical being pumped is isolated by the diaphragm from the working oil or other hydraulic liquid. A built-in pressure relief valve prevents the building up of dangerous pressures; it handles only oil (not the chemical).

The Pulsafeeder is available in two models, and in each of these, in four sizes. Model CPS is a single-head pump and model CPD is a duplex-head pump. The four CPS sizes have capacities of 11, 40, 100, and 330 gallons per hour at discharge pressures of 250, 155, 110, and 100 psi, both respectively. The CPD pumps have capacities twice as great, at the same pressures. The motor rating is $\frac{1}{3}$, $\frac{1}{2}$, 1, and 2 horsepower, respectively. In the duplex models the pistons are opposed 180°, so that the horsepower drive required is the same as for the single-head models.

Proportioning by Control Valves Governed by Meters. There are available proportioning devices which consist of two or more volumetric meters such as the Bowser Xacto 5-cylinder meter, combined with one or several proportioning mechanisms, control valves, and manifold. One meter measures the greater flow, and the other the lesser flow. Let us assume the ratio to be 9 to 1. The first meter carries the proportioning mechanism, which controls the rotation of a threaded horizontal shaft extending half the distance to the second meter, and bearing the control nut. The rotation of the threaded shaft is just equal to the speed at which the slower meter should run, if it is delivering the desired volume. The second meter has a square shaft running half way toward meter 1, and far enough to fit into the square hole on the control nut. The position of the control nut governs the control valve in the delivery line from meter 2. If the second meter runs too fast, the square shaft turns the control nut and alters its location, which causes the lever controlling the control valve to shift, and reduce the free opening of the valve. If the second meter runs at the right speed, the position of the control nut is unchanged, and the control valve undisturbed. If the second meter runs too slowly, the square shaft turns the nut the opposite way, and the control valve opens wider. The liquid passed by the second meter enters the pipeline carrying the discharge from meter 1, and mixes with it as it travels along. Every pound of the first liquid receives the proper proportion of the second liquid. In the example chosen in which the ratio is 9:1, if the second liquid is 10 per cent caustic soda, the resulting mixed solution will then be 1 per cent caustic soda.

The pressure of the second liquid must be greater than that of the first. In the same way as outlined for two liquids, more liquids may be added in definite ratios; the second meter, provided with a proportioning mechanism, will, with the aid of the third meter, control the valve regulating the flow of the third liquid. Similarly, there may be a fourth and a fifth liquid, all entering the main flow at a constant relative rate, in the proper proportions.

The proportioning mechanism installed on a given meter may be set so that the next succeeding meter and control valve will deliver any proportion, from ½ to 100 per cent in steps of ½ per cent, of the amount discharged by the meter on which it is mounted.

For most thin liquids, mixing in the manifold is sufficient to insure complete blending, but for heavy viscous oils, an additional mixing in a small special mixer is recommended.

If for any reason the flow through the second meter should stop, the knockout bar would come into action and permit the spring-actuated master control valve in the main delivery line to close, so that no unmixed liquid could be delivered. In installations in which it is desired to measure and mix definite quantities and then stop, a master meter is used, equipped with a predetermining adapter and a totalizing counter. When the specified quantity has been measured, mixed, and delivered to a tank or to containers, the master meter stops the flow.

Patents

Automatic weighing devices and recording of successive quantities of materials, U. S. Patent 2,132,237; weighing apparatus, for withdrawing a batch or series of batches of pulverized materials, automatic discharge and remote control, 1,911,235; batcher adapted for making concrete, 2,066,012; weighing and filling machine, with auger-like rotating piece, 1,904,652; the original Hoepner patent, for automatic weighing machine, June 4, 1907, 855,578.

Numerical Example

Problem. A hot-water system is to be treated with Sulpho Glucosate for the removal of oxygen. The laboratory reports that 1 pint of Sulpho Glucosate per 3000 gallons of hot water will be required. An H-O-H Feeder, such as described and illustrated in the text, is to be installed at a point in the system where a 2-inch pipe carries the flow. A constant flow of 16.6 gallons per minute travels through the system. The velocity head required to operate the H-O-H Feeder selected equals 0.0268 foot of water. Will the flowing water supply a sufficient head by means of the pitot tubes?

Solution. 16.6 gallons of water per minute in a 2-inch line equals 0.0368 cubic foot per second, equivalent to a velocity of 1,5794 feet per second.

$$\frac{v^2}{2g} = 0.0268; \quad g = 32.174 \text{ ft/sec}^2; \text{ solving for } v \text{ gives } v = 1.306 \text{ ft per sec.}$$

The velocity of the water, 1.5794 feet per second, will be ample since only 1.306 feet per second are required.

Remarks. Flows are seldom constant for a period of 5 days. H-O-H Feeders operate in direct response to the variable flow conditions and not in accordance with a definite lapse of time. It is assumed in this example that the flow of hot water will be constant for the 5-day period. The needle valve is set to proportion exactly 1 pint of Sulpho Glucosate per 3000 gallons of hot water. Therefore, in the period of 5 days, 40 × 3000 gallons or 120,000 gallons will be treated, inasmuch as the Model "B" Feeder selected has a capacity of 5 gallons, or 40 pints of reagent. After that period, the tank is refilled. (*Taken from the H-O-H booklet*).

Reading References

"The automatic proportioning and blending of liquid chemicals in a reclaimed rubber plant," by Henry F. Palmer and James M. Hines, *Trans. Am. Inst. Chem. Eng.*, **36**, 233 (1940).

"Weighing in the chemical industries," by W. A. Benton, *Chemistry and Industry* (*London*), **46**, 741 and 764 (1927).

"Chemicals automatically packed in paper bags," by R. W. Lahey, *Chem. Met. Eng.*, **43**, 318 (1936).

"Automatic mixing and proportioning of gases and liquids," by H. J. Velten, *Ind. Eng. Chem.*, **29**, 1214 (1937).

"Modern packaging," by Carl E. Schaefer, New York, Breskin Publishing Co., (June, 1940).

"Industrial measurements and weighing," by Everett P. Partridge, *Ind. Eng. Chem.*, **21**, 740 (1929).

"An automatic chemical doser," *Industrial Chemist*, (*London*), **21**, 61 (1945).

"Industrial weighing," by Douglas M. Considine, New York, Reinhold Publishing Corporation, 1948.

Some of the names of our prosaic devices suggest distant places. One device got its name from an exclamation of a visitor to whom a new fan working with warm air was being demonstrated. As he stood in the path of the discharge and felt the warm wind, he exclaimed: "Why, that is just like the sirocco" (the wind which blows warm over the Sahara and the central Mediterranean). The fan was so christened forthwith.

8. EQUIPMENT FOR THE PROPULSION OF GASES*

Gases are propelled by means of fans, blowers, and compressors. The terms *fan* and *blower* are interchangeable, but *blower* is not equivalent to *exhauster*. A fan may function either as a blower or as an exhauster. As a blower, it draws its air, let us say, from the room and generally serves it into ducts and pipes; as an exhauster it draws air through a duct or pipe, and delivers it to the free air outside. The same fan serves in either installation; but its housing may differ somewhat. The great majority of fans work against low pressures, such as fractions of an inch of water, or a few inches of water. It must be added, however, that high-speed fans operate also under higher pressures, such as 80 inches of water. Fans are divided into centrifugal fans, and fans with axial flow; to the latter belong disc and propeller fans, to the former, fans with impellers having blades set radially, and either straight or curved.

The turbo-blower may be considered as distinct from the fan, for it depends upon close clearances between impeller and casing, whereas the fan has no close clearances, but relies for its effectiveness upon the shape and curvature of its blades. The high-velocity head developed in the turbo-blower is transformed into pressure head in the diffusers. The air or gas delivered by the fan has no considerable velocity head. Turbo-blowers in the several different constructions develop pressures of between 1 and 6.5 psi.

Compressors begin where the turbo-blower leaves off; thus a medium compressor delivers air under a pressure of 6, 8, or 10 pounds and as high as 30 pounds, overlapping the range of the multi-stage turbo-blower. The normal compressor range is all the way from 1 to 125 pounds pressure and higher; such pressures are developed by rotary compressors of various designs, and by the reciprocating compressor. The reciprocating machines may be single-stage or multi-stage; in the latter, pressures as high as 5000 psi are obtained. In these machines, the air or gas is cooled by means of intercoolers and aftercoolers. Much of the success of a particular make

* The section on fans in this edition, as in the earlier one, has been reviewed by Mr. Albert E. Criqui, Engineer, Buffalo Forge Company, Buffalo 5, N. Y.

of compressor may often be traced to the ample heat transfer wall provided in its construction.

It is very difficult to speak definitely of the meaning of the terms *blower* and *compressor;* some manufacturers call a machine which develops 7 and 8 pounds pressure a blower, while others designate a machine developing pressures measured in ounces of water as a compressor. In the discussion which follows, considerable overlapping must be expected. Even fans are termed "compressors" when they operate at sufficiently high speeds to compress the air materially, and for the purposes of testing and rating compressors the ASME code includes in the compressor class all devices producing over one pound pressure rise.

Fan Laws. A few fundamental fan laws may prove of interest.

The horsepower required to drive a fan may be calculated from the following expression:

$$\text{Horsepower} = \frac{0.000157 \times \text{cfm} \times \text{static pressure}}{\text{static efficiency}}$$
$$= \frac{0.000157 \times \text{cfm} \times \text{total pressure}}{\text{total efficiency}}$$

where cfm is the volume of air in cubic feet per minute, and static pressure and total pressure are in inches of water. The efficiencies are expressed as decimals.

For example, the horsepower is sought for the following performance: 7000 cfm, 3-inch static pressure, 66 per cent static efficiency. Then:

$$\text{Horsepower} = \frac{0.000157 \times 7000 \times 3}{0.66} = 5.0$$

Total pressure equals static pressure plus velocity pressure.

The maximum static efficiencies usually range from 60 to 80 per cent, and the maximum total efficiencies from 65 to 85 per cent.

Each cubic foot of air per minute which moves against a total pressure of 1 inch of water, equivalent to 0.577 ounce per square inch, or 5.19 pounds per square foot, represents the expenditure of energy at the rate of 5.19 foot-pounds per minute. Hence the theoretical power required to maintain this flow is $5.19 \div 33,000 = 0.000157$ horsepower.

"Point of rating" of a fan refers to the position on the fan performance curve where the fan operates for any given system. When a fan operates on a fixed system, it is said to operate at a fixed point of rating.

When at a fixed point of rating, the following fan laws apply:

Cfm varies as the fan speed (rpm);
Static pressure varies as the square of the fan speed;
Horsepower varies as the cube of the fan speed.

For example, consider a ventilating system of 7000 cfm rating, 3-inch static pressure, 800 rpm, and 5 horsepower. In order to raise the capacity of that system to 14,000 cfm, there would be required a 12-inch static pressure, 1600 rpm, and 40 horsepower.

TABLE 39. CLASSIFICATION OF FANS

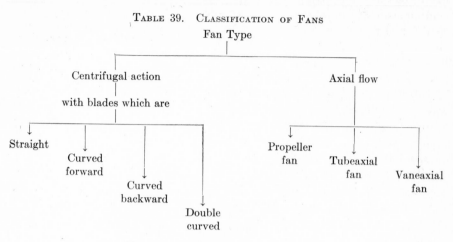

FANS WITH CENTRIFUGAL ACTION

Straight-blade Fans. The straight-blade, or mill-type fan, usually has a small number of blades (5 to 8) on the shaft; in some designs, however, the number may be as high as 16. The blades are straight steel plate of the shape and mounting indicated in Figure 153. The rotor turns in a

FIGURE 153.—A straight-blade fan wheel, such as is used on the smaller fans. It turns in a scroll. The feed is in the center; the discharge is at the tip of the blades.

scroll, a housing with a collecting duct of gradually increasing size. The straight-blade fan is a centrifugal fan; the air enters at the center and is thrown out at the tip of the blade. It is generally slow speed, such as 400 to 600 rpm, and is made in small as well as large sizes, as large as 100 inches wheel diameter. There are straight-blade fans which are operated at speeds as high as 4000 and 5000 rpm.

The straight-blade or radial-blade fan may be a blower or an exhauster. Of special interest are the rubber-lined steel plate exhausters for handling corrosive fumes without damage to the fan. They are especially useful in pulling contaminated air from a workroom. The Buffalo rubber-lined exhausters are lined with "Vulcalock" (see Chapter 5), a superior rubber coating which lasts many years. In addition to rubber-lined fans, those made of corrosion-resisting metal, such as stainless steel, serve well for the removal of corrosive vapors; furthermore, the latter can be run at higher speeds.

Curved-blade Fans. The curvature in the curved-blade fans may be of two kinds. In one type the tip of the blade is curved forward to the direction of rotation; in the other type, the same edge is curved backward. In the single-width fan, there may be 16 blades, carried between the flange and the back plate; in the double-width wheel, the back plate becomes the center plate for the double wheel. The blades on the inlet side are frequently narrower than on the center plate side. One manufacturer uses stationary curved vanes over the inlet.

In Conoidal fans, the blades are curved two ways, forward on the inlet side, and backward at the tip; the tip of the blade is the edge which is last

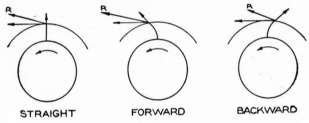

STRAIGHT   FORWARD   BACKWARD

FIGURE 154.—The three types of fan blades.

in contact with the air; it is the edge on the discharge side. The special shape and the curvature of the blades result in a fan which is nonoverloading. A large Conoidal fan is shown in Figure 155; it was installed in the Lincoln Tunnel ventilating building on the New Jersey side of the Hudson in 1937. As the reader views the wheel, fixing in mind the blades at the midpoint and nearest to him, the wheel turns so that these blades rise; the outlet for the air is downward through the floor, in the rear. The stationary inlet vanes are well shown. The capacity is 200,000 cfm with a pressure of 4 inches of water, and the speed is 450 rpm.

Multi-blade Fans. Among the multi-blade fans a well-known make is the Sirocco, a product of The American Blower Corporation. It is a centrifugal type fan with a wheel constructed of a multiple number of narrow curved blades arranged in essentially a drum form. The blades are mounted in the wheel with the curvature forward in the direction of rotation, and pitched so that the inside edge is nearly radial. The outside edge of the blades is inclined forward at the proper angle to give maximum velocity to the air leaving the blade tips.

The Sirocco wheel in the single width has 64 blades which are die-formed and machine-riveted to the back plate and rim. For each size there is a double width as well as a single width; the double-width wheel may be considered as consisting of two wheels with their back plates made into one, now the center plate. The scroll housings are made of

FIGURE 155.—One of the fresh air fans being set in position in the New Jersey ventilation building for the midtown Hudson tunnel, for the Port of New York Authority. (Courtesy Buffalo Forge Co., Buffalo, N. Y.)

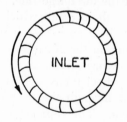

FIGURE 156.—The direction of rotation of the Sirocco multiblade fan wheel.

welded, bolted, and riveted steel in the larger sizes, of steel or cast iron in the very small sizes.

The Sirocco fan is made in 28 standard sizes—8 small ones, 7 medium, and 13 large sizes. Of the latter group, the smallest one is No. 397, single-inlet, single-width, with a wheel diameter of 39¾ inches, and capacities varying with the speed of rotation and static pressure, from 7440 cfm, 129 rpm, and static pressure of ¼ inch, to 31,620 cfm, 622 rpm, and 6 inches static pressure. The largest one is No. 1320, double-inlet, double-width, with a wheel diameter of 132 inches, which delivers 146,400 cfm, 39 rpm, against ¼ inch static pressure, and 622,200 cfm, 189 rpm, against 6 inches static pressure.* At the static pressure of 1¼ inches, to take an example from the pressures normally encountered, the same fan, No. 1320 double-

FIGURE 157.—A view of the single-inlet Sirocco fan. The inlet is inside the wheel; the outlet is at the upper left of the casing. (Courtesy American Blower Corp., Detroit 32, Mich.)

FIGURE 158.—A Duriron exhaust fan, with 14-inch inlet, 12-inch outlet, and a capacity from 200 to 3200 cfm at various speeds and pressures. (Courtesy The Duriron Co., Dayton, Ohio.)

inlet, double-width, would need to turn at the rate of only 83 rpm to deliver a volume of 256,200 cfm.

An exhaust fan with curved blades which is of special design, built of "Duriron," and well suited for exhausting corrosive fumes, is shown in Figure 158.

* Elaborate tables are given by the American Blower Corporation, Detroit, Mich.

FANS WITH AXIAL FLOW

Recently the National Association of Fan Manufacturers has defined the different classes of axial flow fans. As shown in the table of classification (p. 202), there are three classes: propeller fans, tubeaxial fans, and vaneaxial fans.

The *propeller fan* consists of a propeller or disc wheel within a mounting ring or plate. The *"disc fan"* is thus one form of the propeller fan. It has blades which are substantially flat, and set at a slight angle to the plane of rotation; the wheel itself is little more than a disc, and is mounted, without housing, in a steel ring on a knee-type bearing. The fan is used for large capacities against moderate or low pressures; it is usually set directly into the wall. The disc fan wheels are obtainable in sizes from 12 to 144 inches in diameter.

FIGURE 159.—A disc fan, member of the propeller fan family.

The propeller fan wheel usually has its blades mounted on a spider-type hub, or fastened directly to the small hub. The wheel may have 2, 3, or more curved blades, also motor and shaft, a fan ring for mounting, and the necessary carrying arms. It is sometimes referred to as the self-contained electric propeller unit; it serves for the ventilating of engine rooms, boiler rooms, foundries, and the like.

Propeller fan sizes usually range from 12 to 48 inches in diameter, with capacities up to 40,000 cfm, working against pressures ranging from 0 to ½ inch S.P. (static pressure).   An example of a larger size is the Foster Wheeler Axial Flow fan, developed for the propulsion of very large volumes of air at low pressures, with high efficiency.   It consists of an impeller made of "Dowmetal," connected through step-down gears to a motor, the whole carried by a pedestal; it may be mounted in the side wall at the base of a cooling tower, or in the top of a tower where it functions as an exhauster.   An example of the former would be a forced-draft fan with an 11-foot diameter impeller, connected to a 15-hp motor, with an impeller speed of 345 rpm, and a capacity of 106,000 cfm.   An example of the second kind is a recent installation with five cooling towers each

FIGURE 160.—A tubeaxial fan, "Buffalo" type B.   The motor is foot mounted.   Note the absence of stationary directional vanes.

with a fan wheel 14 feet 6 inches in diameter, operating at speeds varying from 104 to 312 rpm; the impeller in this last instance turns in a horizontal plane.

The total head developed at an air velocity of 1200 feet per minute, a typical figure, is between 0.41 and 0.65 inch of water (not mercury). When assembled, the blades are set with their flat side at an angle to the plane of revolution.   There may be either 4 or 8 blades.   An 8-blade impeller 8 feet in diameter, of "Dowmetal," weighs about 165 pounds, whereas the older style multi-blade fan for the same work would weigh over 1000 pounds.

The fan has a low ratio of velocity head to total head; the total efficiency is 61 to 65 per cent, which is greater than that of fans with a higher ratio of velocity head to total head.

Tubeaxial Fan.   The tubeaxial fan is the second type of axial flow fan. It consists of an axial flow type wheel within a cylinder.   The driving motor may be inside the fan, in the case of a direct-driven unit, or it may be V-belt-driven, with the driving motor mounted outside, often fastened directly to the fan housing.   The tubeaxial fan has no stationary guide vanes.   It is selected when more pressure is needed than can be efficiently met by ordinary propeller fans.   The range of pressures is usually from ¼ to 1 inch of water.   Capacities may range up to 60,000 cfm for sizes up to 54 inches in diameter.   The cylinder housing is flanged and drilled for convenient attachment to ductwork.

FIGURE 161.—Inlet end of "Buffalo" type B Vaneaxial Fan, arranged for belt drive. The cast airfoil aluminum wheel provides nonsparking construction.   (Courtesy Buffalo Forge Co., Buffalo, N. Y.)

Vaneaxial Fan.   The vaneaxial fan consists of an axial flow wheel within a cylinder, combined with a set of stationary directional vanes. The vanes may be located either before or after the wheel.   The development of this improved axial flow fan resulted from a close study which indicated that the air leaves a rotating axial wheel blade at an angle to a true axial direction.   A correcting factor must be applied to neutralize the spiral motion which the air has acquired.   The guide vanes placed after the wheel recover the spiral component of the air motion and thus increase the available pressure and the efficiency of the fan.   The vane-axial fan is often used for work where pressures range from ½ to 3 inches.

The capacity and efficiency factors are high.   A large hub is provided which prevents the re-entry losses common to the ordinary propeller fan.

The unit is available for V-belt or for direct drive, and for either vertically down, vertically up, or horizontal discharge. It may be used as a blowing fan, in which case a generous bell inlet is furnished; or it may serve as an exhausting unit, when it is provided with an inlet cone flanged for connection to existing duct work.

The "Buffalo" type B axial flow fan, both vaneaxial and tubeaxial, is made in 10 sizes, from 15 to 54 inches in diameter, and each size may be operated at any speed selected with the aid of available tables, to provide the required capacity.

The axial flow fan is coming more and more into general use for many applications which formerly were covered only by the centrifugal type fan. The development just described has brought about axial flows with efficiencies as high as those of centrifugal fans.

The full type axial flow fan, that is, the vaneaxial, is now capable of producing pressures much higher than was thought possible a few years ago, so that in pressure range it also compares favorably with the moderate pressure centrifugal fan.

Where space is restricted, the axial flow fan has a distinct advantage. Since the flow-through is axial, the fan may be inserted in any convenient location in a straight duct system. The centrifugal fan, which has its inlet at right angles to its outlet, requires more bulky connections if both inlet and outlet are connected to ducts.

The axial flow type fan should be used with caution for exhausting corrosive fumes. The drive is inside the fan, through which the fumes pass, so that the fan must be specially constructed so as to protect the drive from contact with the fumes.

TURBO-BLOWERS, MEDIUM COMPRESSORS, COMPRESSORS

The devices, other than fans, for propelling gases are tabulated in Table 40.

Turbo-blowers. The single-stage turbo-blower is a high-speed centrifugal machine of remarkably small size for its capacity. The impeller wheel is the rotating element, and is usually of the radial-bladed type; it may be a one-piece cast-aluminum alloy. It revolves in a cast-iron or welded steel casing having the shape of a volute, not unlike that of a centrifugal pump with volute; the clearances are close. For pressure from 1 to 3.75 pound gauge, a turbo-blower would be run at 3500 to 3600 rpm, and would be direct-connected to a 60-cycle motor, where such current is available.

The overhung turbo-blower is the most widely used type of single-stage blower operating at speeds of 3500 to 3600 rpm. The impeller mounted in the overhung unit is shown in Figure 162. Examples: an overhung turbo-blower turning at the rate of 3550 rpm driven by a 250-hp

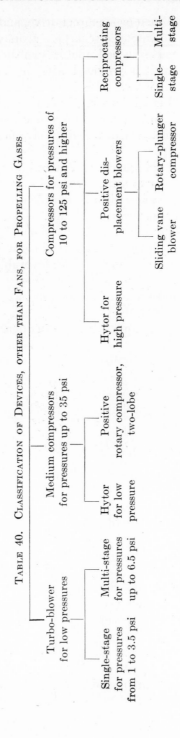

TABLE 40.   CLASSIFICATION OF DEVICES, OTHER THAN FANS, FOR PROPELLING GASES

FIGURE 162.—Single-stage turbo-Blower, "overhung" type, with casing removed, showing method of supporting the overhung impeller on the extended motor shaft. (Courtesy Allis-Chalmers Mfg. Co., Milwaukee 1, Wis.)

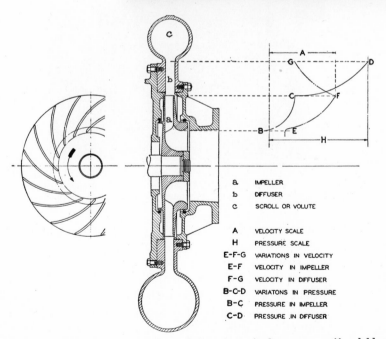

a	IMPELLER
b	DIFFUSER
c	SCROLL OR VOLUTE
A	VELOCITY SCALE
H	PRESSURE SCALE
E-F-G	VARIATIONS IN VELOCITY
E-F	VELOCITY IN IMPELLER
F-G	VELOCITY IN DIFFUSER
B-C-D	VARIATONS IN PRESSURE
B-C	PRESSURE IN IMPELLER
C-D	PRESSURE IN DIFFUSER

FIGURE 163.—Pressure and velocity relations in a single-stage centrifugal blower, a turbo blower, with backward-bladed impeller. In the cross section of the blower, the suction inlet is at the right; the gas passes out through the diffusers and the volute.

motor, delivers 11,000 cfm at 3.5 pounds pressure; another blower with a speed of 3550 rpm, driven by a 100-hp motor, has a capacity of 8600 cfm at 2.0 pounds pressure. The figures for two others are: 2300 cfm delivering air under 1 pound pressure; 18,000 cfm at 3.5 pounds pressure, with speed of 3550 rpm, driven by a 350-hp motor.

For larger capacities, double-inlet blowers with double impeller wheels mounted on a shaft supported between two bearings are provided. Thus a double-inlet blower with capacity of 32,000 cfm at 2 pounds gauge pres-

Figure 164.—An installation view of a turbo-blower, a steam turbine driven pedestal-type blower with a capacity of 10,000 cfm at 5-pound gauge pressure. The impeller turns at the rate of 4700 rpm. (Courtesy Allis-Chalmers Mfg. Co., Milwaukee, Wis.)

sure operating at 3550 rpm direct from a 60-cycle motor would be a typical example.

For pressures above 3.75 but below 6.25 pounds, the single-stage turbo-blower is suitable if driven by a steam turbine, or by a motor and gear. An example would be a pedestal-type turbo-blower driven by a noncondensing, single-stage impulse turbine; it is rated at 10,000 cfm at 5 pounds pressure, running at 4700 rpm (275 hp).

For higher pressures the multi-stage turbo-blower, or turbo-compressor as it is aptly called by many engineers, is well developed, and provides pressures of 10 pounds, for example, to 30 pounds or more. The impeller is enclosed or shrouded (see Chapter 6) and may have three, four, five or more stages. Example: a blast-furnace turbo-blower rated at 40,000 cfm at 30 pounds pressure, driven by a 4600-hp condensing steam turbine turning at the rate of 3630 rpm (Allis-Chalmers).

The following prices are for single-stage turbo-blowers (Allis-Chalmers) exclusively, and are quoted for the convenience in making preliminary estimates.

TABLE 41. RATINGS AND OTHER DATA ON SINGLE-STAGE TURBO-BLOWERS
(ALLIS-CHALMERS)

Rating (cfm)	Discharge pressure (lb)	Motor (hp)	Speed (rpm)	Price*
9,200	1.0	60	3550	$ 4,225
11,000	1.5	100	3550	6,275
12,800	2	150	3550	7,100
11,750	3	200	3550	10,000
24,500	2.5	350	3550	14,600

* Prices as of January 1952, and subject to change without notice.

Multi-stage turbo-blowers which have open impellers instead of the more generally adopted shrouded impellers are also built because they permit higher operating speeds; the shrouded impellers remain the more efficient (Roots-Connersville).

Nash Compressors. Nash compressors are of two types: the low-pressure, usually developing pressures of 8 and 10 pounds, with an upper limit of 35 psi; and the high-pressure, with a normal limit of 75 psi.

The principle of operation will be presented with respect to the low-pressure compressor. The main parts are shown in Figure 166, and consist of the body, the rotor, and the head. The body and the head each bear a cone projecting inward; each cone has two inlet ports and two outlet ports. The compressor is a centrifugal displacement type of pump with an elliptical casing partly filled with liquid, in which the round, multi-blade rotor revolves freely. The curved rotor blades project radially from the hub and form, with the side shrouds, a series of buckets. The rotor revolves at a speed high enough to throw the liquid out from center by centrifugal force, so that there results a solid ring of liquid revolving in the casing at the same speed as the rotor, but hugging the walls of the elliptical casing. This action forces the liquid to enter and recede from the buckets in the rotor at high velocity (see Figure 165). The ports are so placed in the two cones shown in the figure that the expanding buckets can draw air (or gas) from the inlet port, while the buckets in which the gas space is diminishing can deliver the compressed gas to the outlet port. Such a drawing-in of gas, and discharge an instant later, takes place twice in one revolution. Referring again to Figure 165, a complete cycle of operation in a given bucket would be as follows: At A, the bucket is full of liquid (3); as the rotor revolves, the liquid follows the casing, withdrawing from the rotor, so that air or gas is pulled in through the inlet port. At (4), the liquid has been thrown almost entirely from the chamber; the gas space is at a maximum. As the rotation continues, the converging wall (5) of the casing forces the liquid back into the bucket, diminishing the gas space, compressing the gas and delivering it to the discharge port. The bucket is now again filled with liquid (6), and is ready to repeat the cycle. The cycle is repeated during the second half of the revolution.

The rotor shown in Figure 166 is of the divided type, and this is the standard construction except for the smallest sizes. The two parts func-

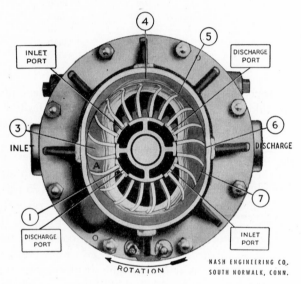

FIGURE 165.—Principle of operation of the Nash Hytor compressor.

tion independently, each one having ports in the cone projecting into it. The ports in the head cone unite with those in the body cone to form the single inlet and outlet, respectively, of the pump; the action is therefore parallel, and the compressor remains a single-stage compressor.

The amount of liquid in the compressor adjusts itself if an excess is provided. Sealing liquid is added to the pump constantly, to take up the heat of compression; a corresponding amount is discharged from the pump with the air, and is removed from the air by a simple baffle separator, before delivery to the conduits.

Although normally used for low pressures, the same compressor may be made to develop a pressure as high as 75 or 80 psi, but it would require about twice the horsepower called for by a reciprocating compressor.

Nevertheless, for certain purposes indicated later, it may be the proper procedure. The capacity at low pressures is as high as 3000 cubic feet per minute; it decreases as the pressure rises, so that the same machine finally furnishes 500 cubic feet per minute at 75 psi.

TABLE 42. CAPACITY, PRESSURE, AND HORSEPOWER REQUIRED BY NASH HYTOR COMPRESSORS; LOW-PRESSURE TYPE, CONICAL (SELECTED ITEMS FROM "K" SERIES)*

Pump Size and Speed	Pressure (psi)	Capacity (cu ft per min)	Motor (hp)	Speed (rpm)
	5	340	15	
K-4	10	339	20	870
	15	310	25	
	5	1020	40	
K-6	10	990	60	570
	15	870	75	
	20	650	100	
	5	2080	75	
K-8	10	1980	125	306
	15	1530	150	

* Data supplied by Nash Engineering Co., South Norwalk, Conn.

The Nash high-pressure compressor has a single undivided wheel, of smaller width, running at a higher speed. The capacity is less; for the largest size it is 410 cubic feet per minute, at 80 psi, with a rotation of 1750 rpm. A few selected items will give additional information.

TABLE 43. CAPACITY, HEAD, AND POWER REQUIRED BY NASH HYTOR COMPRESSORS; HIGH-PRESSURE TYPE; SINGLE-STAGE (SELECTED ITEMS)*

Compressor (size)	Pressure (psi)	Capacity (cu ft per min)	Motor (hp)	Speed (rpm)
621		26	7½	3500
1251	35	120	40	1750
1256		440	100	1750
621		23	10	3500
1251	80	110	50	1750
1256		410	150	1750

* Data supplied by Nash Engineering Co., South Norwalk, Conn.

In volume-pressure performance, the Nash compressor fits between the turbo-blower, which delivers a large volume of air (or gas) at low pressure, and the reciprocating compressor, which furnishes a small volume at an exceedingly high pressure. Its important function, however, is not so much that of an air compressor in the range of medium volumes at medium pressures, as that of a special device. As an air compressor, it is recommended for uses which require that the air be clean and free from dust, oil, and bacteria. The air is cleaned by contact with numerous droplets of water which fill the interior of the compressor and through which the air must travel. In this respect, Figure 165 is misleading; the interior of the pump should be thought of as filled with a spray of water. The absence of any lubricants within the pumping case insures freedom from oil, of major importance, for example, in breweries and carbonated-beverage plants, for a trace of oil enormously reduces the carbon dioxide holding power of the beverages. The air may be used for agitating or blending liquids which must be kept free from impurities and contamination; similarly for volume displacement of such liquids.

FIGURE 166.—A low-pressure Nash compressor, opened, to show the essential parts, body, rotor, and head. Body and head each have a cone with two inlet and two outlet ports. (By permission.)

Air delivered by the Nash air compressor with cold water as the sealing liquid must not be thought of as wet, but rather as relatively dry. The constant addition of sealing water keeps the air cool, and suspended droplets are removed in a separator. The amount of water vapor held by the compressed air is a fraction of the saturation value of free air, because a cubic foot of air contains the same amount of water vapor no matter what the pressure is. If 10-pound pressure air from the compressor were dilated to atmospheric pressure, each cubic foot would contain one-tenth the amount of the water vapor at saturation.

Without additional apparatus, the compressed air delivered is cool, and free from pulsations.

Applications of Nash compressors to the chemical field have been brilliantly successful. The Nash Hytor is the standard pump for moving chlorine from the electrolytic cell to the drying tourilles, with concentrated sulfuric acid as the sealing liquid. The Hytor pumps acetylene from the generator to the reaction vessel, employing an organic solvent as the sealing liquid. It is used for many other gases.

The materials of construction are usually cast iron for the body and bronze for the rotor; for chemical use the compressor may be built of cast iron throughout, or of special metal.

Positive-displacement Blowers. For convenience and clarity, a distinction is made between fans and positive-displacement blowers. In the former the air current is induced, by axial flow or centrifugal force, and the air is served to the fan and delivered by it in a continuous stream. In the latter, a volume of air is cut off from the rest, slightly compressed, and

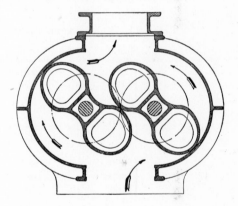

FIGURE 167.—Cross section of a Roots-Connersville blower with involute impellers, showing the travel of the gas.

then delivered to the discharge line, against pressure necessary to overcome resistance in the discharge line due to pipe friction, static head of liquid, or orifices; the volumes succeed each other so rapidly and blend into each other so well that there is but little pulsation.

One of the best known and most important positive-displacement blowers is that developed by the Roots-Connersville Corporation. It may be regarded as a gear pump with two teeth. Its operating principle is as follows. Two interengaging impellers mounted on parallel shafts rotate in opposite directions. Contours and finish of these impellers are such that a clearance of a few thousandths of an inch is maintained by a pair of accurately cut timing gears. These timing gears are also the driving gears, and intermesh; as one is driven by an outside force, the other turns simultaneously. Air is drawn in through the inlet, trapped between the impellers and the casing, and forced positively into the outlet. No internal lubrication is necessary, so that the air or gas is delivered as free from oil or moisture as it is when it enters. There are no restricted passages, no valves, no springs. The action is indicated in Figure 167. Normally the blower is operated with top discharge.

The Roots-Connersville positive-displacement blower is made in a number of models, each having a number of sizes. It should be noted also that the sizes, or better the capacities, are altered not only by changing the gear diameter, but by lengthening the casing so that a longer impeller is accommodated. The standard blower with involute impeller design of special interest to chemical engineers develops pressures of from 1 to 10 pounds, and in the larger sizes, up to 15 pounds. These are single-stage blowers. When desired, two-stage blowers are furnished, which develop, respectively, 20 pounds and 30 pounds pressure. Blower size No. 717 is the sixth and largest in one series; it has 5-inch pipe openings, and at the speed of 690 rpm delivers 700 cfm under a pressure of 1 pound. The same series serves for pressures up to 7 pounds.

TABLE 44.   VICTOR-ACME BLOWERS, LOW-PRESSURE RANGE

No.	Speed (rpm)	At 1 lb Pressure	At 2 lbs Pressure	At 3 lbs Pressure	With Single Pulley
24	860	17 cfm	13	9	$ 75
	1160	27	22	19	
	1750	45	42	38	
36	860	62	52	45	94
	1160	92	82	75	
47	690	80	70	60	136
	860	108	96	85	
	1160	150	145	130	
59	690	180	165	150	220
	860	235	220	205	
615	575	325	300	280	430
	690	400	375	355	
717	490	480	450	410	680
	575	570	540	510	
	690	700	670	640	

V-belt-driven units including motor and rails are higher in price.
The prices are net to the user, f.o.b., Connersville, Ind. good for date of Nov. 1950, and subject to change without notice. Roots-Connersville Corp., Connersville, Ind.

The same operating principle is used in other series for gas compressors, liquid pumps, vacuum pumps, and, reversed, gas and oil meters.

The sliding-vane blower and the rotary-plunger compressor are both positive-displacement blowers; their principle of operation is described in Chapter 19.

FIGURE 168.—Installation view of the Roots-Connersville positive-displacement blower. (Courtesy Roots-Connersville Corp., Connersville, Ind.)

FIGURE 169.—A typical single horizontal compressor arranged with Multi-V-Drive for connection to electric motor.   (Courtesy Worthington Corp., Harrison, N. J.)

Reciprocating compressors also have positive displacement, but are usually classed under a special heading.

Reciprocating Compressors.   The reciprocating compressors furnish air at pressure ranging from a few pounds to high figures, such as 5000 psi. The normal range is from 50 to 150 psi, but these compressors are used for lower pressures as well, e.g., as gas boosters, for pressures of about 10 pounds. The overlap between reciprocating compressors and other types is not infrequently due to local economic factors.

The reciprocating compressor has a piston, a cylinder with inlet and outlet valves, crankshaft, and means of driving it. The piston may be single- or double-acting. The compressor may be single-stage, double-

FIGURE 170.—A vertical angle two-stage air compressor with flange-mounted synchronous motor drive. (Courtesy Worthington Corp., Compressor Division, Buffalo Works, Buffalo, N. Y.)

stage, triple-stage, or more. The drive may be electrical, steam-engine, steam-turbine, gas-engine, and other.

Compressed air is used for many purposes, some of which will be indicated; the definite pressure which it has makes it suitable for certain duties, but unfits it for others. Thus in one plant, a set of reciprocating compressors supplies air at 40 psi for the agitation of heavy slurries, while another set delivers air under 90 psi for the pneumatic transfer of finished cement with the aid of a Fuller-Kinyon pump.

A number of the compressors described, some of which are illustrated, will indicate the various types available.

The motor-driven single-stage compressor (Figure 169) is to be found in almost all foundries and smaller manufacturing plants, for general purposes. It delivers air at 100 psi. It is made in 29 sizes, and has the feather valves described in Chapter 19.

A two-stage, single-tandem, horizontal compressor has a single piston rod carrying both pistons, both double-acting; it has an intercooler and an aftercooler. Piston displacement is 191 cfm, discharge pressure 250 psi,

FIGURE 171.—A 400-horsepower horizontal, duplex, two-stage, double-acting air compressor with direct-connected engine type synchronous motor drive, illustrating the most modern design of this particular type of compressor. (Courtesy Worthington Corp., Compressor Division, Buffalo Works, Buffalo, N. Y.)

volumetric efficiency 77 per cent, actual capacity of free air 147 cfm, brake horsepower 45, motor 50 hp. The cylinder diameters are 9 inches (low pressure) and 4 inches (high pressure), with a 9-inch stroke, and the speed is 300 rpm.

A 600-hp horizontal, duplex, two-stage, 125-pound air compressor is a popular type of medium-sized compressor. Figure 170 shows a vertical angle two-stage air compressor with flange-mounted synchronous motor drive. This unit illustrates very well the modern tendency toward compact installation.

Exemplifying the compressors with gas-engine drive is an angle gas engine gas compressor of four-cycle design, installed in a large oil refinery, and a two cycle gas engine gas compressor, also of angle construction, in operation in a gas plant (Figure 172).

A three-stage compressor for a generated gas, tandem design, with the first stage, double-acting, in the center, the second stage, single-acting, at the crank end, and the third stage, single-acting, at the head end, is shown in Figure 173. Other particulars are: cylinders and stroke, $8\frac{5}{8}$ / $5\frac{1}{4}$ / $2\frac{3}{8} \times 9$ inches; piston displacement 140 cfm, speed 300 rpm, discharge pressure 1500 psi, volumetric efficiency 71 per cent, actual capacity in free gas basis suction 99 cfm, brake hp 52, with intercoolers and motor drive.

Figure 172.—A battery of three 1600-brake horsepower, two-stroke cycle angle gas engine compressors in pipeline gas compression service. (Courtesy Worthington Corp., Compressor Division, Buffalo Works, Buffalo, N. Y.)

The first stage has feather valves; the second and third stages have a ring-and-plate type valve consisting of two special alloy rings, a valve guard and helical springs (see Figure 174).

Figure 175 illustrates a horizontal, duplex, opposed type, six-stage, synchronous motor-driven gas compressor designed for 15,000 psi final discharge pressure.

By decreasing the diameter of the cylinder of a fifth or sixth stage, compressors are designed for the development of still higher pressures.

The uses of the high-pressure compressor are numerous. Air about to be liquefied is compressed to 2800 or 3000 psi; oxygen about to be bottled to 2000 psi; hydrogen and helium similarly. Carbon dioxide to be liquefied and solidified is compressed by high pressures, and the nitrogen-hydrogen mixture for direct ammonia synthesis is compressed to 15,000 psi in at least one process. How important they are may be indicated by

FIGURE 173—A motor-driven horizontal tandem, 9-inch stroke, three-stage gas compressor, installed in a large electrical manufacturing plant. (Courtesy Worthington Corp., Compressor Division, Buffalo Works, Buffalo, N. Y.)

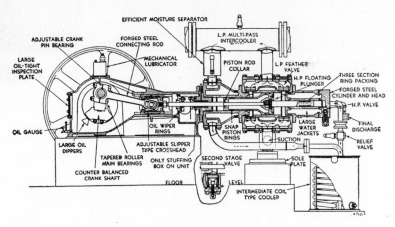

FIGURE 174.—A cross section of the single tandem three-stage horizontal compressor showing a number of additional details. (Courtesy Worthington Corp., Compressor Division, Buffalo Works, Buffalo, N. Y.)

the statement that in the last thirty years, one firm alone has built 672 compressors for pressures above 2000 psi, all but one of them for large-scale operation.

An interesting feature of the Worthington reciprocating compressors is the automatic 5-step, variable-capacity control, which permits the volume discharged to vary from 100 per cent to zero, by automatic mechanism. A properly designed clearance chamber adjoins the cylinder, and is closed by a valve. Three solenoid-operated pneumatic plungers can hold the suction valves and the clearance pocket valve open, when deenergized, and closed when energized. Referring to Figure 176, let No. 1 plunger open the valve to the clearance chamber, which has half the capacity of

FIGURE 175.—A horizontal duplex opposed type, six-stage, synchronous motor-driven gas compressor designed for 15,000 psi final discharge pressure. (Courtesy Worthington Corp., Compressor Division, Buffalo Works, Buffalo, N. Y.)

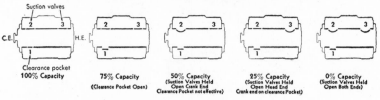

FIGURE 176.—The Worthington 5-step variable capacity control.

the cylinder at crank end; the cylinder will function to one-half its capacity, while the head-end functions at full capacity. There results a 75 per cent capacity. For 50 per cent capacity, the valve to the clearance port stays open, and the suction valve in the crank-end is held open; only the head-end functions now. For 25 per cent capacity, the suction valve at the head-end is held open, while the clearance pocket valve is still open; only the crank-end of the cylinder functions, at one-half its normal capacity. For zero capacity, both suction valves are held open. The governor controls the action of the solenoids.

The automatic variable-capacity control has been applied among others to a compressor installation which is a triple unit of duplex single-stage, with 2000 cfm per unit, hence 6000 cfm in all. The discharge pressure is between 17 and 19 psi. The compressor serves to correct a refinery gas of varying heat value; the value is restored to normal by dilution with air.

FIGURE 177.—An ammonia compressor, for refrigeration and for making ice. The suction valve is in the piston, which sucks on the downstroke, and compresses on the upstroke. The suction line is the lower line between the cylinders; the pressure line is the upper one, both shown in cross section only. (Courtesy Frick Co., Waynesboro, Pa.)

An Askania regulator detects any change in the heat value of the gas, and moves a valve which controls the capacity of the compressor. The capacity of the compressor may be varied from 6000 cfm to zero in 25 steps, with a total spread in pressure of 2 psi.

The variable-capacity control applied to a two-stage compressor must provide for a given event to take place in both stages simultaneously.

There are many other types and styles of compressors; in one of these the suction valve is in the head of the piston. The cross section of an ammonia compressor shown in Figure 177 has such a construction.

Reading References

"Problems of compressors and compressed gases in industry," by R. L. Quertier, *Trans. Inst. Chem. Eng. (London)*, **17**, 80–108 (1939).

"The theory of gas compression and circulation," by D. M. Nevitt, *Ibid.*, **17**, 153–170 (1939).

"Chemical engineering aspects of centrifugal fan design," by Carl V. Herrmann, *Trans. Am. Inst. Chem. Eng.*, **38**, 365 (1942).

"Compressed air for ammonia oxidation," by Donald G. Morrow, *Trans. Am. Inst. Chem. Eng.*, **38**, 377 (1942).

"Gas-moving equipment: Medium pressure compressors," by G. L. Montgomery, *Chem. Met. Eng.*, **44**, 259 (1937); "High-pressure compressors," by C. H. Vivian, p. 263.

"Compression equipment," by Z. G. Deutsch, *Chem. Met. Eng.*, **47**, 317 (1940).

"The axial flow fan and its place in ventilation," by W. R. Heath and A. E. Criqui, from *Journal Am. Soc. Heating Ventilating Engrs.*, delivered at ASHVE annual meeting in New York, January 1944.

"Fans," Chapter 32, "Heating, Ventilating, Air Conditioning Guide," Vol. 28, Am. Soc. Heating and Ventilating Engrs., 51 Madison Avenue, New York 10, N. Y., 1950.

"Reciprocating Compressors," by E. L. Case, Chapter 15, "Chemical Engineering Costs," Zimmerman and Lavine, Dover, New Hampshire, Industrial Research Service, 1950.

Gases occupy considerable volume per unit weight. The removal of matter suspended in gases to be processed involves the handling of vast volumes. It is to the particular credit of the modern engineer that such volumes may be rid of their load of solids in vessels of comparatively small sizes, thanks to clever and purposeful designing.

9. DEVICES FOR THE CLEANING OF GASES

Industrial gases are frequently generated under conditions which leave them charged with suspended matter, for example, iron blast-furnace gas, or carbon dioxide from a lime kiln. The gases must be rid of suspended matter before they can be useful in the next steps, which might be, to continue our examples, the burning of blast-furnace gas in stoves or in gas engines, or the absorption of carbon dioxide in ammoniated brine. The value of the solids collected from the gases may be nil, in which case they are disposed of by dumping on waste land, or it may be just sufficient to permit their reworking after suitable shaping. In either instance, the gas is the primary product of the cleaning operation. Frequently, however, it is the solid material which is of value, not the gas in which it is suspended, for example, certain dusts in air. There are numerous variations of the conditions, and of the interrelation of suspended matter and entraining gas; one is the collection of material precipitated from hot furnace gases by cooling, which must be saved both for itself, and for the prevention of a public nuisance. The devices available differ considerably, and each is especially adapted to a particular duty. The dust may be recovered dry, or in the wetted state; a retaining cloth may or may not be employed. A table of devices is given on page 228. The cleaning of gases from suspended liquids is performed in the same devices as the cleaning of gases from solids. In addition to the contents of this chapter, the reader is referred to Chapter 22, in which installations for gas conditioning are described, some of which are also suitable for gas cleaning.

DEVICES WORKING DRY

The devices used for the cleaning of a gas from suspended shreds, grains, and droplets, and which work dry, include the familiar dust collector which may be seen on the roof of woodworking shops, the dry cyclone, dry filters, multi-bag filters and dust arrestors, and the electrical precipitator. Those which work wet include scrubbers without moving parts, scrubbers with moving parts, and high-speed rotary washers. Some air filters have oil-moistened walls, which might place them in the second class, while other devices combine two working principles.

The sizes of air-borne particles differ widely; they may be as large as

TABLE 45. CLASSIFICATION OF DEVICES FOR CLEANING A GAS

Devices for cleaning a gas from suspended solids and liquids

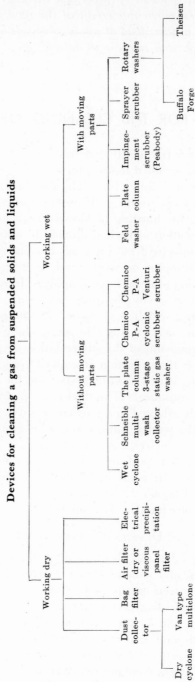

,000 microns in diameter (1 micron equals one thousandth of a millimeter), and as small as 0.01 micron, with all the sizes in between represented.   As the diameter of the large particle given above is 100,000 times
the diameter of the smaller particle, it is no wonder that different devices
are suited to certain sizes and not to others.   Particles 1,000 microns in
diameter and similar sizes may be dropped out of the air current in a
settling chamber; those down to 50 microns in a cyclone collector, cyclones
of special construction retaining particles as small as 5 microns.   Non-
mechanical washers work down to 2 microns, and mechanical washers to
1; gas filters go to 0.1 micron.   Below that, the electrical precipitator still
functions, removing particles no longer visible in the compound micro-
scope, but observable in the ultra-microscope.   Another convenient classification follows.

Dusts contain particles over 10 microns in diameter
Clouds contain particles between 10 and 0.1 micron in diameter
Smokes contain particles between 0.1 and 0.001 micron in diameter.

In the settling chamber particles follow the law of gravity; those separating in the simple cyclone follow the formula for centrifugal velocity;
washers arrest by adhesion to the liquid film; and the electrical precipitator follows electrical laws.   The specific gravity of the particle has an
effect, especially in the larger sizes; the viscosity of the air or gas also.
Formulas for the terminal velocity of particles of various sizes are available, from which calculations of the dimensions of the settling chamber
and cyclone may be made.*

Dust Collectors.   The weight or quantity of solids which air or gas can
carry varies directly as the velocity; the higher the velocity, the greater
the carrying capacity.   The velocity of a dust-laden gas traveling in a
pipe may be lowered by enlarging the pipe; at such enlarged places, the
gas will drop part or all of its load.   The enlargement need not be very
great to produce a considerable reduction; for example, if a 6-inch pipe is
widened to 24 inches, a velocity of 160 feet per second becomes 10 feet per
second; in a 48-inch diameter enlargement, the same gas would have a
velocity of 2.5 feet per second.   The dust collector is such an enlargement.
It is made up of two truncated cones.   The upper cone flares out downward; the lower cone meets the upper one and flares in downward, so that
the box is widest halfway up.   The pipe bringing the gas is so placed that
the air is delivered along the wall and acquires a circular motion as it
travels spirally around and down the box.   The dust drops out and collects at the bottom, while the comparatively clean gas leaves by an internal
pipe set halfway down the collector.   The size of the dust collector must

* "An analysis of mechanical methods of dust collection," by M. A. Lissman, *Chem.
Met. Eng.*, **37**, 630 (1930).   See also "Deposition of aerosol particles from moving gas
streams," by H. F. Johnstone and M. H. Roberts, *Ind. Eng. Chem.*, **41**, 2417 (1949).

fit the volume of air or gas handled, so that the required low in velocity is reached.

Cyclone Dust Collectors. The simple "cyclone" is a cone-shaped box surmounted by an upper circular chamber into which the air enters tangentially, so that a violent circular motion results which resembles that of a cyclone; hence the name. The centrifugal force exerted on a particle of solid is considerable; it is proportional to its mass, and to the square of its velocity. The mass in turn depends upon the size and the specific gravity. The particle is precipitated against the wall, along which it slides down into the conical receptor. For good operation the velocity at the inlet should approach 100 feet per second. The clean air escapes

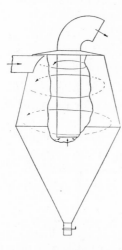

FIGURE 178.—The simple dust collector, suitable for relatively coarse air-suspended matter.

through a central internal pipe reaching into the body of the cone and leading upward to a point above the collector. The collected dust accumulates in the cone and is discharged periodically or continuously.

The simple cyclone is the proper device for treating air containing dusts which are easily retained because their particles are large or because they are heavy. As mentioned previously, air-borne particles of any size down to the range of 50 microns are retained, but smaller ones escape.

Multiclone. The Vane Type Multiclone* is an assembly of small tube-type cyclonic dust collectors. Several tubes are united in a unit, such as six tubes nine inches in diameter, or twelve tubes four inches in diameter, and a sufficient number of units are assembled to handle the volume of gas to be cleaned.

The efficiency of collection for cyclonic equipment is inversely proportional to the cyclone diameter; the centrifugal force (f) increases with de-

* Western Precipitation Corporation, 1016 West 9th Street, Los Angeles 15, California.

creased diameter (r), the mass (m) and the velocity (v) remaining the same:

$$f = \frac{m \cdot v^2}{r}$$

This is the principle of the *small* cyclone tube, which can be as small as 3 inches in diameter. The centrifugal force is greater than in the large, ordinary cyclone separator.

The action is as follows: The gases to be cleaned pass at high velocity through the cast-iron vanes located at the top of each collecting tube. The vanes impart a whirling motion to the gases, causing a downward spiral along the wall, the centrifugal force driving the suspended matter close to and down the wall by radial acceleration. As the gases reach the

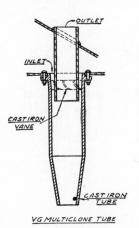

FIGURE 179.—The single VG Multiclone collector tube, showing the vanes which divide the incoming gas into eight smaller streams, for more effective separation of the dust.

bottom, conical portion of the collecting tube, the collected dusts are thrown downward into the hopper. The hopper is a closed box, without outlet of its own, so that the gas in the tube must turn about and rise, still at high velocity and with a continued spiral motion (with a smaller diameter of spiral, however), to the outer tube, and thence to a stack, for example. The gas thus forms within the tube an outer vortex, downward along the wall, and an inner vortex, upward and within the central free space of the outer one. The outlet tube starts a few inches below the top of the collecting tube. The velocity of the inner vortex is increased in direct proportion to the two relative diameters of outer and inner vortices. The velocities of the outer vortex normally approach 90 feet per second.

The dirty gas enters a space leading, through the vanes mentioned, to the outer tubes; after dust deposition, it passes through the inner tubes to another space leading to the stack (see Figure 180).

The Vane Type Multiclone is efficient on small particles, as small as

5 microns; only the Cottrell precipitator and the P-A Venturi tube function efficiently on smaller particles.

Wet Cyclones. The wet cyclone is a cylindrical vessel with tangential entry of the gas, containing means for spraying water into the gas, and outlets for gas and water. An example is a wet cyclone which may be considered a modified spray tower. The dirty gas enters tangentially near the base of an upright cylinder; from the base plate rises a water pipe with spray nozzles; near the top is an outlet pipe for the clean gas, and in the bottom, an outlet for the wash water. As the water sprays play on the turbulent air, numerous contacts between particles and droplets are de-

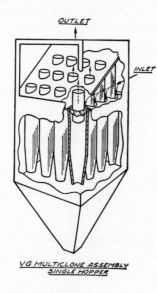

FIGURE 180.—A Multiclone assembly single hopper, with a single inlet and single outlet duct for the assembly. The dust is thrown out of the gas stream by centrifugal force.

veloped, and precipitation is rapid. The sludge delivered from a bottom connection may be settled and its water used over again.[*]

The Hydro-Clone (Sturtevant) is a wet cyclone with spray; the gas travels through vanes which reverse the direction and subdivide the water spray still further.[†]

Bag Filters. The bag filter is a dust-arresting device consisting of bags made of cloth, with a number of them within a housing so set up that the dirty air enters the inner part of the bag, depositing its solids there, while the clean air passes through, or so that the dirty air surrounds the bags and deposits its load on the outer side, while clean air travels through to the inner side, to be pulled away by a fan. Alternatively, the bag filter may be fed by a blower, so that the dirty air is under pressure, and the clean air also. In any scheme, the dust is arrested by the cloth, and the

[*] *Chem. Met. Eng.,* **47,** 324 (1940).
[†] *Chem Met. Eng.,* **45,** 701 (1938).

coating is removed periodically by rapping or shaking the bag; the housing is mounted on hoppers in which the deposits accumulate.

As example of the bag filters, the Dracco multi-bag filter (Figure 181) will be described. Its individual bags are tall cylinders 6 inches across and 9 feet 6 inches high, made of cotton sateen cloth; both napped and unnapped cloth are used. Each cylinder bottom fits over a collar in the floor, and is held in place by a quick detachable bottom band, while its top is fastened to the bag-shaking shaft. Three individual bags are sewn together as one element and this element is referred to as a single filter bag; it measures 17 inches across. The dust-laden air travels over the hoppers

FIGURE 181.—The new Dracco multi-bag filter. The dusty air enters at inlet and travels under the level of platform over the hopper space. The tie rods at the top of the bags are visible, and are part of the shaker mechanism placed in the upper part of the housing. (Courtesy Dracco Corp., Cleveland, Ohio.)

to the inside of the bag, and is pulled through its meshes which retain the dust in the form of a coating. Periodically, a motor-operated shaker mechanism gives the bags an upward and downward motion, loosening the coat of dust, which drops to the hoppers below. The bags are mounted in a housing, which is on the suction side of a fan, so that any repair necessary may be made in dust-free air.

The number of the Dracco multi-bag filters is the number of the filter elements it contains; smaller filters are No. 20 to No. 80; medium ones are No. 200; a large one is No. 400. Large dust-collecting installations are made up of a number of units. For light dust concentrations the ratio of air handled to filter area may approach 3½ cfm per square foot of filter cloth.   For heavy dust concentrations, as from grinding operations, a ratio of only about 2 cfm per square foot of filter cloth is recommended.   In the handling of 250,000 cubic feet of gas per minute in a certain installation, there are provided seven No. 320 filters, with 320 (triple) bags each, and the gas is handled at the rate of 3 cfm per square foot of filter cloth.

The price of a No. 200 multi-bag filter complete with a 3-hp electric bag-shaker motor, dust hoppers, inlet and outlet connections would be approximately $5000.   The filter would have a cloth area of 8000 square feet and could be used for handling up to about 26,000 cfm of air with a low dust concentration, and up to about 16,000 cfm of air with a high dust concentration (1951).

In another model known as the Dracco Automatic Filter, which has compartments and is built in units having from 2 to 12 compartments with 7 to 80 bags in each, the cleaning mechanism is assisted by a small amount of air which causes an air flow through the bags in the reverse direction.* The operation is automatic; the period between rappings may be varied from 2 minutes to an hour, and the rapping with air flow in reverse is performed in 2 to 4 seconds.

Air Filters with Cells Containing Packing.   Among the air filters which work dry are those consisting of an assembly of units, each of which is made up of a cell containing a suitable packing, and fitting into a frame. The frames in turn are arranged to form a bank of many units, such as 20, 60, or more.   The single unit may be 2 feet square and 2, 3, or 4 inches thick; it may be $20 \times 20 \times 2$ inches, $16 \times 25 \times 2$ inches, and of other similar dimensions.   The packing becomes the filter medium, and may consist of cellulose, matted glass fibers laid flat or in V-folds, metal packings of various kinds, small baffles, knitted copper mesh, steel wool, and other materials.   In one group are the *throw-away type filters*, so called because periodically their inexpensive packing, now saturated, is thrown away and replaced by a new one; in another group are the *washable type filters*, in which the filter medium is washed after saturation has been reached, and is used over again many times.   In both groups, the filter medium may be provided with a coat of adhesive liquid in order to retain the dust particles more securely and raise the filtering efficiency; when so provided, the filter becomes a "viscous type" filter.   The *unit type filter* may serve a relatively light duty, such as cleaning air in air conditioning, or for a heavy duty, usually in industrial filtering problems.   The specific filter is selected to fit the purpose.   The velocity of the air traveling through the filter varies with the type and packing of the filter, and with the duty it performs, from perhaps 36 to over 300 feet per minute. Finally, there are unit type filters, all of which are also called package filters, which combine electrostatic deposition with impact filtering.

* Dracco Corporation, Cleveland, Ohio.

In the *Airmat Air Filter*, type P L-24,* the filtering medium is supported in deep pleats (vertical), so that the filtering area is much increased; thus in a unit 2 feet square by 6 inches deep, an effective filtering area of 28 square feet is provided. The filter medium is a laminated cellulose product, made up of felted cellulose fibers treated with a non-volatilizing, adhesive liquid, "Viscosine." The filter medium is supported by a heavy mesh screen with the same serrations, matching exactly those of the Airmat paper. The latter is available in 6 or 10 ply, dry or treated, regular or fireproof. The normal air velocity is 36 feet per minute. When the filter medium has turned black, it is thrown away and a new

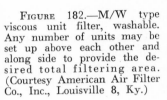

FIGURE 182.—M/W type viscous unit filter, washable. Any number of units may be set up above each other and along side to provide the desired total filtering area. (Courtesy American Air Filter Co., Inc., Louisville 8, Ky.)

packing set in place. The unit list price is $30 (Jan. 1952). The Airmat P L-24 serves mainly in ventilation and air conditioning.

In this as in all American air unit filters, rotary wedge latches hold the unit or cell tightly against felt seals in the frames.

The *American Unit Filter*, type M/W,* is a viscous unit filter for heavy-duty industrial application. Its filter medium consists of two types of metal baffles with graduated air passages, followed by a pad composed of many layers of knitted wire mesh for the final cleaning. First to meet the incoming blast or laden air are herringbone baffles with slits; the baffles form V-shaped pockets (facing the blast) which have large dust-holding capacity. Next, forming the second stage, are several sheets of expanded metal, arranged with their diamond-shaped openings at right angles to each other. The third stage is made up of the knitted wire mesh

* American Air Filter Co., Inc., Louisville, Ky.

of flattened copper wire. The larger particles are caught first, yet leave the passages free for the flow of still partly dirty air; the finest particles are caught last. At intervals, the unit is dismounted, flushed clean, allowed to dry, coated with the special "Viscosine," and replaced. The M/W unit is widely used in railroad car air conditioning where heavy dust loadings ranging from cinders to fine road dust, accompanied by excessive quantities of lint, must be handled. Normal air velocity through the medium is 350 feet per minute. The unit list price for the M/W-4 unit, dimensions 20 × 20 × 5 inches, is $18 (Jan. 1952).

There are at least eight other types of unit filters, each aimed at a specialized duty, or a certain range of general duties. In the Amer-glas* unit the filter pad is completely resilient; it consists of interlaced glass filaments held in place with a thermo-plastic bond to form the pad. When the cell is loaded, it is replaced by a clean one.

The Electro-Cell type electronic precipitator has sectional construction; its collector plates are of aluminum alloy, etched, in order to provide oil retention.

Panel Air Filter. In the panel air filter, the air to be cleaned travels through panels made of woven wire screening. The panels may be made double, so that twice the filtering area is offered. Several panels may overlap, as do shingles on a roof, thus increasing the filtering area still further. A number of panels may be mounted on an endless belt, which may be so actuated as to travel mainly along the vertical, up on one side and down on the other. In such a construction, the air would pass not only through several overlapping ascending panels, but also through the same number of descending ones. The filtering surfaces would thus be greatly increased.

In the *American Multi-Duty Automatic Air Filter,** such a traveling, endless belt bearing overlapping panels, each double and made of woven wire screening, is provided. In addition, the panels are kept coated with an oil which serves to retain the speck of dust or droplet of mist which has impinged upon it. The endless belt does not move continuously, but at intervals, and each time for a short distance, so regulated, however, that the belt makes one complete revolution in 24 hours. The motion is automatic. As the descending panels reach the bottom sprocket, they fall into a vertical position and then move, at the same rate as the belt and in the same manner, through a bath of oil ("Viscosine"). The dust which the panels carry drops off and forms a sludge in the oil basin, to be removed at long intervals. On their upward path, the panels leave the oil bath coated with fresh oil. As will be noted, the filter is self-cleaning and non-clogging.

---

* American Air Filter Co., Inc., Louisville, Ky.

The width of the panel in each single section may be 3 or 4 feet, and as many sections may be assembled as are required to provide the capacity desired. The velocity of the air through the filter is normally 500 feet per minute. A filter with over-all width of 7 feet 1½ inches and 9 feet 4 inches high would have a capacity of 21,700 cubic feet per minute; it would consist of one 3-foot and one 4-foot wide section. The panels are made in three types, and these are interchangeable.

The endless belt is so neatly counterpoised that a small amount of power is sufficient to give it the desired movement.

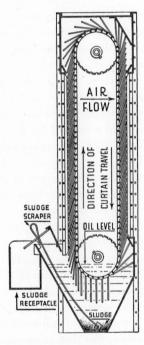

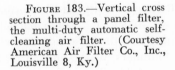

FIGURE 183.—Vertical cross section through a panel filter, the multi-duty automatic self-cleaning air filter. (Courtesy American Air Filter Co., Inc., Louisville 8, Ky.)

The air is drawn through the filter by a fan located behind the filter and connected to it by duct work. The pressure drop for continuous heavy duty service at a velocity of 500 feet per minute is 0.4 inch of water.

Electro-Matic Precipitator. The Electro-Matic* Precipitator is an automatic self-cleaning air filter which electronically precipitates dust and other particles onto coated plates. The collector units of the Electro-Matic, model E-2, precipitator consist of two sets of parallel plate assemblies, one stationary, the other mounted on endless chains so that it may be slowly rotated, in a fashion similar to the rotation of the panel filter. The plates of the stationary assembly are spaced apart sufficiently so that the rotating plates fit in the center of the space and remain so

* American Air Filter Co., Inc., Louisville 8, Ky.

centered as they slowly ascend and descend. The stationary plates are charged with a current of 6,000 volts D. C.; the rotating plates are grounded. The latter are of the same width as the stationary plates, and the curtain is equipped with enough horizontal subassemblies of parallel plates so that these practically touch, and fill, vertically, the space between the stationary plates without coming in contact with them. The air to be cleaned must travel across the narrow channel left between the charged and the uncharged plate; moreover, it must do that twice, once through the ascending curtain, a second time through the descending curtain.

The incoming dirty air meets first a perforated, electrically grounded front grille, which equalizes the air flow over the area of the precipitator; next, it travels through the ionizing zone, made up of very fine, charged tungsten wires (0.008-inch in diameter), each set between two flat grounded electrodes. In a 3-foot section of ionizer, there are 11 ionizing wires. The dust particles acquire an electrical charge, mainly positive, as they travel through the zone; upon reaching the electrostatic field in the curtain, they are attracted by the grounded plate, repelled by the charged plate. The rotating, grounded plates are coated with "Viscosine," which holds firmly all particles which have struck it. Those particles which escape contact in the narrow chambers of the descending curtain must travel through a second set of such chambers, where most of them will be deposited. The ionizing wires are charged with positive D. C. current of 12,000 volts. The ionizing equipment and the front grille form part of a hinged door, which on being opened, breaks the electrical connection to the wires. Figure 184 will clarify many of the statements made.

The curtain moves $\frac{1}{60}$th of its height at 12-minute intervals. Each horizontal group of parallel plate finally reaches a bath of "Viscosine" at the base of the precipitator; with the aid of a comb-like squeegee type wiper through which the adhesive and dirt-laden plates must pass while in the oil reservoir, the dirt is cleaned off. The sludge accumulates at the bottom and is removed periodically. Coated with fresh, clean oil, the uncharged collector plates resume their travel. Most of the deposited dirt precipitated from the air is removed by the traveling plates (80 per cent); only a lesser fraction deposits on the charged plates (20 per cent). A traveling wiper removes this portion from the latter plates.

The Electro-Matic is made in standard sections, 3 and 4 feet wide, less than 3 feet deep, and of any height desired between 6 and 13 feet. There are 44 sizes in all. Two or more sections may be installed together to form one filtering unit. The precipitator is connected to the suction side of an exhauster. At 400 feet per minute velocity, the efficiency is 90 per cent; at 500 feet per minute, 85 per cent; the operating resistance is 0.20

FIGURE 184.—A cutaway drawing of the Electro-Matic, model E-2, automatic, self-cleaning, electronic precipitator for air cleaning. Note hinges on the ionizer which permit swinging open for easy access to the plates; in the ionizer, note the perforated front grille, the flattened grounded electrodes, and the ionizer wires between these latter. Well shown are the stationary, vertical, parallel, uncharged plates, and traveling between them but without touching them, the rotating parallel plates. The rear curtain with the same two sets of plates is visible. Note the oil reservoir and the squeegee wipers. Note in upper third of view the traveling nonconducting wipers which clean the stationary plates of their slight deposit. (Courtesy American Air Filter Co., Inc., Louisville 8, Ky.)

and 0.32 inch water, respectively.   The direct current required is obtained through a power pack.

Precipitron.   The Westinghouse Precipitron* is an electronic air cleaner of the cell type assembly.   The collector cells consist of parallel plates $5/16$ inch apart; every other plate is charged with positive 6,000 volt D. C. current from a power pack, and insulated from the intermediate grounded plates.   Each cell has its own ionizer.   As many cells as needed for the required capacity are assembled in a bank, which may then be enclosed in a steel chamber in which an exhauster functions, drawing dirty air through the collectors and delivering cleaned air to the room. The laden air travels through the ionizing zone, in which the corona discharge of very thin wires at a high positive electrical potential (13,000 v.), placed between electrically grounded tubes, imparts to the air-born particles positive electrical charges.   The charged particles are then drawn into the collector cells where, after repulsion by the charged plates, they are deposited against the oil-coated negative plates (grounded plates). The clean air passes to the exhauster.   After a period, ionizer and collector cell are removed from the bank and cleaned by flushing with hot water.   A new coating is sprayed on the plates, and the cell is ready for further operation.   The cells are made entirely of aluminum, except for insulators, so that they are light in weight and corrosion-resistant.

The electronic air cleaner is primarily intended for cleaning fine dust of low concentration from normal atmospheric air.   Fine particles are more readily affected by electrostatic charges, so that by this device it is possible to precipitate dust as small as $1/10$ micron.   "The electronic air cleaner is not suited to clean air of heavy fly ash, explosive dusts, high temperature flue gases (over 200°F), unpleasant or toxic odors, or highly conductive metallic particles."

The Cottrell electrical precipitation of dusts and mists in gases has been a major achievement in the science of cleaning gases.   The description of the method will be found in Chapter 22 on gas conditioning. In the present chapter grouping, it would fit under the general heading of Devices Working Dry.   It will be observed that the Electro-Matic Air Filter, the Precipitron, and others, combine electrical precipitation with the arresting action of oil-coated surfaces.

Combined Exhauster and Dust Separator.   The Roto-Clone† is a dynamic dust precipitator which combines exhauster and dust collector in a single compact unit.   "The turbine-like impeller has a large number of hyperboloid blades attached radially to a concave base having a center cone to streamline the air flow.   The rotation of this impeller draws in the dust-laden air at high velocity and causes it to turn through an arc of

---

* Westinghouse Electric Corporation, East Pittsburgh, Pa.
† American Air Filter Co., Inc., Louisville 8, Kentucky.

almost 180° before entering the outer scroll. The heavier dust-particles are impinged upon the impeller disc, while the lighter particles are intercepted by the advancing surfaces of the blades. Both light and heavy particles move outward by centrifugal force." The blades extend beyond the edge of the rotating disc, into the scroll. The housing has separate primary and secondary air passages; through the primary pasages, the cleaned air is delivered to the scroll; the dust is arrested by the blades and is collected on the concave side, to be soon thrown by centrifugal force into a narrow annular opening leading to an annular dust chamber

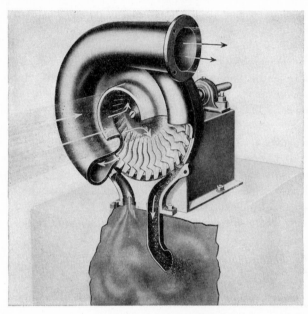

FIGURE 185.—A cutaway section of a Type D Roto-Clone showing method by which dust is dynamically precipitated and delivered to the storage hopper. Note the turbine-like impeller with the hyperboloid blades. (Courtesy American Air Filter Co., Inc., Louisville 8, Ky.)

surrounding it. "The blade tips extending into the dust chamber create a secondary air circuit which conveys the collected material through a port in the base of the Roto-Clone housing to the hopper below." The airtight hopper permits the dust to settle out, while the air later returns to the dust chamber on the far side, to be recirculated.

When the exhausted air, now cleaned, is delivered through the scroll into the workroom to be recirculated, a final fraction of fine dust may be removed from it by means of an after-cleaner, such as a filter with viscous impingement. The cleaned air may alternatively be delivered to a conduit leading to the outside of the building.

Roto-Clone Type D is made in 13 sizes, ranging in capacities from 100 to 15,000 cfm.

While Roto-Clone Type D works dry, Type W provides for water which is sprayed into the dust-laden air before it enters the rotating impeller. Type N, the Hydro-Static Precipitator, provides a water current and thorough intermixing of dust-laden air and water.

DEVICES WORKING WET

Devices for the cleaning of gases which work wet include scrubbers without moving parts, scrubbers with moving parts, and high-speed rotary washers, as stated earlier in the chapter. The devices without moving parts include the spray tower, the multi-wash collector, the wet cyclone, the Pease-Anthony cyclone spray tower scrubber, and the latest addition to the list, the Pease-Anthony Venturi scrubber. The devices with moving parts include the baffle plate scrubber, the Peabody Rotary Sprayer scrubber, and others.

Spray Tower. The spray tower takes many forms. One of the early ones is a square tower built of flat stones, several times as high as it is broad. The wash liquid is introduced near the top through a number of nozzles, so that a fine spray forms and practically fills the tower. The dirty gas enters near the bottom, travels upward countercurrent to the spray, and leaves, clean, near the top. There is no packing. Instead of one tall tower, a number of shorter towers may be used and the gas passed through several of them in series. The wash liquid may be recirculated. Instead of square, the tower may be circular.

The spray tower without packing has the advantage of being non-clogging; also it is simple to build, less expensive and less heavy than the packed tower. It introduces almost no resistance to passage of the gas.

Schneible Multi-Wash Collector. As an example of the class of dust collectors which work wet, the Schneible Multi-Wash Collector or washing tower may be cited. It removes suspended dust particles (and droplets) by contact with water droplets produced in profusion with the aid of its special impingement plates. Along with the washing of the air (or gas) the water droplets also scrub it, that is, remove soluble and miscible impurities, so that the Multi-Wash Collector is both a scrubber and a washer. It could also be described as an improved spray tower. It has no moving parts, hence presents none of the maintenance difficulties which these entail. Its efficiency is high—99.6 per cent on a dust count basis in a number of special tests. Along with other efficient washers it retains particles 10 microns in diameter and smaller, down to perhaps 2 microns.

The Schneible Multi-Wash Collector in the full size is a cylindrical tower with conical bottom, made of steel, cast iron, copper, or other metal. The wash liquid is generally water, but may be any liquid; such other iquids may require special material of construction and some study as to he ease of drop and film formation.   The dirty air enters at the bottom, and the clean air leaves at the top; the water travels down, so that the tower operates on the countercurrent principle.   The tower contains six impingement stages which work wet and one entrainment separator stage surmounting them, working dry.   The impingement stage consists of a conical disk from which are suspended closely spaced curved vanes between which the rising air rushes radially outward, striking the wall, which deflects it upward.   The curvature of the vanes also give it a vortex motion.   A shelf meets the lower ends of the vanes; it is annular, and is tight against the cylinder wall.   The gas cannot travel around the shelf, but must crowd through its central opening.   Water delivered at the center of the top impingement stage runs down from its edge as a circular curtain, over or in front of the curved vanes, reaching the shelf which collects the water and delivers it down the central opening to the top surface of the next impingement plate, where the process is repeated.   The air rushing between the vanes subdivides the water (or other liquid) into a multitude of droplets which offer an increased surface to the foreign suspended particles (or droplets) for contact, and when present, to vapors for solution.

The dirty air enters the tower at the base, tangentially, just above the terminal cone.   The space there acts as a wet cyclone, which gives the air an initial rotary motion, which is further induced by the curved vanes, so that the path upward is that of a spiral.   The heavier particles are deposited in that space.   The air (or gas) on its way upward is deflected by the disk through the vanes, and meets thirteen curtains of wash water which never quite form, because the violent whirling motion of the air forces the liquid off the edges of the disks and shelves in a finely divided spray.   The particles of dust are arrested on contact with the drop wall, or by impingement with the wet film on the surfaces.   After leaving the last wet stage, the gas meets the entrainment separator stage, where suspended water droplets are deposited by impingement; the clean gas free from excess moisture leaves at the top of the tower.   The water flows from the bottom, carrying with it the load of arrested particles (and perhaps dissolved material).

This effluent may be run to waste, or settled and the water used over again, or it may be worked up for the values it contains, in which case the washing operation becomes a source of revenue and a means of conservation.

The Schneible Multi-Wash Collector or other gas washer may be preceded by a dry dust collector, in which the major portion of the suspended material is collected in dry form, leaving only the finest dust to be handled.

A number of further details will be gathered from Figure 186.

There are three standard types, designated as follows: Type "HC" with six impingement stages and one entrainment stage; Type "IC" with four impingement stages and one entrainment stage; and Type "JC" with two impingement stages and one entrainment stage.

The Multi-Wash Collector type "HO," the Senior collector, is made in a complete range of sizes from 1000 to 36,000 cfm capacity unit. The 1500 cfm unit, 2 feet 5 inches in diameter and 10 feet 9 inches high, is listed at $1200; the 30,000 cfm unit, 10 feet 9 inches in diameter and 43 feet high, constructed of steel plate (both), is listed at $9200 (January 1952,

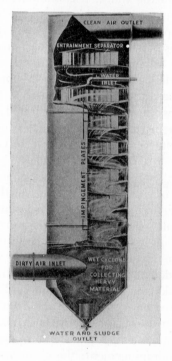

FIGURE 186.—The most recent form of the Schneible Multi-Wash Collector, an example of the wet-type collectors without moving parts. Note the six impingement stages surmounted by the entrainment separator. The gas to be washed enters a wet cyclone separator for the collection of heavy material, forming the base of the tower. (Courtesy Claude B. Schneible Co., Detroit 32, Mich.)

subject to change without notice). The unit is built of steel, stainless steels, "Monel," copper, aluminum, cast iron, or rubber-coated steel.

In the application of the Multi-Wash Unit to the chemical and process industries the projects generally fall into one or more of the following classifications.

(a) Removal of dust by impingement against the wetted interior surfaces of the unit, to be flushed away for disposal or recovery.

(b) Removal of condensible vapors by means of a cool liquid to convert vapors to droplet form, to be removed by impingement.

(c) Removal of soluble vapors or gases through contact with suitable liquid.

(d) Removal of gases or vapors by means of chemical reaction with the recirculated liquid.

(e) For the promotion of a process chemical reaction by means of liquid-gas contact.

Several special arrangements of the Standard Multi-Wash have been developed, each one adapted to one of the classes of service listed. In one to be used for the collection of fumes, the Vari Vanes model, the lower stages have wide vane spacing, the upper stages, close vane spacing.

Recent substantial test data indicate efficiencies on fumes (essentially all in the submicron range) of 88 to 94 per cent.

Pease-Anthony Cyclonic Spray Tower Scrubber. The P-A* cyclonic spray scrubber is an upright cylindrical tower in which spray enters from

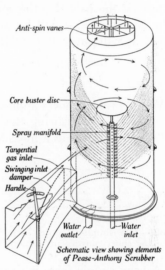

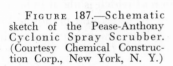

FIGURE 187.—Schematic sketch of the Pease-Anthony Cyclonic Spray Scrubber. (Courtesy Chemical Construction Corp., New York, N. Y.)

Anti-spin vanes

Core buster disc

Spray manifold

Tangential gas inlet

Swinging inlet damper

Handle

Water outlet

Water inlet

Schematic view showing elements of Pease-Anthony Scrubber

central multinozzles. A number of horizontal sheets of spray, separated vertically by 3 to 4 inches, are developed, forming a thick mass of mist through which the gas to be cleaned must pass. The latter enters at the base of the tower and leaves, free of suspended matter, at the top. By means of a specially designed entrance flue, the incoming gas is made to travel tangentially and upward through the thick mass of mist, the rotational motion of the gas causing the droplets to be thrown by centrifugal force to the walls of the chamber. The numerous collisions of particles of dirt and dust lead to their removal by impaction against the surfaces of the droplets of mist.

A central disk called the core buster disk, placed as shown in Figure 187 above the nozzle manifold yet well below the clean gas outlet, prevents

* Pease, Anthony Equipment Company, 29 Grey Birch Terrace, Newtonville 60, Mass.

any tendency of part of the finely divided liquid to "carry upward" along the axis and thereby escape the intimate contact which is essential.* The droplets of suspension or solution, if impaction was followed by solution in the spray liquid, unite and run down the wall of the scrubber, to waste, or to recirculation when conditions are favorable.

An alternate design provides for entry of the dirty gas at the top and exit of the clean gas near the bottom of the tower.

The P-A cyclonic spray scrubber is well adapted to the removal of air borne particles of 1 micron and larger. The denser the dust, the easier it is to catch it; the smaller the particles, the more difficult is their capture The dust collecting efficiency of the scrubber begins to decrease when the suspended particles have diameters below 1 micron. The explanation is offered that "if the particle (the spray droplet) which is in motion relative to the gas is large, it will be surrounded by a streamlined pattern in the gas which will carry the small air-borne particle around it without collision."†

Venturi Tube

The Venturi tube, a novel application of which is about to be described, has been in use for measuring the flow of gases and of liquid for many years. One of its forms as a measuring instrument is presented in Chap-

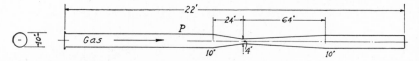

FIGURE 188.—The simple Venturi tube for measuring the flow of gases or liquids Note the short convergent portion, followed by the longer divergent tube.

ter 26. A very simple form is shown in Figure 188; relative dimensions may be varied, but are generally similar to those shown in the sketch. It should be remembered that the velocity of the gas at the throat (marked 4 inches) is higher than in the 10-inch pipe, and that the pressure at the throat is lower than in the pipe. A small tubule is soldered to the throat, and another at P, and both are connected to a U-tube. The pressure differential is the value h in $v^2 = 2gh$, in which v is velocity. From the low at the throat the pressure builds up again as the gas travels through the divergent tube, while at the same time the velocity drops.

Pease-Anthony Venturi Scrubber. The Pease-Anthony Venturi Scrubber is a device of recent development (1946). It consists essentially of a

* U. S. Patent 2,281,254 (April 28, 1942).

† "Removal of salt cake fume from sulphate recovery furnace stack gases by scrubbing," T. T. Collins, Jr., C. R. Seaborne, and A. W. Anthony, Jr., *Paper Trade J.* (June 1947).

Venturi tube in the throat of which a curtain of liquid spray is introduced through numerous openings lining the periphery.   The Venturi delivers to a dry cyclone, where the spray is separated from the gas by centrifugal force, permitting the clean, dry gas or air to reach the suction side of an exhauster; the latter in turn delivers to the stack, or, more rarely, to proc-

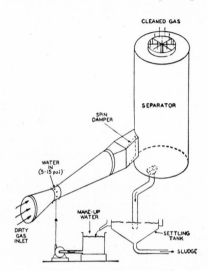

FIGURE 189.—A schematic drawing of a typical P-A Venturi scrubber installation. The separator is a simple dry cyclone, which the gases from the Venturi enter tangentially. Note the adjustable spin damper. (*Ind. Eng. Chem.*, Nov. 1949, p. 2424.)

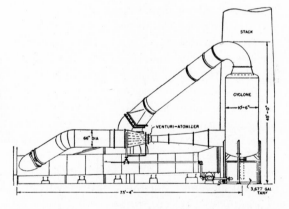

FIGURE 190.—Assembly of a P-A Venturi Scrubber showing the Venturi atomizer, the cyclone separator, the line from the top of cyclone to the exhauster fan; the latter (not visible) discharges to the flue leading to the stack.

ess.   The gas to be treated is generally at an elevated temperature, as, for example, 300°F, or 600°F, and as high as 1800°F (in one pilot plant).

The gas traveling through the Venturi must have a high velocity, such as between 200 and 400 feet per second.   The velocity varies from job to job.   The coarser the dust, the lower the gas velocity may be; the finer the dust, the higher it must be.   Gas velocities have been investigated as low as 130, and as high as 450, feet per second, but most commercial installations thus far have been designed for 250 to 300 feet per second.

The liquid for the spray is introduced in the form of solid jets of water (for example) rather than as a spray; it is the high velocity gas which atomizes the liquid, tearing it, disrupting it, so that the droplets are "briefly, but very violently accelerated." Collisions result from the differential velocities of gas and droplets, and coalescence (of droplets with each other) is favored by the declining velocities of the gas, as it progresses downstream in the diverging tube. Much of the spray water runs out of the bottom end of the Venturi tube already in form of a stream, so that the remaining spray is easily arrested in the cyclone. The particles of dust are arrested by impaction against the walls of the droplets of spray liquid, and are carried along and down with the coalesced liquid. It is in the successful treatment of air-borne dusts with particles below 1 micron that the P-A Venturi has found its field of application.

Originally the throats of all P-A Venturis were made circular, but of late *large* throats are being made rectangular, as for example 8 to 12 inches in width and as long as needed to accommodate the gas volume to be treated. The solid jets of liquid are set along the *long* side, staggered usually opposite each other, with spacings between them, and with internal diameter of the jet and pressure on the liquid so adjusted as to give an average "better distribution" in the throat.

There is a drop in the pressure of the gas to be treated, and inasmuch as the pressure drop is a result in part of the degree of atomization of the liquid, and of its distribution, it has been found promising to study not only the velocity of the gas, but also the pressure drop across the throat region of the Venturi tube. There are three variables which have important effects on the results of the Venturi scrubber: the velocity of the gas, the ratio of liquid to gas, and the distribution of liquid to the throat.[*]

A full-scale V-S installation on salt cake fume from a kraft chemical recovery furnace showed a continuing efficiency of 90 per cent. Another full-scale installation of the P-A Venturi scrubber removing iron oxide fume from the stack discharge from an open hearth steel furnace showed an efficiency of 98 to 99 per cent. In the treating of mists and fogs from sulfuric acid concentrators, and from copperas roasting plants, the average removal efficiency, for the Venturi scrubber alone (with a dry cyclone), is 97.5 and 99.4 per cent, respectively.

The pressure on the system is generally high, and the velocity of the gas also, especially in the throat of the Venturi after the acceleration produced by the shape of the tube. There is a pressure drop, however, and it is nearly always necessary to overcome it; this is the function of the exhauster. In other words, the draft loss in the Venturi scrubber alone, or in the P-A cyclonic scrubber alone, or in the combination installation

[*] Development of the Venturi Scrubber," by William P. Jones, *Ind. Eng. Chem.*, **41**, 2424 (1949).

ɔf the two devices, is overcome (or made good) by the exhauster. In tests performed on a combination installation of Venturi scrubber and P-A cyclonic scrubber, the draft loss was found to be from 16 to 18 inches ɔf water.

Impingement Baffle-plate Scrubber. A gas scrubber which is compact and yet capable of treating large volumes of gas is the Peabody Impingement Baffle-plate scrubber. The gases enter tangentially at the base of an upright cylinder and lose their coarse particles by cyclonic action. They pass next through a zone of water droplets supplied by slowly rotating sprays (5 to 10 rpm), and thence reach the numerous openings of the condenser plate. Each opening in this plate is covered by a fixed baffle some-

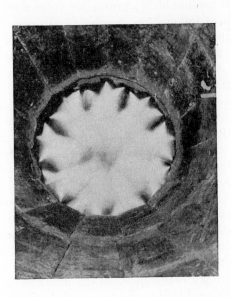

FIGURE 191.—A view of the atomized liquid in a brick-lined P-A Venturi spray scrubber, to show how a large-diameter throat is covered. The throat is 18 inches in diameter, the gas volume 23,500 cfm; the water 40 gpm from upper nozzles and 70 gpm from lower nozzles. (Courtesy Chemical Construction Corp., New York 22, N. Y.)

what larger than the opening, and set just above it with enough free space to permit water to flow over the plate and under the baffles to an overflow. The gas stream is divided into numberless small streams with high velocity, each of which impinges on an individual impact surface, where the wetted dust is trapped by the mass of the cooling water. The cleaned gas next passes the water eliminator, a stationary unit with overlapping curved vanes, where all droplets are deposited, so that the gas emerges free from droplets at the top of the vessel. The water with its load is wasted, or sent to a clarifier, and the clear water recirculated.

Instead of the slowly rotating spray nozzles, stationary nozzles are employed with many gases, while in still other applications the scrubbing water or liquor is introduced above the plate through a free-flowing pipe at no head. The scrubber may be multi-stage or single-stage.. When removing viscous substances, water is replaced by an oil or other suitable solvent as the scrubbing medium.

The scrubber washes the gas free from suspended impurities, and scrubs out soluble vapors; it cools the gas, and dehumidifies it or, on the contrary, humidifies it under certain conditions. The pressure drop i low. The capacity per volume is high; for example, a Peabody Impingement Scrubber 6 feet high and 4 feet in diameter will do the same cleaning duty as a packed tower 8 feet in diameter and 130 feet high.

An investigation of a single-stage Peabody Impingement Plate scrubber conducted by a prominent chemical company in England, consisting of four runs, showed a dust removal efficiency of 99.8 per cent, with an initial dust loading of 7½ grams per cubic meter. The dust had a size distribution as follows: an average of 2½ per cent under one micron, with percentages increasing as the size increased, finally reaching 45 per cent in the 20- to 50-micron range with a negligible amount above that size.

Another test conducted to develop a design for the drying of gases in a contact sulfuric acid plant was run with a three-plate absorber, which was found to remove, with sulfuric acid as contact liquid, 99½ per cent of the moisture in atmospheric air.

Rotary Sprayer Gas Scrubber. The rotary sprayer element, as constructed for the Peabody Rotary Sprayer scrubber is recommended for contacting gases with great quantities of liquid and for cleaning gases heavily loaded with solids. It properly should precede the impingement baffle scrubber, and remove the coarse and medium particles, leaving the impingement scrubber to perform the final clean-up. The rotary sprayer element consists of a shallow sprayer rotor with perforated side wall, rotated at moderate speed (80–300 rpm). Liquid is thrown tangentially from this rotor element and strikes a conical apron attached to the shell, creating a dense spray in the intervening space, which is the gas passage. The liquid strikes the apron with enough force to flow up the apron to a horizontal ledge whence it is returned to the same sprayer, thus establishing recirculation in each spray chamber. It should be stated that the sprayer is generally multi-stage, each stage consisting of a spray chamber. The dirty water may be wasted, or treated in a clarifier and the trapped material recovered, if it has value; the clear water may be used over again.

In Figure 192, a Peabody gas scrubber is shown in which four sprayer scrubbers are mounted, with the rotor on a central shaft turned at high speed by a motoreducer. The upper two sprayers are surmounted by impingement baffle plates. Furthermore, the gas must pass two final impingement scrubbers with cooling-water sprays before reaching the eliminators. In this arrangement, the action of the rotary sprayers is supplemented by that of the condenser plates. It may be noted also that the primary cooling water is distinct from the secondary cooling water, and

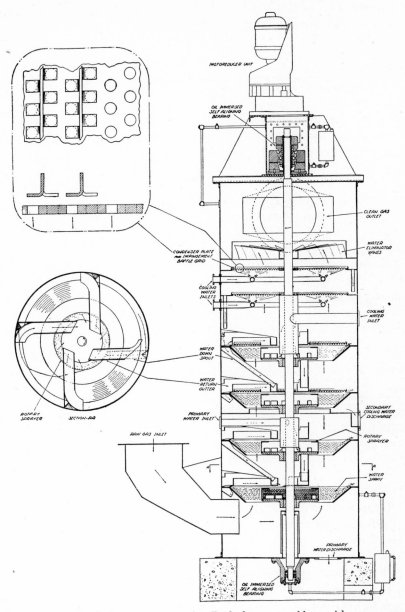

MOTOREDUCER UNIT

OIL IMMERSED
SELF ALIGNING
BEARING

CLEAN GAS
OUTLET

WATER
ELIMINATOR
VANES

CONDENSER PLATE
AND IMPINGEMENT
BAFFLE GRID

COOLING
WATER
INLETS

COOLING
WATER
INLET

WATER
DOWN
SPOUT

WATER
RETURN
GUTTER

ROTARY
SPRAYER

SECTION-AA

PRIMARY
WATER INLET

SECONDARY
COOLING WATER
DISCHARGE

ROTARY
SPRAYER

RAW GAS INLET

WATER
SPRAY

PRIMARY
WATER DISCHARGE

OIL IMMERSED
SELF ALIGNING
BEARING

FIGURE 192.—Typical arrangement of a Peabody gas scrubber, with rotary sprayer elements and impingement baffle plates, both uncombined and combined. Upper left, a top view of condenser plate; middle left, a top view of rotary sprayer element. (Courtesy Peabody Engineering Corp., New York, N. Y.)

that cooling the gases in stages with intermediate removal of all enlarged particles permits the designing of a scrubber for any desired gas cleanliness.

Peabody scrubbers are built in all sizes, to handle from 50 to 120,000 cfm of gas, measured under standard conditions. A medium size would be the 6-foot diameter scrubber, used to clean lime kiln gas at the rate of 10,000 cfm; the large sizes might be represented by scrubbers 21 feet in diameter which scrub furnace gas clean at the rate of 120,000 cfm. In both scrubbers, the gas velocity through the scrubber shell is approximately 6 feet per second.

The *Theisen rotary gas washer* generally follows a dust collector and even a simple spray tower, and cleans such gas down to 0.003 grain per cubic feet. It is a centrifugal machine with a rapidly rotating cylinder (850 rpm). The gas enters at one end, water at the periphery; the clean gas leaves at the opposite end. A No. 6 Theisen washer cleans 30,000 cfm of gas at an expenditure of 4 hp per hour.

The *Feld washer* is a vertical scrubber with a central rotating element carrying disks, while the shell has annular projections so disposed that the scrubbing water cascades from the disk to the annular shelf, which delivers it again to the center of the next disk, where the process is repeated. The dirty gas enters at the bottom, the clean gas leaves at or near the top, while the sludge is drawn away from the lowest point.

GAS COOLERS

The gas scrubbers and washers which have been described are at the same time efficient gas coolers; the cooling effect is due mainly to the consumption of heat as heat of vaporization. In fact, wet washing for blast-furnace gas to be used for stoves and boilers has the objectionable feature of wasting the sensible heat of the gas, which is estimated as 6 per cent of the total heat.

Gases are cooled by passing them through pipes which may be air-cooled; this method is effective enough for extremely hot gases. For lower temperatures, S-bend pipes or other pipes laid in water or cooled by a trickle of water are preferred. The spray tower is a gas-cooling device as well as a scrubbing tower. Gases are cooled in heat interchangers, sometimes by heat exchange with other gases, sometimes by exchange of heat with liquids; in the latter instance, the cooling liquid is in the tubes, the hot gas in the shell.

The Double-Disc gas cooler shown in Figure 193 is made of stoneware, and serves among other purposes for cooling chlorine gas from hydrous caustic electrolytic cells. The cooling liquid, which may be cold brine on the way to the cell, travels inside the discs, which are surrounded by the gas. There are many other coolers for gases, most of which perform two functions: they cool, and they condense moisture, generally unwanted, so that it can be run off as condensate.

A well-known, simple, and useful such cooler is the *Hart cooler*, made of stoneware, for example, for the chlorine industry.   The Hart cooler is

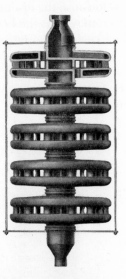

FIGURE 193.—The double-disc cooler made of stoneware, for cooling corrosive gases. (Courtesy General Ceramics and Steatite Corp., Keasbey, N. J.)

FIGURE 194.—The Hart cooler made of heat shock-resistant manifolds and high heat transfer stoneware cooling tubes.   The cascade of cooling water is not shown.   (Courtesy General Ceramics and Steatite Corp., Keasbey, N. J.)

of the cascade type, with a flow of water running over outside of the cooling tubes, fed to the top tube, and trickling down to the others.   It consists of vertical manifolds and horizontal cooling tubes, made of high heat-transfer stoneware.   The gas from the electrolytic brine cells enters, warm and moist, at the lower left manifold (see Figure 194); it rises, and is deflected by a solid plate to the 9 nearly horizontal cooling tubes. The gas reaches the right manifold, again rises, and travels through the upper nearly horizontal tubes from right to left, reaching the upper left manifold and thence the escape line. The tubes are slightly inclined in such directions as to cause the drainings to flow countercurrent to the gas. The dainings are removed at the lower left manifold.

The Hart cooler may be used for other wet gases. The same device may serve as a condenser, as for example for nitric acid; it then becomes the Hart condenser.

In order to remove the remaining moisture from chlorine gas, again as an example, the gas from the Hart cooler is fed to a Green tower,

FIGURE 195.—The Green drying tower, for drying moist chlorine gas; it is made of stoneware in a number of sizes up to 48 inches in diameter. (Courtesy General Ceramics and Steatite Corp., Keasbey, N. J.)

wherein it rises, meeting a flow of sulfuric acid which travels downward. The *Green drying tower* for chlorine is built of numerous shallow stoneware sections (as many as 32), each of which has an internal spreader plate, and a central opening under the plate, through which the drying acid runs down to the next lower spreader. The rising gas must find its way through two curtains of liquid at each plate. There may be several Green towers in series, with the acid similarly in series but flowing countercurrent to the gas.

GAS ABSORBERS

In the gas absorber, a fairly soluble or extremely soluble gas is exposed to a liquid with maximum contact opportunities. The packed tower of considerable dimensions has been used, as for example for the solution of nitre gas in the sulfuric acid chamber process. The tendency today is to use comparatively small vessels, and to provide contact by stirring and baffling.

An example of the packed tower of rather small size is shown in Figure 196; a lean nitre gas is made to travel countercurrent to water, which soon becomes a solution of nitric acid, in several towers.

The Fansteel absorption system (shell and tube design) for rich hydrochloric acid gases, for example, shows the advance made in space

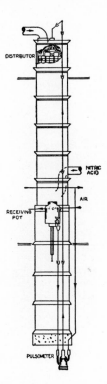

FIGURE 196.—One column in a gas absorption system, for the recovery of nitric oxides from lean gas in a packed tower with recirculation, built of chemical ware and glass. The upper six sections function in absorption; the lower four sections are dummies.

economy. The packing of Raschig rings is contained in a slender tapered vessel of tantalum, which is separated by a narrow annular space, filled with flowing cooling water, from the chemical stoneware case. The absorbing water travels downward, outside the tantalum tube; the gas to be absorbed, upward, and inside the tantalum tube. The heat developed by the absorption process is conducted away as fast as generated. As a result, a plant producing 30 tons of acid per day occupies only 15 square feet of floor space with 21 feet of headroom; it may be operated outdoors.

The Rauh-Klein absorber,* generally employed for hydrogen chloride absorption in water, but suitable for other absorption processes, consists of

* Maurice A. Knight, Akron 9, Ohio.

twenty racks of horizontal cooling 'tubes laid alternately at right angles
to each other. The racks touch each other, and practically fill the space
within the square tower. The tubes may be of "Permanite," "Karbate,"
or other impregnated graphite, or in certain installations of other suitable
material, and are cooled by an internal flow of water. The gas enters at
the base of the tower, itself built of "Permanite" slabs, and rises, meeting
a continuous, regulated minimum volume of absorption water. The heat
of absorption is removed practically at once, so that a strong acid results,
in a single pass.

A material consisting similarly of an impregnated graphite, "Im-
pervite," has a thermal conductivity (K) of 1020, while silver has 2900,

FIGURE 197.—A gas absorber
built of stainless steel; it is 3 feet
in diameter, 7 feet in height, and
has three gas absorber turbines
12 inches in diameter. (Courtesy
Patterson Foundry and Machine
Co., East Liverpool, Ohio.)

carbon steel 460, tantalum 375, ordinary chemical stoneware 10, and glass
7.5.*

Another new type of gas absorber is built, for example, of stainless
steel, and is designed to withstand an internal pressure of 60 pounds and a
jacket pressure of 100 pounds. It has three rapidly rotating turbines
which trap the gas and divide it into small bubbles more readily absorbed
by the liquid. The gas absorber is built of plain steel as well as stainless
steel, and also of a variety of nonferrous metals; a wide range of sizes is
offered.

SOLVENT RECOVERY

Volatile solvents vaporized during a manufacturing process may be recovered and used again. From the mixture of air and vapor, which is

* $K = $ Btu/hr/sq ft/°F/in.

generally the form in which the solvent must be sought, the latter may be condensed to a liquid and trapped away by the application of cold and moderate pressure; the vapor-laden air may be passed through a liquid absorbent such as water or straw oil; or, finally, the mixture may be passed through a sufficiently thick bed of a solid adsorbent such as activated carbon, and later driven off by steam. There are certain conditions which each of these processes meets better than the other two. Condensation by cooling may be properly selected when the concentration of the vapor is very high; absorption in straw oil in a long series of plate towers is the general practice for separating natural gasoline from hydrocarbon gases;

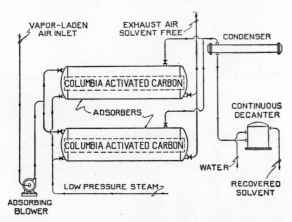

FIGURE 198.—Flow diagram of one type of Columbia Activated Carbon solvent recovery plant. The two adsorbers used in rotation permit continuous operation. (Courtesy Carbide and Carbon Chemicals Co., A Division of Union Carbide and Carbon Corp., New York, N. Y.)

in the general chemical and allied industries adsorption on activated carbon is favored.

An installation for continuous operation by the Columbia Activated Carbon system* consists of a blower; two adsorbers; a condenser; a decanting vessel, to separate solvents which are immiscible with water; and more or less elaborate rectification or distillation equipment for solvents which are miscible with water. The adsorbers are usually built of steel, and may be lagged or left unlagged; the horizontal type is shown in Figures 198 and 199. The vapor-laden air is fed by the blower into one adsorber which contains a bed of 6- to 8-mesh activated carbon granules 12 to 30 inches thick. The air velocity through the bed is 40 to 90 feet per minute. The carbon particles retain the vapor; only the denuded air reaches the exit, and thence the exhaust line. The adsorption is allowed to continue until the carbon is saturated, at which time the vapor-laden air is diverted

* Supplied by the Carbide and Carbon Chemicals Company, A Division of Union Carbide and Carbon Corporation, 30 East 42 St., New York 17, N. Y.

to the second adsorber, while the first adsorber receives low-pressure steam fed in below the carbon bed. The vapor is reformed and carried out by the steam. The two are condensed, and if the solvent is not miscible with water, it may be decanted continuously while the water is run off similarly. After a period which may be approximately 30 or 60 minutes, all the vapor has been removed, the adsorbing power of the charcoal has been restored, and the adsorber is ready to function again, while adsorber No. 2

FIGURE 199.—An installation picture of a Columbia Activated Carbon solvent recovery plant. The equipment is arranged for addition of other adsorbers when increased capacity is desired. (Courtesy Carbide and Carbon Chemicals Co., A Division of Union Carbide and Carbon Corp., New York, N. Y.)

is steamed in turn. The life of the carbon will depend upon the type of carbon employed, upon the solvents and impurities passed to it, and upon the operating conditions. Under favorable conditions, Columbia Activated Carbon may have a life of 10 years or longer. The type of carbon recommended for solvent recovery is a molded carbon of high density, great hardness, and great adsorptive power.

The system may be modified to provide, in addition, a cooling and partial drying of the carbon bed after steaming.

The opening and closing of the valves which divert the vapor-laden air from one adsorber to the other and the corresponding connection and disconnection to the exhaust line may be done manually. When the rate at which the air is fed in is constant, and likewise its vapor content, the system may be operated automatically, on the basis of time. But even when the composition of the vapor-air mixture varies, automatic operation is available by using a sensitive vapor detector in the exhausted air. When the activated carbon in adsorber No. 1 is saturated, some vapor escapes and is detected, whereupon the operation of an electrical device closes the inlet valve and opens or closes all other valves in the predetermined direction and order, so as to send the air mixture to adsorber No. 2. The system is then fully automatic.

Solvents which have been successfully recovered by the activated carbon adsorption method include methanol; ethanol; butanol; nine chlorinated hydrocarbons including perchlorethylene, which boils at 121°C (250°F); ethyl ether; isopropyl ether; the acetates up to amyl acetate; benzene; toluene; xylene; mineral spirits; naphtha; gasoline; acetone; methylethylketone; hexane; carbon disulfide; and others.

The volatile solvents recoverable by the activated carbon system or any other system are nearly all organic, and many of them form flammable or explosive mixtures with air. Such mixtures lie between an upper and lower percentage of the vapor. The activated carbon system avoids the explosive range by staying well below the lowest percentage of vapor which is still explosive; it functions well at very low concentrations. The system also recovers solvents efficiently even in the presence of water; the recovery efficiency is high (98 and 99 per cent is not unusual); it may be fully automatic, as has been explained. The annual maintenance charge rarely exceeds 5 per cent of the cost of equipment. The recovery expense may be as low as 0.2 cent per pound in some installations; it rarely exceeds 1 cent per pound.

In an installation to recover ink solvents vaporized during high-speed rotogravure, the plant has a rated capacity of 1000 pounds of solvent per hour and 22,500 cubic feet of air per minute. Per pound of recovered solvent there are consumed 3.5 to 4.3 pounds of 1-pound steam, 10 gallons of water, and 0.15 kwh of power. The solvent vapor must be collected from a 6-foot drier, through which the printed paper passes at the rate of 1000 feet per minute. The paper is normally in the drier for less than ½ second. The solvent vapor concentration may be 0.4 pound of solvent per 1000 cubic feet of air, unusually low. The plant is a success, the money saving is high.

A few references on liquid-liquid extraction are given under "Reading References" at the end of the chapter.

NOZZLES

Atomizing and Spray Nozzles. The production of a spray of water, oil, or other liquid is most satisfactorily accomplished by means of a properly designed nozzle to which the liquid is delivered under pressure. A spray of water is necessary, for example, to reach every part of a gas which is to be cleaned; the solids in suspension attach themselves to the walls of the droplets. The more droplets there are, therefore, the more efficient is the deposition. Or the spray may be intended for a reaction chamber, such as sulfuric acid lead chambers, when solution and reaction will be the faster, the greater the number of droplets and the greater the wall area exposed per unit mass. Sprays of warm suspensions or warm solutions are fre-

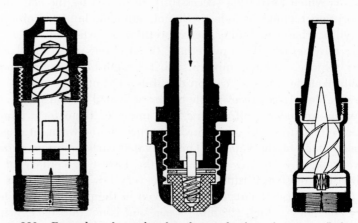

FIGURE 200.—Examples of nozzles for the production of sprays. Left, standard atomizing nozzle, of brass or steel; center, standard Witclay atomizing nozzle, with body of hard lead, and tip of Witclay (akin to stoneware), spiral of lead; right, standard spray nozzle, usually of brass or cast iron. (Courtesy Schutte and Koerting Co., Cornwells Heights, Bucks County, Pa.)

quently formed for the purpose of spray drying, for the drying air will carry the water off the faster, the greater the surface exposed, and hence again the greater the number of droplets (with certain limitations).

The standard atomizing nozzle (Figure 200) has a spiral as shown in the cross section. The water (or other liquid) travels through the spiral at high velocity, and as it leaves the orifice, centrifugal force disrupts the liquid and shatters it into the numerous droplets of the spray. The standard nozzle produces a wide-angle (80°), hollow-cone spray, uniformly atomized. It is recommended for relatively small quantities of liquids, such as 3 gpm and less, which are to be subdivided into a fine mist. For this service, the smaller nozzles should receive the water under a pressure of not less than 60 pounds; the larger ones, not less than 40 pounds. For each pipe size there is a choice of 4 or 5 orifice sizes, given in millimeters.

The pipe sizes fitted by the various size nozzles are ⅛, ¼, ⅜, and ½ inch; the orifice for the ¼-inch nozzle, for example, may be 1¼, 1½, or 2½ mm in diameter. The area covered by the cone from the ⅛-inch nozzle is 2 feet in diameter; from the ½-inch one, it is 6 feet.

For larger capacities and heavier sprays, the standard spray nozzle, which comes in three types, is preferred. Type A of the spray nozzle has a fine-pitched spiral which produces, with water at 60 pounds pressure, a 60° hollow cone spray, with very fine droplets. Type B gives a 45° cone with droplets of medium fineness; type C delivers a 30° cone which has fairly heavy droplets. There are 10 sizes, ranging from ¼ to 3 inches; each has one orifice size, which ranges from 3½ mm diameter for the ¼-inch size nozzle to 30 mm diameter for the 3-inch size. Capacity for the

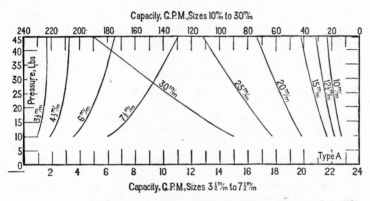

FIGURE 201.—Capacity chart for the standard type-A spray nozzle. The capacity values along the lower line are for the smaller size nozzles; the values along the upper line are for the six larger sizes. (Courtesy Schutte and Koerting Co., Cornwells Heights, Bucks County, Pa.)

10-mm orifice under a 30-pound pressure is 20 gpm; for the 30-mm orifice, under a pressure of 45 pounds, 190 gpm; both are of type A. Further values may be read on the graph in Figure 201.

All the nozzles mentioned and other types not presented are made of brass or steel; most of them are also furnished in "Everdur," "Monel," and other corrosion-resisting base metals. The standard Witclay atomizing nozzle (center in Figure 200) is of special interest to the chemical engineer. It has a body made of hard lead, a tip of "Witclay," which is a ceramic material similar to stoneware, but harder; the spiral is made of lead, and the washer of soft rubber. The Witclay nozzle may be used in an assembly which permits ready inspection without disturbing pipe connections. The assembly includes a lead pipe bearing a bell or cup facing downward and fitting into a cup with the sealing liquid. For inspection, the pipe, bell, and nozzle are lifted out of the sealing cup while an auxiliary bell is placed in the cup temporarily to prevent loss of gas through the opening.

Hard rubber atomizing nozzles of the same design as the standard atomizing nozzles already described have brass bodies, hard rubber tips, and hard rubber spirals. In another form, the body is made of hard lead and bears a bell which fits into a seal cup similar to the one used with the Witclay assembly.

A great variety of modifications, assemblies, and additional types is available; among these may be mentioned the angle-body type instead of the usual spray type, and spray nozzle clusters.

The standard atomizing nozzle ⅛ inch in size, of brass, is listed at $4.40; the same kind, but ½ inch in size, $8.80; the corresponding prices for steel are $12.50 and $19.60. The 3-inch size standard spray nozzle, which is the largest size described, is listed at $70.40 in brass and $77.70 in cast iron. The Witclay atomizing nozzle in the ¼-inch size is listed at $7.90, and the ½-inch size at $16.10 (February 1952).

Reading References

"Gas absorption in bubble-cap columns," by J. F. Walter and T. K. Sherwood, *Ind. Eng. Chem.*, **33**, 493 (1941).

"Absorption of gases by liquid droplets, design of simple spray scrubbers," by H. F. Johnstone and G. C. Williams, *Ind. Eng. Chem.*, **31**, 993 (1939).

"Designing an air filter installation," by the Engineering Department, American Air Filter Co., Inc., Louisville, Ky.; or Darling Brothers, Ltd., Montreal; revised edition, 1941.

"Flow pattern and pressure drop in cyclone dust collectors," by C. B. Shepherd and C. E. Lapple, *Ind. Eng. Chem.*, **32**, 1246 (1940).

"Design of gas-cleaning installations," C. W. Hedburg, *Ind. Eng. Chem.*, **29**, 406 (1937).

"Selecting equipment for industrial gas cleaning," by C. E. Miller, *Chem. Met. Eng.*, **45**, 132 (1938).

"An analysis of mechanical methods of dust collection," by M. A. Lissman, *Chem. Met. Eng.*, **37**, 630 (1930).

"Centrifugal dust collectors—Part I; factors influencing the design," by Henry L. Montgomery Larcombe, *Industrial Chemist (London)*, **18**, 433 (1942), and Part II, same volume, p. 477.

"Gas absorption in a Stedman packed column," by Robert E. White and Donald F. Othmer, *Trans. Am. Inst. Chem. Eng.*, **38**, 1067 (1942).

"Performance of drip-point grid tower packings," by M. C. Molstad, R. G. Abbey, A. R. Thompson and J. F. McKinney, *Trans. Am. Inst. Chem. Eng.*, **38**, 387 and 410 (1942).

"Performance of refinery gas absorbers with and without intercoolers," by R. M. Jackson and T. K. Sherwood, *Trans. Am. Inst. Chem. Eng.*, **37**, 959 (1941).

"Chemico's new pickle liquor process," by F. J. Bartholomew, *Chem. Eng.*, **57**, 118–120 (Aug. 1950).

"New dust filters giving unequalled results," by W. J. Smith and Earl Stafford, *Chem. Eng.*, **57**, 105 (Aug. 1950).

References on liquid-liquid extraction:

"Liquid-liquid extraction employing solvents in the region of their critical temperatures," by A. W. Hixson and J. B. Bockelmann, *Trans. Am. Inst. Chem. Eng.*, **38**, 891 (1942).

"Purification of vitamins—Fractional distribution between immiscible solvents," by R. C. Cornish, E. A. Murphy, R. C. Archibald and H. M. Evans, *Ind. Eng. Chem.*, **26**, 397 (1934).

"Design and applications of liquid-liquid extraction," by J. C. Elgin, *Chem. Met. Eng.*, **49** (May, 1942).

"Columns for liquid-liquid extraction, comparison of the efficiency of packed and spinner type," by W. O. Ney and H. L. Lochte, *Ind. Eng. Chem.*, **33**, 825 (1941).

"Mass-transfer resistances in liquid-liquid extraction," by G. S. Laddha and J. M. Smith, *Chem. Eng. Progress*, **46**, 195 (1950).

There are installations in which favorable dispositions permit the operation of mixing to be brought about by natural laws, without the aid of equipment. Such mixing is reasonably good, but not perfect. In the modern industrial world, however, some piece of equipment is generally necessary, because space and time are limited, and the resulting mixture must be a perfect one. Also, the types of materials which can be united, at least temporarily, by mixing, have increased markedly. For example, air is dispersed in fermentation media in the production of antibiotics, and barium sulfate is suspended in oil well drilling fluid.

10. THE MIXING OF LOW-VISCOSITY LIQUIDS*

At almost every turn in the chemical and allied industries one encounters the operation of mixing. The term "mixing" has a wide scope. It may involve blending two perfectly miscible liquids either in equal or in widely different proportions, i.e., a few gallons of one with thousands of gallons of the other. It may involve promoting the solution of a solid in the solvent liquid, by distributing the concentrated portions near the solid into the more dilute portions at a greater distance. Such operations give homogeneous liquids, which are one-phase systems and are uniform in composition throughout.

On the other hand, "mixing" may involve an insoluble solid and a liquid, resulting in a suspension which is, for a short time at least, of uniform composition. Thus, suspending an impure solid in water, settling it, and resuspending it, in order to remove an impurity, is a mixing operation, as is also the maintenance of a coarse solid in suspension in order to permit a chemical to act on an undesirable component, such as rubber reclaim in a solution of caustic soda. Suspending a solid in a liquid brings about a two-phase system, as does also the distribution of fine bubblets of air in a liquid such as water. The suspension of one liquid in another immiscible one results also in a two-phase system, and is a result of "mixing." All the liquids involved in this brief discussion are assumed to be of low viscosity. The devices and assemblies described in the present chapter are designed for mixing operations involving such liquids.

Low-viscosity liquids, or fluids, as they are often designated, have viscosities below 100,000 centipoises. Most of the common mixing equipment for low-viscosity fluids is intended for those having a viscosity less than 3600 centipoises. The relation between centipoises and more generally known viscosity designations is indicated in Table 46. The poise is the viscosity of a hypothetical liquid such that a force of one dyne per

* In collaboration with James Y. Oldshue, Development Engineer, and Richard D. Boutros, Chief Engineer, Mixing Equipment Co., Inc., Rochester 11, N. Y.

TABLE 46. RELATION OF DIFFERENT DESIGNATIONS FOR VISCOSITIES OF MOTOR OILS
AT ROOM TEMPERATURES

S.A.E. Numbers	Bubble Rise in Tube "E" (Pratt and Lambert) (seconds)	Poises	Centipoises
10	11	1.1	110
20	15	1.5	150
40	26	2.6	260
60	75	7.4	740
70	116	10.6	1060

square centimeter causes two parallel liquid surfaces one square centimeter in area and one centimeter apart to slide past one another with a velocity of one centimeter per second. Water has viscosity of 0.01 poise at 20°C, also called 1 centipoise, but at 25°C, its viscosity is only 0.00895 poise. In general, the viscosity of actual liquids decreases about 2 per cent for each degree centigrade rise in temperature.

There are materials which are so viscous that they are termed pastes; in these, free flow and liquid propulsion methods are impossible. The mixing of pastes requires special equipment, described in a subsequent chapter. Still another type of mixing, that of dry solids with dry solids, is also treated in a separate chapter.

Devices for mixing liquids (over the range specified above) fall into three classes: (1) mixing impellers, (2) recirculation systems, and (3) devices which mix by air agitation. Impellers include propellers, turbines, and paddles. A family grouping of mixing devices is shown in Table 47.

TABLE 47. CLASSIFICATION OF FLUID MIXERS

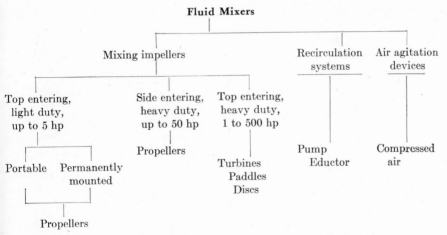

EQUIPMENT WITH MIXING IMPELLERS

In applying mixing equipment to commercial operations there are several factors to be considered. First, the type of vessel must be specified.

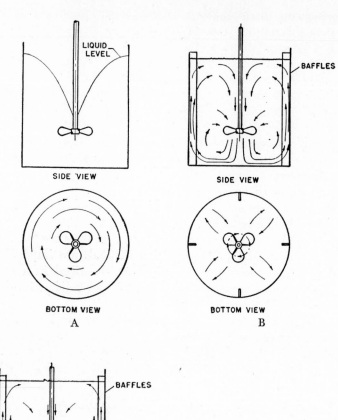

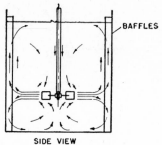

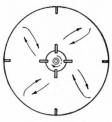

FIGURE 202.—Typical flow patterns of impellers. (A) In an unbaffled tank; (B) of an axial flow impeller in a baffled tank; (C) of a radial flow impeller in a baffled tank. (All figures from 202 to 220 inclusive and not otherwise accredited, are shown by Courtesy of Mixing Equipment Co., 217 Mt. Read Blvd., Rochester 11, N. Y.)

Then, considering the properties of the fluid and the results to be accomplished in a given time, the mechanically most feasible type of mixer drive for a selected impeller type must be determined. Of great importance is the amount of power consumed in the mixing; it will vary with the several sizes and types of impellers and drives. At the same time it must be pointed out that the same amount of horsepower may be consumed with two entirely different types of impellers, as explained later in the chapter; the choice here will depend upon the results obtained. Not only must the kind of duty—heavy or light—be taken into account, but whether for best results the impeller should be top entering, side entering, or portable.

Type of Vessel. Vertical cylindrical vessels are almost universally used at the present time for mixing operations. The bottom may be flat,

FIGURE 203.—Shrouded curved blade turbine with stator ring as used by Turbo Mixer Corporation. The ring surrounding the impeller is stationary and serves the same purpose as wall baffles.

dished according to the ASME code, or of other shape. The most distinguishing characteristic of the mixing vessel is whether it is baffled or unbaffled. Baffled vessels have become accepted practice because they offer two important advantages over unbaffled tanks: (1) They give good top to bottom turnover in contrast to the rotary, swirling flow pattern of an unbaffled tank (Figure 202), and (2) There is no limitation to the amount of power which may be applied to the fluid. Unbaffled tanks are so limited when the vortex first reaches the impeller, in order to avoid pulling in appreciable amounts of air.

The difference between flat and dished bottom tanks is usually negligible. Cylindrical tanks with deep cones or other special shapes require special baffling, which is also true for square or rectangular tanks. The standard baffling for vertical, cylindrical tanks consists of four wall baffles each about one-twelfth the tank diameter. In certain special installations, a stator ring surrounding the impeller may be used in place of baffles (Figure 203).

Impeller Design. A given amount of horsepower may be applied either with a small, high-speed impeller, or with a large, low-speed one. All the power applied to the mixing vessel is absorbed by the fluid. Following the laws of hydraulics, a mixing impeller produces a flow against a certain hydraulic head. The major difference between various impellers is their ratio of *flow* to *head* at a given power input. The flow is the volumetric flow from the impeller, while head is a measure of the turbulence in the immediate zone of the impeller.

It has been found experimentally that large impellers operating at slow speeds give more volumetric flow than do small, high-speed impellers

FIGURE 204.—A flat blade turbine.

FIGURE 205.—Flat Paddle.

at equal horsepower inputs. Small, high-speed impellers give more turbulence in the zone of the impeller than do the larger, slower speed models. It has also been found that the head-to-flow relationship can be altered as much by changing the size of a given impeller type as by changing impeller design. For this reason, equipment manufacturers have chosen impellers which offer mechanically the most feasible design and have learned to apply them in such a manner as to give the desired results.

A flat blade turbine (Figure 204) is a good example of an impeller chosen for good all-around performance, which also has an extremely flexible mechanical design. It can be modified by adding or removing blades; its fabricated construction permits it to be disassembled, passed through small openings in tanks, and reassembled on the inside.

FIGURE 206.—Spiral backswept turbine. This is a 9-foot diameter spiral backswept turbine as used for the agitation of paper pulp.

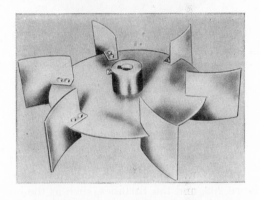

FIGURE 207.—A curved blade turbine.

FIGURE 208.—A three-blade Marine type propeller, typical of the propellers used on portable and side-entering mixers.

Other types of impellers are shown in Figures 205, 206, and 207. The actual choice of a particular design is not too important from the mixing standpoint, provided that the design has been thoroughly studied and its application to a wide variety of operations understood.

Mixing impellers may be grouped into two general classes, those with radial flow, and those with axial flow. Radial flow impellers include turbines, paddles, and discs.* Typical examples of radial flow impellers are shown in Figures 208, 209, and 210. Paddles are essentially large-diameter turbines as far as their operating characteristics are concerned.

FIGURE 209.—Fan turbine as used by the New England Tank and Tower Co.

Axial flow impellers include propellers, one of which is shown in Figure 208, and fan turbines, such as the one shown in Figure 209. Each type of impeller has its sphere of applicability, as indicated in Table 48. The more common types of equipment in use today are grouped into three classifications.

TABLE 48. TYPES OF MIXERS

Position on Tank	Types of Mountings Available		Duty	Horsepower Capacity	Usual Type Impeller	Type of Flow
	Portable	Permanent				
Top entering	X	X	light	⅛ to 3	Propeller	Axial
Side entering		X	heavy	1 to 50	Propeller	Axial
Top entering		X	heavy	1 to 500	Turbine, paddle, discs	Radial

A more complete description of each type of equipment is given in a later section. A few more general remarks follow.

To transmit a given amount of power, high-speed drives are most economical. However, high speeds may present problems because of vibrations of long overhung shafts and mixer mountings. In light-duty

* (See Chapter 11).

equipment, sufficient flexibility of the mounting is inherent or can be provided so that high speeds, 400 to 1750 rpm, can be used. Propellers require high speeds for satisfactory mixing performance, and are universally used on light-duty equipment. In addition, a propeller can be placed in an "angular off-center position" in an unbaffled tank and produce the equivalent flow patterns of a baffled tank. This type of mounting (shown in Figure 210) is very convenient for portable mixers which may be used, for example, in a number of different tanks or in small shipping containers in which the installation of baffles would be very troublesome.

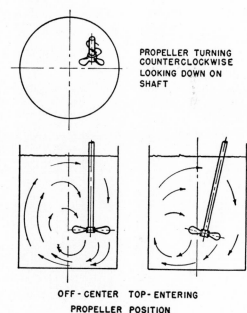

PROPELLER TURNING
COUNTERCLOCKWISE
LOOKING DOWN ON
SHAFT

FIGURE 210.—Flow pattern from a propeller in an angular off-center position.

OFF-CENTER TOP-ENTERING
PROPELLER POSITION

On heavy-duty equipment, rigid, permanent mountings are required, and shaft vibrations must be carefully considered. Turbines have proven to give the best mixing performance at the comparatively slow speeds required to achieve good shaft design. Turbines may be operated at lower speeds and selected with smaller diameters and yet achieve process results equivalent to propellers. Present-day practice in mechanical design, in construction of unit, shaft, and other parts, has led to the choice of a turbine impeller for heavy-duty equipment. Radial flow turbines offer additional advantage in that there is no thrust on the shaft to accentuate shaft deflections.

Power Consumption of Impellers. The results of extensive tests on the power consumption of a wide variety of impellers working in liquids of differing densities and viscosities, have been plotted in the form of a curve[*] which reveals interesting and valuable information. In the *turbulent range*, it is found that power is proportional to the cube of the speed, the fifth power of the diameter, and the first power of the specific gravity, and that viscosity has no effect. The equation below expresses the relations named.

$$P \propto N^3 \times D^5 \times \rho$$

where P is the horsepower turning the impeller shaft, N is the speed of rotation of the impeller, and ρ is the specific gravity.

In the *viscous range*, power is proportional to the square of the speed, the third power of the diameter, and the first power of the viscosity, whereas specific gravity has no effect. The equation is

$$P \propto N^2 \times D^3 \times \mu$$

in which μ is the viscosity.

In the *transition range*, both viscosity and specific gravity have an effect on power consumption.

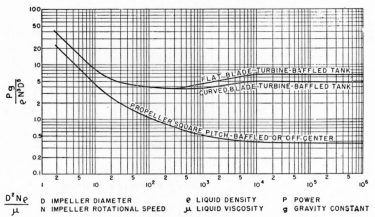

$\dfrac{D^2 N \rho}{\mu}$	D IMPELLER DIAMETER	ρ LIQUID DENSITY	P POWER
	N IMPELLER ROTATIONAL SPEED	μ LIQUID VISCOSITY	g GRAVITY CONSTANT

FIGURE 211.—Plot of Power number $\dfrac{Pg}{\rho N^3 D^5}$ versus Reynolds number $\dfrac{D^2 N \rho}{\mu}$. The Reynolds numbers are the abscissae, the Power numbers the ordinates.

Data such as these allow the accurate choice of impellers for the consumption of given amounts of power at given speeds; they do not tell whether the impeller is accomplishing a given process result when used under these conditions.

Such processes as blending, preparing a solid suspension, and others, depend primarily on volumetric flow, as long as a certain critical stream

* "Power characteristics of mixing impellers," by J. H. Rushton, E. W. Costich, and H. J. Everett, Part I, pp. 395–404; Part II, pp. 467–476, *Chem. Eng. Progress*, 46 (1950).

velocity is exceeded. Others, such as emulsification and gas dispersion, require a much higher degree of turbulence in the stream leaving the impeller. Both of these extreme instances of mixing operations can be handled by a single impeller design by merely changing the size and speed of the impeller for each application. The choice is best made by consulting the field and research information accumulated by the mixing equipment manufacturer and placed at the disposal of the customer.

Agitation equipment is employed in order to promote the transfer of heat from a fluid to vertical tube heating surfaces. By means of dimensionless groups there has been established a correlation of the outside film coefficient with a wide range of fluid properties.* Heat transfer is primarily dependent upon large volumetric flow, and large, slow-speed impellers are preferred.

Other classes of applications of mixing in addition to those mentioned earlier in the chapter are liquid-liquid contacting, liquid-gas contacting, the mixing of fibrous materials with a liquid, the handling of abrasive slurries, circulating within very large tanks, and the maintenance of a solid-liquid suspension after initially producing it; an example of the latter is the agitation of a starch slurry in a compartment storage tank, prior to processing.

Complete Mixer Assembly Types. Laboratory mixers are generally of less than $\frac{1}{8}$ horsepower capacity, usually $\frac{1}{30}$ horsepower and below. Some of the essential features of a laboratory mixer are variable speed, light weight, and a universal clamp. The model shown in Figure 212 obtains variable speed by means of a friction disc drive, and has output speeds from 1750 rpm to zero.

Top-entering, light-duty, portable mixers are usually held to 3 horsepower and less. They may be divided into two classes: (1) direct drive (3600, 1750 and 1150 rpm), and (2) gear drive (431 and 383 rpm). Some of the important features of a portable mixer are a universal clamp so that the "angular off-center position" can be obtained; an outboard bearing to take shaft thrust loads; suitability for many types of electric motors; and light weight. All these requirements are met by the units pictured in Figure 213.

Direct electric drives are the most economical, and represent the best selection for low- and medium-viscosity installations. When the process calls for a higher volumetric flow, the *gear drive portable* is indicated. The portable propeller type units can handle fluids up to 5000-centipoise viscosity.

---

* "Forced convection of heat transfer coefficients on vertical tube baffles," by J. R Rushton and I. R. Dunlap, Dev. Eng. File 1522.2b (Jan 1951), Senior Thesis, Illinois Inst. Tech., Chicago, Ill.

Other pertinent publications will be found included in the Reading References.

FIGURE 212.—"Lightnin" laboratory mixer, $\frac{1}{30}$ horsepower, with variable speed, and friction drive.

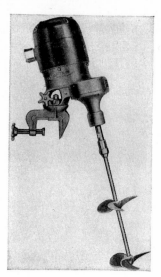

FIGURE 213.—Portable mixers. The unit on the left is a direct-drive portable, **1750** rpm; the unit on the right is a gear-drive portable mixer, 431 rpm.

A direct drive, portable mixer driven by an air motor is manufactured mainly in the light-duty class. *Pneumatically driven mixer impellers* are installed whenever the use of the electric motor might be hazardous because of the danger of explosion from vapors of the material handled or of the solvent employed. Air-driven mixers also have the advantage that the speed can be controlled at any moment by closing or opening the valve admitting the compressed air. The rate of rotation may be varied from a few rotations per minute to 3200 rpm (without load).

The geared model drives operate at lower speed with increased power.

Turbo-type up-thrust, turbo-type down-thrust propellers, and many others, are available in a variety of sizes and constructed of any one of many corrosion-resisting metals, some of them plated.*

Figure 214.—Permanently mounted light duty "Lightnin" mixer, with gear drive.

Top-entering, light-duty, permanently mounted units are essentially modified portable mixers (Figure 214). As may be noted, the universal clamp arrangement has been replaced by a tripod or other type of permanent mounting. The same units may be used with stuffing boxes on closed tanks, as well as on open tanks. Their field of application is similar to that of the portable mixers previously described.

Attempts to extend the capacity of permanently mounted, top-entering, light-duty units into the range of heavy-duty equipment are usually not satisfactory. The initial savings on first costs are more than offset by increased maintenance costs and decreased life of the equipment.

* Eclipse Air Brush Co., Inc., 390 Park Avenue, Newark 7, N. J.

FIGURE 215.—The Unipower agitator drive. The gears of the speed reducer work in an oil spray visible at all times through bull's-eyes. The Unipower combines motor, reducer, and agitator suspension in one heavy-duty unit. (Courtesy Patterson Foundry and Machine Co., East Liverpool, Ohio.)

FIGURE 216.—"Lightnin" heavy-duty, top-entering mixer with turbine impellers. The lower turbine has a stabilizing ring.

Top-entering, heavy-duty, permanently mounted mixer units are the proper selection when equipment requiring over 5 horsepower is needed. Such a unit is mounted to the tank or other supports; its impeller is usually of the turbine type, operated through a gear reduction.

The most recent development in this type is the "Lightnin" E series drive (Figures 216, 217). Among its features are an independent shaft support which eliminates the transmission of all shaft vibrations to

FIGURE 217.—A typical installation of "Lightnin" mixers. Each of the units shown is rated at 5 horsepower, with a speed of 1750 rpm, and is equipped with a single 30-inch diameter turbine having 6 flat blades. The units are equipped with integral stuffing boxes. (Courtesy Mixing Equipment Co., Inc., Rochester 11, N. Y.)

FIGURE 218.—A set of "change-gears" which serve to change the speed of the impeller, in the top-entering, heavy-duty, permanently mounted mixer shown in Figure 217. The distance from the center of the drive shaft to that of the pinion or driven shaft is always the same.

the gear set, and an extremely flexible "change-gear" provision. By means of "change gears" (Figure 218), reached most conveniently by removing a cover plate without disturbing the mounting, 16 different speeds, from 420 to 16½ rpm, can be obtained, and the change can easily be made within 20 to 30 minutes. For closed tank operation, these units are provided with stuffing boxes similar in construction to those described under "side-entering mixers," described below.

It is very important to have accurate data on the critical speeds of shafts on these units. When liquids are being withdrawn from the tank while the mixer is running, a severe vibration is set up as the fluid interface passes through the impeller. A stabilizing ring (Figure 219) may be added to the impeller to prevent this vibration; the stabilizer, in addition, allows the use of longer unsupported shafts than would normally be possible. For extremely long shafts it is sometimes necessary to use steady bearings in the bottom of the tank. It is always desirable to avoid this condition because steady bearings present an additional maintenance duty.

The *Pachuca tank* is a cylindrical tank with conical bottom in which agitation is provided by means of a central smaller draft tube in which a propeller agitator works. The liquid or suspension travels up the tube, while in the comparatively large annular space along the sides it travels

FIGURE 219.—Stabilizing ring which serves to avoid shaft vibrations when the liquid surface passes through the impeller.

down. It gives very satisfactory mixing results; sludge is enabled to gather in the cone, out of the way.

Side-entering, heavy-duty, permanently mounted mixers normally run at 420 rpm. Propellers are always used. Side-entering mixers have a submerged stuffing box, an additional piece of equipment which requires attention and maintenance, and therefore is used only when top-entering equipment is not feasible because of the particular process and installation specifications.

The same "Lightnin" E series unit which serves for top-entering agitators is available in a form suitable for side entering; an example is shown in Figure 220.

A typical stuffing box for a side-entering unit is equipped with a shut-off device and a flushing diaphragm seal. The shut-off device enables the operator to shut off the tank contents by turning the jack handle at the end of the mixer, thereby forcing a collar and gasket against the front of the stuffing box, effectively sealing off the tank from the rest of the mixer. The device saves many times the work involved in the draining of thousands of gallons of tank contents for minor repair work, which would otherwise be necessary.

FIGURE 220.—Side-entering propeller type "Lightnin" mixer. (All illustrations from Figure 202 to this one inclusive, and not otherwise accredited, are shown by Courtesy of Mixing Equipment Co., 217 Mt. Read Blvd., Rochester 11, N. Y.)

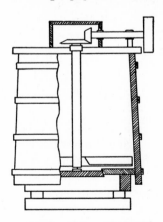

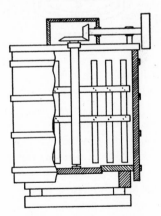

FIGURE 221a.—Tank with a simple paddle agitator made of wood.

FIGURE 221b.—Tank with a gate agitator made of wood.

Another type of side-entering mixer consists, among other parts, of a motor-reducer and an independent shaft bearing.

The simple *paddle mixer* (Figure 221) today occupies a modest position among its brilliant and versatile descendents.   It is still useful, however, partly because of its simple construction and its inexpensiveness. It serves very well for the stirring of a bottom deposit such as an alloy from which a portion is to be dissolved; the stirrer serves to expose fresh surfaces to the action of the acid. As to liquids, an investigation made some years ago led to the conclusion that "a plain paddle stirrer is a much more efficient mixer for miscible liquids than is usually supposed,"[*] and this has been confirmed by others.[†] Suggestions as to the best width, length, and distance from the floor of the tank have been made.[‡]

Another slow-moving agitator of the paddle type is the gate agitator (Figure 222). It consists of a number of horizontal members carried by a vertical mast, with additional vertical members connecting the horizontal ones, so that a gate-like assembly, with two gates at right angles to each other, results. Upon rotation, this structure disturbs directly every cubic foot of liquid in the tank or still.

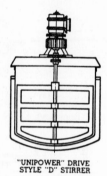

"UNIPOWER" DRIVE
STYLE "D" STIRRER

FIGURE 222.—An agitator of the slow-moving type, combining a sweep with cross arms in a single structure. (Courtesy Patterson Foundry and Machine Co., East Liverpool, Ohio.)

Colloid Mills and Homogenizers. As mentioned previously, small, high-speed impellers produce the maximum amount of turbulence in the immediate zone of the impeller. It is for this reason that high-speed impellers are used, when operating in open mixing vessels to produce emulsions, dispersions, and other systems. The extension of this type of equipment is the colloid mill which contains extremely high-speed rotors, revolving with close clearances to produce extreme turbulence. A typical example of a colloid mill is shown in Figure 223.

Generally, a preliminary emulsion is formed, with simple hand-stirring. This is then fed to the colloid mill in which it travels through

[*] "The measurement of stirrer performance," by J. C. Wood, E. R. Whittemore and W. L. Badger, *Chem. Met. Eng.*, **27**, 1176 (1922).

[†] "Dependence of reaction velocity upon surface agitation," by A. W. Hixson and J. H. Crowell, *Ind. Eng. Chem.*, **23**, 923 (1931).

[‡] "New data on design of simple paddle agitation," by A. McLaren White and S. D. Comerford, *Chem. Met. Eng.*, **43**, 370 (1936).

a gap between a high-speed disc-like rotor and a stationary companion piece; it is this shearing action which reduces the size of the oil droplets (in an oil-in-water emulsion, for example).

The gap is adjustable. The rotor and stator may be of the smooth-surface, truncated-cone type, or they may have grooved or otherwise roughened surfaces. The speed of the mill is 3600 rpm or so for large rotors such as 15 or 21 inches in diameter, 10,000 rpm for rotors up to 10 inches, and as high as 14,000 to even 17,000 rpm for 3 and 4-inch diameter rotors. The uses of colloid mills are many and are constantly being extended.

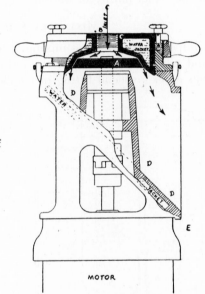

Figure 223.—Cross section of Premier colloid mill.

The same type of action may be produced by a pressure-type homogenizer. The forcing of fluid through a small area at high pressure produces extreme turbulence similar to that produced by a high-speed impeller or a colloid mill. The homogenizer is an accurately ground poppet valve which is held against an accurately ground seat by spring pressure. When the pressure on the liquid is sufficiently high (such as 2000 or 3000 psi), the valve lifts and provides a passage of definite, limited dimensions through which the oil droplets and the water continuous phase (to select the same example as above) may pass. The oil droplets are reduced to a smaller and reasonably uniform size, governed by the size of the passage, which is adjustable. The valve and valve seat were originally made of agate, then of bronze; today they are generally made of "Stellite." Homogenizers are used extensively in the dairy, ice cream, food, and cosmetic industries, also for making polishes and for other purposes.

General Remarks on Impellers. The application of mixing impellers to processing problems is just beginning to progress from an art to a science. As can be seen from the foregoing discussion, the choice of any part of a mixer must be considered from the standpoint of the unit as a whole. The choice of an impeller must be made with a consideration of the availability of mixer drives, and vice versa. The savings in processing time and cost which have resulted from the proper application of mixing impellers has stimulated much research in this field and is shedding much light on the exact nature of the mixing phenomena.

MIXING BY CIRCULATION

An important example of mixing by circulation is the blending of sulfuric and nitric acids of various strengths to produce a mixed acid. The two acids enter a special fitting in which partial mixing takes place, then

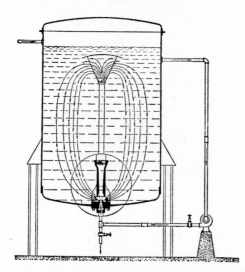

FIGURE 224.—A mixing eductor in batch mixing tank. The central portion showing the eductor tube is enlarged. A portion of the liquid in tank is drawn by the pump and fed to the nozzle of the eductor; entrainment takes place as shown. (Courtesy Schutte and Koerting Co., Cornwell's Heights, Bucks County, Pa.)

travel through a cooler which delivers to the storage tank. A centrifugal pump takes liquid from a low point in the tank and delivers it, generally through another cooler, to a high point in the tank. The circulation and incident mixing are continued until the liquid is homogeneous in density and composition. Mixing by circulation may not require the cooling mentioned here. The return from the pump may to advantage be dropped to the top surface of the liquid in the tank. The location of feed and delivery for the pump will be chosen so as to provide maximum natural disturbance due to difference in densities. Mixing by circulation with the aid of a pump is the selected method in special duties, and is particularly suitable where removal of heat resulting from the mixing must be done simultaneously. In general it may be remarked that the power to drive a turbine or propeller mixer is a fraction of that required to drive a pump to accomplish the same result. Nevertheless there will be instances when mixing by circulation will be indicated, regardless of power consumption.

Water jet eductors are useful for lifting, pumping, mixing, and agitating liquids. An example shown in Figure 224 illustrates an eductor which mixes the liquids in a tank.

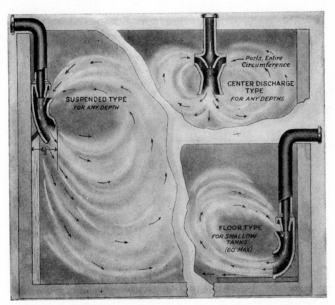

FIGURE 225.—Several adaptations, designated in the sketches, of the Durco Steam Jet, for mixing and for heating. (Courtesy The Duriron Co., Inc., Dayton 1, Ohio.)

Steam jets for heating and mixing the liquid contents of a tank are in use (see Figure 225). The jet shown at lower right is a floor type; a second type is the wall type which is set in the wall so that only the jet itself lies within the tank.

AIR AGITATION

A stream of air delivered near the bottom of a tank through a sparge ring rises and, with low viscosity liquids, causes a limited amount of agitation. Observations in transparent plastics tanks have shown that such agitation is not nearly as effective as the use of mixing impellers.

An example of air agitation which is beneficial and is the only feasible method for that purpose is furnished in the portland cement plant which works on the wet process. After the slurry of raw materials has been adjusted in composition, and while the adjustment is being made, a stream of compressed air is allowed to escape from a rubber hose plunged in the mud.

With very heavy ores and slurries, an air lift may be used to produce a mild circulation. Combined with paddle agitation, air agitation gives good results. In Figure 226 the air lift is placed at the sides of the tank, and works in conjunction with the paddle. There are other combinations which have the air lift in the center. The Denver tank shown is made in ten sizes, which run from 10 feet in diameter and height, to 35 feet in diameter and 20 feet in height.

It might be observed here that air agitation may serve for the separation of materials instead of for mixing, as for example in the separation

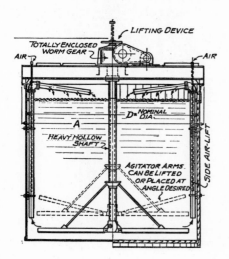

FIGURE 226.—The Denver side airlift agitator which combines the mechanical paddle or rake with air agitation and circulation. The paddle rotates; it may be set at any angle. The complete shaft assembly may be lifted. The air agitators are stationary. The tank is round, and may be of wood (right) or of steel (left). (Courtesy Denver Equipment Co., Denver, Col.)

of mineral particles from each other in a "liquid pulp." Small air bubbles are formed which attach themselves to the selected particles and carry them upward into a froth which is floated off; the gangue remains in the flotation cell, and is discarded. Several cells work in series. Two of the many *froth flotation cells* in use today are the Fagergren Subaeration flotation machine, and the Denver Sub-A Fahrenwald flotation machine. In the Denver cell, a rotating impeller working under a stationary hood sucks air down a standpipe, mixes air and pulp, and provides circulation.*

Reading References

"Propeller-type mixers," by E. S. Bissell, *Ind. Eng. Chem.*, **30**, 493 (1938).

"The role of blending in the production of aviation motor fuel," by E. S. Bissell, *Refiner Natural Gasoline Mfr.*, **21**, (January 1942).

* The Fagergren Subaeration flotation machine or cell will be found illustrated in *Ind. Eng. Chem.*, **32**, 647 (1940).

"The unit process of mixing," by J. P. Asquith, *Ind. Chemist* (*London*), **19**, 280 (1943).

"Oxygen transfer and agitation in submerged fermentation; effect of air flow and agitation rates upon fermentation of *Penicillin chrysogenum* and *Streptomyces griseus*," by W. H. Bartholomew, E. O. Karow, and M. R. Sfat, and R. H. Wilhelm, *Ind. Eng. Chem.*, **42**, 1810 (1950).

"Oxygen transfer in submerged fermentation," by A. W. Hixson and Elmer L. Gaden, Jr., *Ind. Eng. Chem.*, **42**, 1792 (1950).

"The performance of agitated gas-liquid contactors," by C. M. Cooper, G. A. Fernstrom, and S. A. Miller, *Ind. Eng. Chem.*, **36**, 504 (1944).

"Jet pumps with liquid drive," by Richard G. Folsom, *Chem. Eng. Progress*, **44**, 765 (1948).

"Application of free jets to the mixing of fluids in bulk," by H. Fossett and L. E. Prosser, *Proc. Intern. Mech. Engrs.*, **160**, 128.

"Heat transfer data for kettles with jackets and coils," by A. S. West and G. H. Cummings, *Ind. Eng. Chem.*, **42**, 2303 (1950).

Every pound in a 1000-pound lot of sweet chocolate must have the same proportion of cocoa liquor and powdered sugar as every other pound, and this uniformity of composition must be achieved in a short time. The mixing of such thick, pasty masses is made easy by the clever devices now available.

11. MIXING, KNEADING AND BLENDING EQUIPMENT FOR PASTES AND SOLIDS

The mixing of viscous liquids and viscous suspensions or pastes cannot be done with the same ease as in the case of thin liquids, because the former do not transmit the propulsive impulse. Rotating a propeller at high speed in one part of the mass would affect but a small volume of it; the greater part would be either unmoved, or moved very slightly. Viscous liquids and pastes must be worked by devices which reach every part of the mass, and disturb it by pushing portions of it into other portions. The pastes especially must be worked very much as bread dough is worked; in fact some of the mixers to be discussed presently resemble the dough mixer; others are developments along new lines. Agitators designed for such service are therefore slow-speed and sturdy.

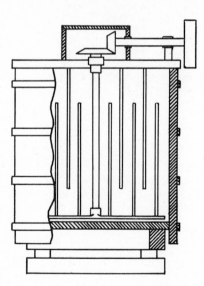

Figure 227.—A mixer for viscous liquids, with four stationary fingers reaching down, and six vertical fingers carried by a lower rotating crosspiece. An example of the intermeshing-stationary fingers type.

MIXERS FOR VISCOUS LIQUIDS

Viscous liquids may be mixed by a multi-bladed agitator moving between stationary fingers set close to the moving paddles. Thus a vertical

286

cylindrical tank, jacketed or unjacketed, may have a six-bladed vertical paddle and twenty stationary horizontal fingers set four on a level, 90° apart, fixed on the wall. Every time the blade passes close over the fingers, the mass in between is drawn out thin and spread into new material. The dissolving of lacquer scrap in "Cellosolve" or other solvent, as well as the solution of cellulose nitrate in such solvents, is essentially a mixing operation of the kind described here. The strong solution surrounding the nitrated fibers must be spread out so that fresh solvent may reach it and the residual solid. Another arrangement provides stationary

FIGURE 228.—View looking down into the Day Hero rubber cement mixer, showing the heavy blades. (Courtesy J. H. Day Co., Cincinnati 22, Ohio.)

vertical fingers attached to the cover plate, while vertical blades set on a rotating lower cross-piece move between them. Finally, an upper cross-piece carrying vertical blades may be rotated in one direction, while vertical blades set to pass between the upper ones are carried by a lower cross-piece and rotated in the opposite direction.

There are numerous modifications in the form and purpose of this kind of mixer. Equipped with massive blades, the Day Hero rubber cement mixer requires a comparatively short time for dissolving a batch of rubber. Four sets of stationary blades, spaced at 90°, extend downward from the top frame. Two sets of blades, spaced at 180°, extend upward from a special casting located in the bottom and rotate with the vertical shaft. The clearance between the stationary and the moving blades is so close that the rubber is sheared into smaller and smaller pieces, constantly exposing more surface to the action of the solvent.

The disc agitator, included in the classification of mixers in the preceding chapter, is well adapted to the mixing of thick liquids. Thus, for example, it can be used for incorporating a thinner in pigment paste. In the disc agitator, two discs close together and held apart by spacers, are mounted on a rotating shaft. The diameter of the discs is small, such as 5 or 6 inches, to work in a tank 5 feet in diameter. The discs have several openings close to the shaft. As they rotate, liquids are drawn in by these openings and thrown with a high velocity from the circular space between them. They are remarkably effective, and complete mixing results in less than an hour.

FIGURE 229.—Double-motion, positive-scraping agitator, with a heavy-duty worm drive. The agitator has two sets of paddles which rotate in opposite directions, at different speeds. (Courtesy Buflovak Equipment Division, Blaw-Knox Co., Buffalo 11, N. Y.)

The Sweep Agitator. The sweep agitator conforms in shape to the vessel in which it works. The clearance between agitator and vessel wall is made small, e.g., $\frac{3}{8}$ or $\frac{1}{4}$ inch so that any material settling out is constantly disturbed. The sweep has particular value in the handling of pastes or thick creams, for these materials cling to the wall. When the vessel is not only a mixing, but also a heating or cooling vessel, such a stagnant layer acts as an insulator. The sweep that scrapes avoids this difficulty; a special form of this device is shown in Figure 229. The sweep not only travels close to the wall, but carries blades which press on the metal and remove all adhering material at every contact. The result is good heat transfer, as well as more thorough mixing. This agitator has two sets of paddles which revolve in opposite directions. The sweep has horizontal cross-arms and is driven from its top by a hollow, vertical shaft which extends down through the uppermost cross member. Within the short, hollow shaft is a solid inner vertical shaft which carries the second set of paddles. One set of paddles is pitched to give a lifting action, the other to force the material down. The effect of these oppositely pitched elements revolving in opposite directions is to give heavy pasty materials a sort of squeezing and rubbing action which is very effective in making smooth, homogeneous products. The sweep with scrapers is usually driven at 15 rpm, while the inner paddles may travel at the rate of 25 or 30 rpm. A kettle in which this agitator works is shown in Figure 449.

For the preparation of emulsions which have the consistency of shaving cream at room temperature there may be used an open-jacketed, glass-

FIGURE 230.—A jacketed kettle-fitted Dopp-style "A-D" double-motion combination paddle and screw agitator, with positive-scraping. The photograph shows the one-piece construction and the staybolts which stiffen the jacket. (Courtesy Buflovak Equipment Division, Blaw-Knox Co., Buffalo 11, N. Y.)

lined kettle with a simple sweep agitator having several cross members either made of flat, noncorrosive metal, or tin- or nickel-plated. The frame of the sweep and the cross members are pitched at various angles calculated to produce upward and downward motion as well as forward.

Superior mixing is obtained in a model in which the sweep has planetary motion superimposed upon the rotary motion. For this purpose, the sweep is made some 3 or 4 inches smaller in its width than the diameter of the kettle. The assembly includes a cast-iron base with an upright which carries a movable overhead arm supporting the motor, the speed reducer, and the agitator; by raising the arm, the agitator may be raised vertically out of the kettle. The latter has trunnions resting on arms projecting from the base plate so that it may be tilted. The capacity of the kettle is 25 gallons; by making several batches per shift, a fair daily production may be shown.   The motor has three rotating speeds, 30, 60, and 120 rpm.

Another medium-sized model is an open, jacketed, stainless-steel kettle equipped with a double-motion agitator of the sweep-and-paddle type. The sweep carries spring steel blades which lift all material adhering to the wall; it rotates one way, while the two paddles rotate the other way. The kettle has a lip, and may be tilted, in which case the agitator and the upper gear move with it.   The capacity is 50 gallons, and it is used for concentrating milk, condensed milk, and similar materials to a paste.

An open kettle with the combination of paddle and screw agitator shown in Figure 230 is used for viscous liquids or light and medium pastes,

Figure 231.—Looking down into a kettle with double-motion positive scraping, just after a batch of soap was discharged from it.   Note that although the soap is of heavy consistency, as shown by the material adhering to the paddles, the kettle wall has been scraped clean.   (Courtesy Buflovak Equipment Division, Blaw-Knox Co., Buffalo 11, N. Y.)

such as melted soaps, which must be mixed or in which additional ingredients must be incorporated.   The paddles are horizontal and run from the sweep to the central drum, while the screw runs within the drum at a higher speed.   The sweep usually travels at the rate of 15 rpm and the screw at 100 or 125 rpm or more, depending on the consistency of the material.   The sweep carries Dopp-type adjustable, spring-tempered scrapers, alternately arranged; the scrapers bear against the metal wall and scrape it free of material, so that mixing is more rapid and thorough, the heat transfer is improved, and the operation is shortened.   Separate pulleys drive the individual pinions and bevel gears; separate motors and speed reducers may be used instead.   A view looking down into this kettle just after a batch of soap was discharged shows the clean state of the wall (Figure 231). This agitator is used for mixing a heavy material with a lighter one, as the screw continually draws the heavy material away from the bottom of the kettle. Also the troweling action of the screw effectively rubs out small lumps of soap fillers, wood flour, clay, powdered asbestos, and the like.

An agitator well adapted to kettles for thermosetting resins in the primary uncured stage is shown in Figure 232. It consists of a sweep carrying scraper blades, and of cross-arms made as thin as possible. The positive scraping action prevents the deposit of a hard, insulating scale, which otherwise must be removed by hand at a great cost of time and labor. The notch in the scraper at the base is for the projection of a thermo-

FIGURE 232.—Modified Type "J" single motion agitator with scrapers, used in kettles for the polymerization and dehydration of thermosetting resins. A thermometer well, which extends down from the cover of the still, is also shown. (Courtesy Buflovak Equipment Division, Blaw-Knox Co., Buffalo 11, N. Y.)

couple, which gives temperature readings. This agitator is usually driven at the rate of 15 rpm. The kettle in which this scraper agitator works is shown in Figure 444.

Only kettles made of cast metal are suitable for scraper agitators with heavy steel blades.

In the design of a urea resin plant,* a nickel-clad steel was selected for the kettle body, and a horseshoe-shaped agitator with one cross member for the agitating device. The clearance between agitator and kettle wall was ¼ inch, and the rotation was 41 rpm.

Muller. The muller is described later in this chapter, but it is used also for the mixing of heavy pastes. Thus, to give a definite example,

* "Design of a urea resin plant," by A. Brothman and A. P. Weber, *Chem. Met. Eng.*, **48**, (1941).

the mixing of powdered sugar with cocoa liquor (crushed cocoa nibs) is performed in a muller called *mélangeur*. In a circular pan, two cylindrical stones weighing 500 pounds each are set on edge and held in position by connections to a central post which permit a slight up and down movement. The pan rotates, but the stones are stationary. Inner and outer plows, also stationary, direct the soft mass to the base of the stones. From the mélangeur, the paste passes to a five-roll mill where further mixing takes place with simultaneous reduction of particle size. The product from the roll mill goes to a double-arm kneader where some "liquor" or liquid cocoa butter is worked in to produce the desired degree of plasticity; the mass then goes to the roll mill again. This operation is repeated several times.

Other Types of Mixers. The pony mixer is used for thin pastes, and for the preliminary mixing of paints; it consists of a drum which revolves in one direction, and an agitator which revolves in the other. The agita-

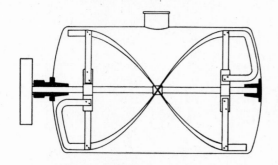

FIGURE 233.—A ribbon mixer, for pastes or viscous liquids, with S-shaped scraper agitator of the ribbon type. (Sketched from the corresponding Koven mixer.)

tor has four vertical blades, and a scraper blade. The mixer is built in· 40-, 50-, 80-, 100-, and 125-gallon sizes (Day).

The ball mill, which is described elsewhere, is an excellent and important device for mixing solids and liquids, including difficult combinations. It is used in the preparation of ready-mixed paints.

In the paint factory also, there are in use five-roll mixers, which intimately mix pigment and vehicle. The rolls are horizontal, and revolve at different speeds so that there is a rubbing as well as a pick-up action. Every particle of pigment must be wetted by the vehicle. The rolls are hollow and water-cooled; the temperature depends upon the flow of water and the thickness of the metal.

The ribbon mixer shown in Figure 233, which is a modified screw mixer, is used successfully for the mixing of thick liquids and of pastes thin enough to flow easily under the conditions of mixing. In a ribbon mixer having an inner ribbon (of stout construction) driving the material one way, and an outer ribbon pitched in the opposite direction, a mass may be subjected to mixing for hours or days, if advisable.

KNEADERS

Mixers intended primarily for medium to heavy pastes are termed kneaders by many manufacturers. The kneader consists of a bowl, which may or may not be jacketed, in which the mass is worked by a single slow-speed, horizontal agitator, or twin slow-speed agitators, of various shapes. The effectiveness of the mixing operation is usually measured by the time required for a small portion of dyestuff to color the entire mass. The kneading operation for very viscous masses requires considerable energy, exceeding 1 hp per 5 gallons.

A modern bread-dough mixer is an example of a kneader with a single agitator carrying on one shaft two bars which differ in thickness, and a

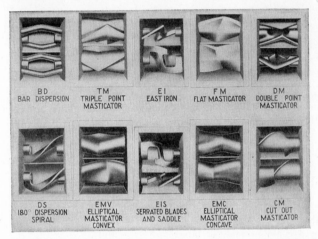

FIGURE 234.—Several types of agitators used in mixing and kneading which fit interchangeably in the Day Mogul kneader and mixer. (Courtesy J. H. Day Co., Cincinnati, Ohio.)

swing bar. The agitator works against a stationary bar, and rotates at a speed of 65 rpm, which is a high speed for these mixers.

The Day Universal dough mixer No. 6½ is equipped with a "flat agitator," a single-arm agitator of elaborate design which rotates at the speed of 25 rpm. The capacity of the mixer is 650 pounds of dough.

All kneaders with two agitator arms have a low saddle in the bowl, which forms two half-cylinders in the bottom; each agitator works in its trough. The shape of the agitator arms varies; several are visible in the illustrations in this section; best known are the S-shaped, Z-shaped, and Sigma-shaped. The two agitators overlap and force the material to travel up at the sides and down in the center of the bowl, while at the same time they give a folding-in action which alters the relative disposition of the

FIGURE 235.—A view of a heavy-duty vacuum mixer processing a tough plastic mass using Sigma blades. Size 15 JUMM Universal Mixer with "U" type dispersion drive, with fabricated steel-jacketed shell, hydraulic tilting machine for discharge, pyramidal cover for vacuum operation, pedestal mounted, direct-connected drive to 100 horsepower, 900 rpm motor. (Courtesy Baker Perkins, Inc., Saginaw, Mich.)

TABLE 49. CLASSIFICATION OF MIXING DEVICES

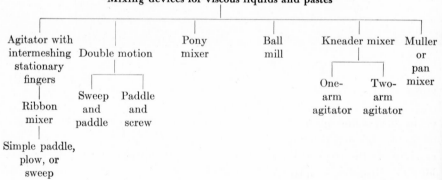

Mixing devices for viscous liquids and pastes

Agitator with intermeshing stationary fingers | Double motion | Pony mixer | Ball mill | Kneader mixer | Muller or pan mixer

Ribbon mixer — Sweep and paddle — Paddle and screw

One-arm agitator — Two-arm agitator

Simple paddle, plow, or sweep

Mixing devices for blending dry powders

Tumbling drums with sloping walls | Screw conveyors with rakes | Ribbon conveyor Ribbon mixer | Muller or pan mixer | Pebble and ball mill | Mixing cone masses, leading to the final homogeneous whole. The agitators sweep the surface of the trough clean, one-half of each half-trough at a time. Replaceable wearing strips may be attached to many of the mixing arms.

By altering the relative angle at which the arms are mounted, the overlap may be made to disappear; by setting the two arms parallel, tangential mixing is secured. Various mixing actions may be secured by changing the relative position of two given agitator arms, as indicated in Figure 236. The rate of rotation in one of the less elaborate open mixers is in the neighborhood of 20 rpm.

The kneader is also constructed for vacuum operation, permitting the removal by evaporation of moisture or solvents at low temperatures. For

Position 1   Position 2   Position 3

FIGURE 236.—By changing the position of two agitator arms, various mixing actions are secured with the same agitators. Position 1 uses little power, heats material slightly, requires long mixing period. Position 2 requires moderate increase in power, greater heating of material, and relatively shorter mixing period; it also produces some masticating action. Position 3 increases masticating action, causing increase in power consumption, and consequently greater heating of material, decreasing mixing time. (Courtesy J. H. Day Co., Cincinnati, Ohio.)

temperature regulation, the agitator arms may be cored for circulation of cooling or heating liquid, in addition to placing jackets on the bowl. The vacuum kneader-mixer also permits operating in an inert gas atmosphere, or under elevated pressure. By fastening an extension over the bowl, the capacity of the regular kneader may be raised, for example from 290 gallons to 650 gallons. Any suitable metal including stainless steel may be used for the bowl and agitator arms.

The Kneadermaster shown in Figure 237 is one of a series of mixers made in almost any batch capacity up to 1500 gallons, in 60 different combinations of frames, sizes, and horsepowers. It is a double-arm mixer with a totally enclosed mechanism and a built-in piping system for circulation in the jackets. The Kneadermaster is suited for mixing operations requiring cooling, heating, pressure, or vacuum; it is particularly useful for mixing and treating heavy plastics and tenacious materials.

FIGURE 237.—The Kneadermaster mixer of latest design. (Courtesy Patterson Foundry and Machine Co., East Liverpool, Ohio.)

FIGURE 238.—JYIM Universal mixing and kneading machine, size 16, with a vacuum connection located in the cover; the latter is pedestal-mounted for easy removal. (Courtesy Baker Perkins, Inc., Saginaw, Mich.)

A kneader is transformed into a shredder by mounting a replaceable serrated nose casting on the saddle; close clearance between the agitator arms and the serrations insures even, fine shredding. Like the kneader, the shredder may be water- or cold brine-cooled by circulation in the jackets.

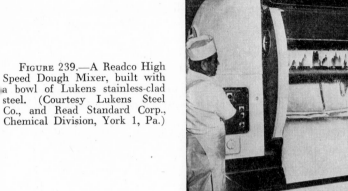

FIGURE 239.—A Readco High Speed Dough Mixer, built with a bowl of Lukens stainless-clad steel. (Courtesy Lukens Steel Co., and Read Standard Corp., Chemical Division, York 1, Pa.)

FIGURE 240.—A tilting-bowl double-arm acetylator with special bronze bowl and agitators; latest model. Capacity 425 gallons total; weight 25,200 pounds. (Courtesy Read Standard Corp., Chemical Division, York 1, Pa.)

In addition to mixing and shredding, a reaction may be performed in the kneader. The acetylator shown in Figure 240 is a tilting-bowl mixer entirely closed, in which the reaction between cellulose and acetic anhydride takes place to produce cellulose acetate. Bowl, agitators, and hood are of a special-analysis bronze. The saddle in the bottom bears a serrated nosepiece against which the agitators work, shredding the cellulose and promoting the reaction; the heat evolved is removed by cold brine circulating in the jacket which surrounds the bowl, including its sides. The agitators turn toward each other, and as they do so, they mix the charge, and bring new masses against the saddle. The arms sweep the bowl clean, thanks to the close clearances between agitator and bowl cast-

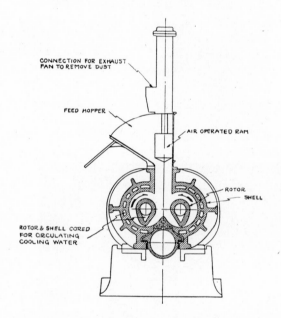

CONNECTION FOR EXHAUST
FAN TO REMOVE DUST

FEED HOPPER

AIR OPERATED RAM

ROTOR

SHELL

ROTOR & SHELL CORED
FOR CIRCULATING
COOLING WATER

FIGURE 241.—A cross-sectional view of the Banbury Mixer. (Courtesy Farrel-Birmingham Co., Inc., Ansonia, Conn.)

ing; heat transfer as well as mixing is thus improved. The working capacity of the acetylator shown is 300 gallons (425 gallons total).

Among the many other modifications and constructions for special purposes might be mentioned a mixer with worm-type agitators which move the material along one trough, transfer it to another trough, there move it in the opposite direction, transferring again, and repeating. The transfer paddles are integral with the worms. Another type of mixer has all-steel gears and special heavy-duty, double-arm agitators for working battery pastes, pigments, and plastics. A mixer used for manufacturing triple superphosphate from phosphoric acid and ground phosphate rock has cast-steel agitators faced with "Stellite." The mixing bowl of another heavy-duty machine has cast jackets for the circulation of oil at 500°F.

Extremely heavy mixing requires agitator drives at both ends of the arms. A number of mixers have provision for tilting the bowl as shown in the illustrations; others have a stationary bowl with bottom discharge or other provision. The rotation of the arms may be reversible.

For plastic masses, overlapping action is preferred; the two arms must rotate at the same speed, although the degree of turn of one arm with respect to the other may be selected according to the duty, as already indicated. There are materials which may be handled to advantage by tangential action with arms rotating at different speeds; such a decision requires a comprehensive study of the materials to be handled.

Banbury Internal Mixer. The Banbury internal mixer properly follows the two-armed kneaders and mixers, for it is itself a heavy-duty, two-armed mixer. One of the many industries in which it has been successfully applied is the rubber industry, where it does the same work as the open two-roll mill but with much greater efficiency. The latter is described later. The Banbury mixer is a completely enclosed kneader chamber with cored walls to permit the circulation of either cooling or heating fluids, and with a ridge in the bottom, similar to the saddle in the two-arm kneader. The mixer has two rotors turning toward each other; each has a tip or blade over which the stock must pass as the rotors revolve. The normal speed of the drive rotor for mixing is 20 rpm; there is a small differential between the two rotors so that the driven rotor runs at a slightly lower speed. Some machines are equipped with a two-speed motor, so that double the standard speed, or 40 rpm, can be obtained for masticating crude rubber. The cross section of the rotors is shown in Figure 241. Longitudinally, the rotors are formed in an interrupted spiral which, combined with the speed differential, produces a constant circulation of the stock while it is being worked. The rotors themselves are cored for water or heating agent circulation. Over the mixing chamber is the feeding hopper, and in the neck of the feeder is a floating weight operated by compressed air, which serves to keep the material within the sphere of mixing action and to exert pressure on it.

In handling certain plastics, such as "Vinylite," the mixing chamber is heated by steam or hot oil. In masticating rubber or compounding it, the mixer is cooled by water in the jackets. It is also possible to cool the bowl and discharge door while the rotors are heated, and vice versa.

A new Banbury mixer for mixing operations which require cooling is the spray-cooled type, in which better cooling is produced by giving the mixing chamber thin steel sides and playing a spray of water on them. An example is the Banbury No. 11 (Figure 242), with an approximate capacity of 300 pounds of crude rubber per batch. The standard machine for rubber is equipped with spray cooling of the sides and circulating system for the rotors and the discharge door.

The time required for thorough mixing is astonishingly short. Thus in mixing cork dust or wood flour with linseed oil in the manufacture of linoleum, the mixer does in 2½ minutes what formerly required 1½ hours on a series of devices. Asphalts and gilsonite loaded in cold lump form into a hot Banbury become a stiff plastic in from ½ to 1½ minutes; fillers and fibers may be added and the mixed batch dumped in about 6 minutes over-all. Pigments may be mixed with nitrocellulose, synthetic resins,

Figure 242.—The latest design of No. 11 Banbury mixer. When used for working rubber, the sides of the bowl are spray-cooled from nozzles behind the curtain, shown in center. (Courtesy Farrel-Birmingham Co., Inc., Ansonia, Conn.)

varnishes, or heavy-bodied oils in from 6 to 20 minutes, instead of in 24 or more hours by other methods. In mixing high-grade tire tread stock, five No. 11 Banbury mixers, with five 84-inch roll mills for sheeting, mix and sheet 194,280 pounds of stock per 24 hours, whereas formerly nineteen 84-inch roll mills had to be used for the same production in the same period.

The progress of the mixing is followed by watching the position and movement of the tell-tale rod attached to the floating weight, and by other means. The mixer is discharged by opening a sliding discharge door in

he bottom of the mixing chamber; the operation of this door may be made
ιutomatic. A number of recording and controlling devices may be in-
talled.

There are eight standard sizes of Banburys. The largest, No. 27,
aking a 600-pound crude rubber batch, is equipped with a 500-hp motor.

Mixing Mills. The heavy duty two-roll mill, with open rolls (Figure
ι43), was the sole standard device for mixing rubber, until the advent of
he Banbury internal mixer in the early 1920's. It is also called a plastics
nill. There are a number of sizes, but in general, the rolls are 22 or 24
nches in diameter and from 48 to 84 inches long. The mill shown in
ℱigure 243 is a 22 by 60 inch; the cylinders are chamber-bored and when
nilling rubber are water-cooled. The relative speed of the two rolls may
vary from even speed to a differential as high as 3 to 1. For average con-

FIGURE 243.—A heavy-duty two-roll mill, with open rolls, also called a plastics mill or
plastics rolls. (Courtesy Farrel-Birmingham Co., Inc., Ansonia, Conn.)

ditions the drive roll (the rear roll on the mill shown) turns at between
20 and 22 rpm, while the front or driven roll turns at approximately 16
or 17 rpm; the differential is 1¼ to 1. The rubber is not only worked,
but may be compounded on these rolls; in either case it becomes quite hot,
in spite of the water-cooling. The method of mixing consists in allowing
the front roll to coat itself with the plastic, then cutting along the face of
roll with a sharp knife and folding over to the top of the rolls; material
collected in the pan below is also continuously fed back to the rolls.
The rolls may be adjusted forward as well as back, and the gap between
them altered at any time; graduated dials on the adjusting screws indicate the amount of movement of the front roll.

This mill may be run at high temperature as well, by heating the
rolls, the surfaces of which may be chrome-plated. The pan under the
rolls may be made of stainless steel. The mill is driven by an electric
motor through an enclosed reduction unit and cut spur bull gears which

run in oil; a series, or "line," of such mills may be driven by a single main shaft actuated by a motor. Celluloid is one of the plastics handled successfully on this mill.

MIXING OF SOLIDS WITH SOLIDS

Blenders and Tumblers. The blending of different solids is performed in several ways, each of which is exhibited in the corresponding device.

In the conical-type dry blender, of which a new example is shown in Figure 244, the solids are tumbled against sloping walls so that their relative disposition is constantly changed. In this machine, uniformity is reached in a short time, and when additions as small as one or two per cent

FIGURE 244.—A conical dry blender for mixing or blending dry powders with improved facilities for loading, discharging, and cleaning. The blender rotates on a horizontal axis. (Courtesy Patterson Foundry and Machine Co., East Liverpool, Ohio.)

are made, they are incorporated in the larger quantity in the same period, and a homogeneous product results. The blender shown has an improved method of loading and discharging; it is built of plain steel, stainless steel, and other metals.

Another tumbling mixer* consists of a round-cornered square box mounted on a horizontal shaft at such an angle that none of its sides is parallel to the shaft. As the box revolves, the material is thrown to each of the sides of the box in turn, so that the batch travels from one end of the mixer to the other. The batch is further subjected to violent mixing by the revolving mixing knives which are mounted in opposite corners of the box. This mixer will incorporate one half of one per cent of any

* Aurelio Tanzi Engineering Co., 235 Fourth Ave., New York.

particular dry material in a batch of several ingredients of different specific gravities, so that a homogeneous mixture results. The Day Oblique Revolving Drum is also so mounted that the charge tumbles on sloping walls, and travels from end to end. Baffles are furnished if desired. The drums are made of plain steel or stainless steel, and in a wide range of sizes.

The Patterson Triplex Dry Blender operates on the principle of dividing the material into thirds by geometric progression. In addition, the material undergoes the conventional mixing process during its travel, because of the rotation of the cylinders. The construction of the blender is shown in Figure 245. The material fed to the blender at the left enters a single helicoid screw flight fastened to the outer shell, traveling one-

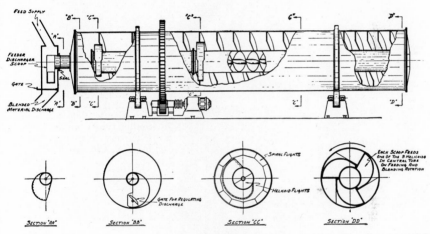

FIGURE 245.—The Patterson triplex dry blender, for mixing and blending dry materials. (Courtesy Patterson Foundry and Machine Co., East Liverpool, Ohio.)

third the length of the blender, where it enters a double helicoid screw flight, thus becoming divided into two streams. When the third compartment is reached, the material enters a triple helicoid flight, and division into three distinct streams is accomplished. Each of the three compartments of the outer cylinder is equipped with an individual scoop which picks up one-third of the material and deposits it in the inner cylinder. Again it is divided into sections traveling left toward the starting point the length of one compartment, or one-third the length of the blender, where one stream is permitted to return to the outer cylinder and a double stream is carried through the second compartment. Another stream is dropped at the end of the second compartment and the third near the feed end of the machine. The result is mechanical division in thirds, four cycles causing eighty-one divisions, or practically complete mixing. One cycle averages approximately fifteen revolutions. Discharge is accomplished by reversing the direction of rotation, through the feed opening; or it may be arranged at the opposite end.

Two solids may be mixed, or rather, simultaneously ground and mixed, in a ball mill or pebble mill, which have been described elsewhere. Solids are mixed, as well as moved to a discharge point, by the plows in a mechanical shelf burner, and in a one-floor roasting furnace, such as the Mannheim.

Pan Mixers or Mullers.   Mulling is the second way in which solids may be mixed with solids.   The mulling action is comparable to the rubbing,

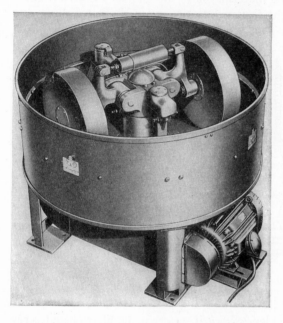

FIGURE 246.—An interior view of the new No. 2 F Simpson Mix-Muller, an intensive, muller-type mixer, (1952). (Courtesy National Engineering Co., Chicago 6, Ill.)

kneading, or smearing action of the mortar and pestle; no grinding is involved. The machine for mulling consists of a circular stationary pan in which is mounted a special combination of mullers and plows which revolves (Figure 246). The mullers are flat circular members running on their edges. They are adjustable, and are mounted on rocker arms so that they are free to ride on the material, creating pressure and an intensive rubbing action as they revolve, and are pulled in constantly by the central post out of their normal forward path. At the same time, the plows rake the material into the path of the runners, turning it over at the same time (a shoveling action). The mixing is rapid, thorough distribution and diffusion of the various elements in the mix producing a strictly uniform product. After preparation, the material is discharged, by the action of the plows, through a door at the bottom of the pan. The cycle of operations—loading, mixing, and discharging—for a 4-foot 6-inch diameter pan mixer, when handling core and facing sands in a foundry, is 3 to 5 minutes. The mullers are generally of metal, such as high-carbon rolled steel tires shrunk on cast-iron centers (Simpson), or alloy-steel tires; they are also

Figure 247.—A 24-inch diameter Simpson intensive mixer arranged for vacuum operation and equipped with electrical heating elements. (Courtesy National Engineering Co., Chicago, Ill.)

made of stone, as already described, and of other materials. The weight of the muller is great, and varies with the size of the mixer, as shown in Table 49a. Instead of the pair of mullers generally used, a single muller

Table 49a. Simpson Intensive Mixers

No.*	Diameter of Pan (feet)	Weight of Muller (lbs)	Diameter of Muller (in)	Face (in)	Rpm of Vertical Shaft
1	4	375	26	5	37
2	6	1000	30	9	25
3	8	2200	36	11	19½

* There are two larger sizes, and several intermediate ones.

may be used in 3- or 4-foot diameter pans, to afford maximum clearances for efficient mulling. The capacity varies with the length of the cycle which depends upon the duty; a 4-foot 6-inch diameter mixer produces 5 to 6 tons of core or facing sands per hour.

Mullers are used in many industries. One recently developed example of its use for dry solids is the mixing of vitamin products. Inasmuch as the amounts of vitamins blended into flour and other bulk foods are minute, it has been found advisable to use a pre-mixer for blending these small amounts with the base ingredients (Simpson). The blending of powdered metals is an interesting application of the same mixer, as is also the preparation of coatings for welding electrodes.

Mullers are made not only in a number of sizes, but also in different models, for example, an open model, a closed model for vacuum applica-

FIGURE 248.—Side view of No. 2 Simpson intensive mixer, a pan mixer or muller, showing driving mechanism and discharge apron. (Courtesy National Engineering Co., Chicago, Ill.)

FIGURE 249.—Two different kinds of mixing and stirring conveyor flights. Upper, cut and folded flight conveyor; lower, conveyor with mixing paddles. (Courtesy Link-Belt Co., Chicago, Ill.)

tion for de-airing clays, and a model with jackets in the walls of the crib for water or steam. Use of a muller in the mixing of pastes has been described.

Screw Conveyors. Solids are also mixed with solids by the screw conveyor. The primary task of the screw conveyor is to move the solids from the place of entry to the discharge spout, but besides the lateral motion, much mixing unavoidably takes place. The mixing action is accentuated y using spirals which are suitably notched or carry small rakes on the haft. Two such mixing conveyors are shown in Figure 249.

Ribbon Agitators. A fourth way of mixing solids with solids is by means of the ribbon agitator, of which one example is shown in Figure 50. The multiple-ribbon mixing conveyor consists of four ribbons of lifferent diameters opposite in hand, one set inside the other. The mateial is carried forward by one ribbon and then backward by another, and becomes thoroughly worked and mixed. The multiple ribbon shown eads to end discharge, and serves for continuous operation. There is also center discharge construction. When the material is heavy, alternate ections of the outer ribbon are left out so that the movement of the gitator through the material is made easier.

FIGURE 250.—Multiple-ribbon conveyor, for mixing and stirring solids. (Courtesy Link-Belt Co., Chicago, Ill.)

Ribbon agitators may be used in the usual conveyor trough with rounded bottom, or in batch mixers which have the shape of a section of the trough but are larger in dimensions, and are made of iron, or for certain products such as starch, of cypress wood.

Mixing Cones. Very fair mixing is obtained in a simple way, suitable for example for the preparation of mixed feeds for poultry. The several materials are deposited from overhead storage bins onto a moving conveyor belt at a definite rate corresponding to the relative amount in the final mix. The same belt receives all the materials, one above the other, as it passes under the several bins. At the turn of the belt, all of its load is dumped onto a cone, down the sides of which the material runs, becoming mixed at the same time. It is screw-conveyed from the base of the cone to the bagging machines.

Reading References

"Processing of viscous materials," by Harold A. Levey, *Chem. Met. Eng.*, **46**, 371 (1939).
"The flow of pseudo-plastic materials," by R. V. Williamson, *Ind. Eng. Chem.*, **21**, 1108 (1929).

A comparatively new science in the separation of solids from liquids—the science of settling—has grown up in the past 40 years, and based upon this science, a large and still increasing number of devices have been made available to the chemical plant engineer. Now thickeners which not only concentrate a slurry, but wash it economically, are in daily operation.

12. SEPARATION OF SOLIDS FROM LIQUIDS

I. SETTLERS AND THICKENERS

The devices generally associated with the separation of solids from liquids are filters, discussed in the next chapter, and centrifugal baskets which follow in Chapter 14. A separation of solids from liquids is possible, however, by simpler means, namely by settling the suspended material, which permits the decantation of the supernatant clear, or more or less clear, liquid and the collection of the suspension in a more concentrated form. The latter may then be fed to a filter, for separation of further quantities of liquid from the solid.

A settling tank is indeed a valuable device for this separation. It may be built rather tall, with a cone-shaped bottom, and with a number of outlets at different levels; thus it is possible to find the lowest layer of clear liquid, and to run off a maximum quantity. The operation is by the batch, and is interrupted each time a new batch is introduced. By installing a number of settlers, a continuous supply of clear liquor may be provided.

A settling tank wholly in the form of a cone has been devised. It has continuous feed, continuous discharge of clarified liquor, and intermittent discharge of thickened sludge, yet it is without mechanism. An example is the Allen cone. As the density of the thickening sludge rises, a float finally is lifted, and with it, levers and connections which open a plug valve at the base, allowing a thick sludge to escape. The thinner slurry follows the sludge downward, bringing about a fall in density, so that the float drops, which in turn causes the valve to close.

Batch settlers and even continuously operated cones have been found unsatisfactory for a number of duties. Settlers with mechanical scraper arms for the discharge of the mud have been developed; they offer more regular action and greater convenience of layout. In these newer forms of settlers, settling is made to take place in shallow vessels, for it has been demonstrated that tanks of equal diameter produce substantially the same quantity of clear liquid irrespective of depth.

Continuous mechanical settling units are generally known as thickeners or clarifiers, depending on whether their main purpose is to separate the liquid from a fairly concentrated suspension, such as one with 1 to 25 per cent solids, or to clarify a liquid containing a small percentage, often measured in parts per million, of suspended solids. The mechanical principle is the same in both, except that clarifiers, used primarily in water softening and sewage purification, are of lighter construction than thickeners. It is the latter which are more frequently encountered in the chemical and metallurgical fields.

TABLE 50. CLASSIFICATION OF SETTLERS, THICKENERS AND CLARIFIERS

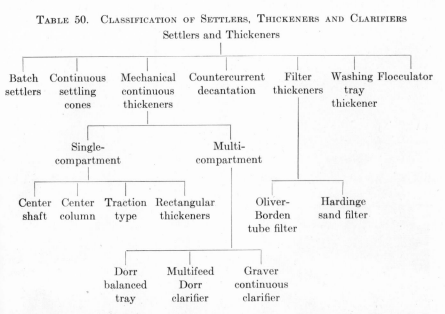

Mechanical Continuous Thickeners, Single-compartment. Mechanical continuous thickeners are used primarily for large-scale continuous operation, and are built in sizes ranging from 6 to 325 feet in diameter. They are essentially settlers with continuous discharge, by mechanical means, of the more concentrated mud, and with continuous run-off of the supernatant liquid; the latter may be crystal clear, or slightly turbid. The many virtues of the mechanical continuous thickener have led to its introduction in the strictly chemical field, for the handling of large, medium, and even small volumes of slurries.

It must be remembered that the thickener does nothing to accelerate the settling; improvements in the rate of settling—a matter of the greatest importance in the design and operation of thickeners—must be obtained in the processing of the slurry.

As an example of large mechanical thickeners, one installed in the open for a cement factory will be described. The function of the thickener is to concentrate the raw materials slurry destined for the cement kiln. The thickener (Dorr) consists of a circular concrete tank 125 feet in diameter with vertical sides about 12 feet high and the bottom sloping to a central discharge hopper. A central concrete column carries the mud-raking mechanism which consists of four radial arms fitted with inclined scraping blades. The arms are rotated by a gear mechanism supported by the central column, and make one revolution in 30 minutes.

The slurry is delivered to a central feedwell by means of an inclined radial feed launder. The liquid moves toward the periphery at a pro-

Figure 251.—A 125-foot Dorr continuous thickener, single compartment, installed at a cement plant. The raw material slurry is thickened in this unit before being fed to the kilns. (Ideal Cement Co., Devil's Slide, Utah.)

gressively decreasing speed, allowing the suspended material to settle to the bottom. The clear liquid finally leaves the tank through an annular overflow launder with suitable outlets. The settled solids are moved by the rotating arms toward the central hopper, from which a diaphragm pump draws them away.

The thickener described is one of three similar units installed at one plant. It receives 875 tons per day of finely ground raw cement materials as a suspension with about 15 per cent solids, and thickens this to a consistency of about 70 per cent solids.

The Dorr thickener just described is known more specifically as the

Torq thickener. In the Torq thickener, the rake arms are secured to the central rotating cage by a hinge-like mechanism which allows them to tilt upward and backward should they encounter an obstruction. When that happens, the arms continue their rotation by climbing over the obstruction, which consists of an accidentally formed heap of mud. While passing over the heap, the plows at the same time dig in and remove a portion. After several more revolutions, the obstruction is swept away and normal operation is resumed. All these operations are automatic. For certain duties* the Torq thickener is recommended in place of the

FIGURE 252.—An outstanding example of continuous thickening in the chemical industry. At this plant, thousands of tons per day of milk of lime are thickened from 12 to 27 per cent solids in the 150-foot diameter Dorr thickener shown in the foreground. The thickened sludge is then used to precipitate magnesium hydroxide from several thousand gallons per minute of sea water, and the suspension obtained is reduced to one fortieth or less of its original volume by thickening in four 200-foot diameter Dorr thickeners seen at the center of the picture. This plant was installed in 1940 by the Dow Chemical Company at Freeport, Texas.

Traction thickener. Dorr Torq thickeners are available in sizes ranging from 30 to 200 feet in diameter.

The Hardinge clarifiers and thickeners may embody the *Auto-Raise* feature, by which the scrapers are automatically raised when an overload occurs. The drive mechanism and scrapers may be supported by I-beams placed across the tank, or by a structural steel truss. For large tanks, usually 60 feet and more in diameter, a combination of I-beam and center column structure is favored. The center-drive works in a circular tank which may have any dimension from 6 to 150 feet in diameter. The

* Seventy-two Dorr Torq thickeners, 125 feet in diameter, were installed at the All-American Canal desilting plant near Yuma, Arizona.

thickened sludge is moved to the center where a hopper collects it, from which it is removed by a sludge pump. The tanks may be of wood, steel, or concrete. For resistance to corrosive solutions, the Hardinge scraper assembly may consist of wood and "Monel" metal, for example.

A time-proved apparatus, well suited to chemical plant operations, is the *Denver spiral rake thickener* which comes with either a single or a double spiral rake. The raking mechanism imparts a continuous turning motion to the thickened pulp which conveys it in one revolution from the circumference of the tank to the center cone. The thickeners between 5

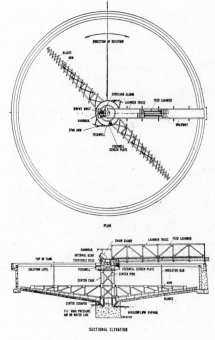

FIGURE 253.—The Dorr Torq thickener. The rake arms are hinged to the center cage and raise automatically when actuated by the torque of an overload, which may be caused by an obstruction or by a too heavy accumulation of sand.

and 40 feet in diameter have a low superstructure, consisting of two heavy structural steel members; the large thickeners, 40 to 75 feet in diameter, have a bridge superstructure. All of them have steel tanks, with a circular launder inside the top edge for the effluent. The feed is in the center near the surface; the thickened pulp collects in the center cone in the base and is conveyed thence to the pump.

The Dorr Torq thickener, which has been described, is a center-column thickener. *Dorr type A thickener* is a single-compartment thickener with center-shaft mechanism. It is made in sizes ranging from 6 feet to 40 feet in diameter, of standard or heavy-duty construction.

In the *Dorr traction thickeners* the main raking blades are carried by a rotating truss supported at one end by a bearing on a central post, and at the other by a motor-driven carriage with two traction wheels traveling on a rail along the periphery of the tank. The current for the driving motors is brought in through a conduit in the central post to slip rings which are in contact with brushes on the rotating truss. Other conduits bring the current from the brushes to the motors. The principal application of the Dorr traction thickener is in the 200- to 325-foot diameter ranges.

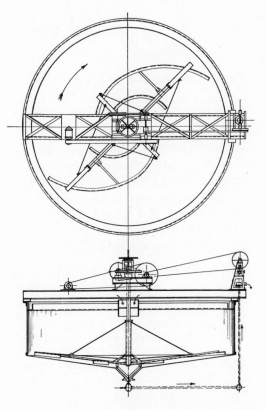

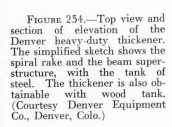

FIGURE 254.—Top view and section of elevation of the Denver heavy-duty thickener. The simplified sketch shows the spiral rake and the beam superstructure, with the tank of steel. The thickener is also obtainable with wood tank. (Courtesy Denver Equipment Co., Denver, Colo.)

Thickeners are available with square tanks, in which rake arms sweep a circle, leaving the four corners to fill, or with rectangular tanks, in which a scraper is carried back and forth by a bridge crane, the scraper working on one trip only. As an example of the latter, the *Hardinge crane type rectangular clarifier* may be selected.

On a rectangular tank 10 by 30 feet, let us say, there will be provided a bridge crane spanning the narrow width of 10 feet, traveling forward the length of the tank (30 feet) and then returning. The sludge collector consists of a scraper blade carried by the crane, traveling slowly along the bottom of the tank and pushing the mud ahead of it very gently until the mud falls into a collection hopper (or two hoppers side by side) set below the tank level. At the end of the trip the direction is reversed automatically, and the scraper blade turned 90°, so that on the return trip it

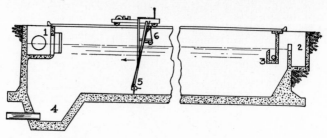

FIGURE 255.—A rectangular tank clarifier or thickener. *1*, influent; *2*, outfall of clear water; *3*, scum trough; *4*, sludge hopper; *5*, scraper blade in operating position, crane bridge traveling as shown; *6*, skimmer blade, not working on the return trip; blade *5* is horizontal, and blade *6*, vertical. (From Hardinge model.)

leaves the mud undisturbed. The bridge crane also carries a skimmer blade traveling along the surface; this works only on the return trip. It pushes any floating matter toward a scum trough, placed at the surface near the starting point of the forward trip. The slurry enters at the surface just over the mud hopper; the clarified effluent leaves at the surface at the other end, just behind the scum hopper, as shown in Figure 255.

The tanks are built in sizes from 10 to 65 feet for the narrow dimension, with the long dimension preferably 3 to 5 times the narrow one.

TABLE 51. PERFORMANCE OF THICKENERS AND CLARIFIERS*

No.	Size (ft)	Slurry	Mesh	Rate of Feed (tons/day)	Solids in Feed	Solids in Under-flow(%)	Remarks
4	6 × 5	Paint pigment	300	39	5.7%	33	Solubles washed out
3	16 × 8	Iron oxide	300	162	10	33	C.C.D. washing
1	20 × 8	Zinc, copper, lead ore	99.5% −200	400	20	40	
2	25 × 10	Calcium carbonate	200	450 each	10	38	Feed is 14° Bé caustic liquor
1	40 × 10	Flotation tailings	65% −200	800	20	55	To recover the water
1	40 × 12	Flotation mill concentrates		1050	25	56	
Clarifiers			(gallons/day)				
12 × 60 rectangular		Sewage	300,000	141 ppm	4.2	66% of solids removed	
28 × 8 round		Aerated sewage	350,000	330 ppm	7	40 ppm in effluent	
30 × 30 sq round mech.		Softened water calcium carbonate sludge	800,000	0.01%	8	Producing clear water	
66 × 12 round		Waste water from de-inking plant	1.2 million	0.12%	8	To retain settleable matter	

* Data supplied by the Hardinge Co., York, Pa.

In the rectangular clarifier it will be noticed that the flow of the slurry and liquor is across the tank, from one side to the other. This is the regular method for rectangular tanks.

Where process and plant layout conditions permit, Dorr square clarifiers are designed for radial rather than transverse flow.

Mechanical Continuous Thickeners, Multi-compartment. In the *Dorr balanced tray* thickener there are two (or more) compartments over each other in one tank, each with its own slurry feed and clear liquor overflow. A central shaft carries both sets of rake arms with their plows. The box on the left in Figure 256 divides the feed equally between the

FIGURE 256.—A two-compartment Dorr balanced tray thickener.

two settling chambers, and that on the right collects the two overflows. Settled solids from the upper chamber fall through the central boot to a discharge cone, common for all chambers. Units of this type with two to five settling chambers, or compartments, are available. The two-tray unit has a settling capacity almost twice that of the same tank fitted out as a single unit.

The *Dorr Multifeed cane juice clarifier* and the Dorr Multifeed carbonation thickener are special types of multi-compartment thickeners applied to the defecation of sugar juices. These essentially similar machines consist of a cylindrical upright steel tank with trays sloping toward the center and dividing the tank into a number of chambers: a flocculating chamber at the top; from one to four clarifying chambers in the middle;

and a combined clarifying and mud thickening chamber at the bottom. The raw juice enters the flocculating chamber at the top. Clarified juice is drawn from the upper zones of all the chambers, the amount withdrawn being regulated by adjustable sleeves in the overflow box, located on the outer side near the top of the tank. The settled mud, raked to the center of each tray, flows through annular passages around the central tube to

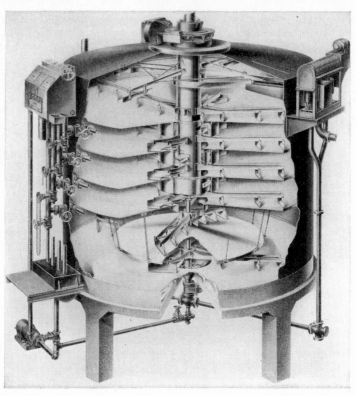

FIGURE 257.—The Dorr Multifeed cane juice clarifier. Limed juice from the upper or flocculating chamber flows into the central tube and is distributed radially into the four settling chambers below.

a mud-thickening cone hanging in the bottom chamber, and is finally raked to a common mud-discharge cone on the tank bottom.

In the *Graver continuous clarifier*, advantage is taken of the fact that there is greater yield, per volume of slurry, of clear juices in shallow vessels; thus the clarifier is given shallow compartments which are bell-like, with sloping tops, between two and five in number, according to the magnitude of the operation. Mechanical arms remove the settled mud from each shelf. A coagulation compartment is provided at the top of the clarifier as a first level, where the gentle movement of arms and loose-hung paddles promotes the formation and growth of floccules. The top of each bell is the floor of the clarifying compartment above it (see Figure 258).

The Graver continuous clarifier is circular, and has a slowly rotating central shaft with arms and plows at each tray. The rate of rotation of the main shaft is from 3 to 12 revolutions per hour. The plows gently

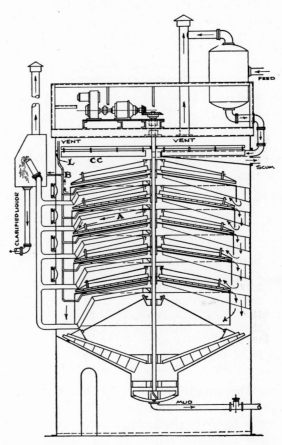

FIGURE 258.—A simplified sketch of the Graver continuous clarifier, which illustrates a continuous settling unit, with mechanical propulsion of sludge. Note the eight bells whose tops bear the sludge, which is removed very gently by the rotating arms. *A*, clarifier liquor drawoff; *B*, vent pipes; *C*, coagulation chamber; *L*, level of the slurry feed in the coagulation chamber. All other compartments are filled with liquor.

push the mud toward the circumference, where it drops slowly down, finally reaching the cone-shaped bottom.

The coagulation chamber is only partly filled. A trough 12 inches wide and 8 inches deep, for example, with sloping bottom, is constructed near the liquid surface and under the feed pipe. The rotating paddles sweep the scums into the trough, whence they are conducted to an outside storage tank.

In the clarifier with five compartments the five floors (bell tops) slope downward toward the circumference; the bottom plate slopes toward the center, where an auxiliary bottom for mud drawoff is provided for the elimination of clogging. When the liquors must be kept hot, the clarifier may be readily insulated.

The clear juice is drawn from the uppermost zone in each of the clarifying compartments. Each bell is vented. Provision is made for the recirculation of a certain proportion of the mud in processes which require it (such as certain water clarifications), and for drawing off all the contents of the clarifier (liquidation).

The clarifier is made in 9 sizes, as indicated in Table 52.

TABLE 52. THE GRAVER CONTINUOUS CLARIFIER*

Model	Diameter (ft)	Height (ft)	Chambers	Settling Area (sq ft)	Holding Capacity (gallons)
2630	26	30	5	2200	81,000
2428	24	28	5	1815	65,800
2227	22	27	5	1500	49,500
2026	20	26	5	1200	40,450
1826	18	26	5	825	33,370
1525	15	25	5	614	22,060
1220	12	20	4	299	11,150
10-½-18	10½	18	3	158	6,800
10-½-16	10½	16	2	105	5,100

Height is for tank proper; holding capacity is effective holding capacity. (By courtesy of Graver Tank and Mfg. Co., Inc., East Chicago, Indiana.)
* In the metric system, the figures are:

Model	Diameter (meters)	Height (meters)	Chambers	Settling Area (sq m)	Holding Capacity (liters)
2630	7.93	9.15	5	204.38	306,620
2428	7.33	8.53	5	168.61	249,100
2227	6.71	8.23	5	139.35	187,400
2026	6.10	7.93	5	111.48	153,120
1826	5.49	7.93	5	76.64	126,340
1525	4.57	7.62	5	57.04	83,520
1220	3.66	6.10	4	27.78	42,200
10-½-18	3.20	5.49	3	14.59	25,740
10-½-16	3.20	4.88	2	10.31	20,835

The capacity in delivered clear liquor depends on the rate of settling, and varies with other circumstances. Only by choosing a standard juice can a figure be cited which will serve as a guide. For the raw sugar juice from Louisiana canes, the throughput of No. 2630 clarifier is approximately 550 to 600 gallons (2080 to 2270 liters) per minute, which is the equivalent of the amount of juice provided by 3000 tons of sugar cane per day (2725 metric tons), with approximately 30 per cent maceration water. The throughput figure is based on a settling rate of 1.5 inches (3.81 cm) or more per minute, maximum clarity of overflow, and density of underflow. The Graver continuous clarifier finds its main application in sugar cane juice clarification.

Continuous decantation produces an overflow which in most cases is found to be sufficiently clear for use without further mechanical treatment.   When a crystal-clear liquid is wanted and cannot be obtained by decantation alone, clarifying filters of various kinds, including sand filters, may be used.   Some of the sand filters are constructed as thickeners, with a scraper assembly which works on the top layer of sand (for example, the *Hardinge sand filter-clarifier*, bull. 30-B).   Any solids which the influent carried originally are retained by the sand on its upper surface, and are scraped away by the rotating mechanism.   The scraper is lowered a fraction of an inch per day, so that it may remove the portion of the sand which has become clogged by particles of the solids.   The sand scraped away is removed with the sludge through a central submerged outlet.   The filter-bed is thus restored to its original porosity and to its free-filtering quality.

Continuous Counter-current Decantation.   The mechanical thickeners lend themselves well to installations for counter-current washing and decantation with continuous operation.   In a set of three thickeners, for ex-

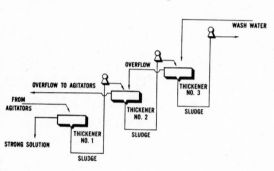

Figure 259.—A continuous countercurrent decantation flowsheet. (Dorrco.)

ample, the first would produce a final, strong liquor as overflow, and a sludge still rich in soluble substances.   The sludge is pumped into a repulper, where a weaker overflow is used to produce a slurry, which is thickened in the second thickener (at a higher level).   The sludge from the second thickener is pumped to another repulper, where it meets water, and then enters the third thickener, whose underflow now contains no more soluble matter; it may be wasted, or it may be processed further. The overflow from the third tank travels by gravity to the repulper at tank 2; the overflow from tank 2 is applied to the material to be extracted, usually in agitators.   In the decantation plant, the sludge and liquor travel counter-current to each other; in Figure 259 the sludge travels from left to right, the water and liquor from right to left.

The pumps used to handle the sludge are generally of the diaphragm type, especially designed for this service (Denver, Dorrco).

Dorr Washing Tray Thickener.   The Dorr washing tray thickener is a multi-compartment thickener in which the various compartments are connected in series so as to provide for countercurrent washing of the sludge. From two to seven trays may be used. Water is introduced into the lower compartment and travels upward following the path schematically indicated by the arrows in Figure 260, and meeting the descending sludge at each tray. The sludge travels downward, falling directly from one compartment into the next. A sludge seal at the center of each tray prevents the water and wash solutions from passing directly upward through the central openings, which would interfere with the sedimentation process. The actual path of water and wash solution is through outside pipes and control boxes, clearly visible in the illustration. High-pressure air and water lines may be connected to the underflow piping for cleaning purposes.

The thickener just described is the standard type. There are also "combination" types in which the sludge is removed separately from the top tray and mixed with wash solution outside. Other "combination"

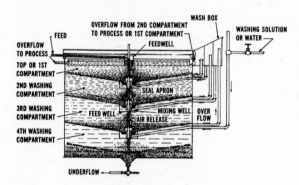

Figure 260.—An illustrative drawing of the Dorr washing tray thickener, standard type. (All the pictures and sketches of Dorr equipment by courtesy of The Dorr Co., Engineers, Barry Place, Stamford, Conn.)

types combine the features of the Dorr balanced tray thickener with those of the Dorr washing tray thickener, thus providing for large settling capacity and countercurrent washing in a single unit of relatively small diameter.

"For rough and very preliminary estimating purposes, the cost of a Dorr thickener, f.o.b. factory, consisting of iron and steel mechanism, steel superstructure, and open steel tank, may be taken at from $4 to $10 per square foot of settling area. Accessories such as pumps, tank covers, motor-drive units, piping, insulation, and others, are not included.

"Special materials of construction, such as lead or rubber-covered steel, wood, hard lead, and special alloys, alter the unit cost to such a wide extent that no reliable estimating figures may be given for thickeners of such special construction."*

Dorrco Flocculator. Solids which are very finely divided and in low concentration settle with difficulty unless the individual particles coalesce

---

* Quoted from J. H. Perry's "Chemical Engineers' Handbook," 3rd ed., p. 944, New York, McGraw-Hill Book Company, 1950.

in the form of flocs. In many cases, such flocs form spontaneously, or else their formation may be caused by the addition of suitable coagulants. To enhance the process and promote the formation of denser, fast-settling flocs, mechanical flocculation is used. A typical example of the kind of equipment available for this purpose is offered by the Dorrco Flocculator, a device often used in connection with the purification of municipal and other waters. The Dorrco Flocculator consists of a number of slowly re-

Figure 261.—A municipal water softening installation including Dorrco "Flocculators" and Dorr Clarifiers.

volving submerged paddles mounted on shafts resting on short piers installed in the sedimentation basin in the path of the slowly moving mass of water. The shafts are rotated by a chain and sprocket at the side of the basin. The paddles lie transversely to the travel of the water. Baffles reaching part way down from the surface are provided between the paddles, and in the sort of compartment so formed, a motion of the water similar to a gentle barrel roll is produced. The flocs sweep back and forth and have the maximum number of chances of being brought into contact with the fine dirt; as a result they grow in size, and trap essentially all the suspended matter. At the end of the basin, the well flocculated, cleaned water enters a clarifier or thickener. A portion of the well flocculated water (with its floccules) is swept back along the bottom of the tank to the influent end, where it joins the new water, providing some of the nuclei for further floc formation.

Figure 261 shows a municipal water softening installation including Dorrco Flocculators and Dorr Clarifiers. In operation, raw water mixed with chemicals flows across the three rows of Flocculator paddles, visible in the foreground, and dense, fast-settling flocs of precipitated matter are formed. The water then passes directly into the square-tank Dorrco clarifier, on the left of the picture, where the flocs settle. A duplicate identical system, used for secondary treatment, is visible in the background.

The following designations, Flocculator, Multifeed and Torq are trademarks of the Dorr Company, Reg. U. S. Patent Office.

Reading References

"Methods for determining the capacities of slime-settling tanks," by H. S. Coe and G. H. Clevenger, *Trans. A.I.M.E.*, 55, 356 (1916).

"Technique of settling separations," by Anthony Anable and Chester L. Knowles, *Chem. Met. Eng.*, 45, 260 (1938).

"Solid-liquid separations," by J. V. N. Dorr and Franklin P. Lasseter, in "Colloid Chemistry," J. Alexander (ed.), pp. 782–799, New York, Reinhold Publishing Corp., 1946.

"Thickening—art or science?" by E. J. Roberts, *Mining Eng.*, 1, 61 (March 1949).

"Chemical Engineers' Handbook," by J. H. Perry (ed.), pp. 937–955, New York, McGraw-Hill Book Co., 1950.

In the simpler days of yore, the central piece of apparatus in the chemical plant was the filter. It was the filter which permitted the separation of the valuable precipitate from the generally valueless solution, and in other processes, of the prized clear solution from an undesirable mud. Today there are many huge operations which do not require the services of the filter. Nevertheless, filters, filter presses, and suction filters have been developed and so well adapted to modern processes that they retain a prominent place among apparatus serving the chemical industries.

13. SEPARATION OF SOLIDS FROM LIQUIDS
II. FILTERS

In the broadest sense, filtration is the separation of suspended particles or droplets from a fluid by passage through a pervious membrane. Dust may be filtered from air, thus purifying the latter; oil droplets may be filtered from water, or from a gas; solids suspended in water or salt solutions may be removed from the liquid by filtration. The apparatus to be described in this chapter, and most of the discussion, will concern itself with the third kind of separation.

The separation of a liquid, perhaps containing valuable constituents in solution, from the accompanying solid, which may or may not have value, is an operation which must be performed repeatedly. When there is no time limit, and the scope of the operation is modest, settling tanks may serve; an accelerated settling brought about by judicious treatment of the reacting substances and made to take place in mechanical settlers with continuous operation, has extended the usefulness of settling apparatus, as described in the preceding chapter. Generally, however, the time is very limited and, there is no provision for extensive storage, so that the separation must be performed without delay. A filter is then imperative.

The slurry—the suspension of solids in either water or a solution—is fed to a filtering device for the purpose of separating it into a clear liquid (the filtrate) and the solids, called the cake, the latter being wet. The wet cake retains much liquid in its interstices; when the liquid carries valuable materials in solution, it is advisable to recover it. This may be done partially by blowing with air or steam, or more thoroughly by washing. Most filters are therefore so conceived as to allow these operations. The discussion of filtering devices will thus include remarks on slurry, filtrate, wash, and cake, and to these must be added filter medium, which is the surface against which the cake deposits and through which the filtrate runs. The commonest filter medium is filter cloth of cotton duck or twill.

In the majority of chemical processes, the solution is so rich in dissolved materials that its floating power will be considerably greater than that of water; therefore, the settling out of the suspended solids will be less easy and the slurry will be more stable. It is desirable that the. slurry be reasonably stable, so that it may be passed through a pump (or a blow case, now less favored than formerly), and through pipelines with their cocks and valves, on the way to the filtering device. The varied needs of the chemical and process industries in general, including metallurgical plants, have stimulated a number of ingenious inventions and developments of filtering devices, of which the typical ones will be found in Table 53.

Simple Funnel Filters. The funnel with its filter paper used in the analytical laboratory is a gravity filter; larger funnels, 6 inches across and as much as 10 or 12 inches high, are used for small batches, in the fine-chemical industry, for example.

Sand and Gravel Gravity Filters. In the purification of municipal water, a filter plant contains in many instances a number of filter beds constructed of gravel and sands, which retain the "alum floc" and any suspended solids. Example: a filter 40 feet by 33 feet in area may have at the bottom a perforated underdrain pipe overlaid by 16 inches of gravel made up of five graduated layers, and overlaid by 26 inches of sand whose grains range from 0.38 to 0.45 mm in diameter.

Gravity sand filters have been used in the filtration of dilute phosphoric acid from suspended calcium sulfate.

Sand Filters with Pressure. A similar bed of gravel and sand may be placed inside a steel shell, and water under pressure forced through it from the top downward. The dirt is retained on the sand, and is flushed out periodically by reversing the flow. Such a sand filter serves almost exclusively for water filtration; for the removal of suspended matter from river water destined, for example, to be passed through the water jackets of a blast furnace; or for other cooling purposes in the factory. Except for this cleaning period, the operation is continuous.

It is the general rule to use essentially a constantly increasing pressure on a pressure filter. Inasmuch as the thickness of the cake increases and consequently the resistance also, it is necessary to gradually increase the pressure in order to maintain the filtration rate. In addition to the sand filter just discussed, the pressure filters include the plate and frame press, the shell and leaf press, and certain forms of edge filters and clarifiers. The latter devices are grouped in a section by themselves, as their duties and problems differ markedly from filters proper.

TABLE 53. CLASSIFICATION OF FILTERS

Filters

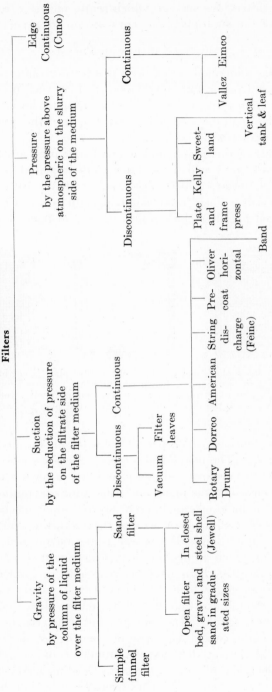

In suction filters, the suction, which really means a fractional part of the pressure of the atmosphere, is kept constant for a particular duty.

PLATE AND FRAME PRESSES

The familiar plate and frame press is a pressure filter. The slurry is fed to the filter from a pump or blow-case; however, in certain installations it is fed from the reaction tank set at a higher level, and allowed to flow under the hydraulic head so provided, into the press. This procedure will be described on p. 327.

In the fundamental design, a plate and frame press of cast iron consists of grooved plates over which the filter cloth is placed, alternating with frames. The latter are at first empty, but gradually fill with cake as the filtration proceeds. Each frame stands upright between two plates; each plate is covered by filter cloth which extends to both sides. Plates and

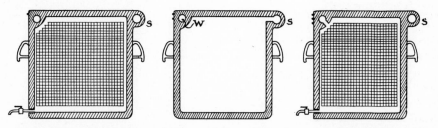

FIGURE 262.—Press plates and frame. Left, a filter plate, a one-button plate; right, a wash plate, a three-button plate, which is a filter plate adapted for washing; center, a frame, marked by two buttons. *S* is the slurry conduit; *W*, the water conduit. Only the frame has a port to the slurry line; only the wash plate has a port to the water line.

frames have extensions which permit them to ride on the two horizontal bars of the press. The heavy end pieces of the press, one stationary and the other movable, are grooved and channeled to form a half-plate each. The movable piece and the plates and frames may be pushed together and held tight by a hand-operated screw or hydraulic mechanism. Plates and frames have machined surfaces, so that with the cloth as gasket, the closed press is liquid-tight. Plates and frames have a widened edge at an upper corner in which an opening is provided, so that, when the press is closed, after the filter cloths have been suitably perforated to fit, a conduit is formed through which the slurry travels. Only the frames have ports in this conduit, so that the slurry enters them only. The clear liquid travels through the cloth and runs down the grooves to reach a port leading to an outlet cock. An "open delivery" press has such cocks, and the filtrate is in view at all times. A launder runs the full length of the press and collects the flow from the cocks, leading it to a receiving tank. A 36-inch press has plates 36 inches overall; each plate has a machined surface edge 1¼ inches wide, so that the actual filtering surface is 33½ inches square.   It may have 50 plates and 50 frames to match.

When it is required that the cake be washed, two kinds of plates must be provided, differing only slightly: one has an inner port through which water may be introduced, while the other one lacks it.   The former is called a wash plate, the latter a filtrate plate; the wash plate acts as a filtrate plate until the time for washing arrives.   All plates and frames are provided with an opening in the upper left-hand corner, for example, which forms a second conduit with the other corresponding openings when the press is closed; through this, water for washing may be introduced.   Only the wash plates are provided with an inner port leading to the line; the filter plates lack it (see Figure 262).   When washing, the delivery cock at the bottom of the wash plate is closed.   As a result, the wash water travels along the grooves of the wash plate, through the filter cloth into the cake, through the cake, and through the next filter cloth to the grooves of the filter plant, there escaping through its cock.   The flow is indicated in Figure 263.   Some manufacturers cast a little button on the outer side of the plates and frames.   In that system, the filter plate is a one-button plate, the wash plate a three-button plate, and the frame a two-button plate; this is a great convenience in giving directions.

The press just described is made of cast iron, which indeed is the material most frequently used.   But there are numerous liquids or solids which must not be contaminated by even a trace of iron; for these, wooden plates and frames, resting on steel bars, continue in favor.   There are many such wooden presses in daily use giving excellent service; their defects are that they wear fast and sometimes warp.   It is in such presses especially that the feed may be by gravity from the slurry tank set at a higher level.   An example is the separation of aniline dyes and other dyes from the liquid of reaction.   Washing has been mentioned, but for water-soluble dyes it is out of the question; instead, as much as possible of the liquid is driven out by applying a steam blow or an air blow to the press through the slurry line.   Practically all the contaminating mother liquor is removed.

The *operation* of the plate and frame press is as follows: When the press has been made ready, the slurry is fed in until the cake fills the frames, when the flow decreases and finally stops.   If washing is to be done, the water is sent in, after closing every other cock, as already explained.   The density of the wash is taken periodically; after it has reached the designated point, the water is turned off, and the press is opened.   Two men work together on presses with 36-inch plates; they push the plate away from the frame, then move the frame out a little and tilt it, to drop the cake; a rapid stroke with a large spatula or knife cleans the frame completely, and it is shoved away.   When all the frames are emptied, any crust discovered is removed with steam, any defective cloth is replaced by a new one, and the press is closed. The period of the cycle varies. A slurry with 5 per cent solids may run on a 9-hour cycle: 8 hours on the filtrate, and 1 hour to open, clean, and close. A slurry with 20 per cent solids may deliver filtrate for 3 hours, and require 1 hour to open, clean, and close—a cycle of 4 hours. For both these examples it will be noted that no washing period is provided. The duration of the cycle depends not only on the percentage of solids in the slurry, but also on the thickness of the frames; the wider, thicker frames will accommodate more cake, and permit a longer cycle.

The method of working will differ from one process to another. When the cake has value, and the liquor none, a great simplification is

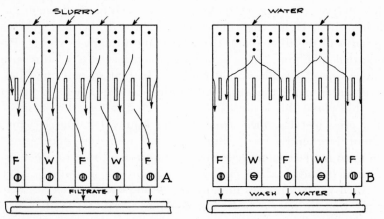

Figure 263.—Disposition of the outlet cocks in a plate and frame press. *A*, when filtering; *B*, when washing; *F*, regular filter plates; *W*, wash plates.

introduced; similarly, when the liquor has value, and the cake none. In the latter case, washing will generally be required, after which the cake may be dumped into a hopper set under the press, as the frames are tilted in cleaning; or the cake may be dropped directly into a sump tank, where a flow of water and an agitator reslurry it and a discharge spout delivers it to the sewer. This is an attractive method, which lowers the cost of handling, but it is dangerous, for any leak in the press will allow the valuable filtrate to reach the sump and be lost. Corrugated iron plates pushed under the press will diminish the loss, but constant care is required. In the third group of processes, both the cake and the filtrate are valuable, and it is these which make the most insistent demands for perfection in operation.

Wash-water Volume and Reslurrying. When the filtrate is to be saved, and the cake is not, to take a simple instance, the volume of wash water must be limited; otherwise the cost in fuel for concentration to crystallizing strength might be greater than the value of the solute. The effort is always made to have no concentration expense at all. This is done by using the wash for the solution of the next quantity of original material, so that the wash is constantly absorbed by the process, producing an equivalent volume of filtrate.

Strictly speaking, washing in the press means the removal of all remaining strong solution adhering to the inert solid; a certain amount of soluble, desirable material may be dissolved at the same time. Should there be present in cake a great deal of soluble material which is desired, it will be difficult, if not impossible, to remove it. The removal by solution of sizable quantities of soluble matter leaves the cake irregular; the wash water seeks the free channels, and after a while, there is no washing. Cake rich in soluble matter which must be recovered should be reslurried (dumped into water and agitated), and this slurry filtered and washed.

As a first approximation, the volume of wash water should not exceed that of the filtrate.

There are many *variations in the design*. The plates are generally square, but not infrequently they are circular. The frames, square or circular, may be cast with standard edging or with extra-wide edging, depending upon the pressure to be applied; the corresponding plates likewise. Plates and frames may be provided with a lug bored to provide the passage for the slurry; such a press is said to have side feed. More often this opening is provided within the square, as in the illustration of plate types (Figure 262). When there is an opening in each of the four corners (slurry, first wash, second wash, filtrate), the plates are said to be "four-eyed." The press may also have "center feed," the standard arrangement in the "recessed plates," that is, plates that are deep and require no frames, the cake collecting in the recess space available between two plates.

Open delivery of filtrate is the simpler design, but closed delivery is often favored because the filtrate, still under pressure, may be delivered under its own head to a distant or moderately elevated crystallizer. Closed delivery is achieved by providing plates and frames with one more horizontal opening in the lower left corner, for example; this opening with all the corresponding ones forms the new conduit for the filtrate.

The capacity of the press for cake is varied by changing the width of the frame; it might be 1, 1½, 2, 3 or even 4 inches. The edging of plate and frame is machine-faced, and the filter cloth laid over the whole of the plate forms a gasket, so that with the press closed a tight closure is assured, as has already been emphasized; nevertheless, designs are available with grooves for rubber or other gaskets.

The surface of the plates may have parallel grooves, as already suggested, or other designs, for each of which an advantage may be pointed out; it may have radial grooves, "pyramids," or other corrugation.

Plates and frames which are cored permit *heating* by steam circulation, or *cooling* by brine circulation. Vented plates are obtainable.

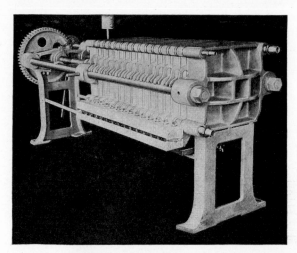

FIGURE 264.—A Sperry filter press, of leakproof construction for filtering volatiles and valuable substances. The feed is at upper right; filtrate discharge at lower left, with special protective housing for visible closed delivery. A washing fluid inlet is shown at upper left. (Courtesy D. R. Sperry and Co., Batavia, Ill.)

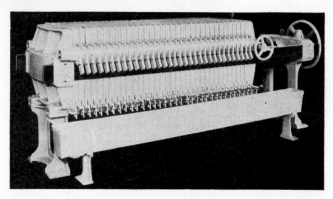

FIGURE 265.—A side feed, open delivery, washing type filter press. (Courtesy T. Shriver & Co., Harrison, N. J.)

The press may be closed by a simple screw turned by hand, with the aid of a lever which permits the application of considerable power; it may be closed by ratchet and thrust block, or in the larger sizes by hydraulic power. Distinct from the latter is the hydraulic filter press (Chapter 23).

Cast-iron plates and frames may be 7, 12, 18, 24, 30, 36, 42, 48, and 56 inches square; the actual filtering surface is less by the space occupied by the edging. The plates may be as few as six, and as many as 100, or even

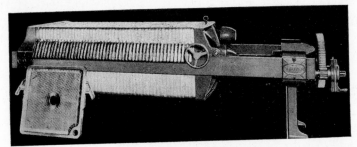

FIGURE 266.—A Shriver filter press with recessed plates and center feed.

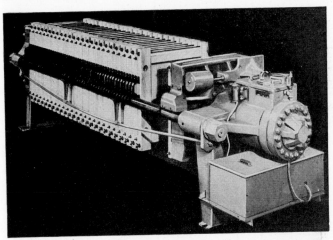

FIGURE 267.—A wood plate and frame filter press, with closed discharge, and with electric hydraulic closing device. Filter cloths not in place. The feed inlet and discharge outlet are in the fixed head on far side of press, not visible in the photograph. (Courtesy D. R. Sperry and Co., Batavia, Ill.)

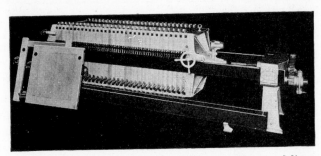

FIGURE 268.—A wood filter press, with corner feed, and with open delivery. (Courtesy T. Shriver & Co., Harrison, N. J.)

more. In petroleum refineries, the press in which paraffin wax is separated from lubricating oil (both chilled) may have 350 circular plates, each five feet in diameter. The press is closed and opened by machinery. The cycle is one day.

The materials of construction for the plates and frames are not limited to wood and cast iron; they may be hard rubber, semi-hard rubber,

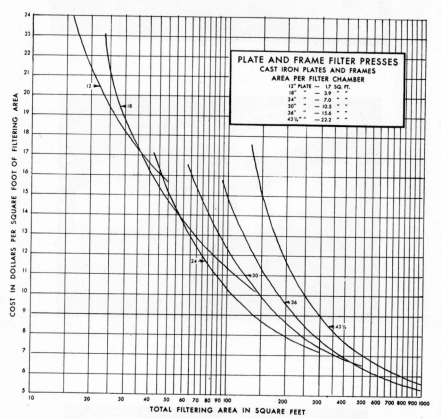

FIGURE 269.—Chart showing the cost per square foot of filtering area in square feet, for cast-iron plate and frame filter presses. (Courtesy T. Shriver & Co., Harrison, N. J., July 17, 1951.)

bronze, aluminum, "Ni-Resist," lead, stainless steel, and combinations of these. There should be added, furthermore, cast-iron plates and frames coated with nonferrous metals, such as block tin, zinc, porcelain enamel, and others. As to wood, there is a choice of yellow pine, hard maple, cypress, ash, oak, redwood, and others. In order to minimize the corrosive action of acids, acid-containing cakes are washed with cold water.

The plate and frame press has several *advantages*. Its first cost is low. It is a well-known device. Its operation is comparatively simple.

It requires only ordinary untrained labor. Its auxiliary apparatus is modest, consisting of a slurry tank, a pump for the slurry, a water line, and storage tanks for filtrate and wash. All parts are easily replaced, and granted such replacements, the life of the press is without limit. In the open-delivery type, the filtrate may be watched, and a plate which runs muddy may be shut off without decreasing the capacity of the press ma-

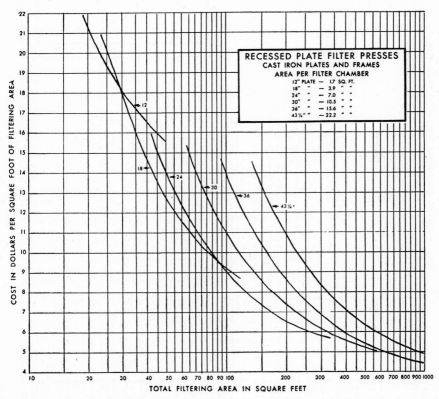

FIGURE 270.—Chart showing the cost per square foot of filtering area for total filtering areas in square feet, for cast-iron recessed plate and frame filter presses. (Courtesy T. Shriver & Co., Harrison, N. J., July 17, 1951.)

terially. In the closed-delivery type, the same advantage may be insured by means of a glass return bend or test and shut-off cock attached to the lower part of the plate. The plate and frame press is truly a pressure press, the standard cast-iron plates and frames being able to withstand a pressure of 100 psi (up to 200 psi in the small sizes), and specially constructed plates and frames a pressure of 750 psi and even higher. The pressure on the two sides of a plate is balanced, in the ordinary run, which explains how the thin casting can withstand such pressures. Occasion-

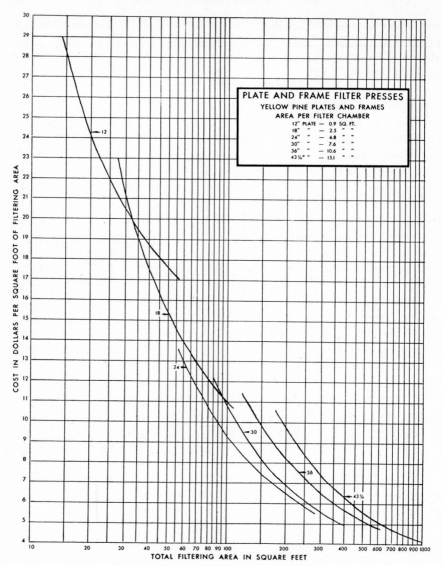

FIGURE 271.—Chart showing the cost per square foot of filtering area for total filtering areas in square feet, for yellow pine plate and frame filter presses. (Courtesy T. Shriver & Co., Harrison, N. J., July 17, 1951.)

ally a plate will give way and break because of the failure of a frame to fill, leaving the pressure on one side unbalanced.

Other advantages are as follows: The filter press may be varied in capacity of cake and filtering area at will, below a maximum, by using only as many chambers as desired, and blocking the balance. There is no danger of overloading the filter press with cake, as may happen in pressure leaf filters. Any kind of filter medium may be used, cotton, synthetic resin, or metallic, and each remains easily accessible for inspection.

The *disadvantages* of the plate and frame press are headed by a higher labor cost, but this cost is higher than that for the vertical or horizontal leaf pressure filters only when sluicing of the filter cake is permissible in the latter, for quick removal. Where the cake is valuable and is desired as dry and firm as possible, no other type of filter can be operated more economically as to labor. The plate and frame press has numerous potential leaks if the closing of the press is done carelessly; on the other hand, plates with leakage grooves or equipped with gaskets are available, to prevent leakage with certainty. Compared with continuous filters, the plate and frame press suffers because of the discontinuity of its operation; for processes which are themselves discontinuous, this disadvantage disappears. Also, where the viscosity of the liquid is high, or the solids content relatively low, or batches of material are to be filtered intermittently, the filter press definitely finds its field.

An estimate of the cost of a filter press may be made by consulting graphs (Figures 269, 270, and 271) which show the cost per square foot of filtering area against total filtering area in different sized presses. The effective filtering area per filter chamber, which has two filter-plate surfaces as walls, is listed; by dividing the total filtering area by the area per filter chamber, the number of chambers is determined. As an example, a 24-chamber cast-iron 24-inch square plate and frame filter press would cost $1400 (as of July 17, 1951).

The area required for a given volume of slurry is determined experimentally on a small filter press.

Prices for filter presses made of the corrosion-resisting metals may be estimated from the following figures, based on the prices for cast-iron presses:

For aluminum, add 40%
For bronze, add 100 to 170%   } to the prices of
For lead, add 100 to 240%   } cast-iron press.
For stainless steel (18–8), add 250 to 600% }

SHELL AND LEAF PRESSES

In the shell and leaf press, the cake is deposited on the outside of the filter leaves. The leaf assembly may be pulled out in a few seconds, or the lower part of the shell may swing on a hinge; the cake is dropped by a slight shaking of the leaves by means of a pole and finished by a stream of water, all in a very few minutes. In one model, the Vallez, the filter leaves are circular and rotate; when it is time to dump the cake, it is scraped off within the shell, and moved by a right-and-left screw to a central discharge door; the entire operation takes place without opening the filter. The shell and leaf press has only one gasket, which is readily kept tight and free from leaks; therein lies another advantage over the plate and frame press.

The Kelly Filter. The earliest shell and leaf press was the Kelly. It consists of a horizontal steel cylindrical tank enclosing 6, 8, 10, or 12 rectangular leaves. The leaves are set vertical, and are made of heavy wire screening fastened to a frame which has at its lowest point a pipe connection to the movable head for delivery of the filtrate. The frames are supported by a carriage forming one piece with the head, and the whole

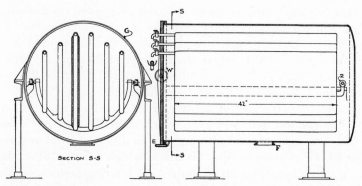

FIGURE 272.—The Kelly press, much simplified. Right, side view, with half the shell removed, showing the filter leaves; the cradle carrying them is supported on wheel *R*, an inner wheel resting and running on a rail fastened to the inside of shell, and on the movable head. The head travels on outer wheel *W*. *F* is the entry of slurry feed. *E* indicates the eyes placed along the shell body to receive the fingers of the toggle joint (not shown) carried by the head. In section *S-S*, the third leaf is shown with the cake formed on it. *G*, is the groove with gasket into which the circular lip on the head fits, forming the only joint in the press.

assembly is pulled out along two rails outside of the shell, when the press is opened, by a small air motor and chain drive; the rear of the carriage travels on two rails within the shell. On closing, the carriage is pushed in, until a toggle joint comes into operation which forces the head tightly against the shell. The head has a protruding circular lip which fits into a corresponding groove in the casting forming the surface of the shell, and containing a rubber (or other) gasket. This is the only joint.

The shell has a pipe connection at its base, through which the slurry is fed, and through which also the last shellful is returned to storage when the press is about to be opened. The filtrate from each leaf runs into a small gutter, and may be observed. A leaf running muddy is replaced by one covered with fresh filter cloth. The cloth is held by iron clamps.

Kelly filters are made in four sizes as single units, and the two larger sizes are also built as twin units. In a twin unit, the heads face each other, the two carriages are on a single frame, and there is one common dumping hopper. As the carriage from one press is pulled out, the other carriage is pushed home in the other press. One of the two presses in the unit is working at all times.

TABLE 54. SIZES OF KELLY FILTERS (inches)

	30 × 49	40 × 108	48 × 120	60 × 108
Number of frames	6	8	10	12
Spacing between frames (in)	4	4	4	4
Filter area (sq ft)	50	250	450	650

The lower labor cost may be based on the average of many days' work in actual full-scale operation, as illustrated by the following figures:

A Kelly press, 48 × 120 inches, dumps 6000 pounds of unwashed mud every 70 minutes; labor on the press floor, two man-hours. For every 1000 pounds of mud, there are required.................... 0.417 man-hour

A plate and frame press, nonwashing, 36 × 36 inches, 4-inch frames (extra large), 24 plates and 25 frames, dumps 4000 pounds every two hours. Labor, on the press floor, 5 man-hours. For every 1000 pounds of mud, there are required............................. 1.25 man-hours

The virtue of the Kelly type pressure press which has been emphasized over others is the evenness of the cake-building operation. At all points the slurry is under equal pressure; it is moving at a certain rate thanks to the filtrate withdrawal. The thickness and texture of the cake are uniform. The wash water may be introduced by turning on the water to the pressure feed pipe before turning off the latter, so that an even flow under a similar pressure may follow. The success of washing is then practically assured, another great advantage of the shell and leaf press.

The Sweetland Press. The Sweetland press has a split pressure shell. The two halves are hinged together, and the lower half is counterpoised. The upper half is stationary and carries the pipe connections. The press is opened by dropping the lower half, exposing the filter leaves; it is closed by raising the lower half, which is made tight against the single gasket by a twist of an eccentric. The slurry is fed in through the stationary upper half. The leaves are circular, and are made of coarse iron wire covered on each side with finer wire screen, which in turn supports the filter cloth; the latter may be fitted on bag-fashion, or else circular pieces of cloth may be caulked into grooves provided in the frame of the leaf (lead wire, or soft iron wire). The leaf is suspended from a fitting bearing a valve, a sight glass, then another valve leading to a common discharge manifold. There are two types of leaves, those with top drainage, and those with bottom drainage (see Figure 273). The filtrate passes through the cloth, toward the top of the leaf, for the leaves with top drainage, then upward through the stem, through the sight glass, and to the filtrate escape line. The leaves with bottom drainage deliver their liquor to a point at the base of the leaf, from which an internal riser takes it to the stem and the filtrate delivery line. Leaves with bottom drainage are recommended when the cake must be as dry as possible.

When the rate of filtration has diminished considerably, the cake may be considered thick enough; the feed is interrupted and the slurry remaining in the shell is returned to storage. The press is ready to be opened; if it is desired to wash the cake, the wash water is admitted and the shell again emptied at the end of the wash.

The press is opened in a matter of seconds; the cake drops off, aided by a slight blow-back through the leaves, or it may be loosened by a rap with a pole or washed by a hose to a hopper below, and thence to a screw conveyor, or to a sump tank. The latest of the several methods for cake removal, when a dry cake is not desired, is the automatic sluice discharge,

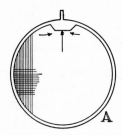 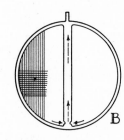

FIGURE 273.—Filter leaves for the Sweetland filter. *A*, top drainage leaf, the standard form; *B*, bottom drainage leaf, for cake which must be as dry as possible. The filter cloth fits over the leaf in bag-form, or, it is applied as a circular piece on each side of leaf, and caulked in place. As shown, the leaves are uncovered.

which permits flushing away the cake with the press remaining closed. A pipe mechanism in the upper part of the press, receiving a rotary and a reciprocating motion, directs streams of water against every part of the surface of every leaf.

Comparison of Kelly and Sweetland Presses. The Sweetland press is designed for pressures not exceeding 50 pounds; the Kelly press, on the other hand, is designed for pressures as high as 500 pounds; it is the pressure press par excellence.

Except for this consideration, the Sweetland press would seem to have the advantage. Its filter leaves are circular and all of one size, a moderate one (see Table 55). The Kelly press has leaves of three different sizes; in the larger presses, the largest leaf is 4 by 10 feet, which is not easy to handle.

The Sweetland has less free space around the leaves, and less material need be returned preparatory to opening than from the Kelly. The filtering area of the Sweetland is greater than that of the Kelly. Both have one gasket only. For a slurry containing not too large a percentage

TABLE 55. STANDARD SWEETLAND FILTER

No.	I.D.* (in)	Length of shell (in)	No. leaves 2″ space	No leaves 4″ space	Filter area 2″ spacing (sq ft)	Filter area 4″ spacing (sq ft)	Total weight† of filter (lbs)
1	10	20½	9	5	8	4½	550
2	16	36½	18	9	46	23	2150
5	25	61	30	15	185	92	7300
7	25	82	41	20	252	123	9350
10	31	109	54	27	523	262	16500
12	37	145	72	36	1004	502	29600

* Diameter of leaf one inch less.
† Filled with water.

of solids, which must be recovered in as dry a condition as possible, the Sweetland is indicated. For average plant work the Sweetland has been found more generally applicable.

Shell and Leaf Filters with Rotating Leaves. The Vallez filter is the best known of the pressure-leaf filters with rotating leaves. The filter leaves are mounted on a hollow shaft, with openings for each leaf; the leaves are circular. Shaft and leaves rotate within a substantial, pressure-tight casing. The operations of filtering, washing, sluicing off the cake, and removing the latter are all conducted without opening the press. The leaf rotation has two good results: the suspension, or slurry, is kept in agitation so that settling is avoided, and the cake forms evenly. These are the advantages which the rotating-leaf pressure filter may claim over the Kelly or Sweetland. For certain operations, the Vallez filter serves admirably, for example, in the filtration of sugar liquors. On the other hand it must be noted that the delivery from each individual leaf is not visible, and furthermore, that the removal of a filter leaf is a more difficult operation in this filter than in the Sweetland.

Some additional information will be afforded by Table 56.

TABLE 56. VALLEZ FILTER (LARGEST SIZE ONLY, 20 FEET LONG, 7 FEET HIGH, 7 FEET WIDE)

Spacing of Leaves (in)	No. of Leaves	O.D. of Leaf (in)	Filter Area (sq ft)	Cake Capacity (cu ft)
3	52	52	1232	65
4	39	52	924	72
5	31	52	734	79
6	23	52	546	92

There are smaller sizes with leaves the outside diameters of which are 44½, 36, 30, and 22 inches; for the 30-inch leaves, four lengths of shell are available.

Another filter which combines pressure filtration with filter-leaf rotation is the Swenson rotating-leaf pressure filter; still another is the Conkey rotary leaf pressure filter.

In all pressure filters, especially in the Kelly with its large leaves, a steady flow of slurry at an even pressure should be maintained during the filtration period of a cycle. If a blow-case is used, it should be large enough to furnish all the slurry required, without refilling; two smaller ones may be used, however, by putting on No. 2 before No. 1 is quite empty and before shutting of the cock to No. 1. No. 1 may again be put on using the same precaution; a flow approximating that from a pump is thus provided.

Continuous Rotary-drum Pressure Filter. A continuous rotary pressure filter has been developed for the filtration of propane-wax slurries. This operation must be conducted under pressure, for otherwise the propane would volatilize and no longer be available for carrying the oil in solution. It consists of a rotary drum with a rotary valve, essentially like the drum and valve of the rotary-drum suction filter (see p. 343), placed inside a pressure vessel with a removable head, fitted with a conveyor for moving and discharging the cake. The pressure vessel acts as a slurry tank. The filter medium is cotton cloth. Cold, fresh propane is carried into the vessel and is sprayed onto the cake for wash. The pressure differential is kept low, 2 to 3 pounds, in order not to crush the wax crystals. The rate of filtration is 4 gallons of dewaxed oil per sq ft per hour. One rotation of the drum requires 1 minute with certain slurries and up to 8 minutes with others. The cake is discharged directly into the suction of a gear pump; some liquid propane is added—just enough to make the wax suspension pumpable. Views and sketches will be found in the reference below.*

Another example of a pressure filter is the *Niagara filter*, a totally enclosed, *vertical pressure-leaf filter*. The leaves may be precoated, or not, as required. The Niagara filter has a series of double-faced filter leaves properly spaced by a peripheral spacer bar, set in an upright cylindrical pressure vessel with removable top. There are two main types of leaves: style C, in which a central wide mesh backing screen is covered by a cotton or other cloth bag, enclosing the whole leaf, and style A, which has a fine metallic filter screen, the actual filtering surface, over the backing screen. The leaves are bound by a heavy tubular frame which provides a flow channel for the filtrate. The leaves fit into a manifold at the base of the tank, through which the filtrate escapes. The slurry to be filtered enters at the base of the tank.

For many filtrations, such as those of cloudy vegetable oils, it is necessary to add a filter aid. Among the several methods of procedure available, one provides for a precoat of the diatomaceous earth applied to the leaves; in addition, the cloudy oil may be treated with filter aid by body addition (direct addition) in an open feeder tank equipped with an agitator. The treated oil is then pumped into the filter. After a period, the pressure rises very suddenly, indicating the filling of the cake space between the leaves with solids, to, for example, 65 pounds. The liquid in

---

* "Liquid propane-use in dewaxing, deasphalting, and refining heavy oils," by R. E. Wilson, P. C. Keith, Jr., and R. E. Haylett, *Ind. Eng. Chem.*, **28**, 1065–1078 (1936).

the tank (the heel) is forced back to the feeder, after which the cake is discharged. This may be done without opening the filter tank if it is equipped with an auto-sluice, a special spray nozzle header which has both a rotary and a reciprocating motion, so that streams of water spray reach all the surface on both sides of every leaf. The cake slurry leaves the tank by the same pipe which is the inlet for the oil slurry. When so equipped, the device becomes the *Niagara "Auto-Sluice" filter*, a self-cleaning pressure filter; the accumulated cake is removed and disposed of without opening the filter.

The Niagara filter may be built of steel or stainless steel, especially the latter, and, optionally, of a variety of metals. In size it ranges from 50 to 20,000 gpm. Batteries of multiple units occupy a minimum of floor space.

A still newer type is the Niagara "H" style filter, which permits easy discharge of cake which must be recovered and processed as such. The shell has a horizontal axis, and the leaves pull out with the carriage. The filter leaves are circular, and are set at right angle to the axis of the shell.

The *Oliver pressure filter* has flat leaves in a cylindrical shell set upright. The filter leaves may be covered with a precoating of diatomaceous earth or other material. It is made in the smaller sizes, with 25 to 100 square feet of filter area. The simple construction lends itself well to sterilization.

Suction Filters

Suction filters fall into two classes, (a) those with discontinuous operation, and (b) those with continuous operation. To the former class

Figure 274.—A stationary suction filter, made of chemical stoneware, for acids and corrosive liquids. (Courtesy General Ceramics and Steatite Corp., Keasbey, N. J.)

belong the Moore filter leaves—narrow, flat, rectangular chambers similar to the Kelly leaves but arranged in clusters of six or eight, which may be lowered into a slurry tank; by the application of suction, the filtrate is drawn through the filter medium stretched on the leaves, while the cake deposits on the outside. After a period, the cake is of the required thickness and filtration is interrupted. The leaves are hoisted out of the tank and if the cake must be washed, lowered into another one containing water, which is drawn through the cake by again applying suction. Next the leaves are hoisted away and scraped or flushed free from cake. In the recovery of magnesium from sea water in a war plant, a magnesium hydroxide mud is collected by means of Moore filter leaves of such size that an overhead crane is necessary.

Filter leaves of smaller sizes are also available, and it is feasible to use only one tank for moderate scale operations; the slurry may be withdrawn after the cake forms, and water for washing may be introduced into the same tank. The operation of the leaf filter is discontinuous, and requires much space.

To the same class belongs the stationary suction filter, in which a suitably supported filter cloth retains the cake, while suction is applied to the chamber below, drawing the filtrate through. The stationary filter is made of lead, of stoneware, or of other material. The stoneware filter, which is widely used, is shown in Figure 274. This consists of a lower chamber with outlets for the suction line and for the filtrate, and an upper chamber with the supporting multichanneled stoneware arch bearing the filter medium (not shown) between them. The operation is intermittent. The stationary suction filter is highly favored for small and medium-sized batches.

The laboratory Gooch and the Buchner funnel are suction filters.

Class (b) suction filters are those with continuous operation, and these devices may be exhibited with pride by chemical engineers. There is a variety of such filters, and several of them may be modified for certain needs, so that the number of designs available is large. How economic forces favored the development of the suction filter with continuous operation may be reviewed briefly. The plate and frame press has the great defect of entailing a high labor cost. The shell and leaf press requires less hand labor than the filter press, but this lesser amount may still be too much. The ideal installation, from this point of view, would be one which discharges the cake as rapidly as the filtrate is separated from it, without any interruption, and with opportunity for washing—all without any operating labor charge whatever. These far-reaching expectations have been met with the rotating suction filter, developed along several different lines. All varieties have this in common, however: the appli-

TABLE 57. OPERATING LABOR FOR DUMPING 1000 POUNDS OF MUD
(*An Example from Plant Practice*)

From plate and frame press	From shell and leaf press	From continuous rotary suction filter
1.25 man-hours	0.417 man-hour	0

cation of suction, continuous operation, and no operating labor. For all of them, the withdrawing of filtrate, formation of cake, aerating, washing (if required), and discharge of the cake, go on simultaneously. In normal running, there is no interruption.

Continuous-suction Filter with Rotating Drum. The earliest (1907) and probably the best-known rotating-drum suction filter, with its filtering surface on the outside, is the Oliver, and it will serve as the representative of its type.

The rotary-drum suction filter consists of a cylinder lying on its side and rotating about its axis. The cylinder is mounted on a horizontal shaft, set on a slurry tank, in which the drum dips to varying depths. The surface of the cylinder is made up of shallow compartments which terminate in a pipe first running radially, then turning along the shaft to reach the stationary part of the automatic valve. Each compartment is so connected. The compartment offers numerous points of support to the filter medium, a cotton filter cloth, for example, which covers in one piece the entire surface of the cylinder. As a drum compartment enters the slurry, the automatic valve connects the suction line to it, after which the filtrate is drawn in and pulled to a separator and receiver; the cake is deposited against the surface. This continues while the compartment is submerged; the suction remains connected for a short distance after it emerges, in order that all adhering filtrate may be sucked in. A spray of water meets the compartment as it slowly rises away from the tank. Suction is again applied by the automatic valve; the wash water is sucked in and pulled away through a second line to a second separator, receiver, and pump. The cake now approaches the discharge knife; a pressure line brings a positive-pressure air blow which bulges the filter cloth outward, loosening the cake, so that when it reaches the knife, it is scraped off with comparative ease. The various zones are indicated in Figure 280.

The rotary-drum suction filter is possible only because of the *automatic valve,* which places a compartment under suction alternately for filtrate, for wash, and blowback for bulge. It consists of a rotating part *A* (see Figure 275) which turns with the drum and has a port for each row of compartments, and of a stationary part of which *B* is the inside view, and which positions the dividing bridges; *C* shows the outside of the stationary part, a cover piece which bears the liquor, wash lines, and the compressed air connection. A stud with a spring holds the stationary part tight against the rotating part. Both rotating and stationary parts are machine-faced and make a perfect fit; the surface is lubricated by a grease cup. The rotation is slow, so that the wear is slight, yet there is wear, and in the latest constructions, the Oliver has a "wear plate" between the rotating part and the stationary part. The wear plate takes the wear, and may be changed readily when required.

The slurry line feeds the tank at a rate which is a little greater than

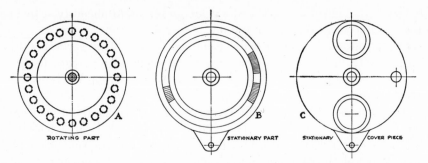

FIGURE 275.—The automatic valve in the rotary-suction filter, as used in the Oliver continuous filter. *A*, rotating part; *B*, inner view of the stationary part; *C*, the stationary part of the valve, a cover piece in which the suction lines are fitted.

FIGURE 276.—Two rotary drum suction filters, 8-feet diameter by 10-feet face, filtering sewage and sludge at the City of East Chicago, Illinois. Note the conveyor belt receiving the discharged cake. (Courtesy The Eimco Corp., Salt Lake City 8, Utah.)

that of filtration, so that with the aid of an overflow pipe, the level remains constant. An agitator is provided, which prevents settling. The level selected will depend upon the percentage of solids in the slurry. For a thin slurry, a high level will be maintained in order to allow more time for the formation of a thickness of one-eighth of an inch or more, as high as half an inch. The thickness of one-eighth of an inch is favored because it permits a better washing. For a thicker slurry, the level in the pan may be lower for the deposition of the same thickness of cake. But another way would be to decrease the rate of rotation for the thin slurry, which would permit more time for the filtrate to be drawn off, while the cake would have also more time to form and grow. An adjustment in the bridging in the valve would be a third means of control.

The wire winding over the surface of the drum was standard practice for many years, and served its purpose. The wire-wound drum, however, has been largely displaced by the panel type drum, because of the latter's ability to discharge thin cakes.

FIGURE 277.—The Oliver continuous vacuum filter, panel type. (Courtesy Oliver United Filters, Inc., 33 W. 42 St., New York 18, N. Y.)

In the wire-wound drum suction filter, the discharge knife rides on the wire, thereby saving wear on the filter cloth, but at the same time leaving an unscraped portion of the cloth between adjacent windings, which are close together. In the *panel type drum suction filter*, the cloth, which is divided into covers for each of the drum divisions, is slightly inflated at the moment it meets the scraper knife, and all of the cloth meets the knife.

The construction of the panel type drum suction filter is as follows: The drum shell is covered with filter screen strips of narrow width, such as 10 inches, and as long as the face of the drum. The strips are held in place by longitudinal blocks of rubber set in metal holders. Over the screen the filter cloth is stretched and caulked in the drum division strips. As the observer faces the drum, which has its axis horizontal, the drum sections are relatively narrow panels, running from left to right. Each panel is a chamber of the same dimensions, also running horizontally. There is a filtrate outlet pipe from each section. An air blow into the chamber inflates the cloth to meet the scraper which removes the cake completely (see Figure 278).

The Oliver rotating-drum filter is made in fourteen sizes, ranging from the small size of 3 feet in diameter and 2 feet in width of face, to

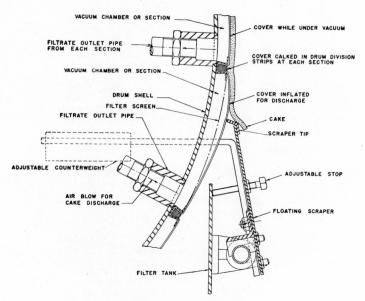

FIGURE 278.—Details of the panel type drum, with floating scraper discharge. (Courtesy Oliver United Filters, Inc., 33 W. 42 St., New York 18, N. Y.)

the largest one, 14 feet in diameter and 24 feet in width. A popular intermediate size is 5 feet 3 inches in diameter and 6 feet in width, with a rotation, subject to endless modifications, of 1 revolution in 6 minutes.

The drum suction filters are usually made of wood, or of cast iron, but they may be made from any workable material. The filter screen is generally 8 mesh to the inch. The filter medium may be cotton duck, cotton twill or other weave, metal-woven cloth, plastic covers, "Vinyon N," nylon, "Saran," "Dynel," "Orlon," "Acrilan," and others. Nylon does not blind as readily as some of the other media, while "Vinyon N" has better heat resistance than other filter cloths.

As indication of the cost of a drum suction filter the following may serve: an Oliver continuous drum suction filter 5 feet 3 inches in diameter and 6 feet wide on the face (the popular size mentioned previ-

FIGURE 279.—A rotary drum suction filter, handling sewage and sludge at the City of Stevens Point, Wisconsin. (Courtesy The Eimco Corp., Salt Lake City 8, Utah.)

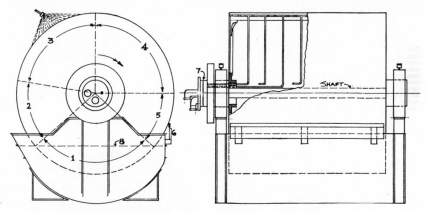

FIGURE 280.—The low submergence rotating-drum continuous-suction filter. Left, end view, showing valve, part of drive mechanism, end of slurry tank; *1*, filtrate removal zone and cake building zone; *2*, aerating zone; *3*, wash zone; *4*, drying and aerating zone; *5*, vacuum broken, pressure atmospheric; *6*, invert discharge knife. Right, side view, showing the compartment suction lines running to the rotating valve, *7*. The level of slurry is labeled *8*. Conveyor for removal of cake not shown.

ously), in wood drum construction but with steel tank and agitator, would cost, in round figures, $5000. This price includes the filter and agitator drives. The same size filter in a steel drum construction with steel tank and agitator is $6000. The auxiliaries, consisting of receiver, filtrate pump, and vacuum pump would be approximately $2300 including the drives, for cast iron and steel construction. (June 13, 1951).

Low-submergence Drum Suction Filters. In some of the latest models of the Oliver and other drum suction filters, the slurry basin is smaller and is set lower than in previous designs. By this arrangement, several desirable results are secured: a lengthening of the drying and washing periods, and a free-falling cake at discharge, for the discharging knife may now be set at a point well below the central horizontal plane of the cylinder, and in a vertical position. The cake drops off largely by gravity, which means less wear on the filter medium. This is called an invert

FIGURE 281.—The rubber-tipped metal scraper which is now used with the low submergence rotating-drum filter. (Oliver design.)

discharge. In order to compensate for the shorter filtrate removal and cake-building zones, the low-submergence drum is rotated faster. The output of cake and of filtrate is maintained at the old figure, washing is better through the thinner cake, and, as has been said, the discharge is easier and the life of the cloth longer.

Other recent innovations are the insertion of a section of rubber tubing in the suction line, relieving strains, and the covering of the discharge knife with a long rubber tip (see Figure 281).

There are numerous modifications of the drum suction filter to meet certain requirements, for example the two which follow.

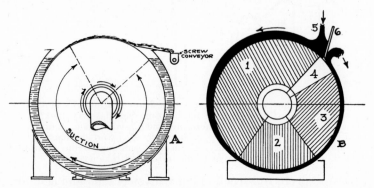

FIGURE 282.—Modified drum-suction filters. Left, suction filter with high submergence, such as may be used for white-water in the pulp mill, where it bears the name of saveall. Right, top-feed drum-suction filter for thick slurries. 1, zone with suction for filtrate removal; 2, for wash; 3, for wash removal and aeration; 4, blowback to loosen cloth; 6, discharge knife. The feed is at 5. (System Humboldt, Cologne, Germany.)

The top feed* drum suction filter is specially suitable for thick slurries, which the standard drum would not pick up. For example, drying of the cake by means of a hood and hot gas may be combined in one machine which then becomes a "drying filter" (Oliver Topfeed).

The Peterson TFR filter is a drum suction filter with top feed; its top feed reservoir is a patented feature. The drum has no filter cloth. The Peterson, like other top feed filters, is recommended for slurries with fast-settling solids, so fast in settling that they are not picked up on bottom feed reservoir type filters.†

String Discharge Suction Filter. In the rotary drum suction filter with string discharge, the cake is lifted from the filter and discharged by a system of endless strings which pass around the drum, over the filter cloth. No discharge knife scraping the cloth is required.

The drum is covered with its filter cloth, and then equipped with numerous endless strings spaced about ½ inch apart. The strings are long enough to travel off the drum to a small roll, the discharge roll, where they reverse, then travel through an aligning comb and over another roll which presses them tightly against the filter medium, whence they repeat their trip around the drum. The cake forms over the strings; the latter are all of exactly the same length and under the same tension, so that the cake is carried by them as by a woven cloth. The sharp turn at the discharge roll causes the cake to drop off, without benefit of scraper or backblow, onto the filter cloth.

The suction drum is fitted with longitudinal, shallow compartments as

* Patent references to top feed:

Drying filter. C. W. Moore and C. W. Crumb, ass'rs, to Oliver United Filters, Inc. U. S. Pat. 1,943,168, 16/1/34, appl. 4/1/32. Slurry is fed to zenith of a rotating drum which is elsewhere confined in a casing supplied with heated air which is withdrawn axially.

Continuous rotary vacuum filter. C. S. Robison to Oliver United Filters, Inc. Brit. Pat. 411,900, 14/12/32; U. S. Pat. 2,067,415, 12/1/37. The slurry is supplied in a comparatively thick layer to the upper part of a rotating permeable drum in certain inner compartments of which a vacuum is maintained. As the outer layer of cake dries off it is removed by a knife . . . set a certain distance . . . another knife set closer . . . An internal cellular structure preventing run-back of filtrate on the dried cake and a trough device for feeding prefilt to near the crown of the drum.

Continuous vacuum filter. W. Mauss. Brit. Pat. 481,815, 29/9/36. Feed applied to the crown; the cake is rinsed by dipping and is discharged only after rising out of it.

Reversal in valve. U. S. Pat. 1,917,818, 11/7/33. S. E. Woodworth. The multiport disk valve is caused to change quickly from suction to pressure by imparting a slight oscillation to the nonrotating part of the valve.

On half trough. Brit. Pat. 400,080, 18/3/33; Ger. Pat. 1/4/32. Apparatus for applying liquids to a rotating drum. Half a trough is applied to the rising side of the drum with a suitable liquid-tight packing.

† Peterson Filters & Engineering Co., 137 Motor Avenue, Salt Lake City, Utah.

FIGURE 283.—A rotary drum suction filter with string discharge. Note the endless strings traveling to the discharge roll and turning there to return to the drum surface. Aligning comb not shown. At the top of the drum, the compression belt and compression rolls are shown, which make possible the removal of additional moisture from the cake. (Courtesy Filtration Engineers, Inc., Newark 4, N. J.)

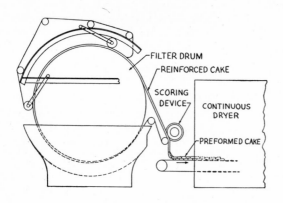

FIGURE 284.—A FEinc drum suction filter with string discharge, combined with scoring device for feeding the cake to continuous drier. (Courtesy Filtration Engineers, Inc., Newark 4, N. J.)

in the standard rotary drum suction filter; the cake may be washed. The valve is an automatic valve with rotating members and a stationary member (FEinc); a type of spirally woven wire drainage supports the filter cloth and provides much more open area than the conventional square mesh screen. The FEinc string discharge filter may be combined with a drier, providing a continuous feed of cake for the drier's continuous operation, as illustrated in Figure 284.

Horizontal suction filters (Lurgi, Oliver) serve best for the filtration of free-filtering solids.

The Oliver horizontal filter, a rotary filter, is essentially "a pan into which are set pie-shaped filter sections with outlets to a common valve in the center of the pan." Each filter section has a rapid drainage member covered by the selected filter medium. The stationary part of the valve has bridging and pipe connections which permit the separate removal of filtrate and wash. The pan rotates, and with it the rotary part of the valve. The cake builds up on the filter cloth (to a depth of as

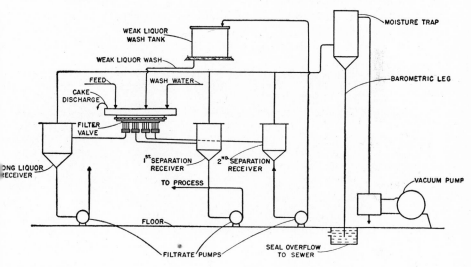

FIGURE 285.—Schematic arrangement for the Oliver horizontal rotary suction filter.

much as 4 inches, or more, if desired), and is discharged by means of a scroll over the edge of the pan. The filter is under suction, but the removal of the liquid also conforms to the pull of gravity; hence it is not surprising that the hydraulic capacity is high, for example, 200 gallons per square foot per hour. The tonnage of cake capacity is from 2 to 7 tons per square foot per day.

The filter may be built of steel, of lead-protected steel, of stainless steel; it has been applied to the filtration of calcium sulfate from phosphoric acid, zinc sulfate from a zinc sulfate-chloride solution, sodium chloride from a caustic soda solution, and other salts.

The Lurgi horizontal filter is a band filter, the fine screen and its backing screens being in the form of endless belts whose horizontal travel takes place over a horizontal suction box.

The *Conkey Hopper Dewaterer* may be classed with the drum suction filters. It is a rotary drum suction filter which has radial side-hopper extensions, one over each longitudinal compartment, so that over each a box-like hopper is formed in which a great deal of material may be held. The description may be clearer if it is said that it resembles an old-fashioned overshot water wheel. The Dewaterer is well adapted to the rapid removal by suction of water or solution accompanying a small amount of solids which could not be built up into a cake on the regular drum filter. The Hopper Dewaterer has top feed, and the drained material, corresponding to the wet cake, drops off by gravity.

There are other modifications of the drum suction filter which are interesting and important. Certain thick slurries which settle out fast may be handled on top-feed drum filters, in which the settling action of

Figure 286.—The Oliver horizontal rotary filter. (Courtesy Oliver United Filters, Inc., 33 W. 42 St., New York 18, N. Y.)

gravity works in the same direction as the suction (system Humboldt, Cologne, Germany, illustrated). The Dorrco (discussed below) possesses the same advantage. A twin-drum filter with the feed between the drums and at their tops offers a similar advantage (system Gerlach, Nordhausen, Germany, shown in Figure 287).

Dorrco Filter. The Dorrco continuous suction filter is also a rotary drum filter, but in contrast to the Oliver, its filtering surface is on the inside of the drum, and the suction lines on the outside. The drum is lying on its side and is rotated about its horizontal axis; one end is closed and carries a trunnion; the other end is open, for the entry of the feed and the discharge of the cake. There is no slurry tank; the slurry is carried in the space formed by the inner cylinder and part of the end walls. The filtrate is carried by the suction lines to a rotating valve, not unlike the one in the Oliver, located in the trunnion, and from there to receivers and pumps.   The cake may be washed, and the wash water drawn away separately.

The drum is supported by a trunnion bearing at the closed end, and by a large ring around the drum at the open end.   The motion is imparted by a worm gear at the trunnion end, and the ring rides on rolls.

The filtering surface consists of filter cloth mounted in panels, each underlain by one or more shallow troughs terminating in the suction pipe through which the filtrate, as well as air, is pulled away to the receivers and pumps.   The slurry lies in the basin formed by the filtering medium, and is kept at a definite level; the feed line enters through the open end. The cake forms both by the effect of suction and by gravity settling of the heavier particles.   No attempt is made to keep the slurry agitated in

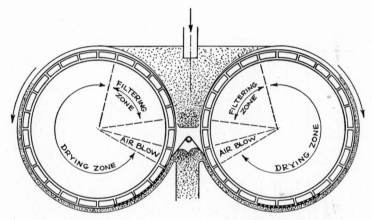

Figure 287.—Twin-drum rotary-suction filter for rapidly settling slurries, with top feed. As shown, the filter is nonwashing, but may be altered for washing.   Suitable for certain slurries only.   (System Gerlach, Nordhausen, Germany.)

order to prevent settling; on the contrary, settling is welcomed, for it works with suction to build the cake.   Provision is made for washing.

Rotating-leaf Continuous Suction Filters.   The rotating-leaf continuous suction filter, of which the American continuous suction filter is an example, presents a greater filtering area for a given floor space than any other type.   It consists essentially of a number of vertical disks mounted on a horizontal shaft within which longitudinal channels are provided. The shaft is carried by a slurry tank; the disks are rotated and travel not quite half submerged in the slurry.

The slurry tank is semicircular in cross section; furthermore, one half of it, let us say its forward half, has crenelations, one for each disk.   The disks revolve so as to enter from the top the narrow chamber provided by the crenelation.   The shaft is rather stout, and might perhaps better be described as a compartmented, circular, rotary, shaft-like chamber. Originally a casting, there is now supplied a fabricated shaft on request.

Each disk is composed of ten (or more) sectors, and each of the sectors on one disk has its own channel in the shaft. For a number of disks, corresponding sectors in the several disks feed into the same channel.

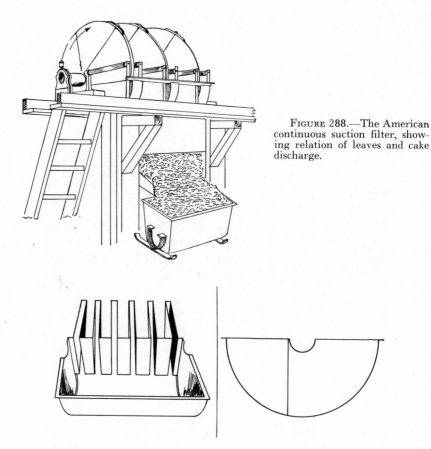

FIGURE 288.—The American continuous suction filter, showing relation of leaves and cake discharge.

FIGURE 289.—The crenelated slurry tank for the American filter, a rotary-disk filter, shown on the left; on the right, an end view.

The sector is made of wood or metal, and has up and down grooves all leading to the special casting which is carried by the shaft, and in which a tube collects all drainage. At the outer edge, two sectors are held together by a clamp carried by a radial rod, itself screwed into the shaft. The filter cloths are in the shape of bags fitting the sectors, and sewed around all the edges.

The shaft carries a circular "rotating" valve, the same as the Oliver.

The rotating half has ten ports which are connected at regular intervals, at one time to the filtrate lines, at another to the compressed air line carried by the stationary half, by the disposition of removable bridges and permanent cast-in ribs. Suction is applied to the disks through the rotating valve, the channels in the shaft, and the short nipple carrying the sectors. When the cake is to be washed, which is readily done by applying a spray to the disk as it emerges from the slurry, the wash water may be collected by a separate line from the rotary valve.

Figure 290.—View of the American continuous vacuum filter, disk type. (Courtesy Oliver United Filters, Inc., 33 W. 42 St., New York 18, N. Y.)

The discharge of the cake is facilitated by a pair of radial blades—tapered idling rolls set horizontally, and touching the disk, one on each side. As the shaft revolves and the sector nears the radial blades, an air-blow bulges out the filter cloth; the blade flattens out the cloth below the bulge so that the cake falls off and drops, guided by a deflector, through the spaces provided between the crenelations to a chute or conveyor.

The slurry is fed to the tank from above, and its level kept high enough to submerge completely every sector which enters it. The rotating disks act as agitators.

The sectors are built of California redwood or cedar, carried by the light cast-iron drainage cap; the shaft is of cast iron. The sectors are sometimes made of cast iron, cast aluminum, bronze, and other materials. The dimensions and number of disks will be apparent from Table 58.

TABLE 58. SIZES AND AREAS OF AMERICAN CONTINUOUS VACUUM FILTER

Diameter of Disk (ft)	General Max. No. of Disks	No. of Rotary Valves	Total Filtering Area (sq ft)	Total hp/sq ft of Filter Area	Total hp/filter (mean)
4	4	1	88	0.15–0.09	10.5
6	6	1 or 2	300	0.08–0.06	21
8½	6	1 or 2	600	0.06–0.05	30

The following distribution of power requirements for average conditions will serve as a guide, although it is not necessarily applicable to any specific installation: filter drive, 4 per cent; vacuum pump, 67 per cent; filtrate pump, 14 per cent; wash water pump, 11 per cent; blower, 4 per cent. The filter may be driven by any of the standard methods. Its speed may be as low as 1 rpm and as high as 20 rpm, with an average of 6 rpm.

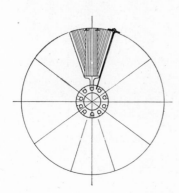

FIGURE 291.—A disk in the American continuous suction filter showing a sector frame made of wood and a cross section of the compartmented shaft with channels for the filtrate.

The American disk filter has been successfully operated in portland cement plants, starch plants, sugar houses, and pigment plants; it is also used in dewatering flotation concentrates and in the filtration of cyanide solutions. It finds its best field in nonwashing operations.

Pressure Filters vs. Suction Filters. Filtration means pushing the liquid through the passages, capillaries, microcapillaries, and large passages of the cake at a certain rate. Increasing the pressure, as may be done in pressure filters, increases the rate. This is indeed effective in many installations, but there are instances in which added pressure not only does not accelerate, but actually retards the flow. The reason is that many solids are not rigid; they are soft enough to be deformable. The higher pressure squeezes them so that they cover and fill channels which otherwise might have remained open. In this respect, the suction filter, which is limited to a modest range of pressures, generally in the neighborhood of 10 pounds, has the advantage. What is more, a given pressure applied in the form of suction on the underside of the filter cloth has less deforming effect than the same pressure applied on the cake side.

In the suction filter, the filter cake is generally thinner. The 1-inch and 1½-inch cake (or thicker) of the pressure filter is replaced by the ⅛-inch, and even 1/16-inch, cake, through which the filtrate flows more readily, and to which wash may be applied more uniformly. In the thick cakes of the pressure filters, there is danger that a weak area will carry all the wash, depriving other parts of the cake of their water, and effectively nullifying the washing effort.

In the plate and frame press, the cake sometimes builds up from the bottom, where it then is denser. Near the top, the frame fills last, and sometimes not completely, because the filtrate near the end of the period flows so slowly that it may become economically inadvisable to continue. In the suction filter, the cake forms all over the surface at the same time, and with uniform density.

On the other hand, there have been complaints that the filtrate on the drum suction filter and disk filter runs muddy, that it is not crystal clear as it is from the plate and frame press or the Kelly, for example. For such installations, if the difficulty persists, a special port with a cloudy filtrate line may be installed.

The filter medium on the suction filter may become clogged from particles of solid which become wedged into the meshes of the cloth by physical force. The remedy is to use a better filter medium, such as nylon, for example, and to give it a submerged blow. The filter with string discharge has less tendency, or none, to show this defect, and the panel type drum suction filter also has little of this tendency.

The superiority of the pressure filter lies in the greater velocity of the liquid through the available channels in the cake, hence in its higher rate of filtration per unit filter area. In the shell and leaf press, the cake forms uniformly, thus insuring thorough washing. The cake is 1 or 1½ inches thick, and hangs on a vertical surface 3 by 6 feet or so. It should be remarked that the cake sometimes drops off the leaf, and on opening the press, one finds the heavy mud in the bottom. Such a dropped cake is rare.

Against the suction filter, it has been argued that its cake develops cracks which interfere with proper washing. One remedy is the application of rollers which press the cake and fill the cracks by squeezing. Another is an accessory of great efficiency yet equally great simplicity, an *open mesh cloth* extending part way around the drum; it lies on the surface of the drum, fastened to an outside sized member, and is laid in the direction of rotation, but is unable to move. It therefore drags on the surface of the cake, preventing the wash water from running down and away too fast, at the same time smoothing the cake and closing cracks [Leno Washnet (Oliver), Dragnet (Lurgi)].

The rate of filtration in the chemical processes is about ¼ to ½ gallon per sq ft filtering surface per minute. A rate of 1½ to 4 gallons per sq ft surface per minute reported for a large drum suction filter working on very thin slurry in a paper mill would be unusually high.

Washing the Cake. Strictly speaking, washing the cake means the removal of filtrate adhering to an insoluble solid by replacement with water. There are countless instances, however, in which the cake has values which are soluble, or in which the filtrate on cooling deposits crystals which must be recaptured. A certain amount of dissolving is expected to be performed while washing. When the cake is rich in solubles, and wash is applied to remove them, the cake structure is weakened, and the cake is said to "rot." Such a rotted cake may fall off the filter leaf surface. When the solubles in the cake are high, and have

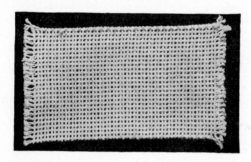

FIGURE 292.—The open mesh cloth "Leno" Washnet, patented by Oliver Filters, used for better washing of the cake in the drum suction filter. (Courtesy Oliver United Filters, Inc., 33 W. 42 St., New York 18, N. Y.)

value, good practice demands that the cake be reslurried and passed to another filter.

The following scant figures will perhaps be of value to the reader in connection with the percentage of solids in slurries.

The percentage by weight of solids in weak sodium sulfide slurry is 10. The slurry consists of a first cake, unwashed, which has been made up with water for the second filtration. The percentage of solids in a trisodium phosphate slurry is 7. A filter cake of basic magnesium carbonate contained 12.5 per cent of solids; unscreened, spirit-type distillery waste had 29 per cent of solids.

Calculations. The engineer in charge of operations will determine the size of filter he needs from a preliminary test on a small test filter, sometimes home-made. For the suction filters, for example, he will use a circular section of the filter medium suitably mounted and having an area of one-tenth of a square foot. Applying a measured suction for a given number of seconds or minutes, with the filter medium placed face down in a well-stirred pail containing the slurry, he will obtain a relation between the volume of the filtrate, the weight of the deposited cake, and the time required. From these, and from the area of the test filter, he can compute the filter area required to handle a given volume of slurry. Similar tests are made on small shell and leaf presses, obtainable on loan from the manufacturers; also on small rotary suction filters, on small Dorrcos, and others.

Equations expressing the rate of filtration in terms of the pressure applied, the area, the viscosity of the filtrate, the weight of the cake, and a proportionality factor, have been proposed,* as well as modifications of the original ones.† The difficulties are great, but further advances are expected in the near future.

TABLE 59. CAPACITY OF SUCTION FILTERS FOR CAKE DISCHARGE

	Lbs/sq ft/24 hours	Moisture (%)
Calcium carbonate cake from caustic soda liquor	500–1200	35
Anhydrous calcium sulfate cake from wet process for phosphoric acid	2000–4000	27
Settled mud cake in cane sugar juice	1000–2000	
Lithopone cake	200– 400	

FILTER MEDIA

Cotton duck and cotton twill are the most widely used filter media; they may be smooth, or may be obtained with a nap. For strongly alkaline solutions, woven iron wire cloth is successfully substituted for cotton; even better is the more expensive "Monel" wire cloth. For acid solutions, woolen filter cloths are used. A still newer material is nylon fiber cloth which possesses chemical-resisting properties similar to those of wool. "Vinyon" fibers made into cloth serve well in certain installations; in others, "Vinyon N" (a copolymer), "Saran," "Orlon," "Dynel," "Acrilan," and others are used, as already mentioned. Asbestos cloth is used, and also a woven nitrocellulose fiber cloth which must be kept under water. Wire filter cloth is obtainable in all standard weaves, plain or twilled, crimp, triple warp, braided, Dutch twilled, or corduroy, in meshes of any count from 1 to 500 per square inch. Nonwoven fabrics are obtainable in a variety of grades.‡

A new kind of metallic cloth suitable for filters is Jelliff patented "Lektromesh."§ It is made in the finer meshes, such as 25 to 400 holes per inch, so that it will supplement mechanically perforated plates.

* "Principles of Chemical Engineering," by Walker, Lewis, McAdams, and Gilliland, 3rd ed., New York, McGraw-Hill Book Co., 1937.

† "Filtration as a unit operation," by P. C. Carman, *Trans. Inst. Chem. Eng.,* (*London*) 12, 229–241 (1934).

‡ The Chicopee Mfg. Co. A general supply firm is National Filter Media, 1717 Dixwell Avenue, New Haven 14, Conn.

§ The C. O. Jelliff Mfg. Co., 200 Pequot Ave., Southport, Conn.

"Lektromesh" is produced by electrodeposition of copper, nickel, or other metal on a suitable design produced on a metal plate, on which the "holes" are nonconductors, while the solid portions representing the wire are conductors. The thickness is governed by the current used and the length of time they are plated.

A wire cloth with rolled selvage is on the market, but only in the narrower widths. Combinations of materials are used, such as metal wire interwoven with cotton or with rayon. Certain pigment manufacturers and seed oil extractors find it to their advantage to continue to use filter mats made of Chinese hair.

Except for coarse grains of hard texture and free from fines, the filter medium is not the filter cloth itself, but the first deposit of solids which covers the meshes of the cloth. It is in fact generally noted that the filtrate runs slightly cloudy at first, but that it clears after several minutes. The cloudy filtrate is returned to the slurry tank.

EDGE FILTERS

An example of the edge filter would be a stack of paper or metal disks perforated at their center so that an internal upright tube-like chamber is formed. The stack of disks is set in a casing with suitable inlet and outlet, and is under pressure from above and from the periphery of the disks. The dirty liquid surrounds the stack and finds its way to the central chamber, assisted in some models by suction; the suspended particles reach the edge of the disks and there are stopped, because the space between the disks is too small to admit them. The arrested solids form a cake at the edge of the disks; the cake is discharged at intervals by reversing the flow for a short time and running the heavy suspension to waste. There are several refinements in design represented by commercial edge filters.

The Cuno Filter or Strainer. The Cuno filter* or strainer is an edge filter which has the distinction of being "continuously cleanable." The most important representative of the several models is the Auto-Klean Strainer. Its disks are generally of metal, brass, bronze, or stainless steel, and are cut according to a pattern shown in Figure 293. Each disk is separated from its neighbor by a spacer which varies in thickness in the different models, beginning at 0.0035 inch, through eight gradually increasing sizes, to the stoutest one, 0.062 inch (ten sizes in all). Disks and spacers are stacked on a central shaft with which they form a single assembly called the cartridge. The disks and spacers are placed so that their cross arms are just over each other, forming vertical free passages. The shaft of the cartridge is surmounted by a handle; by turning the handle, the whole cartridge turns. The cartridge fits in a "head" with

---

* The Cuno Engineering Corp., Meriden, Conn.

inlet and outlet, and the head fits on the casing or "sump." The latter has a drainage plug or line at its bottom.

On a vertical rod fixed to the interior of the casing are stacked the "cleaner blades," of such thickness and alternating with such spacers that each blade just fits between two disks. The cleaner blades are held rigidly in place; they are stationary at all times, and each engages the space between two disks in the cartridge. Turning the cartridge is equivalent to scraping the circular spaces with a thin blade, ejecting the dirt.

During operation, the dirty liquid enters the outer casing at the top right (let us say), travels down between casing and cartridge, and moves toward the edges of the disks where the dirt is stopped because the space is too small to allow entry, while the clear liquid continues to the inner vertical passages and thence to the outlet at upper left.

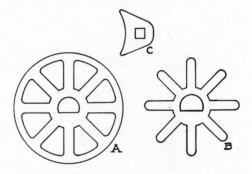

FIGURE 293.—Parts for the Cuno filter. *A*, the metal disk, perforated; *B*, the spacer; *C*, the cleaner blade. *A* and *B* with the shaft make up the cartridge. A stationary stack of *C*-blades engages the cartridge, each blade reaching in between two disks.

In order to clean the filter, the handle is turned, which turns the cartridge, allowing the cleaner blades to sweep the dirt away from the edges, causing it to drop into the sump. The dirt from a number of cleanings may remain in the sump, which is drained at longer intervals. While cleaning, the flow of the liquid is not interrupted. The accumulated dirt is called the cake.

It has been observed in practice that many of the smaller particles, too small to be stopped at the entrance to the space between the disks, that is, by edge filtration proper, are nevertheless removed by deposition on the surfaces of the disks. The percentage of the smaller particles so deposited depends upon the fluid velocity and upon the viscosity of the liquid. The endeavor of the Cuno design, and the choice of size of filter for a given duty, is to keep the velocity of the liquid through the slots in the neighborhood of 3 feet per second, for water and similar liquids. In general, liquids with higher viscosities call for lower velocities. The cleaner blades remove the surface-deposited dirt along with the edge-deposited cake.

The Cuno Auto-Klean strainer is made in a wide range of capacity sizes and may be fabricated from a variety of materials, steel, brass, or stainless steel. The strainers will handle from a few gallons to more than 4,000 gallons of fluid per minute under pressures which may be as high as 500 psi. Special units are available for building into equipment. All units can be continuously and automatically cleaned by turning the cartridge either with a motor, or through mechanical accessories.

A first estimate of the cost of a Cuno may be based on the following statement: The price of a standard hand-operated filter of cast-iron and steel construction is approximately $1.50 per gallon of liquid treated per minute, with the rated flow based on water. Complicated design, special

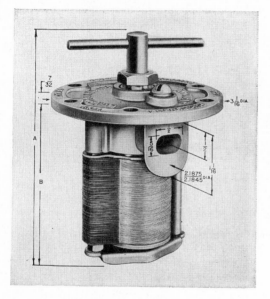

Figure 294.—Cuno integral strainer, hand operated, with the housing removed. Note the stack of disks and, to the left, the stack of cleaner blades. The outlet to the right is for removal of the filtrate or clean liquid. (Courtesy Cuno Engineering Corp., Meriden, Conn.)

material, or motorized operation will increase this figure; quantity production on standard units will decrease it (1951).

The Cuno models include the Flo-Klean filter and the Micro-Klean filter. The latter has a cylindrical, replaceable cartridge made of fibers felted so as to produce a graded density, lower at the periphery, higher near the center. The cartridge resembles in outer shape the disk assembly in the Auto-Klean. The felted fiber is bonded in place by a resinous impregnation which is set by heat, also setting the felted fiber in place. Such a cartridge removes particles down to 1 micron.

Metafilter. Another well-known edge filter is the Metafilter. In its original form, there was provided a wedge-shaped space, wider at the edges, between metal disks. It was soon discovered that the service of the filter could be greatly extended by filling the space with a suitable filter aid, such as diatomaceous earth or charcoal powder. In the current models, the turbid liquid enters between the casing and the disks; the clear liquid makes its way inside to the vertical escape, while the solids are trapped at the edges or in the filter aid. When the filter is plugged, the pressure on the disks is released and the flow of the liquid reversed; dirt and the bed material are swept out into a sump. Before resuming filtration, a fresh deposit of bed material is formed. The excellent results obtained are given in Table 60.

TABLE 60. SIZES OF PARTICLES REMOVED BY THE METAFILTER, AND RATES OF FILTRATION*

Bed Material and Dimension of Its Particles (microns)	Material Filtered	Concentration of Suspended Matter	Particle Size of Suspended Matter (microns)	Rate of Filtration (gals/sq ft; pressure 10 lbs/sq in)
Metasil A 3–85	Barium sulfate suspension	0.05%	0.1–1	75
Metasil B 3–75	Water	Bacteria	0.5–5	60
Metasil A	Beer	Hazy (yeast and bacteria)	4–8	40
Metasil A	Cloudy varnish	Faint haze	3–30	1.75
Charcoal 70–190	Carbonized crankcase oil	0.2–0.5%	1–4	0.5

* "Metafiltration," by J. A. Pickard, *J. Soc. Chem. Ind.*, **49**, 260T (1930). (Metasil is a standardized grade of diatomaceous earth.)

CLARIFICATION FILTERS

By clarification is meant the removal of the small amount of solids from 0.5 down to 0.05 per cent and less, which cause a permanent or relatively permanent turbidity in a liquid. Clarification may be achieved by the addition of filter aids, followed by filtration; by filtration on a precoated filter; with a mass filter; or with a napped filter cloth for certain solutions.

The substances most generally used as filter aids are diatomaceous earth ("Silocel," "Celite," "Kieselghur," "Metasil," "Diatomite"); powdered charcoal usually pretreated in one of various ways; cellulose fibers; asbestos; and the like. The filter aid is stirred into the solution to be clarified; the particle of filter aid attaches itself to the suspended impurity, forming an aggregate large enough to be arrested by regular filtration, whereas the untreated impurity would have passed through. There are other ways to use filter aids—their use in the Metafilter has already been given; their use in precoat filters follows.

Precoat Filters. Precoat filters may be pressure filters, or suction filters, generally the latter. They are designed for the filtration of slurries carrying, for example, colloidal matter, chiefly hydrated emulsoids, which are soft and not retained by the standard filters. The colloidal material is retained at or near the surface of the precoat, while the clear filtrate travels through. An example of such a filter, which is really a clarifier, is the Oliver precoat drum suction filter. It consists of a standard drum suction filter whose drum has been provided (by suction) with a thick cake of precoat, diatomaceous earth, about 2½ inches thick. As the drum rotates, it meets a moving knife which peels off a thin layer of precoat with the adhering or contained solids, so that the permeability of the precoat is continuously restored. The Oliver precoat filter may be hooded, and in another modification, may be enclosed in a pressure-resisting housing, so that pressure may be applied.

A number of other filters may function as a precoat filter, as, for example, the Niagara filter, previously described.

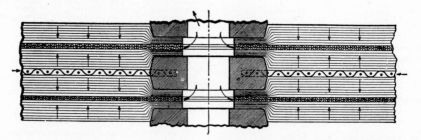

FIGURE 295.—Cross section of the central part of the filtermasse plates in the Kiefer beer filter, or clarifier, showing two plates, with inlet passage for the cloudy beer formed, and a coarse circular metal screening reaching to the outer edge of the plates. The travel of the beer through the mass, and the escape of the clear filtrate to the central passage, are indicated by arrows. The passage for the clear filtrate extends only part way to the periphery of plates. (Courtesy Karl Kiefer Machine Co., Cincinnati, Ohio.)

A clarifying filter which has been in use for many years is the so-called *"filtermasse" filter*, in which the turbid liquid must traverse a thick mass of wood pulp, cotton fibers, or other suitable fibrous material. The filter mass consists of a number of thick pads, cells, or disks, about 1½ inches thick, and 12 to 24 inches in diameter, with a central channel; it is placed inside an upright cylinder set on a platform, with or without wheels, and surmounted by a yoke. The disks are compressed by a screw working in the yoke. The "filtermasse" filter, in other words, resembles closely the edge filter, and the direction of travel of the liquor is the same: the cloudy liquor enters between the casing and the filter cells, travels through the filter mass, and escapes by the inner vertical channel. While traveling through the filter mass, the suspended solids (in the case of beer, dead yeast cells) are retained by the fibrous mass by adsorption; the clear liquid reaches the inner channel. A reduction in the solids carried is not enough; all the solids must be removed. The "filtermasse" filter does this, and produces a brilliantly clear filtrate.

An example of this kind of filter is the Karl Kiefer double plate (meaning double filtering surface) filter. In the largest size, the filter cells are 24 inches in diameter, No. 52, and weigh 175 pounds in filter mass alone. The filter mass is made of pure cotton fiber; the customer receives it in the form of a cake which softens in water, and is then formed into layers, or cells, in a special hydraulic packer. The Kiefer filter has a number of improvements over the older simple "filtermasse" filter. Each cell contains a circular disk of copper screening reaching almost but not quite to the periphery; the screen is placed on the lower half of the cell pad while being formed, and is covered by the upper half. The cells are separated by a circular screen, also of copper wire, set in a compressor ring. When the cells are assembled and compressed, a tight packing of the mass around the buried, smaller screen results. No turbid liquor can reach the escape channel along the larger screen, for it ends in a solid ring; nor can it reach the smaller screen without first traveling through an inch or so of filter mass. Hence only brilliantly clarified filtrate reaches the inner channel.

The "filtermasse" filters are operated under pressure. Periodically, the mass is washed in a special washer, and may then be used over again.

Capacities and dimensions for the Karl Kiefer double plate filters are listed in Table 61; the four sizes listed there range from $1310.00 to $3665.00 (August 1951).

TABLE 61. FILTERMASSE SUCH AS CELLULOSE MASS CLARIFYING FILTERS AND KARL KIEFER DOUBLE PLATE FILTERS
(FIGURES SIMPLIFIED AND ROUNDED OFF)

Double Plate	No. 1	2	3	4
Number of cells	24	22	44	52
Diameter of cells (in)	12	24	24	24
Amount of filtermasse required (lbs)	25	85	140	175
Height over all (ft)	4	$5\frac{2}{3}$	$7\frac{1}{6}$	$8\frac{1}{6}$
Capacity per hour				
Beer (bbls)	10–20	35–50	60–90	90–120
Syrups (gals)	400–600	700–1000	1200–2000	1500–2500
Whiskey (gals)	1000	1500	3000	3500
Gelatine (gals)	400	800	1500	1700
Wine (gals)	1000	1700	3500	4000

The Adams clarification filter* has as filtering element an upright porous tube and is suitable for acid and corrosive liquors. The tube may be mounted singly in a steel shell, the cloudy liquid reaching the outer tube wall and traveling through the medium to yield crystal-clear liquid in the inner part of the tube; or a number of tubes may be set up in a steel shell which may be rubber- or lead-lined. Several types of media are available; "Poro-Stone," a manufactured product with silica bond for

* R. P. Adams Co., Inc., 242 East Park Drive, Buffalo 17, N. Y.

water filtration, "Poro-Carbon" for the clarification of caustic solutions, and "Poro-Screen," of "Monel"-woven cloth with heavy "Monel" wire backing for medium water filtration.

Originally designed for removal of water from compressed air and for water filtration and clarification, the Adams filter has been adapted to the chemical services by lining the steel pressure tank with rubber or lead, or by building it of "Monel," nickel, or stainless steel. Accessory equipment for precoating is available.

Reading References

"Fundamental principles of industrial filtration (A Critical Review of Present Knowledge)," by P. C. Carman, *Trans. Inst. Chem. Eng. (London)*, 16, 169–188 (1938); theoretical mainly, with a bibliography of 179 titles.

"Filtration as a unit operation," by P. C. Carman, *Ibid.*, 12, 229–241 (1934); numerous graphs and many practical suggestions.

"Filtration: Accuracy of plant operation from test data," by E. L. McMillen and H. A. Webber, *Trans. Am. Inst. Chem. Eng.*, 34, 213–241 (1938).

"Mechanism of paraffin wax filtration. Continuous drum filter dewaxing of cylinder stocks in propane solution," by J. Griswold, *Ibid.*, 35, 505–515 (1939).

"Attempt to derive general expression for rate of washing filter cakes," by F. H. Rhodes, *Ind. Chem. Eng.*, 26, 1331 (1934).

"Experimental study of factors affecting cloth resistance and initial resistance. Application of filtration equation in practice," B. F. Ruth, *Ind. Eng. Chem.*, 27, 708, 806 (1935).

"Physikalische Grundlagen, Probleme und derzeitiger Stand der Filtration," by Fr. Prockat, *Chem. Fabrik*, 9 No. 35/36, 401–420 (Sept. 2, 1936).

"An analysis of recent filtration equations: Filtration at constant pressure," by M. G. Larian, *Trans. Am. Inst. Chem. Eng.*, 35, 623–634 (1939).

"Filter rates of clay-oil slurries," by H. H. Bible, M. A. White and J. W. Donnell, *Ind. Eng. Chem.*, 31, 1007 (1939).

"Filter media," by F. J. Van Antwerpen, *Ind. Eng. Chem.*, 32, 1580 (1940).

"Evaluating filter aids," by R. N. Cogger and H. M. Merker, *Ind. Eng. Chem.*, 33, 1233 (1941).

"Zur Theorie der Filtration von Flüssigkeiten," Friedrich A. Friedel, *Chemie-Ingenieur-Technik*, 21, 382–383 (1949), mainly as to wetting.

"Cost data correlated," by C. H. Chilton, *Chem. Eng.*, 56 No. 6, 97–106 (1949).

"Auto-Sluice precoat leaf filter," by M. P. Edrington and S. Weinstein, *Sugar*, 43, 35–39 (1948).

"The requirements of rotary-drum vacuum filters," by L. E. Brownell and G. B. Gudz, *Chem. Eng.*, 56 No. 9, 112–115 (Sept. 1949); see also L. E. Brownell and H. E. Crosier, *Chem. Eng.*, 56 No. 12, 124 (Dec. 1949).

Chemical Engineering, "Unit Operations Review, Filtration," *Ind. Eng. Chem.*, 42, 13–76 (1951).

"Flow of fluids through porous media, III—Application to rotary vacuum filtration," by Lloyd E. Brownell and Donald L. Katz, *Chem. Eng. Progress*, 43, 703 (1947).

Centrifugal force has been put to work for the chemist in the rugged, dependable batch centrifugals; indeed, certain separations of solids from liquids would not be possible on the modern factory scale were it not for centrifugal force. In devices having continuous operation, the same force renders greater service, with less labor, in consonance with the aims of modern technology.

14. SEPARATION OF SOLIDS FROM LIQUIDS
III. CENTRIFUGALS

The purpose of centrifugal machines is to cause solids to separate from liquids by centrifugal force. There are two main types of centrifugals. One has a perforated basket which revolves rapidly; the solids remain in the basket, while the liquids are whirled away at right angles to the axis of rotation, through the perforations. The other type has an imperforate or solid basket, against the rapidly rotating sides of which the solids build up as a cake, while the liquid is drained off by a skimmer pipe or by flowing over the top of the basket. Both types have batch operation, in which the basket is stopped in order to discharge the solids, and continuous operation, in which the solids are discharged while the basket continues its rotation. A general classification of centrifugal separators is given in Table 62.

Batch Operation Centrifugal Separators

Centrifugals with Perforated Baskets. The standard centrifugal for the separation of solids from liquids in the chemical industry has overhead suspension and bottom discharge. The slurry, generally rather thick, is fed from above into the basket, which is started from rest and rotated at moderate speeds while being loaded. After the full load is in, the rotation is increased to the maximum and held there for some time. Surrounding the basket is a monitor case, or curb, with an annular gutter at the bottom, provided with a discharge pipe; the mother liquor is whirled through the perforations in the basket, strikes the casing wall, runs down to the gutter, and escapes through the discharge line. The basket is lined with a metal-wire screen, in order to increase the drainage surface; against the screen there rests a filter medium, such as a fine metal-wire cloth, or cotton duck. The filter cloth may be pinned or sewed in place. The crystals or other solid particles are stopped by the cloth, and build the cake. The solids may be washed most efficiently by spraying water up and down the vertical wall of the revolving mass. After a few moments of whirling to remove the last of the wash water, the brake is ap-

TABLE 62.   CLASSIFICATION OF CENTRIFUGAL SEPARATORS (SOLIDS FROM LIQUIDS)

Centrifugal Separators

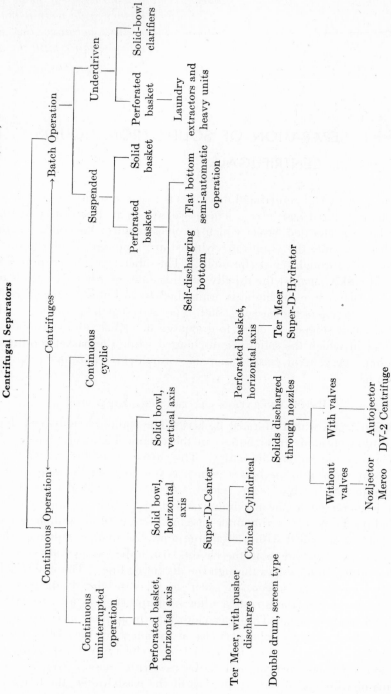

plied, and the basket is stopped. The broad annular valve which forms part of the bottom is lifted and hung out of the way; the contents are unloaded through the spaces between the three metal ribs (Figure 298) in the bottom. The solids drop to a chute, to a conveyor, or to a rotating screen if dry enough. If they must be dried by heat, they may be dropped directly into a drier. The annular valve is lowered into place, and the cycle is completed: the basket is then ready for the next load.

The cake may be discharged by hand, generally by holding a broad spatula or a wooden spade against it while rotating the basket at slow

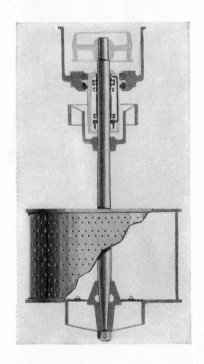

FIGURE 296.—Assembly of basket, spindle, and head of a 40-inch-diameter centrifugal, overhead-suspension type with bottom discharge. (Courtesy Geo. L. Squier Mfg. Co., Buffalo, N. Y.)

speed. It is quicker and more satisfactory to have a "plow" fastened to the curb, with a rack and pinion, to allow up-and-down movement, and a hinge for sidewise motion; the plow is lowered into the basket and pressed against the cake, which is peeled off in a few seconds. An example of the cycle with duration and speeds is presented in Figure 300. There are many variations to suit the various products.

The wash water may be allowed to mix with the mother liquor, or it may be deflected into a branch in the discharge piece by turning a butterfly valve.

There are "self-discharging" baskets which have a conical bottom. When the basket has been loaded and is stopped, the crystals forming the

FIGURE 297.—A 30-inch centrifugal separator, perforated basket type, with overhead suspension and individual motor drive. (Courtesy Geo. L. Squier Mfg. Co., Buffalo, N. Y.)

FIGURE 298.—Two views of a centrifugal basket, perforated type. (Courtesy Geo. L. Squier Mfg. Co., Buffalo, N. Y.)

cake slip down and out through the bottom spaces. The self-discharging baskets have no annular valve-forming bottom. As only a very free-flowing crystal will run out in this way, the applications are few.

The American standard sizes are 30, 40, and 48 inches; baskets are made in all sizes, however, such as 18 inches for small ones; 42, 56, and

ven 84 inches for large ones. The last size is used in a standard centrif-
ıgal clarifier. Generally the 40-inch basket is favored. For light ma-
erials, such as nitrated cotton, a larger basket is desirable, since the
ounds per basket are few; but even for this operation the 40-inch basket
s selected by many factories because it is made on a "production basis"
ınd hence is cheaper, and parts are more easily obtained. As indicated,
he size of the basket is governed in part by the specific gravity of the

FIGURE 299.—View of the "plow" for rapid unloading of the cake in the centrifugal
basket, with rack and pinion. Note the chute for loading at right rear. (Courtesy
Geo. L. Squier Mfg. Co., Buffalo, N. Y.)

product; this is illustrated further by the centrifugal baskets in commercial laundries, which are 60 and 72 inch. In the British Empire, the
standard sizes are 24, 36, and 42 inches.

A basket 30 inches in diameter and 14 inches deep, with a 3.5-minute
cycle, has a total capacity of 3 cubic feet, and will hold 200 pounds of
dischargeable solids of medium specific gravity. It may have a top speed
of 1500 rpm.

If the material weighs about 65 pounds per cubic foot, then the 3 cubic feet would be 195 pounds, the amount of discharge per basket of charge, with a cycle of 3½ minutes (17 cycles per hour), the hourly capacity would be 3300 pounds of discharged solids. A machine having this capacity would require about 7½ hp with a 25-cycle current. By means of a controller, the basket may be revolved at 1500, 750, or 500 rpm.

A basket 40 inches in diameter and 24 inches deep (capacity 9 cubic feet) would hold 500 pounds of a solid such as sugar. The fine screen for sugar work is chosen with 400 holes to the square inch.

Centrifugal separators are driven either by direct connection to individual vertical motors, or by a belt. In chemical plants, belts are avoided as much as possible, and therefore nearly all centrifugal separators are motor-driven. A 30-inch machine generally requires 5 to 25 hp; a 40-inch one, between 15 and 75 hp. The power requirement depends upon

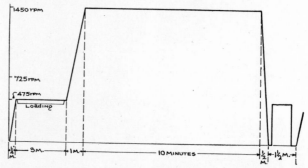

FIGURE 300.—An example of a time graph from the chemical industries; three-speed motor, 16¼-minute cycle, for the centrifugal separation of a very fine-grained solid. Loading, 3 minutes; whirling at top speed, 10 minutes, during which all liquor whirled off, material essentially dry; no washing; unloading, 1½ minutes. Batch centrifuge. With a better crystal structure, the 10-minute period is decreased.

basket speed, time taken to attain that speed, weight per cubic foot of the material in the basket, and length of the cycle. A shorter cycle, in which the basket must be brought to speed in fewer seconds, calls for greater power. The motors for centrifugals are nearly always specially designed to suit the individual application.

When a number of centrifugal separators are operated, there is a choice between direct-connected motor drive and belt drive. From the standpoint of power economy, placing six centrifugals in a battery and running belts from a jack shaft driven from a single motor is preferable. The reason is that great power is needed for starting, but considerably less for maintaining the speed, once it has been reached. As only one basket is started at a time, the prime mover need have the excess power for starting for only one basket out of six. Thus for a given basket on a 3-minute cycle, to make 1800 rpm requires 75 hp, but to run, only 30 hp. The six-belt-driven machines may be driven by one prime mover of 6 ×

30 plus 45 hp, total 215, while for those with individual drive, $6 \times 45 = 450$ hp would be needed. In original cost there is the same sort of advantage.

There is this great advantage to the individual drive system, however—when a motor gives out, only one basket is immobilized, not six. The individual drive, moreover, avoids the nuisance of belts.

The load must be evenly distributed in the rapidly rotating basket if it is to run smoothly. In a basket running at the rate of 1450 rpm, where

Figure 301.—An installation picture of the Tolhurst suspended centrifugal. (Courtesy Tolhurst Centrifugal Div., American Machine and Metals, Inc., New York, N. Y.)

the centrifugal force is about 1000 times gravity, the unbalance becomes serious, throwing the basket out of its orbit. The overhead suspension allows for oscillations and the bearing absorbs them. A feature of the latest design and type of bearing is the self-lubricating, graphite-impregnated synthetic resin called "Insurok," cut to form a segment of a sphere, the radius of which would be the distance to the center of oscillation. The segment faces upward, and becomes the annular bearing on which the basket rotates and rests. Full-floating flexible couplings compensate for the oscillations of the spindle. In another type of machine, the oscillations are taken up by rubber packing.

The underdrive-type of centrifugal is still very much in use. The basket rests on the head of a short upright shaft, provided with a pulley at its lower end. The drive is by a crossed belt from the motor pulley, with the motor mounted on the same base as the centrifugal. In the newer models, the motor shaft is vertical, and a V-belt runs from it to the centrifugal shaft. Laundry centrifugals are underdriven; the top of the basket is entirely free for the introduction of the pieces to be whirled.

Construction. The perforated basket is made in two designs. A light wall material with strengthening rings is the older type; a heavy wall which does not need rings is the modern tendency. In the latter construction, shown in Figure 298, the plate must be ½ inch thick for most metals,

FIGURE 302.—The perforated centrifugal basket, with strengthening rings. (Courtesy Geo. L. Squier Mfg. Co., Buffalo, N. Y.)

so that it may withstand the centrifugal strain both of itself and of the load. The ringless construction is preferred because it offers more area for draining. The material is bronze, stainless steel, or special alloys. An example of a special alloy is the special stainless steel 19-9, which contains 19 per cent chromium and 9 per cent nickel, the balance iron. All parts which serve in the construction of the basket are annealed before fabrication. After complete fabrication and machining the basket is pickled, heat-treated at 1950°F, and water-quenched. It is then dynamically balanced and passivated. Such a basket is specified in certain processes for nitrated cotton.

Automatic operation. Nearly all the high-production centrifugals, as for example for sugar (sucrose), are automatically controlled. When the operator starts a cycle by turning on the motor, or by pushing the clutch-actuating lever on belt-driven machines, an automatic timing device is started. The operator opens the massecuite valves and loads the basket while it rotates at a speed gradually increasing from 300 to 900 rpm. The massecuite is a slurry with a high content of solids, generally 50 per cent; it is ideally suited for centrifugal basket separation. The slurry distributes itself in the smoothly running basket about as fast as it enters; the basket is filled nearly full. The operator walks away and starts another machine. In the meantime, the timing device turns on the wash water at a set time, for instance when the machine reaches full speed, 1800 rpm, and washes the sugar with a predetermined volume of water. The timing device also applies the brake and the machine comes to rest. The operator now returns, lifts out the valve at the bottom of the basket, and dis-

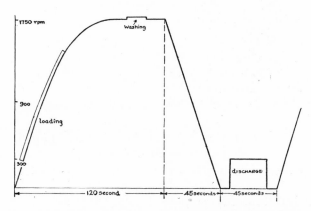

FIGURE 303.—An example of a time graph from the sugar industry, for a first sugar, slurry preheated. Constant-speed motor, with two speeds, 1750 and 575 rpm. Batch centrifuge. Total time 3½ minutes.

charges the sugar by means of a hand-operated plow, called a Universal type unloader. He rotates the basket slowly, while the plow moves along the crystals, downward. He then replaces the valve in the bottom and begins a new cycle. With high-grade sugar, and with other well-crystallized materials, the cycle is completed in 2½ minutes or less. With low-grade sugar, the same cycle may take half an hour, because of the slow flow of low-grade molasses. In the 40-inch diameter basket, 24 inches deep, the charge of sugar ready to be unloaded is 500 pounds.

Among recent innovations might be cited the Bird Hydraulic Unloader, which is carried across the face of the basket by an hydraulically operated ram. Safety stops prevent any possibility of injury to basket or filter linings; the operator throws a valve, and the unloader performs its function and returns automatically to an out-of-the-way position.

The centrifugal basket separator is suitable not only for the separation or filtering of relatively free-draining crystalline and granular substances, but also for free-draining fibrous materials.

Calculations.* The horsepower required by the centrifugal machine is found from the formula

$$\text{Horsepower} = \frac{T \times N_s}{5250}$$

in which T is the torque in foot pounds, and N_s the maximum speed. The torque is expressed as follows:

$$\text{Torque} = \frac{W \times R^2 \times N}{307 \times t}$$

W being the weight and R the radius of gyration of the basket which may be taken as 77 per cent of the basket radius; the radius of gyration for the load may be taken as 86.6 per cent of the basket radius.

Extraction takes place rapidly, so that the load reaches approximately 62 per cent of its original value at the end of the accelerating period. For that reason it is sufficient to consider the average load during acceleration, that is, 81 per cent of the total load at start. The total load is made up of the charge and all the rotating elements—basket, spindle, brake pulley, and others. Its value times 81 per cent is the W used in the expression $W \times R^2$.

The value of N is taken as 90 per cent of the maximum running speed. The expression for the torque given above is the theoretical constant torque required to bring the machine up to a given speed N in a given time t.

The centrifugal force is computed by the formula

$$\text{C.F.} = \frac{W \times V^2}{g \times R}$$

in which W is the weight in pounds, V is the velocity in feet per second of a point on the rim of the basket, g is 32.16, and R the radius of the basket in feet.

Centrifugals with Imperforate Baskets. The imperforate basket in centrifugal separators has solid side walls as well as solid bottom and top flanges, but otherwise it is similar in shape and contruction to the perforated basket. As the basket revolves, the solids are thrown against the side, while the liquid, unable to leave through the side wall, climbs to the top flange and travels there to the edge or down the outer side of the basket, flying off to a curb which collects it and guides it to a delivery piece. The solids, in the meantime, accumulate along the wall; after a while, a plow, hand or mechanically operated, dislodges the solids and causes them to drop out through the bottom opening, just as in the perforated baskets. The load in the imperforate basket is a liquid, and is

---

* *General Electric Review*, **22**, 416 (1919).

FIGURE 304.—A solid or imperforate centrifugal basket. (Courtesy Fletcher Works, Inc., Philadelphia, Pa.)

FIGURE 305.—A 48-inch suspended centrifugal installation with solid or imperforate basket skimming nozzle, feed pipe, and unloader. (Courtesy Fletcher Works, Inc., Philadelphia, Pa.)

subject to "tidal waves" which throw the basket out of balance; to prevent the waves, horizontal annular baffles, with numerous perforations, are attached to the inner sides of the basket.

The Fletcher Solid Basket centrifugal has an adjustable skimming nozzle which permits the removal of all the liquid in the basket at the end of a run. A 48-inch suspended centrifugal with solid basket, skimming nozzle, feed pipe, and unloader is shown in Figure 305. The solid bowl is shown in Figure 304.

Not only solids from liquids, but two immiscible liquids, perhaps forming an emulsion, may be separated in the centrifugal solid bowl. In such a separation, both liquids may be siphoned off continuously, the lighter one from the center, the other from a point at the periphery.

Not only that, but solids may be classified by means of the centrifugal solid bowl; by feeding the slurry at a fairly rapid rate, so that there is not enough time for the finest particles to be thrown against the wall, a slurry with these finer particles may be drawn off continuously, while the coarser particles are left behind. Such a use of the bowl would make it a classifier.

There is in process of development a *centrifugal with fluid drive*, which is expected to have among its many advantages a smoother start, adaptability to control, low maintenance, and reliability.

In ploughing centrifugals,* the basket is inclined, so that after centrifuging, the solids in the basket may be removed by a plough and dropped directly to a chute or conveyor. A perforate basket is used for free-filtering slurries, an imperforate basket or bowl with skimmer gear for slurries which will not filter.

Continuous Operation Centrifugal Filters and Separators

During the past ten years automatic continuous centrifuges have largely superceded batch operation machines. One can distinguish between the centrifuges with truly continuous functions, that is, in which

Figure 306.—Outside view of the Sharples Super-D-Canter. (Courtesy The Sharples Corp., Philadelphia 40, Pa.)

feed, discharge of solids, delivery of filtrate or liquor, and wash, proceed continuously and uninterrupted, and those in which a cycle of operations, each run for a period and then interrupted, and controlled by a timer mechanism, is repeated over and over, while the basket or bowl spins on. A further distinction can be made within the first group between those in which a relatively dry cake is discharged, continuously, and those in which enough liquor accompanies the cake so that the discharge mixture can flow through discharge ports or nozzles. All these distinctions will be clearer after the several devices have been described.

* Thomas Broadbent and Sons, Ltd., Huddersfield, England.

The *Sharples Super-D-Canter* is a high-speed horizontal centrifuge for the continuous removal of solids from slurries and suspensions. It is manufactured in two distinct modifications. The *Conical Super-D-Canter* has a solid bowl which is conical in shape, lies on its side, and rotates about a horizontal axis at the rate of 3,250 rpm. Within the cone, a screw conveyor fits its inner walls, and rotates in the same direction, at a slightly lower speed. The slurry enters through the hollow shaft and is delivered at a point about half-way down the bowl; the sedimented solids are moved uphill by the conveyor, toward the small end of the cone, out of the liquid, and into the solids-discharge ports. The liquid collects in the lower, wider part of the cone, reaching the adjustable filtrate ports, through which it leaves (see Figure 307). The centrifugal force developed by the rotation given is 2,100 times gravity. The conical bowl is most suitable for solids which pack tightly; it yields its solids in a relatively dry state.

FIGURE 307.—Sketch illustrating the working principle of the Sharples Conical Super-D-Canter.

The *Cylindrical Super-D-Canter*, an equally remarkable device, has a cylindrical bowl rotating at the same speed and developing the same centrifugal force. Within the bowl, a cylindrical screw conveyor turns, again in the same direction and with a slightly lower speed, moving the accumulated solids forward toward the solids-discharge ports, which lie above the liquid line, as indicated in Figure 308. The solids are forced out of the liquid by the cumulative pressure exercised by the rapidly revolving screw flights. The liquid, now freed of its suspended solids, moves in the opposite direction and leaves through the liquid-discharge ports. The cylindrical type is meant for the processing of comparatively soft or plastic solids; it is applicable especially to solids which "do not pack tightly, yet dry to a degree by compression rather than by draining." It may be said further that the Cylindrical Super-D-Canter is used where the dryness of the discharged solids is a secondary consideration. Both Super-D-Canters have truly continuous operation.

The Baker Perkins "Ter Meer" centrifugals are manufactured in three categories: continuous centrifugal, filtering centrifugal, and universal centrifugal clarifier. They are named after Dr. Gustav ter Meer, the original designer.

The *Baker Perkins "Ter Meer" Continuous Centrifugal* has a perforated bowl rotating about a horizontal axis. The entering slurry is separated into the solids, which are retained by the bowl, and the liquid, which escapes through the perforations into prepared chamber spaces in the housing. For the discharge of the cake, no scrapers, rakes, or plows are used; the cake is pushed out by numerous short strokes (for example 15 to 30 strokes per minute for the smaller sizes, 8 to 16 for the largest size) of a pusher actuated by a hydraulic servo-motor which is part of the main shaft. The latter is horizontal (see Figure 309). The pusher carries the slurry inlet funnel on equally spaced lugs. The wide end is close to the pusher; the narrow end is away from it, and receives the slurry. The funnel rotates with the pusher and by virtue of its shape, gradually accelerates the slurry, so that friable crystals do not suffer

FIGURE 308.—The working principle of the Sharples Cylindrical Super-D-Canter.

breakage as they would if the acceleration were sudden. As the pusher moves forward, it pushes the cake forward the length of one stroke (thus 1½ inches for the medium size); on the return stroke, a space is left into which the entering slurry flows, soon filling it with solids, so that on the next forward stroke, the cake is again pushed forward. On the way, it passes under a wash spray (which may or may not be operated), then continues, drying in the meantime, to the outer edge of the filter drum where it flies off into the dry-salt collecting housing. The thickness of the cake is set by the difference in diameter of the outer edge of the slurry feed funnel and the slotted screen lining of the drum. The output of cake varies with the size of the centrifugal, of which there are five, from a fraction of a ton to 24 tons per hour; in each size, it depends also upon the slurry, the nature of its crystals, or granules, and the rate of feed, as well as upon the size of the basket. In general, the coarser the crystals or granules or cake, the more frequent the strokes may be, and the greater the output. When washing is done, the washings are collected in a separate chamber (see Figure 309).

The frequency of the pusher stroke is adjustable and is set to give a displacement of solids somewhat greater than the feed volume. This done, the control valve is placed at two-thirds to three-quarters of maximum, to provide a reserve margin of capacity for handling unusual peak load conditions.

The horsepower required is moderate; thus for a medium size, such as S-19.5, with a nominal capacity of 12,000 pounds per hour, a 20 horsepower motor is listed for the drive.

It may be observed that in the "Ter Meer" Continuous Centrifugal, a number of factors insure the preservation of a delicate crystal or granule

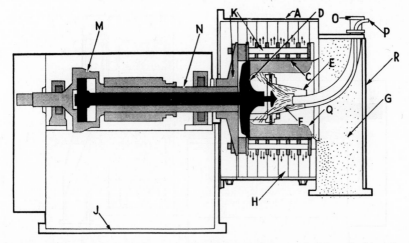

FIGURE 309.—A vertical cross-sectional sketch of the type S Baker Perkins Continuous Centrifugal for free draining materials. *F*, inlet for the raw slurry; *K*, rotating perforated drum; *D*, pusher which rotates with the drum; *M*, hydraulic servo motor which give through piston rod *N* the short reciprocating motion to the pusher; *C*, wedge slot screen which lines the rotating drum; *A*, wet housing which collects the liquor; *Q*, the cake, which the pusher forces forward, so that part of it flies off into dry collector housing *G*; *H*, opening for discharge of mother liquor; *P*, wash feed pipe leading to wash funnel *E*; *R*, hinged access door for inspection. (Courtesy Baker Perkins, Inc., Saginaw, Mich.)

structure: the slurry is brought to drum speed gradually, the pusher action is smooth, and there is no tearing or cutting by any extraneous mechanical device. The number of installations is constantly increasing. The variety of adaptations is indicated by the products handled—ammonium sulfate, muriate of potash, grainer salt, and ethyl cellulose, among those in the United States; cellulose acetate, Glauber salt, copperas, calcium nitrate, disodium phosphate, and citric acid, among those in Europe.

The *Baker Perkins "Ter Meer" Universal Filtering Centrifugal* is different from the device just described. It includes a perforated bowl, enclosed in a housing, and rotating about a horizontal axis. The bowl is lined with filter cloth. While the basket is spinning at full speed, slurry enters, and the cake builds up in the bowl. The filtrate is collected in a compartment as shown in Figure 310. After a predetermined thickness has been attained, the feed is stopped and the cake allowed to spin dry; if desired, the cake may be washed (see figure) and the wash collected separately. The cake is discharged by raising the hydraulically operated peeler; after the discharge the feed is turned on again and the process repeated. It will be noted that the operation is of the batch type; the feed is discontinuous, and the cake is discharged periodically. The cycle of

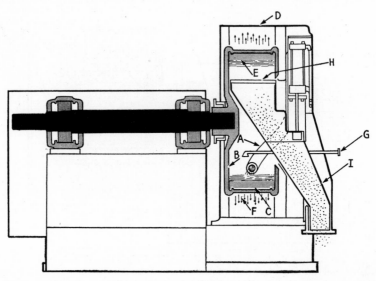

FIGURE 310.—Cross-sectional drawing of the Baker Perkins "Ter Meer" Universal Filtering Centrifugal. *A*, charging pipe; *B*, drum; *C*, filter medium (cloth); *E*, deposited solids; *F*, filtrate passing through perforations (not shown); *G*, wash pipe; *H*, peeler knife; *I*, chute for removal of peeled filter cake. The cycle of operations is repeated continuously through the operation of the timer mechanism, supplied with each machine.

operations, however, may be run automatically and repeated by means of timing control and operation mechanism. It should be observed further that the centrifugal bowl spins continuously throughout the cycle; there is no starting torque at each cake discharge.

The *Baker "Ter Meer" Centrifugal Clarifier* is intended for slurries containing solids which are unfilterable. An imperforate drum while rotating about a horizontal axis receives enough slurry to fill it. Under the influence of centrifugal force, the solids are quickly deposited against the wall, and the clear liquid is removed by the hydraulically operated skimmer pipe. The solids are recovered by the action of a hydraulically operated discharge knife (see Figure 311), after which a new quantity of slurry is admitted and the cycle of operation repeated. If the amount of suspended matter is small, the bowl may be filled several times before removing the collected solids. Excess slurry overflows at *F* and is returned to the slurry tank. The procedure described constitutes the *skimmer system.* The clarifier may also be used in the *overflow system,* if the amount of solids to be thrown against the bowl wall by centrifugal force is small, and the solids are of the quick settling type. In the overflow system, the slurry is fed in for long periods (several hours) and the clear liquor allowed to overflow over the edge of the bowl. The "Ter

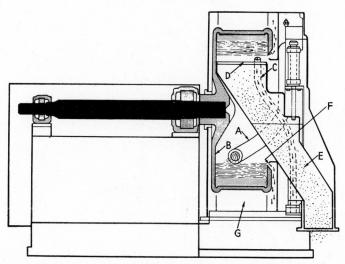

FIGURE 311.—Cross-sectional drawing of the Universal Clarifier, skimmer system, for nonfilterable solid-liquid slurries; automatic, but not continuous. *C* is the skimmer pipe; *D* the hydraulically operated discharge knife; *E* chute. *F* is the overflow when a slurry with low solids is clarified, permitting a run of several hours before the accumulated solids are discharged, illustrating the overflow system. (Courtesy Baker Perkins, Inc., Saginaw, Mich.)

Meer" centrifugals are suitable for operation up to about 1000 times gravity.

The centrifugal clarifier is also well adapted to the separation of two immiscible liquids differing in specific gravity, in which application the heavier liquid separated against the drum may be removed by means of the skimmer pipe *C*, leaving the lighter liquid in the bowl or allowing it to overflow as shown.

The *Merco centrifuge* or *Merco Continuous Separator* has as its primary function the separation of solids in liquid suspension from the carrying liquid; its outstanding merit is continuous separation and delivery of the solids, and continuous separation of the liquid from a continuous feed. The separation of the solids may be carried to the point just beyond which the thickened pulp would no longer flow.   The Merco centrifuge consists of a massive rotor, statically and dynamically balanced, suspended and driven from above, which spins in a housing as shown in Figure 312. The feed enters from the top.   The slurry on being rotated yields its solids, which are thrown to the outermost space of the rotor by centrifugal force and leave, with a certain predetermined amount of carrying liquid, through the nozzles (20) in the rotor and thence through the underflow pipe.   The liquid passes through the inclined vanes nearer the center of the rotor, rises, and reaches the overflow collecting and delivering pipe. The wash, which may be water or a special solution, enters at the bottom of the housing and of the rotor.   In the larger types, with through-put capacities of 350 gpm, the speed of the rotor may be 2000 rpm, for example; in the smaller types, with, for example, a stainless steel rotor and

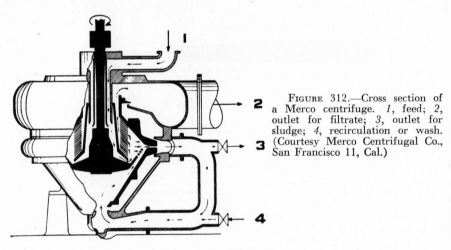

FIGURE 312.—Cross section of a Merco centrifuge. *1*, feed; *2*, outlet for filtrate; *3*, outlet for sludge; *4*, recirculation or wash. (Courtesy Merco Centrifugal Co., San Francisco 11, Cal.)

an acid-proof bronze housing, and with a through-put capacity of 10 gpm, the rotor spins at rates of 6000 rpm and higher.

The Merco centrifuge has three general chemical applications.   In one, the purpose is to collect a valuable solid, as free as possible from contaminating soluble impurities, and includes washing.   The wash liquid functions by displacing, more or less completely, the carrying liquid, and leaves with the overflow.   In another, the purpose may be the recovery of valuable dissolved material and its separation from a suspended solid which may or may not be of value.   The dissolved material is collected in the overflow, which will include any wash liquor applied.   A third application is the classification of solids in a suspension or mother liquor, involving, for example, the collection in the overflow of fine crystals, essentially of one size, and separate delivery of oversize in the underflow.   Very neat particle separations can be made, at high feed rates, in desired sizes, for example, —3 microns in the overflow and from +3 microns in the underflow, with a high efficiency in the recovery of the smaller sized particles.

In the separation of two solids from each other, for example, gluten and starch, the Merco has functioned successfully and continues to do so. The gluten leaves in suspension by the overflow; the heavier starch, collected also as a suspension, leaves in the underflow. It should be noted that the Merco has high capacity, that the residence time is low, and that while being processed the slurry is enclosed, reducing to almost zero the opportunity for contamination. The latter consideration is important in the processing of fruit juices (pineapple).

Instead of washing, a portion of the underflow may be recycled by means of the return circuit (see Figure 312). The Merco may be automatically controlled, with provision for compensating for rate of feed and composition.* The operation of the separator may be varied by changes in the rate of feed, rotor speed, and nozzle size, and by altering underflow draw-off and return wash by means of manually controlled external valves.

The Merco continuous separator may be thought of as a thickener with almost instantaneous settling; its concentrated pulp may be delivered to a filter for further dehydration. There are furthermore two-stage and three-stage installations applied to certain separation and thickening duties.

The continuous separation of solids from their suspending liquids may be performed in a screen type continuous filter, in which two concentric drums, lying on their sides, revolve. The outer drum is the filter drum; the inner drum is the conveying member; it carries a series of plows and rotates just a little slower than the filter drum, so that the plows, mounted to form a screw conveyor, move the deposited cake along the filtering surface toward the discharge. The liquor passes through the openings in the drum and collects in the housing which encloses the filter drum.

Of greater importance to-day is the *Bird continuous solid bowl centrifugal filter* which separates solids from liquids by centrifugal sedimentation. The solids must have a specific gravity greater than that of the liquid, and their particle size must be sufficient so that they will respond to centrifugal separating forces which may be as high as 1700 times gravity. The bowl is a section of a cone with its axis laid horizontal, about which it rotates. An inner screw conveyor rotates in the same direction, slightly less rapidly. The feed of slurry is continuous; the solids move uphill to the small end of the cone and are there discharged, while the liquid moves to the wide end and leaves through adjustable

* "Starch and Sugar from Milo Maize," by Robert L. Taylor, *Chem. Inds.* (June 1949).

filtrate ports. Nozzles on the conveyor flights permit washing of the cake.

The Bird solid bowl centrifugal filter is built in a number of sizes; solids through-put may be as low as 300 pounds per hour, or in the larger sizes, as high as 60 tons per hour. The clarified liquor delivered may vary anywhere from 1 gallon per minute to 400. It has found application in the separation of 75 commercial chemical products.

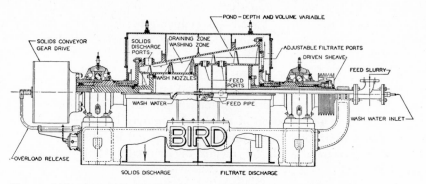

FIGURE 313.—A special sketch of the Bird solid bowl centrifugal filter, in part cross sectional, showing the construction and working principle. (Courtesy Bird Machine Co., South Walpole, Mass.)

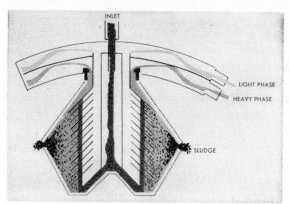

FIGURE 314.—Flow diagram of the Sharples Nozljector. Note the separation into light phase from heavy phase liquid, and the sludge, the latter also discharged continuously. (See text.)

The *Nozljector* (*Sharples*) is a disc type centrifuge which separates a slurry of two immiscible liquids containing solids into the two separate liquids and the separate solids besides. The Nozljector has a rotating bowl with its axis vertical, containing conical discs surrounding the hollow shaft and sloping upward toward it. The discs permit separation according to the stratification principle. The bowl widens in steps, so that its widest part forms a belt-like chamber, below which it narrows again.

The solids are thrown to the outermost edge of the belt and leave through the nozzles located there, while the two liquids stratify in the passages between the discs, the heavier one leaving by a separate port, the lighter one by the uppermost port. The bowl rotates at the speed of 6000 rpm, and the centrifugal force created is larger than any quoted in previous descriptions in this chapter.

The *Autojector* has a similarly shaped bowl with internal sloping discs and discharges solids through ten valves located around the periphery of the bowl. The accumulated solids cause the valves to open for a period, allowing the solids to discharge, after which they close.

In the *DV-2 Centrifuge*, the bowl, again similar in outline and main internal features to that of the Nozljector, and having the sloping discs, separates the solids from a suspension or slurry and discharges them

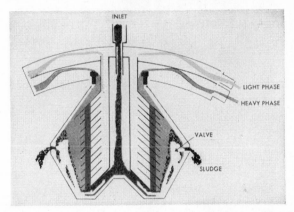

FIGURE 315.—Flow diagram of the Sharples Autojector, with self-acting valves controlling the discharge of the sludge. Here too the separation is into three phases.

through ten valves located at the widest diameter of the bowl which are operated by externally controlled water pressure. The DV-2 Centrifuge is applicable to clarification of a liquid, or to the separation of two immiscible liquids.

Another well-known device which has proven its worth over a number of years is the *Sharples Super-D-Hydrator*, a centrifuge with continuous cyclic operation. Into a rotating perforated basket, a measured amount of a suspension of crystals, such as ammonium sulfate in its pickle, is introduced; the crystals collected on the wall of the basket are whirled free of pickle, rinsed with a small volume of water, spun dry, and then discharged by an automatically operated knife which removes all the crystals except a thin layer to provide a filter medium for the next portion of suspension. The cycle then begins again with a delivery of slurry. The several steps in the cycle are controlled by precision timers, and each step may be varied independently by an adjustment. The complete cycle may take one minute, and it is repeated indefinitely. The slurry of crystals may be stored in a feed tank and pumped through circulating pipe; the centrifugal baskets are fed from T connections in the pipe on the pressure side of the pump.

FIGURE 316.—View of the S h a r p l e s Super-D-Hydrator, opened to show interior construction. The perforated bowl with horizontal axis is seen at the right; at the left, a leveling rake, and the discharge knife over the outlet for the dry salt. (Courtesy Sharples Corp., Philadelphia 40, Pa.)

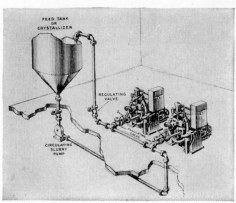

FIGURE 317.—Closed circulation feed system of the Sharples Super-D-Hydrator. The crystal slurry is kept circulating, and a measured amount is admitted periodically to each D-Hydrator. The operation is automatic, and the slurry is always at the proper condition for centrifugation. (Courtesy Sharples Corp., Philadelphia 40, Pa.)

The Super-D-Hydrator is made in two sizes, one with a 20-inch, the other with a 27-inch inside basket diameter. The speeds are 2100 rpm for the smaller centrifuge, 1800 rpm for the larger one.

Centrifugal Extractor. In the centrifugal countercurrent, multi-stage, solvent extractor, two liquids are contacted for liquid-liquid extraction and separated in one compact centrifugal contactor-separator. "The lighter of two liquid phases is admitted to the outside of the rotor, while the heavier is entered at the center. The heavier phase flows to the outside of the rotor, displacing the lighter phase and causing it to flow towards the center. The action of the "contacting elements" within the rotor is to alternately mix and separate, in multi-stage fashion. "Quiet" zones near the center and at the larger diameter provide clarification of

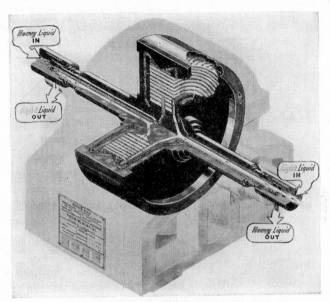

FIGURE 318.—Diagram illustrating flow of fluids through Podbielniak solids-handling centrifugal contactor. (Courtesy Podbielniak, Inc., Chicago 11, Illinois.)

either or both streams as they leave the rotor. Centrifugal force, ranging from 2000 to 5000 times gravity, permits satisfactory handling of phases with as little as 0.02 specific gravity difference."*

Reading References

"Centrifugal machines," *General Electric Review*, 22, No. 5, p. 416 (May, 1919).

"Which centrifugal, and when?," by L. P. Sharples, *Ind. Eng. Chem.*, 31, 1072 (1939).

"The tools of the chemical engineer. VI. Centrifugal machines," by D. H. Killeffer, *Ind. Eng. Chem.*, 19, 287 (1927).

"Centrifugation as unit operation reviewed," by James O. Maloney, *Ind. Eng. Chem.*, 39, 16 (1947).

"Centrifuge selection for chemical processing," by J. C. Smith, *Ind. Eng. Chem.*, 39, 474 (1947).

"New development in centrifuge applications," by C. M. Ambler, *Chem. Eng. Progress*, 44, 405 (1948).

"The centrifuge, its process potential," by Charles M. Ambler, *Chem. Eng. Progress*, 46, 549 (1950).

"The evaluation of centrifuge performance," by Charles M. Ambler, *Chem. Eng. Progress*, 48, 150 (1952).

* Quoted from the official literature of Podbielniak, Inc., 341 East Ohio Street, Chicago 11, Illinois.

It has been said in homely language that the battle goes to the side which "gets there first with the mostest men." By analogy, the motto for the evaporation engineer might well be "the most evaporation in the leastest time." The emphasis in the modern design is rapidity; while in the old days one spoke of evaporation cycles in terms of hours, one now also speaks of them in terms of minutes, and of very few of these. Great benefits flow from the shortness of the period which a liquid must spend within the evaporator.

15. EVAPORATORS*

The task of concentrating a solution by the evaporation of part of the solvent is one which must be repeatedly performed in the chemical industries. Most frequently the solvent is water, and the task of the evaporator is the vaporization of part of the water with the resulting production of a concentrated solution. In other instances, the task of the evaporator may be the evaporation of all the water, with the production of a crystalline salt. The vapor is of no use except, perhaps, for its heat value, as will be seen later; it is the residual product which is important. A distinction can thus be made between what is here called an evaporator, and a still, for in the latter it is the vapor which has value, while the residue has either no value, or little value in comparison. There are however some still operations in which the residue has considerable value.

The heating agent is generally steam, and more particularly, steam at low pressure, such as 5 to 40 pounds. It is, furthermore, saturated steam, that is, steam without superheat, for superheat reduces heat transfer to that of a dry gas until the saturation point is reached, and also does not furnish sufficient additional heat units to be of importance. For example, the total heat content of saturated steam at 40 pounds gauge is 1169.4 Btu per pound, while 40 pounds gauge pressure steam with 100° superheat has a total heat content of 1218.4 Btu. The latent heats of both steams are equal, hence it is to the great store of heat in the form of latent heat, also called heat of condensation, that the task of vaporization is delegated, and not to the superheat.

One of the standard forms of evaporators is an upright cylinder, within which a nest of upright steam tubes is placed. An earlier form has a rectangular base with a dished dome, and contains a bundle of horizontal steam tubes. The latter are also built into the upright cylinder body. Instead of tubes, suitably placed coils within which steam circulates are

* In collaboration with Mr. D. J. Van Marle, Buflovak Equipment Division, Blaw-Knox Co.

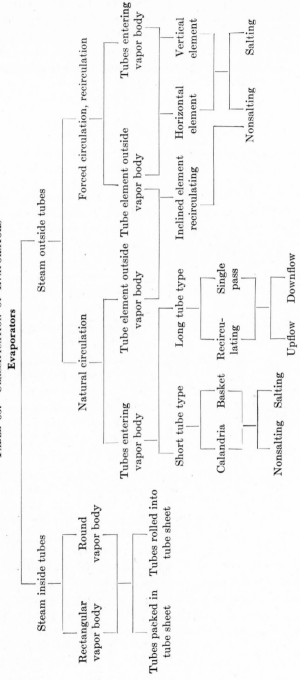

TABLE 63. CLASSIFICATION OF EVAPORATORS

installed, for small-scale and for batch operation. Certain evaporators have both tubes and (at a lower level) coils. Before considering the modern aims in design and type of evaporators, four evaporators of older design, yet still in favor and useful for certain purposes, will be described. These are: two natural circulation short tube evaporators; the basket type evaporator; and the horizontal tube type. Numerous examples of long-tube evaporators with slender bodies and high evaporative efficiencies will follow.

<h2 style="text-align:center">SHORT TUBE EVAPORATORS</h2>

An example of the upright cylindrical type is the *natural circulation short-tube, nonsalting evaporator*. It is made in many sizes varying from 2 feet 6 inches to 18 feet in diameter, depending upon the capacity de-

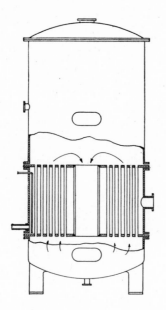

FIGURE 319.—A natural-circulation vertical short-tube nonsalting evaporator. T h e tube sheets are fastened to the body. The tube sheets and tubes make up the steam chest proper.

sired. In the so-called short-tube evaporators, the tubes vary from 2 to 6 feet in height, while their diameter may range from 1 to 3 inches. In general, the relation of the dimensions of the various parts will be similar to those of a specific example, such as one 8 feet in diameter and 18 feet high in which the tubes are 5 feet long and 2 inches in outside diameter. The tube dimensions given would be averages for those used in the chemical industries. The liquor is inside the tubes, and the steam is on their outer walls. The tubes are set in an upper and lower tube sheet which forms part of the body. A wide, central space in the chest, called the downtake, is provided, down which the liquor travels, while in the tubes, the boiling liquor travels upward.* There is thus provided a natural circulation which constantly disturbs the film clinging to the inner wall of the tubes, sweeping it away (at least in part), and replacing it by fresh liquor—actions which promote evaporation. The cross section of the downtake is generally 50 per cent of the total cross section of the tubes, but may be more. The steam chamber has an inlet for steam, an outlet for the condensate, and a vent to purge the noncondensable gases.† The body has an inlet for the weak liquor, an outlet for the strong liquor, an outlet for the vapors, gauges for pressure or vacuum and for liquor level, hand holes, manhole, and a generous covering of insulating material to reduce the loss of heat by radiation.

The *natural-circulation short-tube, salting-out evaporator* is like the one just described, except that its bottom is conical; the salt separating as a solid during the concentration collects by gravity in this cone, from which it may be removed into a salt box or by means of a pump to a point further away. This evaporator, when constructed for the manufacture of common salt, NaCl, has been made as large as 24 feet in diameter (Manistee).

The steam chest in the natural circulation, short-tube evaporator is called the calandria, and the evaporator is not unfrequently spoken of, in the trade, as a *calandria-type evaporator*. The steam chest in any form which has straight vertical tubes is classed by many specialists as a calandria, as opposed to a heating element in the form of coils. In Figure 319, the tube sheets are held between the sections of the body.

In the *basket type* of evaporator, the heating tubes are again vertical and "short," but they are placed close together to form a unit smaller in diameter than the evaporator body. The annular space so gained becomes the downtake; there is no central opening in the basket. This type has two points in its favor: the removability of the tube element and the uniform distribution of the steam from the center to the inner periphery of the steam chest. In the type shown in Figure 319, which has the steam inlet on the side of the steam chest, boiling is more vigorous near the steam inlet.

By changing the base to a cone-shaped piece, the basket type becomes an acceptable device for salting out liquors. When comparing the merits of the calandria type with those of the basket type, all that can be said,

* There are other special designs for the downtake; for example, a crescent-shaped one placed close to the body wall [*Chem. Met. Eng.*, **26**, 1211 (1922).]

† Venting becomes a complicated problem in a large-diameter cylindrical body because the accumulation of permanent gases in pockets is blanked off by steam flowing directly from the steam inlet to the air or gas vent. In an improved design a spiral baffle guides the steam through a gradually narrowing space to the outside of the downtake, maintaining a more uniform steam velocity and more complete venting (Webre).

perhaps, is that the latter is not built in the very large sizes and that it is more expensive in construction.

The natural circulation in the calandria type may be increased by installing a stirrer in the central downtake; this accelerates the downward movement. For either type, a propeller may be installed under the tubes, driving the liquor through them with greater speed. In the basket type again, a deflector plate over the tubes is very effective in reducing entrainment of droplets by the outgoing vapors. Entrainment means the carrying away by the vapor of bubbles and droplets of liquid. When the boiling is quiet, there is essentially no danger of entrainment;

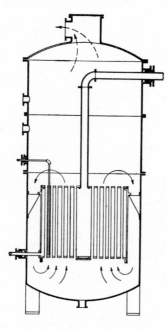

FIGURE 320.—A natural-circulation short-tube basket-type nonsalting evaporator. The tube bundle forms a separate unit, which is removable. The tubes are vertical. The steam enters at upper right. The horizontal cross section of the evaporator is circular. The arrows show the circulation of the liquor. Note the annular space between the steam chest and the unheated outer wall, which acts as a downtake.

with dilute solutions, boiling may be violent, however, and the high velocities favor entrainment. A baffle over the tubes counteracts this. For the calandria type, the baffling is more difficult.

The *horizontal-tube* type of evaporator is illustrated by a cast-lead evaporator with nickel or lead tubes suitable for the concentration of corrosive liquors. It should be noted that this is the only type which has steam inside the tubes and liquor outside. All the other evaporators have liquor within the tubes and steam around them. The horizontal-tube evaporator is made in a rectangular shape, besides the more common round one, and there still are a good many such installations in the industries, although this design is now largely superseded. In the horizontal-tube evaporator, with upright cylindrical body, space for down-

ward circulation of the liquor is available between the tube bundle and
he wall; in the rectangular body, spaces are arranged between the tubes.
t should be pointed out, in favor of the horizontal-tube type, that its
ubes are easily replaceable, especially so because they need not be expanded in place, but, since such a joint lies in the steam chamber, may
be packed with gaskets and ferrules.* The statement regarding circula-
ion, moreover, should be qualified by saying that the Lillie evaporator, a
horizontal-tube evaporator invented in the United States but in favor
mainly in England, has mechanical circulation of the liquor over the
ubes.

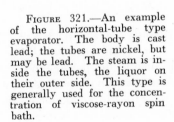
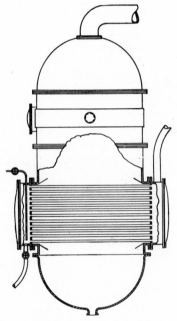

FIGURE 321.—An example
of the horizontal-tube type
evaporator. The body is cast
lead; the tubes are nickel, but
may be lead. The steam is inside the tubes, the liquor on
their outer side. This type is
generally used for the concentration of viscose-rayon spin
bath.

General Considerations. It will be noted that in the older designs,
essentially in those just presented, the steam chest and vapor space are of
the same diameter and form a single unit of cylindrical shape, and rather
stout. Separation of liquid and vapor takes place by gravity. Frequently fine drops of the liquid are carried along by the vapor, particularly when operating under a high vacuum and at high vapor velocities. To prevent this entrainment, there are provided, in addition to deflector plates already mentioned, special entrainment separators either as
separate units or built into the top of the vapor chambers.

* The ferrule has a male thread which fits into a female thread tapped in the wall of
the hole.

The older designs have a number of disadvantages. In handling foamy liquids, loss of product becomes serious and cannot be stopped by the ordinary entrainment separator. Liquids containing scale-forming impurities such as calcium sulfate or carbonate, form a coating on the heating tubes which soon reduces heat transfer and is troublesome to remove. In evaporators producing crystalline salts, the heating surface in time often becomes incrusted with crystals.

The newer designs have as their aim the removal of the disadvantages just listed, and also the establishment of a higher rate of heat transfer, and shorter hold-up time (defined later on), the latter especially important for heat-sensitive liquids. Natural circulation of the liquid in the older evaporators is rather slow, which results in low heat transfer rates, especially serious when viscosity of the liquid increases rapidly with concentration. To provide better heat transfer, two methods for increasing circulation have become available: the lengthening of the tubes, and "forced circulation." A few words on heat transfer will precede a closer examination of the newer designs.

The function of the evaporators just described, as well as of those which are to come, is to transfer heat, mainly the latent heat of steam as discussed in the introduction, from the steam side through the metal to the liquor on the other side. The resistance to the passage of the heat is not only that of the metal, which is indeed very small, but also that of the condensed steam film on the one side, and of a film of liquor on the other side. The condensed steam film, which is essentially hot water, has a moderate resistance to heat, partly because its thickness is low; hence its coefficient of transfer is medium high, such as 2000 or 3000. Until recently, at least, the engineer "did not need to worry about it"; demands for higher heat transfer rates may force a new examination of it. The liquor coefficient in the evaporators which have been discussed may be as low as 200, but it varies over a wide range. For the metal, in similar units, in a thickness of ⅛ inch, a coefficient of 3200 may be taken for steel or nickel, 22,000 for copper or silver. Studies and inventions in the newer designs have been directed toward raising the liquor film coefficient, always the lowest of the several coefficients concerned. Values for over-all coefficients in modern practice will be found in the "Numerical Example" at the end of the chapter.

LONG-TUBE EVAPORATORS

By increasing the tube length from a maximum of 5 or 6 feet in the short tube evaporators to 8, 10, 14, 16, and 20 feet, the active boiling within the tubes drives slugs of liquid upward (for the vertical tube types) at a rapid rate. By increasing the length of the heating tube, more vapor is formed, increasing not only its velocity but that of the liquid carried along. The higher velocity brings about a greater scouring of the stagnant film of liquor, hence a transfer of a greater amount of heat per unit of wall surface. The design is particularly useful for foamy liquids in that the higher velocity breaks up the foam.

In the new designs, at the same time, the size of the evaporator body has been decreased, as may be noted from the several illustrations which follow, so that its volume is smaller. By feeding in a limited amount of liquid and keeping the liquid level in the tubes (vertical) low, the time spent within the evaporator by any one gallon (the hold-up time) is decreased, a valuable feature for materials which may be damaged by prolonged heating.

The vapor chambers need not be of the same diameter as the evaporator body. They may form a dome over the top of the main body, and have a greater diameter, or they may be entirely separate. The latter arrangement permits introducing the vapors tangentially to the periphery of the separator, causing a circular motion, with separation of the liquid by centrifugal force. Another advantage of separate construction is that the tubes in the evaporator body are more accessible for cleaning.

In long-tube evaporators which are to be applied to viscous liquids, the direction of flow may be reversed, downward through the (vertical) tubes, whereby the liquid is spread over the inside of the tube in a thin layer, which causes it to flow down by gravity (see later section).

In Figure 322, a distinction is made between the evaporator body proper which contains the steam chest (and is sometimes referred to as the steam chest), and the vapor body, entirely separate, with tangential entry of vapors, and wherein the separation of dry vapors and entrainment takes place.

The ideal method of concentration would be to have only a single pass of the liquid through the heating tubes, after which the intended concentration would be complete. There would be separation of vapor from entrained liquor, but no return of liquor from the base of the vapor body to the bottom of the evaporator proper, and no recirculation. To restate: a *one-pass type evaporator* is one in which the total concentration takes place in one single pass through the boiling tube. It is rarely possible to accomplish this. To concentrate a 10 per cent solution to 20 per cent requires an evaporation of 55.5 per cent of the water in the original solution and a ratio of about 1 pound of vapor to 1 pound of liquid leaving the tubes. Such a high ratio of vapor to liquid seldom can be obtained even in a multiple effect evaporator providing several single passes in series. For larger concentration ranges, such as from 10 to 50 per cent, conditions are even more unfavorable.

Several other examples of these newer forms are shown in the accompanying illustrations.   The *natural-circulation long-tube evaporator,* shown in Figure 322, has special alloy tubes set in a steel body whose inner surfaces are covered with rubber.   It serves for the concentration of acid solutions, such as of sulfuric acid containing salts besides acid (e.g., the coagulating solution used in the viscose process for making rayon).   The tubes are vertical and are placed outside the body; the latter has been diminished to a vapor head in which the liquid disengages itself from the vapors.   The liquid may be drawn off or returned to the base of the tubes for further evaporation.   The feed may be regulated and sent in continuously, and the strengthened liquor may be drawn off

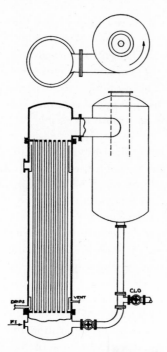

FIGURE   322.—A   natural-circulation long-tube film-type evaporator of special materials.   At the left is the evaporator body proper, containing the steam chest. The tubes may be of special alloys, and the steel body may be rubber-lined, for the concentration of corrosive liquids. The amount of liquid present within the evaporator is small.   At the right is the vapor body, with tangential entry of the vapors, which promotes separation of droplets from the vapor.   The same design   in   stainless-steel   construction   is typical of black liquor recovery installation   in   paper   mills.   *FI*,   feed   inlet; *CLO*, concentrated liquor outlet.   The dry vapors leave at the top of vapor body.

continuously, giving an evaporator with continuous operation.   It will be noted that the liquor space in the evaporator is small.

   The evaporator shown in Figure 323 has a vapor head over the tubes and a baffle which arrests the upward rise of the stream of steam and liquid.   The vapors pass into a separator where entrained drops are deposited, collected at the base, and returned to the evaporator.   The level of liquid retained in the evaporator is controlled by the selection of one of the three valves shown.   The lower the level in the tube chamber, the less the period of contact with the hot tubes, so that a single pass may be all that the liquid must make.   The original long-tube evaporator is the Kestner, much favored in France and England.

The Conkey Integral evaporator is a *long-tube evaporator* with natural circulation, and which is *self-supporting*, as shown in Figure 324. It is also built for forced circulation if desired. The single effect evaporator is assembled at the factory and sent to the purchaser as a single, complete unit which is ready for erecting, by a simple upending operation, on a prepared foundation. It is one example of the modern types of evaporators in which the vapor head is of the same diameter as the evaporator body. The Integral evaporator may be set up in double and in multiple effects as well as in a single effect. The multiple effect evaporator has been erected out of doors in several installations.

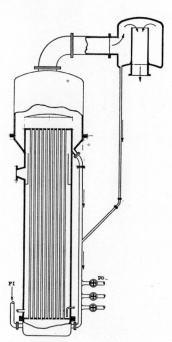

FIGURE 323.—A natural-circulation long-tube vertical film-type evaporator. The amount of liquor present in the evaporator is controlled by running off from one of three valves, which set the level in the evaporator. The circulation is so violent that a baffle must be provided over the tubes, which are 16 feet long, and 1½ inches in diameter. *FI,* feed inlet; *PO,* product outlet.

In the *forced circulation evaporator*, a pump is installed below the tubes, and the liquor is forced at a definite velocity through the tubes. The latter may be vertical or horizontal, each position having certain advantages. The velocity is kept high in order to obtain the desired reduced liquid film, with the consequent increase in its transfer coefficient; yet it must not be made too high, for the friction drop through the tubes varies directly as the square of the velocity, as does the power required for the pump.

The heat required in the evaporator in order to evaporate a certain amount of water (with the latent heat of evaporation at the pressure maintained in the evaporator, frequently under vacuum), is expressed as the product of the area of the heating surface (A), the temperature difference between the circulating liquid and the steam in the chest (ΔT), and the over-all heat transfer coefficient (U) (see also Chapter 20). In absorbing this heat, the liquid circulating through the tubes is raised in temperature, but the designer limits this increase, in order to prevent, in the horizontal tube evaporators, any boiling of the liquid. Instead, the liquid, heated to above its boiling point (by 10°F for example) is allowed

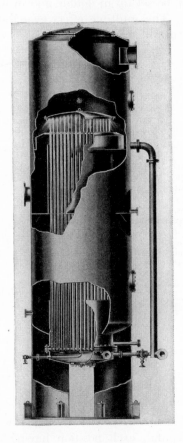

FIGURE 324.—Conkey, long-tube film-type evaporator, of the self-supporting t y p e. (Courtesy Process Equipment Division, General American Transportation Corp., 10 E. 49 St., New York 17, N. Y.)

to flash in the vapor body. The level of liquid in the evaporator proper is kept high enough to provide a hydrostatic head, effectively preventing flashing within the horizontal tubes. In forced circulation with vertical tubes, the latter are generally filled with liquid to very near the top.

The amount of liquid to be circulated is calculated; the selected velocity then governs the cross section of the heating tubes, operating in parallel, and their number, assuming a single pass.

The example which follows is for a forced circulation evaporator with horizontal tubes set in a separate steam chest, and operated under reduced pressure.

Example

The evaporator is operated under a vacuum

Amount of water to be evaporated	1500 lb/hr
Latent heat of evaporation	1000 Btu/lb
Amount of heat required	1,500,000 Btu/hr
Steam pressure available for heater	35 lb ga.
Steam temperature in heater	275°F
Temp. of liquid entering heater at b.p. of liquid	150°F
Temp. of liquid leaving heater, allowing a 10° rise	160°F
Temperature difference (ΔT)	120°F
Heat transfer coefficient (U)	250 Btu/hr/sq ft/°F
Heating surface required (A)	50 sq ft
Amount of liquid to be circulated, 10° rise, sp. ht. 0.75	200,000 lb/hr
Amount of liquid to be circulated, sp. gr. 1.5 (volume)	0.60 cu ft/sec
Velocity of liquid desired	6 ft/sec
Internal cross section of tubes required	14.4 sq in
Internal cross section of 1-inch O.D. 16 ga. tube	0.595 sq in
Number of tubes in parallel (horizontal)	24
O.D. surface of 24 1-inch O.D. tubes	6.28 sq ft/ft length
Length of tubes required to provide 50 sq ft	8 ft
Number of passes	1

The velocity of the liquor in the forced circulation evaporators ranges from 6 feet per second, as in the installation just described, to 18 feet per second. In the long-tube evaporator with vertical tubes, a recent installation with forced circulation provided for an average time of contact of not more than 4 seconds; in the natural circulation short-tube (vertical) evaporator, the time of contact may be hours.

Vertical and horizontal heating elements have been described. There are also evaporators with the heating element inclined at an angle with the vertical, which may be large, small, or intermediate. From time to time, such "inclined evaporators" are designed and installed to serve special purposes.

A *forced-circulation evaporator* adapted for high-viscosity salting-out liquors is shown in Figure 325. The evaporation produces a suspension of solid salt; a portion is pumped over at all times to the separating chamber which retains the solid, while the supernatant clear liquor is returned to the suction line of the pump. Into this same line, the fresh feed is led. The apparatus has continuous operation, continuous feed, and continuous discharge of the salt.

A somewhat different construction is shown in Figure 326. The liquor, also a viscous, salt-producing one, is heated in horizontal tubes through which the pump sends it at a high velocity so that no deposition of salt can take place.   The liquor enters the vaporization chamber where the vapor forms, dropping the liquid and the grains of salt.   The latter collects in the salt box below the cone bottom, while part of the clear liquor is discharged, and part returned to the pump together with feed liquor to be sent through the heating tubes again.

In the *Downflow evaporator*, the liquor to be concentrated is distributed to the several tubes by a special device, in such a way that the liquor travels down the walls of the tubes without filling them.   Vapor

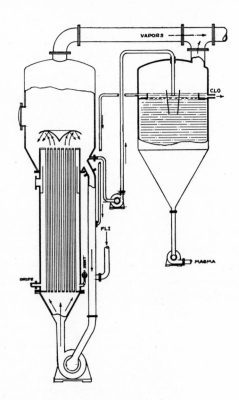

Figure 325.—Swenson salting-out forced-circulation evaporator. A suspension of salt in liquor is formed; part of it is passed to the separator, where the salt is retained, while the other part is recirculated through the heating element. From the separator, part of the clear liquor is discharged as finished liquor; another part is returned to the evaporator. *CLO*, concentrated liquor outlet; *FLI*, feed liquor inlet.

which gradually forms and increases in amount also travels downward (which it must do, for the only outlet is near the bottom of the evaporator body), increasing the velocity of both liquor and vapors to a maximum. The liquid and vapor mixture leaving the bottom end of the tubes is conducted to a vapor separator of the same tangential entry design as that used in the standard long-tube evaporator.   Part of the liquor is pumped back to the top of the tubes to be recirculated, and the balance enters the next effect, if there is one, or goes to storage and shipment.   The Downflow evaporator frequently is built for single effect, and is operated under vacuum; when a thermo compressor is employed (see further), an econ-

omy in steam is realized which equals that of a double effect. The
Downflow evaporator may also be installed in multiple effects. The operation may be continuous, or batch.

A second feature of the downflow evaporator is that it permits evaporation to proceed at low temperatures, enabling the processor, for example,
to concentrate orange juice or other fruit juices while conserving unal-
tered their natural delicate flavor. In such a *low-temperature evaporator*,
the evaporation is performed at temperatures of 50 to 70°F, under a

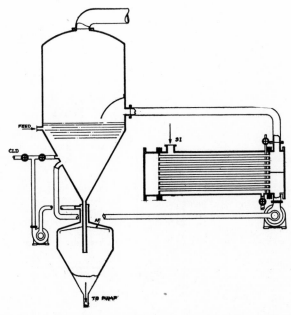

FIGURE 326.—An evaporator for electrolytic caustic with outside horizontal submerged tubes, and with forced circulation. The separated salt enters the salt box, where
the salt deposits, and clear liquor passes up past the baffle *AF*, to be discharged as finished liquor, or in part, returned to the separator. *CLD*, concentrated liquor discharge;
SI, steam inlet. (A Buflovak design.)

vacuum which is maintained high, over 29 inches of mercury. The
vapor issuing from the liquor at such low temperatures and pressures
cannot be condensed by means of cooling water which in the summer is
usually above 70°F itself. The problem is solved by compressing the
vapor in a thermo-compressor, with the aid of boiler steam, to a point at
which it can be condensed. A portion of the vapors from the vapor body
may be compressed, also thermally, to the pressure maintained in the
steam chest proper (hence around the tubes), and then fed into the chest
to become the source of heat. The temperature furnished by the steam
must also not be too high; it may be, for example, 140°F. The vapors

may also be recompressed mechanically, if boiler steam should be unavailable.

The Downflow, low-temperature evaporator avoids building a hydrostatic head on the liquor to be boiled, by constantly emptying the tube so that a column of liquor cannot accumulate; the hydrostatic temperature loss which would otherwise result is avoided. On the other hand,

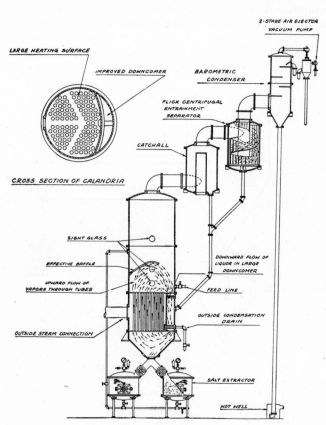

FIGURE 326a.—A single-effect salting out evaporator with natural circulation, operated under vacuum. Note location and shape of the downcomer; the Flick separator; the barometric condenser with 2-stage steam jet ejector. (Courtesy Wurster and Sanger, Inc., Chicago 15, Ill.)

a larger heating surface must be provided because temperature difference in a thermo-compression evaporator generally is lower than in an ordinary evaporator using higher steam pressure.

Another method of boiling at low temperatures consists in combining the evaporator with a refrigerating cycle.*

* See "Buflovak Evaporators," p. 40, Catalog 351, Buflovak Division, Blaw-Knox Company, Buffalo 11, N. Y., 1949.

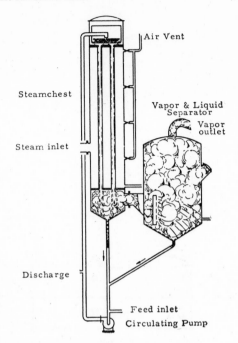

Air Vent

Steamchest

Vapor & Liquid
Separator

Vapor
outlet

Steam inlet

FIGURE 327.—Sketch show-
ing the working principle of
the Buflovak Downflow Evaporator. (By permission.)

Discharge

Feed inlet
Circulating Pump

MULTIPLE-EFFECT EVAPORATORS

All evaporators so far described have been single-effect devices. Each consists of a single vessel, operating, unless distinctly stated otherwise, at near-atmospheric pressure. The outgoing vapors, which are steam, may be discharged into the atmosphere. But any one of the evaporators shown, in addition to the downflow and low-temperature evaporator, may be operated at subatmospheric pressure. This involves passing the vapors to a surface condenser or a barometric condenser where they condense (collapse) and thus produce a more or less perfect vacuum. In addition, a suitable pump is provided to remove air and noncondensables entrained by the liquor or entering through leakage. As the liquor is now able to boil under (or against) a lower pressure, the boiling temperature is lower, and consequently the temperature difference is greater, which means a higher heat transfer (between the steam chest, whose tempera- ture remains the same, and the liquor outside of it), and an increased rate of evaporation. A well-known example of the single effect being oper- ated under such conditions is the single-effect vacuum pan in a sugar house. A vessel to be operated under reduced pressure must be strong enough to withstand atmospheric pressure (14.7 pounds to the square inch).

There is another way of disposing of the vapor from an evaporator besides condensing it. The vapor leaving the solution in a single-effect

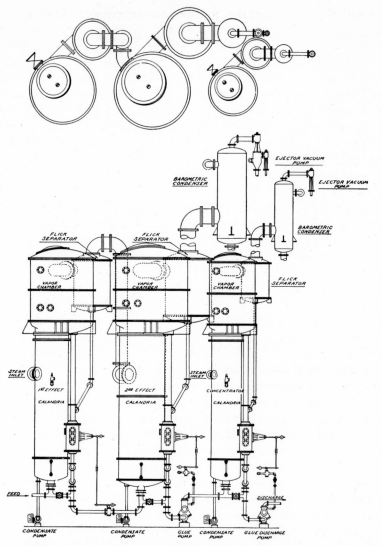

FIGURE 328.—A W&S continuous glue evaporator with a double-effect evaporator followed by a concentrator, high-velocity, long-tube, one-pass, climbing film type. Note from the plan the tangential connection from vapor chamber to Flick separator. The three vessels differ in size to meet the changing conditions of gravity and viscosity of the liquor. The high vacuum provided permits the use of comparatively low temperatures. (Courtesy Wurster and Sanger, Inc., Chicago, Ill.)

evaporator might be piped to the steam chest of a second single-effect evaporator, there to condense and give up its heat to evaporate an equal quantity of liquid. It would be necessary to reduce the pressure on the second effect in order to bring about a temperature difference and insure boiling at all pressures—preferably, fairly rapid boiling. The incoming steam will be cooler than the original steam from the boiler house, and the vapor raised in the second effect will be cooler than the steam entering the chest. With this arrangement, one would have a double-effect evaporator. The designer might go a step further and pipe the steam from this second effect to the chest of a third one, there to produce in its turn vapor from the surrounding liquor. Here too, the pressure would have to be lowered by a considerable amount below the temperature of the vapor of the second effect. Such an arrangement is then a triple-effect evaporator. An example of its temperature and temperature differences is shown later. There are also quadruple and quintuple effects.

A double-effect evaporator with the second effect just above atmospheric pressure, and discharging directly into the atmosphere, is feasible and satisfactory. The first effect must receive steam at 40 pounds pressure or so. Triple effects working above atmospheric pressure are not ruled out, as long as sufficient temperature differences can be set up. In fact there is at least one firm in the United States which recommends and builds high-speed pressure evaporators in which condensers and vacuum pumps are unnecessary and are left out. It is even possible to use the low-pressure steam discharged from the last effect for process purposes.

In a multiple effect evaporator, only the pressure of the steam supplied to the first effect and the pressure in the last effect are fixed, the first by the available boiler or exhaust steam pressure, the second by the temperature of the available cooling water for the condenser. Intermediate temperatures and intermediate pressures will then take care of themselves.

The adjustment takes place in accordance with the amount of heat, Q, passing through the heating surface in each effect.* In the expression $Q = U \times A \times \Delta t$, Q is the amount of heat in Btu's transferred per hour, U is the over-all heat transfer coefficient expressed as Btu's per square foot per hour per degree, A is the area of the heating surface, and Δt is the temperature difference between the steam in the steam chest and the vapor. If Q is to remain the same in each effect, and A has been built the same, then when U becomes smaller (as it does when we move from one effect to the next one), Δt must become correspondingly larger. An example with figures is given in Figure 329.

Of interest in connection with temperature studies is the "boiling point rise." Solutions boil at temperatures higher than water; dilute solutions boil slightly higher, and stronger solutions considerably higher. The difference between the boiling point of water at any one pressure and the boiling point of a solution at that pressure is called the "boiling point rise." With a number of substances, especially those of high molecular weight, the boiling point rise is of no great moment; with cer-

---

* A variation is caused by a certain amount of heat liberated in flash or absorbed in heating the liquid, as the case may be.

tain inorganic substances, especially sodium hydroxide, it is very large. The boiling point rises in the various vacuum effects must be deducted from the total temperature difference between initial steam and the vapor in the last effect, in order to arrive at the useful temperature difference available for actual heat transfer.

Of minor importance is the superheat carried by the steam from a solution which exerts a large boiling point rise; the steam leaves the solution at its boiling point, under a certain pressure, but soon drops to the temperature of water which on boiling would produce steam at that pressure.

The temperature differences distribute themselves, as already stated, between the several effects so that the quantity of heat leaving one effect in the vapor is equal to that passed through the heating surface of the

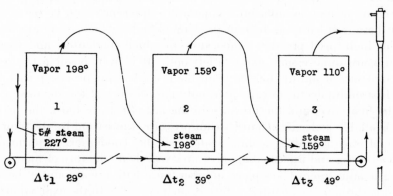

FIGURE 329.—The temperatures and temperature differences in a typical triple-effect evaporator.

succeeding effect per hour. However, all the heat leaving one effect need not be vaporization heat. In parallel flow (which see), a certain quantity of vapor is due to the flash of the hotter liquid upon entering the next effect whose temperature is somewhat lower. For each pound of liquor, such a quantity of water is transformed into steam as will use exactly the amount of heat released when each pound of solution drops from the upper to the lower temperature. The sensible heat of the liquor becomes latent heat of vapor. Vapor so formed also travels to the next chest, there to perform the act of vaporization. Only in the last effect is the heat value of the flash a total loss. Evaporation by flash may also be called self-evaporation.

The liquor levels are set at will and regulated either by hand or automatically by means of gates or butterfly valves actuated by floats. High levels mean longer contact between the liquor and the heating surfaces. The height of the liquor in the tubes brings about a temporary increase in temperature above the boiling point, known as the hydrostatic head loss. This loss is most pronounced in short-tube evaporators in which the height of the liquid is a large proportion of the total length of the tubes; it is much less pronounced in long-tube evaporators and absent in forced circulation evaporators.

With the distribution of temperature goes the *distribution of the reduction in pressure* dependent essentially upon the temperature of the boiling liquid. When first started, the air is pulled out by a vacuum pump, for example, by the one attached to the barometric condenser; auxiliary vents allow steam chests and bodies to be interconnected and evacuated.

It is customary to condense the vapors leaving the final effect in a low-level jet condenser or in a barometric condenser. In the latter the vacuum pump, referred to above, connected to the condenser head, pulls out the noncondensable gases as fast as they accumulate. A surface condenser is employed when the condensate is to be saved. The jet condenser requires more cooling water than the surface or barometric condenser for the same amount of heat removal.

The low-level jet condenser with wet vacuum pump produces a vacuum of 26 inches of mercury; the barometric jet condenser with dry suction pump gives a 27-inch vacuum or better. There is another method, widely used, for the removal of the vapors from the final effect, and that is by means of a steam jet ejector, fully discussed in Chapter 19.

Returning to the consideration of the multiple-effect evaporator, it may be of interest to point out that the second effect may be viewed as a condenser in which the entering vapor is condensed, as it would be in any condenser. There are these differences, however: the cooling agent is not water, but liquor, and the heat absorption is not by a rise in temperature, i.e., a rise merely in sensible heat, but mainly by vaporization, i.e., by the consumption of latent heat. Similarly, the steam chest in the third effect is a condenser for the vapors leaving the second effect.

In multiple-effect evaporators, the heating surface in each effect generally is made the same, because it is cheaper to build several effects of the one size than of different dimensions.

Occasionally the several effects differ in size, when for any reason the temperature in one of the effects has to be kept below or above a fixed value; for example, in evaporating milk in a double-effect evaporator, the temperature in the first effect must be held below the point at which proteins start to coagulate and coat the tubes.

The main benefit in using multiple effect evaporators is the saving in cost of steam; the amount of steam is reduced, roughly, in proportion to the number of effects, as will be shown later by means of figures. Multiple effects are assembled in any one of the types which have been described. as single effects, either all of one type or a combination of types, depending on the service to be rendered. Boiling is less violent than in an equivalent single effect, because Δt is smaller in the several effects. Danger of entrainment therefore is less.

Direction of flow of liquor. There is a choice in the flow of liquor through the several effects of a multiple-effect evaporator; there may be forward flow, backward flow, parallel feed, and a combination of these (see Figure 330). The reader is reminded that numbering the effects is based on the steam flow. The selection of the kind of liquor flow will depend upon the temperature of the feed, the temperature difference between steam chests and corresponding liquor, the temperature-viscosity

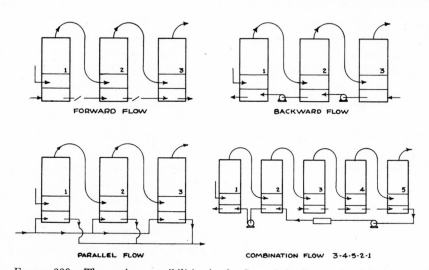

FORWARD FLOW   BACKWARD FLOW

PARALLEL FLOW   COMBINATION FLOW 3-4-5-2-1

FIGURE 330.—The various possibilities in the flow of the liquor through the several effects of a multi-effect evaporator. The sketches will explain themselves. Note that the combination flow is the only one which has an outside heater.

relation, the heat transfer coefficients, and other circumstances. If the feed temperature is low, the backward flow will be more economical, for the temperature of the feed will approximate, presumably, that of the last effect. If the temperature of the feed is high, the forward flow will be favored; the feed will enter the first effect at a temperature presumably only slightly higher or lower than that of the boiling liquor therein.

The advantage of forward flow is that only two pumps are required —the feed pump and the product pump. Backward flow requires as many liquor pumps as there are effects, plus one for the removal of the concentrated liquor. Parallel feed is the proper method when the liquor fed in is saturated, when little or no concentration is needed and the saturation does not vary greatly with temperature; the only evaporation required is that for the separation of the solid phase, as in making sodium chloride crystals from brine. Backward flow is most desirable in single-pass evaporation which requires low liquid levels, for these can be maintained more readily by this method. Both back flow and mixed flow are practiced when the concentrated liquor has a high viscosity, or if it is desirable to discharge at an elevated temperature.

In quintuple-effect, forward flow would be 1, 2, 3, 4, 5; backward flow would be 5, 4, 3, 2, 1; both are used. It may be desirable to have the order 2, 3, 4, 5, 1, which would place the final concentration at the highest temperature level instead of at the lowest, but would otherwise conform to forward flow. In other installations, 3, 4, 5, 2, 1, may be the right selection; if so, and if the evaporator is of the long-tube type, a preheater might well be placed between 5 and 2, in order to raise the temperature of the liquor to that of effect No. 2, for a preheater can furnish such heat cheaper than the evaporator. One good reason for adopting the 3, 4, 5, 2, 1 order would be that the viscosity of the liquor after the concentration reached in three effects becomes high at the lower temperatures, but is reduced at the temperature of effects 2 and 1 sufficiently so that better heat transfer takes place. Forced circulation for the final effect or for the last two effects may lead to the best evaporation figures.

TABLE 64.   COMPARATIVE STEAM CONSUMPTION (POUNDS OF STEAM REQUIRED FOR THE EVAPORATION OF 1 POUND OF WATER) FOR VARIOUS FLOWS OF LIQUOR IN A QUADRUPLE EFFECT*

	Forward Flow	Combination Flow 2, 3, 4, 1	Backward Flow
For 50% evaporation	0.455	0.445	0.36
For 90% evaporation	0.37	0.345	0.295

* The radiation loss, usually estimated as 10%, is not included. The high figure in the first item, 0.455 pound, is due to the low temperature of the feed.

Factors Affecting the Transfer Coefficient. The over-all heat transfer coefficient is made up of three separate parts. In the evaporator, these parts are the film coefficient on the steam side, the conductivity of the metal, and the liquor film coefficient. A number of pertinent remarks have been presented earlier (p. 396). There might be added the following: The *liquor film coefficient* is by no means a constant. It depends on many factors, some involving the nature of the liquid, others the method of operation and the design of the multiple-effect unit. Among the first are concentration, viscosity, and temperature of the liquid. As concentration increases, the coefficient drops, largely because the viscosity increases; under reduced pressure and consequent reduced temperature, the coefficient also is lowered. Among the factors involving operating method and design are the velocity of the liquid, and the measures taken to reduce the bad effect of high viscosity by special construction or by the proper selection of the direction of flow of the liquid. For instance, to reduce the bad results due to high viscosity, the effect in which the final concentration takes place may be split in two sections operating in series at the same vapor pressure. Part of the evaporation takes place in one section at an intermediate concentration at which the viscosity is still not too high, permitting good heat transfer, while the balance of the concentration takes place in the other section at high viscosity and low heat transfer. Such an arrangement is advantageous if the two units cost less than a larger single unit operating at the minimum rate. This has been done with distillery waste by splitting the first effect, operating 2-3-4-1; and again in the concentration of glue, which may be finished at low temperature in a forward flow evaporator with split last effect. Whatever the problem, final selection always must be based on a balance between the cost of the equipment and the cost of operation within the limits set by the nature of the product and local conditions.

Table 65 illustrates the variation of over-all heat transfer coefficients in an experimental evaporator corresponding to quadruple-effect concentration of a paper mill waste liquor, with steam at 5 pounds pressure and a vacuum of 27 inches of mercury, concentrating from 14 to 50 per cent.

TABLE 65. OVER-ALL HEAT TRANSFER COEFFICIENTS (SEE TEXT)

Flow	1	2	Effect 3	4
1-2-3-4	750	680	420	135
2-3-4-1	265	700	540	295
4-3-2-1	265	490	540	405

The surface of the transfer wall must be clean for maximum heat transfer; any scale will push down the value of U. Roughness rather than smoothness promotes heat transfer, since bubbles can form more readily on protuberances, thus minimizing the superheating of the liquid at the tube wall. Superheating would decrease the temperature difference. However, smooth surfaces are preferred for the concentration of food products to permit thorough cleaning and the maintaining of sanitary conditions.

A departure from the conventional tubular heating surfaces is made in the *Flat Plate Heating Surface Evaporator* in which the heating element is made up of narrow rectangular sections confined by flat plates. Provision is made for switching the boiling liquid from one chamber to the next. Every other chamber has boiling liquid, while the alternate chambers receive the steam. The boiling liquid on concentration deposits a scale on the flat surfaces of its walls, but after a while the switch occurs, and steam is admitted. The steam then cleans the surface and restores the original high heat transfer through the wall. The Flat Plate Heating

Surface Evaporator was developed for duties involving scaling of heating surfaces. In the multiple-effect Flat Plate Evaporator, the liquid side of the unit is switched with the condensing steam side with the aid of reversing valves at each end of the multiple-effect unit; this is done during a short shut-down during which liquid is transferred to what had been the

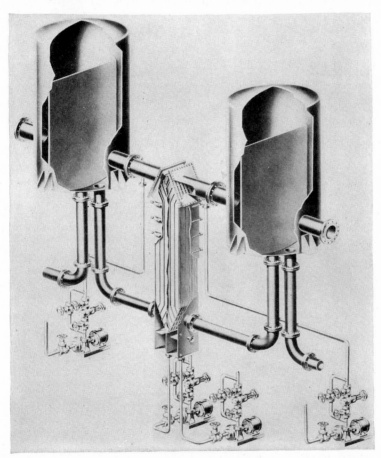

FIGURE 331.—Conkey Flat Plate Heating Surface Evaporators, the Rosenblad Channel Switching System—patents applied for. (Process Equipment Division, General American Transportation Corp., 10 E. 49 St., New York 17, N. Y.)

steam side. The interval between switchings is determined by the rate of deposition of the scale (see Figures 331 and 332).

Materials of Construction. As to materials of construction, a number of them have been mentioned in the course of the discussion. Mild steel is used as the least expensive material; the lower cost is due in part to the fact that the seams may be welded. Cast iron is more expensive than steel, because patterns have to be made first.   Cast iron resists mild corrosive action better than steel.   When corrosion becomes serious, or contamination of the product by iron must be prevented, more expensive metals like "Monel" and "Inconel" have to be used.   Copper tubes and cast bronze tube sheets are standard in sugar houses.   The list also includes nickel-clad steel, rubber-lined steel, lead (generally cast), and aluminum.

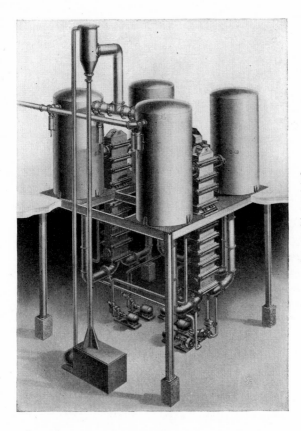

FIGURE 332.—F o u r-Body Triple Effect Conkey Flat Plate Heating Surface Evaporator, reproduction of a wash drawing showing the c o m- p l e t e assembly. (Courtesy Process Equipment Division, General American Transportation Corp., New York 17, N. Y.)

A special mention must be made of stainless steel.   It is used in the concentration of milk and in the food industries in general, and also for the concentration of pharmaceuticals and for corrosive chemicals.   Its heat conductivity is low, but that is overcome by making the tube thin, less than $\frac{1}{16}$ inch.   The most economical form is mild steel clad with stainless steel; it goes by the name of stainless-clad steel.*

In dimensions, the evaporator may have anywhere from 100 to 10,000

* For other comments on the economics of the several clad steels, see Chapter 24.

square feet of heating surface to each effect. For the concentration of 75 tons of caustic per day, from 10 to 50 per cent sodium hydroxide, a triple-effect evaporator would be required with a 40-horsepower circulating pump on each effect, and with 2100 square feet of heating surface in each effect.*

In a kraft paper mill there are large quantities of weak, spent liquors from the digesters which must be concentrated for the recovery of their salts and caustic. One such plant uses a multiple-effect, single-pass, continuous feed and draw evaporator which evaporates two and a half million pounds per day. This is followed by a forced-circulation machine, because the viscosity has become too high for natural circulation; there the viscous product is further concentrated, after which it is passed to the furnace for combustion and recovery of its alkaline ash.

In design, in dimensions, and in materials of construction, there is an endless variety, so that money figures mean little. The following may, nevertheless, serve in a limited way as a guide. A single-effect, long-tube rapid evaporator, made of stainless steel throughout, with covers over the heating tubes on hinges for ready cleaning, with heating element outside, and with 350 square feet heating surface, would have cost $12,500 in 1949; the same construction, also of stainless steel throughout, in double-effect would have cost at that time about $21,500. These estimates are for the complete evaporator in each instance, but without auxiliary equipment.

Multiple- versus Single-effect. In the multiple-effect evaporator, a considerable saving in fuel may be realized, for a given amount of steam from the power house does the work of vaporization as many times, or at least approximately as many times, as there are effects. Unfortunately, the case for the multiple effects is not as one-sided as might be inferred from this statement, because the high first cost and the upkeep costs of three effects instead of one must be included in the consideration. In a single effect, although with more steam (about threefold), the weight of water vaporized from the solution in a given period is just as great as in the three effects combined. If fuel is cheap and installation costs are high, it may be more economical to install only one effect and consume three times the fuel which the triple effect would have required. If

---

* Informative tables of dimensions of the evaporator and its parts with the volume of milk which may be concentrated from 2 volumes to 1, from 3 to 1 or from 4 to 1, are given by the Buflovak Equipment Division, Blaw-Knox Co., Buffalo, N. Y. The steam required for the concentration of a given volume is given for a single effect, and for a double effect, for continuous operation. The single effect only is given for the lower four sizes, which take from 890 to 6,680 lbs of milk per hour. The next eight sizes are listed with both single and double effect; they will take (also for 2 to 1 concentration) from 8,530 to 35,600 lbs per hour. For greater concentrations, the amounts taken per hour are smaller. Three other tables list the capacities and steam consumption for batch-type evaporators of all sizes.

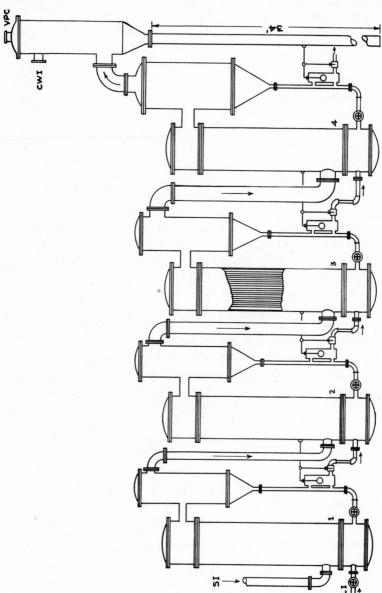

Figure 333.—A quadruple-effect natural-circulation vertical long-tube rapid evaporator, with continuous operation and automatic regulation of liquor levels. Steam from the power house enters effect *1*; steam raised in *1* travels to the heating element in *2*; the steam raised in *2* goes to *3*; while the vapor raised in *3* heats the last effect *4*. The vapor leaving effect *4* is condensed in the barometric condenser. The evaporator has forward feed. *DLI*, dilute liquor inlet; *SI*, steam inlet; *CWI*, cold water inlet; *VPC*, vacuum pump connection. Note the relative sizes of the separators, the unlike diameters of the vapor lines between the several effects, and the equal size of the tube elements. The valves in the liquor lines are shown directly controlled by the floats; in practice, the

fuel is high and installation purchase and erection costs are reasonable, it would be of greater advantage to invest the larger sum and consume less fuel. A balance must be struck between the recurring cost of the fuel and the first cost of the several effects. The cost of cooling water should also receive consideration; the amount of cooling water per effect decreases with an increase in the number of effects.

The reason why a single effect does the same work as the three effects is that the greater temperature difference allows a greater transfer of heat. Per unit surface, three times as much heat is transferred in the single effect as in the triple effect. Stated in other words, the triple-effect evaporator would have essentially the same evaporative capacity as one single-effect with the same end conditions. A single-effect evaporator with vacuum is the choice in the evaporation of a substance sensitive to heat. A low temperature may be maintained, and its exact location will depend upon the vacuum applied. Thus, 125°F will be the temperature for a 26-inch vacuum, which may be maintained with a parallel current jet condenser. The temperature listed is for water, so that for a solution of moderate strength a temperature near 130°F will be obtained. A temperature of 101°F may be produced by a 28-inch vacuum which will require a counter current jet condenser (again for water). The multiple-effect evaporator would not do for such a purpose, because in its first effect, and probably in the second, the temperature would be too high. The single-effect evaporator, furthermore, is suited to small installations and to operations which require close control and regular application of heat to regulate the formation of crystal nuclei and the growth of grains on these nuclei, such as in the "finishing pan" in a sugar house.

TABLE 66. A COMPARISON OF THE NUMBER OF POUNDS OF STEAM* REQUIRED TO EVAPORATE 1 POUND OF WATER IN SINGLE-EFFECT VERSUS MULTIPLE-EFFECT EVAPORATION (FORWARD FLOW)

Effect	Temperature of Feed	50% Evaporation	90% Evaporation
Single	70°F	1.29	1.23
	180°	1.03	1.09
Double	70°	0.75	0.65
	180°	0.52	0.53
Triple	70°	0.59	0.49
	180°	0.36	0.36
Quadruple	70°	0.51	0.42
	180°	0.29	0.29

* These figures include 10% for radiation loss.

Recompression. There has been a renewal of interest in recompression. In this system, a part of the vapors given off during evaporation is recompressed, either mechanically (in Europe) or thermally (in America) and returned to the steam chest. If the evaporation must be conducted at a low temperature, such as 120°F, or if the steam economy must approach

Numerical Example: First Calculation

Effect	1	2	3	4
Effective temp. diff. (Δt)	26.5	26.5	26.5	26.5
Steam temp., °F	267	237	205	169.5
Liquor temp., °F	240.5	210.5	178.5	143
Boiling point rise, °F	3.5	5.5	9.0	18.0
Saturated vapor temp., °F	237	205	169.5	125
Latent heat of steam, Btu/lb	934	954	975	996
Latent heat of vapor, Btu/lb	954	975	996	1022
Specific heat of liquor	.86	.81	.76	.65
Heat transfer coefficient (U), Btu/hr/sq ft/°F	900	750	500	300
Feed liquor, lb/hr	100,000	$100{,}000 - x$	$97{,}650 - 1.955x$	$93{,}250 - 2.848x$
Evaporation by direct heat transfer	x	$x\frac{954}{975} = .978x$	$(2350+.955x)\frac{975}{996}$ $= 2300+.935x$	$(4400+.893x)\frac{996}{1022}$ $= 4300+.871x$
Flash	0	$\frac{26.5\times.86}{975}\,(100{,}000 - x)$ $= 2350-.023x$	$\frac{26.5\times.81}{996}\,(97{,}650 - 1.955x)$ $= 2100-.042x$	$\frac{26.5\times.76}{1022}\,(93{,}250 - 2.848x)$ $= 1950-.057x$
Total evaporation	x	$2350 + .955x$	$4400 + .893x$	$6250 + .814x$
Discharge	$100{,}000 - x$	$97{,}650 - 1.955x$	$93{,}250 - 2.848x$	$87{,}000 - 3.662x$

To find x $87{,}000 - 3.662x = (100{,}000 \times 14) \div 50 = 28{,}000;\ x = 16{,}100$

	1	2	3	4
Heat transfer through heating surface, Btu/hr	$\frac{954x}{15{,}350{,}000}$	$\frac{975\times.987x}{15{,}350{,}000}$	$\frac{996(2300+.935x)}{17{,}300{,}000}$	$\frac{1022(4300+.871x)}{18{,}700{,}000}$
For warming feed 60.5°	5,400,000			
Total (Q)	20,750,000			
Surface $A = \dfrac{Q}{U \times \Delta t} =$	870	775	1305	2350
Ratio of surfaces	1	.89	1.50	2.70

Numerical Example: Second Calculation

Effect	1	2	3	4
Effective temp. diff. (Δt)	18.3	15.2	22.9	49.6
Steam temp., °F	267.0	245.2	224.5	192.6
Liquor temp., °F	248.7	230.0	201.6	143.0
Vapor temp., °F	245.2	224.5	192.6	125.0
Latent heat of steam, Btu/lb	934	949	962	982
Latent heat of vapor, Btu/lb	949	962	982	1022
Heat transfer coefficient (U), Btu/hr/sq ft/°F	900	800	600	300
Feed liquor, lbs/hr	100,000	$100,000 - x$	$98,365 - 1.971x$	$95,530 - 2.926x$
Evaporation by direct heat transfer	x	$x \frac{949}{962} = .987x$	$(1635 + .971x)\frac{962}{982}$ $= 1600 + .980x$	$(2835 + .955x)\frac{982}{1022}$ $= 2720 + .917x$
Flash	0	$\frac{18.3 \times .86}{962}(100,000 - x)$ $= 1635 - .016x$	$\frac{15.2 \times .81}{982}(98,365 - 1.971x)$ $= 1235 - .025x$	$\frac{22.9 \times .76}{1022}(95,530 - 2.926x)$ $= 1625 - .050x$
Total evaporation	x	$1635 + .971x$	$2835 + .955x$	$4345 + .867x$
Discharge	$100,000 - x$	$98,365 - 1.971x$	$95,530 - 2.926x$	$91,185 - 3.793x$
To find x		$91,185 - 3.793x = (100,000 \times 14) \div 50 = 28,000$; $x = 16,650$		
Heat transfer through heating surface, Btu/hr / Heating liquid	949x · 15,800,000 · 6,050,000	962(.987x) 15,800,000	982(1600 + .980x) 17,600,000	1022(2720 + .917x) 18,350,000
Total (Q)	21,850,000			
Surface, sq ft (A)	1330	1300	1280	1235
Steam consumption	21,850,000 ÷ 934 = 23,400 lbs/hr			

70°F Cooling water: $\dfrac{(4345 + .867x)(1022 + 5)}{(120 - 70) \times 500} = 770$ gpm

Average surface $A = 1286$ sq ft.

that of multiple effects, which are ruled out by the temperature limitation, the recompression unit may be recommended.

The recompression unit is meant to give double-effect economy for the single effect. The double-effect economy is 0.55 pound of steam applied for the evaporation of 1 pound of water from the solution; in the single effect it is 1.05. For the realization of the double-effect economy in recompression, the ratio of steam to vapor must be 1.1, in order to compress 0.5 lb of vapor by means of 0.55 lb of high pressure steam to produce 1.05 lb of low pressure steam for the steamchest, allowing the other 0.5 lb of vapor to flow to the condenser. At 26 inches of vacuum in the evaporator, the recompression to about 22 inches in the steam chest will allow this ratio. The temperature difference in the evaporator will be 152 — 125 = 27°F. When operated normally, the single-effect evaporator without recompression, at 26 inches of vacuum with 5-pound steam, would have a temperature difference of 227 — 125 = 102°F. Hence, the recompression evaporator must have 102 ÷ 27 = 3.75 times the heating surface of the ordinary single effect in order to possess the same evaporation capacity. The recompression is done by means of steam at boiler pressure sent through a small converging-diverging nozzle into a small chamber receiving the 26-inch vacuum vapor, which is then carried through a larger converging-diverging nozzle from which it emerges as 22-inch vacuum steam, slightly superheated. Superheat in the compressed vapor is removed by spraying in a small amount of water. The balance of the vapor from the evaporator is sent to the condenser.

If steam is cheap and low-pressure steam is available, it is just as well to use the single effect evaporator (without recompression) which is smaller and therefore cheaper. If the plant has only high-pressure steam, it may be most economical to use recompression.

Numerical Example

When the chemical engineer or manager is faced with an evaporation problem involving new installation, he desires to make an estimate at his desk, in order to obtain an approximation of the size of the apparatus required, the most advantageous direction of flow of liquid through the evaporator, or the most economical number of effects. He knows what steam pressure is available, and what the temperature of the cooling water is. He may know the over-all temperature coefficients from previous plant operations; if not, he may be able to obtain them from another operator or have them determined in the laboratory. It is the temperature distribution which he does not know; hence it would seem logical that the temperature difference be distributed evenly between the several effects, for a first calculation.

For the calculation of the heating surface, the area A in $Q = U \times A \times \Delta t$, is sought. A simplified form of such a calculation, which leaves out all the items not absolutely necessary to exhibit the method, is given on pages 418 and 419. This method has the advantage of employing simple mathematics, of following a logical sequence, and of being easy to check.

In this equation it is necessary to assign values to U and to Δt for each effect of a multiple-effect evaporator. Values for U vary widely for different products and for different operating conditions. In the absence of any available data, at least relative values for U may be obtained by tests in an experimental unit. To arrive at values for Δt, it is not sufficient to select these in inverse ratio to the values of U, because Q also varies materially in the several effects. For this reason it is simpler to make a first calculation of A by making Δt equal in all effects, and then make a second calculation with the Δt's in the same relation to each other as the values for A found in the first calculation. In doing this, the liquor temperature in all effects except the last is changed considerably, and it is advisable to make an adjustment in U before Δt for the second calculation is established. Other refinements may be introduced as desired. The method is applicable if supplementary feed enters any effect, or if vapor is withdrawn from an effect. By carrying Δt to the first decimal, the second calculation will be sufficiently close for most practical purposes. In making these calculations, the unknown x is always the evaporation by direct heat transfer in the effect in which the feed liquor is introduced. In forward flow it will be the first effect; in backward flow, the last; in mixed flow 2-3-4-1, the second effect, working forward to the last effect and backward to the first.

The following reasoning is used after the first calculation to determine Δt for an evaporator with the same heating surface in all four effects. In making this calculation an adjustment is made in the heat transfer coefficient to allow for the change in this coefficient when the temperature of the liquid changes.

Effect	1	2	3	4
Δt for equal heating surface and the same U	17.5	15.5	26.1	47
Liquor temperature	249.5	230.5	199	143
U_1 at this liquor temperature	900	800	600	300
Ratio old U/new U_1	1	1.07	1.20	1
Ratio A/ratio U/U_1	1	.83	1.25	2.70
Δt for second calculation, for equal A and new U_1	18.3	15.2	22.9	49.6

Computation of the heating surface in a quadruple-effect evaporator, with forward feed, for the concentration of a liquor with 14 per cent solids to 50 per cent, is presented on an adjoining page. The feed is 100,000 pounds per hour, its temperature is 180°F. Steam pressure is 39.7 pounds absolute. Vacuum 26 inches, which corresponds to a temperature of 125°F. Consideration has been given to the boiling point rise. The large figures are rounded figures.

A second calculation is made, with temperature differences obtained in the reasoning and computation just preceding; it is shown on page 419.

Reading References

"Boiling-heat transfer in natural convection evaporators," by G. A. Akin and W. H. McAdams, *Ind. Chem. Eng.*, **31**, 487 (1939).

"Heat transmission in evaporative condensers," by A. K. G. Thomson, *Trans. Inst. Chem. Eng. (London)*, **17**, 137–152 (1939).

"A study of entrainment in a forced-circulation evaporator," by O. C. Cessna and W. L. Badger, *Trans. Am. Inst. Chem. Eng.*, **30**, 256 (1934).

"Verdampfen, Kondensieren und Kühlen," by E. Hausbrand, 7th ed., revised by M. Hirsch, Julius Springer, Berlin, 1931.

"Solution cycles," by W. H. Sellew, *Trans. Am. Inst. Chem. Eng.*, **30**, 546 (1934).

"Heat transfer and evaporation," by W. L. Badger, New York, Chemical Catalog Co., Inc. (Reinhold Publishing Corp.), 1926.

"Evaporation," by A. L. Webre and C. S. Robinson, New York, Chemical Catalog Co., Inc. (Reinhold Publishing Corp.), 1926.

"Heat transfer and crystallization," by W. L. Badger and G. E. Seavoy, Harvey, Illinois, Swenson Evaporator Co., 1945.

"Process heat transfer," by D. Q. Kern, Chapter 14, New York, McGraw-Hill Book Company, 1950.

"Factors affecting boiling in a liquid," by R. F. Larson, *Ind. Eng. Chem.*, **37**, 1004–16 (1945).

"Heat transfer to boiling liquids," by F. H. Rhodes and C. H. Bridges, *Ind. Eng. Chem.*, **30**, 1401–6 (1938).

"Liquid film heat-transfer for coefficients in a vertical-tube forced-circulation evaporator," by L. A. Logan, N. Fragen, and W. L. Badger, *Ind. Eng. Chem.*, **26**, 1044–47 (1934).

"Heat transfer coefficients in vertical-tube forced circulation evaporators," by N. Fragen and W. L. Badger, *Ind. Eng. Chem.*, **28**, 534–37 (1936).

"Boiling film heat transfer coefficients in a long-tube vertical evaporator," by G. W. Stroebe, E. M. Baker, and W. L. Badger, *Ind. Eng. Chem.*, **31**, 200–206 (1939); *Trans. A.I.C.E.*, **35**, 17 (1939).

"Liquid velocity and coefficients of heat transfer in a natural-circulation evaporator," by A. J. Foust, E. M. Baker, and W. L. Badger, *Ind. Eng. Chem.*, **31**, 206–214 (1939); *Trans. A.I.C.E.*, **35**, 45 (1939).

"Steam-film heat transfer coefficients for vertical tubes," by E. M. Baker, E. W. Kazmark, and G. W. Stroebe, *Ind. Eng. Chem.*, **31**, 214–218 (1939); *Trans. A.I.C.E.*, **35**, 127 (1939).

"Vapor recompression systems for evaporators," by W. L. Badger, *Chem. Met. Eng.*, **28**, 26–31, 73–78 (1923).

"Heat transfer in a long-tube vertical evaporator," by O. C. Cessna, J. R. Lentz, and W. L. Badger, *Trans. A.I.C.E.*, **36**, 759 (1939).

"Some aspects of the economics of evaporation," by H. B. Caldwell and W. D. Kohlins, *Trans. A.I.C.E.*, **42**, 495 (1946).

"Design of multiple effect evaporators for minimum area and minimum cost," by C. F. Bonilla, *Trans. A.I.C.E.*, **42**, 407 (1946); **41**, 529 (1945).

"Heat transfer at high rates to water with surface boiling," by W. H. McAdams, W. E. Kennel, C. S. Minden, Rudolf Carl, P. M. Picornell, and J. E. Drew, *Ind. Eng. Chem.*, **41**, 1945–53 (1949).

"Heat transfer in stable film boiling," by L. A. Bromley, *Chem. Eng. Progress*, **46**, 221–7 (1950).

"Heat transfer," by W. H. McAdams, *Chem. Eng. Progress*, **46**, 121–30 (1950).

The formation of a crystal from a water solution involves the construction of a crystal lattice by the atoms concerned at a rate which is stupendous. The lattice forms with certain distances between its planes, in every direction; it accepts only the atoms which are of a certain kind and size, and rejects all others, dislodging them if they are already seated. It is this self-cleansing property of the lattice which makes possible the formation and growth of crystals—a synonym for pure substances.

16. CRYSTALLIZERS

A crystallizer is a vessel in which a hot solution of proper strength is allowed to cool and form crystals. As a rule, after crystal separation, there remains a mother liquor which may be run off, and with it the soluble impurities. The crystallizers for inorganic salts which belong to the heavy chemicals class are rectangular boxes without covers, made of wood, of steel, or lead-lined, and provided with an opening for running off the mother liquor. The dimensions vary, but are typically 6 by 10 feet, with a depth of 18 or 24 inches. The box is mounted on horses, and tilted slightly so that when the run-off plug is removed, the mother liquor may run out to a trough which leads to a collecting vessel. The crystals left in the crystallizer are shoveled over the edge onto buggies, or small cars on rails, and these are dumped through an opening in the floor to a storage room or shipping room below.

The moisture, or mother liquor, which clings to the crystals is removed first by sending the crystals from the buggy or rail car to centrifugals; from this the comparatively dry crystals are discharged at the bottom, and enter a rotating cylindrical screen to separate them into sizes. A screen with three sizes of perforations furnishes four sizes of crystals.

The stationary crystallizer is still in use and will continue to be, because of its simplicity and inexpensiveness. It has, however, at least two defects; one is that much hand labor is required, and the other, that several sizes of crystals are formed, while only one size may be saleable. A third, though less serious, defect is that much time is required for the crop of crystals to deposit.

Jacketed-trough Crystallizer with Agitators. The stationary crystallizer is cooled by natural evaporation and by air-cooling of its walls and bottom. More rapid cooling is obtained by using cold water in a jacket, and a better heat transfer is assured if a scraper is used to keep the walls free from crystals. The jacketed crystallizer may then take the form of a trough in which long-pitched ribbon scrapers turn. There is discharged from the trough a slurry of crystals and mother liquor which is sent to the centrifugal; the discharge may be continuous, if hot liquor is con-

423

TABLE 67. A CLASSIFICATION OF CRYSTALLIZERS

Crystallizers

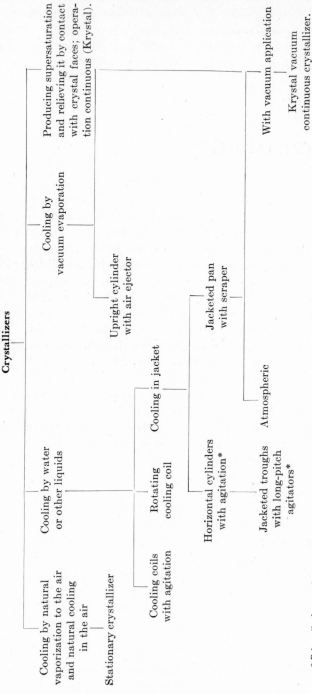

- Cooling by natural vaporization to the air and natural cooling in the air
  - Stationary crystallizer
- Cooling by water or other liquids
  - Cooling coils with agitation
    - Rotating cooling coil
  - Cooling in jacket
    - Horizontal cylinders with agitation*
    - Jacketed pan with scraper
    - Jacketed troughs with long-pitch agitators*
    - Atmospheric
- Cooling by vacuum evaporation
  - Upright cylinder with air ejector
  - With vacuum application
    - Krystal vacuum continuous crystallizer.
- Producing supersaturation and relieving it by contact with crystal faces; operation continuous (Krystal).

* Primarily for continuous operation.

tinuously fed in at the other end of the trough. Thus a crystallizer with continuous operation results. The trough is generally 24 inches wide by 26 inches deep and 10 feet long; four sections fitted together give a deck 40 feet in length, generally the maximum. If the flow of the liquor must be more rapid than the wall area permits, a second or third deck is provided, and the incompletely crystallized liquor from the first is cascaded to the second, and thence to the third deck.

Double-pipe Crystallizer. The double-pipe crystallizer consists of fully jacketed pipes with long-pitch agitators, set up in tiers of three or more, each tier operating in series. The inner pipe may be 24 inches in diameter surrounded by a suitably larger pipe, both roughly 10 feet long; sev-

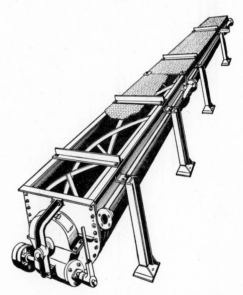

FIGURE 334.—Single-deck Swenson-Walker mechanical crystallizer for continuous or batch operation. The jacketed trough contains a long-pitch ribbon conveyor. The solution is fed in at one end; the crystals are discharged at the other. The solution moves countercurrent to the coolant in the jacket. (Courtesy Swenson Evaporator Co., Harvey, Ill.)

eral lengths, generally three, are assembled to form one single horizontal length. Three such lengths are set one above another; the hot liquor fed to the upper one moves along the length of the pipe, drops to the intermediate level, travels through its length, and then drops to the lowest level, where it moves again over its whole length to reach the outlet. The cooling water or brine may be fed countercurrent to the flow of the liquor, or each level may receive fresh cooling medium. If both pipes are cast-iron, the outer pipe carries baffles in the annular jacket space which force the water to travel in a spiral path; when the outer pipe is of cast iron and the inner one of steel, stainless steel, or similar metals, a steel rod is welded to the outer side of the latter pipe to form a spiral and produce the same flow in the cooling water. As the liquor moves along the pipes, crystals form, and a slurry is discharged at the outlet which may be handled in

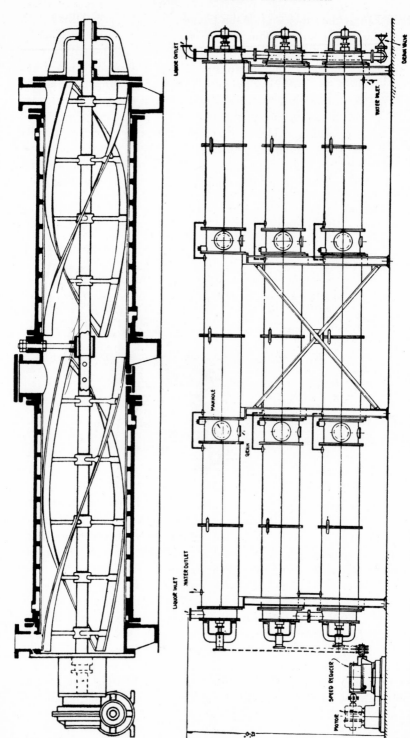

FIGURE 335.—Upper figure, vertical cross section through one section of a double pipe crystallizer, showing the scraper-agitator; the adjustable support of the shaft bearing; the baffles in the cooling jacket. The scraper is adjusted to scrape the bottom of the pipe. Lower figure, a side elevation of a complete double-pipe crystallizer, consisting of two vertical rows of three pipes each, 24 inches outer diameter, 36 feet length, with liquor or slurry outlet brought to the same level as the inlet. The agitators are driven by sprocket chains.

one of two ways. It may be sent past a restricting valve to a magma tank at a lower level, or a riser may cause it to reach the level of the upper tier, there to be discharged into a magma tank. In Figure 335, a double-pipe condenser is shown which has such a riser. By using the latter, the velocity of the liquor is made to depend solely upon the rate of feed. The agitators are driven by sprockets and chains, in the assembly shown. The shaft of the agitator is adjustable, and the provision which makes this adjustment easy is visible in Figure 335; the adjustment is such that the bottom of the pipe is continuously scraped clean. The rate of rotation of the agitator varies between 5 and 30 rpm, depending upon the material handled.

The operation of the crystallizer is continuous; liquor is fed in at the top inlet and slurry is collected from the outlet, both continuously. The

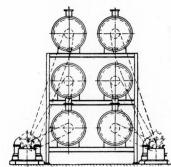

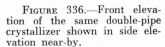

FIGURE 336.—Front eleva-tion of the same double-pipe crystallizer shown in side ele-vation near-by.

crystallizer may readily be made a link in a sequence of operations, all continuous.

It will be noted that the double-pipe crystallizer has a large cooling surface, nearly double that provided in the trough crystallizer; the whole circle of the pipe is cooled. The cubical content per linear foot also is greater by 25 per cent than that of a trough crystallizer of the same diameter.

	Cooling Surface per Lineal Foot	Cubical Content per Lineal Foot
Double-pipe crystallizer (24 in)	6.3 sq ft	3.15 cu ft
Trough crystallizer (24 in)	3.7 sq ft	2.57 cu ft

Another feature of the double-pipe crystallizer is that the cooling is entirely by the jacket; no evaporation takes place, so that there is no change in the ratio of solute to solvent. That the composition of the liquor or slurry should remain unchanged may be of importance in certain crystallization problems.

The double-pipe crystallizer may be operated under pressure.

The jacketed crystallizer may also have the form of a jacketed circular pan in which a scraper agitator slowly rotates. Water applied to the jacket brings about cooling while the crystallization proceeds. The construction of the pan crystallizer is similar to that of the vacuum pan drier shown in Chapter 17. Its main purpose is the production of uniform, rather small crystals, as for example the rice-size "hypo." This crystallizer is of the batch type. A jacketed kettle with sweep agitator makes an excellent crystallizer for certain installations.

Batch Crystallizers with Coils. A second way to cool the crystallizer with cold water is by means of one or several stationary coils through which the water circulates, while an agitator keeps the liquor in motion, preventing coating and consequent insulation of the coil walls, and bring-

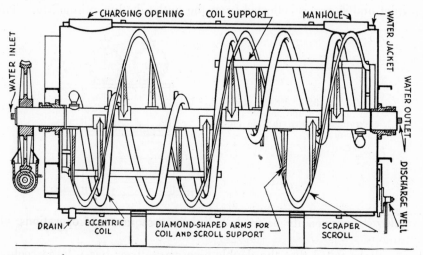

FIGURE 337.—The new type eccentric-coil crystallizer showing the eccentric coil, the diamond-shaped arms, and the scraper-scroll. (Courtesy The Kilby Mfg. Co., Cleveland, Ohio.)

ing new hot layers into contact with the cold walls. The cooling is rapid and the crystals formed are small and uniform. The resulting slurry remains in the vessel until crystallization is complete, when it is discharged to centrifugals or other devices for separating the crystals from the mother liquor.

The Kilby eccentric coil crystallizer consists of a horizontal cylindrical vessel with a horizontal shaft on which is mounted a cooling coil in a position eccentric to the shaft. The latter also carries an agitator scroll by means of diamond-shaped, self-cleaning arms; this rotates with the coil. The cooling water enters and leaves the coil through the hollow shaft. The mass to be cooled is introduced through the charging door at the top, and discharged through the opening in the end plate near the bottom.

The rotation of the coil is generally slow; in the field in which the crystallizer has been most successfully adopted of late, i.e., in the crystallization of cerelose sugar and cane and beet sugars, the rotation varies from ¼ to ½ rpm. The time of retention has been lowered from the earlier 144–168 hours in other types of crystallizers to 96–108 hours in this one. The coil is divided into two halves which are mounted on the shaft so that their eccentricities differ by 180°.

FIGURE 338.—The Kilby patented eccentric-coil crystallizer with end plate removed to show the shaft, coil, and scroll agitator. The charging opening is at top front. (Courtesy The Kilby Mfg. Co., Cleveland, Ohio.)

In the crystallizer with a "patented equalizing coil," the water enters the hollow shaft and thence is introduced into individual, pear-shaped, tubular heating elements. The coils and arms are of extra-sturdy construction and the coil is stiffened by a cross-piece, for use in very heavy masses of 98–99° Brix. The equalizing eccentric coil has served in the equalization of the temperature of a mixture of pulverized coal and distillation oil.

The *process of crystallization* is more than a matter of cooling a liquor until crystals form. Also, the process of crystallization varies from one substance to another and even for one substance when crystallized from various mother liquors. Three phases may be distinguished: the first involves cooling the liquor to the temperature at which the nuclei are about to separate out; the second is the further cooling which leads to the forma-

FIGURE 339.—A single-shell crystallizer 7 feet by 22 feet, equipped with a 3½-inch extra heavy steel temperature equalizing cooling coil for very heavy sugar massecuite. (Courtesy The Kilby Mfg. Co., Cleveland, Ohio.)

tion of nuclei; the third is the period of growth during which the temperature is held constant. Over the latter stage, the heat evolved by crystallization is removed, but the temperature is not allowed to drop. The importance of observing these phases, and the time to be allowed each, will depend upon the particular process at hand. A relatively pure liquor will require less time for crystal growth than a second mother liquor, and the second one in turn will require less time than the third.   The time element has a great effect on the yield, for unless time is allowed, the growth of the crystals will be incomplete, and crystallizable material will remain in solution and leave with the mother liquor.   In order to reach a high yield, then, a longer time of contact between crystals and mother liquor must be allowed, or the temperature must be lowered.   As has already been implied, the amount of impurities and also the pH of the solution have an effect on the yield.   These are all reasons why batch crystallization remains of value.   Furthermore, batch crystallization is of importance whenever precise control of purity is necessary, for it per-

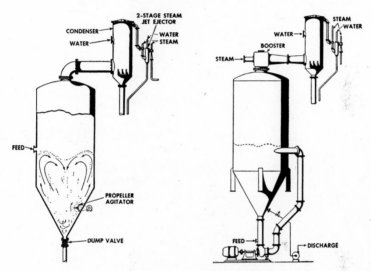

FIGURE 340.—Left, a batch vacuum crystallizer without booster, but with baro-metric condenser; right, a single-stage continuous vacuum crystallizer with booster. The methods of feed and discharge are indicated.   (Courtesy Swenson Evaporator Co., Division of Whiting Corp., Harvey, Ill.)

mits the examination of every batch before acceptance.   In a continuous process, it would be difficult to maintain exactly conditions which would confine impurities to the narrow limits sometimes set.

Delayed-action Crystallizers.   Certain substances like sugar may re-quire a long period of contact between the small crystals, which are to grow, and the mother liquor.   This period is provided in a crystallizer with slow agitation, such as 1 rpm.   The mass remains in the crystallizer for many hours, certain qualities (C sugar) for 2 or 3 days.   Other sugars generally require 2 to 5 hours.

Vacuum Crystallizers.   In the vacuum crystallizer, the cooling of the liquor is brought about by vaporizing some of the water or solvent.   The heat consumed by the process of vaporization is taken from the liquid, which gives up heat from two sources: its sensible heat, and its heat of crystallization. When a crystal forms from solution, there is liberated a certain amount of heat equal to the cooling effect produced when the crystal is dissolved. As the heat is removed, the solution becomes gradually cooler and crystallization continues until finally it is complete.

In the vacuum crystallizer with batch operation, a volume of hot solution is introduced, and a vacuum developed by the functioning of a baro-

FIGURE 341.—A rubber-lined vacuum crystallizer, 8 feet in diameter, crystallizing under acid conditions. Note the two propeller shafts entering the cone. A steam-jet ejector booster is connected in the cover of the vessel, on the floor above, and is not shown. Note level gauge, thermometer, and operator standing at right rear. The method of discharge of product is by a slurry pump pulling from the lowest part of the cone. (Courtesy Swenson Evaporator Co., Division of Whiting Corp., Harvey, Ill.)

metric condenser. A certain low in temperature is reached, corresponding to the pressure in the crystallizer. If the specifications call for a lower liquor temperature, it becomes necessary to install a booster steam-jet ejector. The booster has the effect of lowering still further the temperature of the liquor; it is able to continue to remove water vapor even when the temperature of the liquid is 60 or even 50°F. The booster is not used if it is not necessary.

The crystallizer consists of an upright cylindrical steel tank with a conical bottom, and two side-entering propeller agitators placed in the cone. The tank is closed, and the barometric condenser, or the booster, is connected to the center of the cover. The propellers keep the slurry in motion, prevent deposition of crystals on the walls where they might otherwise grow to larger sizes, and move warmer portions of the liquor to the surface. A similar agitation may be provided by circulating a large stream of the liquor by means of a pump. After crystallization is complete, the slurry is discharged to a magma tank with agitators and thence, as needed, to centrifugals, or possibly to a rotary suction filter. The steam-jet ejector and the booster are fully described in Chapter 19, where essential relations between the cooling water available and the vacuum obtainable are also presented.

FIGURE 342.—A vacuum-crystallizing kettle, approximately 6 feet in diameter and 4 feet deep. The parts coming in contact with the material are made of stainless-clad steel; the jacket is of carbon steel. (Courtesy Buflovak Equipment Division, Blaw-Knox Co.)

The steel tank may be lined, as with rubber, when acid solutions are to be concentrated—for example, the viscose rayon spin bath for the recovery of sulfuric acid and Glauber salt. Crystallizers and steam-jet ejectors are also built of acid-resisting metals when required. Batch operation may require two or more crystallizer bodies to accommodate the volume of liquor.

The vacuum crystallizer is adaptable to continuous operation as well as to batch operation. Continuous operation is recommended for volumes of liquor exceeding 200,000 gallons per day. Continuous operation requires that hot, concentrated liquor be fed in continuously, and a corresponding volume of slurry removed. The hot liquor may be introduced near the surface, when considerable flash takes place, which is an advantage; it is recommended by many operators that there be recirculation

by means of a pump, and that the feed enter the vessel with the recirculation stream. In continuous operation, it is desirable to install several
cooling stages, each having its own steam-jet ejector, and the liquor moving (pumps) from No. 1 to 2, 3, and finally 4. This last will have the
coolest liquor, the highest vacuum, and the thickest slurry. Only for the
last stage (in this example) will a booster be necessary; the earlier stages
deliver steam which the barometric condenser removes successfully. The
slurry from No. 4 cooling stage goes to a magma tank, and from there to
a centrifugal or a suction filter; the mother liquor may be returned to No.
1 stage.*

Compared to mechanical crystallizers, vacuum crystallizers for
equivalent performance are lower in both installation cost and operation
cost. An instance is given under "Numerical Example."

A vacuum pan with external calandria and bed of seed crystals is
shown and discussed as part of a study on the formation and growth of
crystals.†

Crystallization as presented in the preceding pages has concerned itself solely with crystals formed from a hot solution by lowering the
temperature. The salt, or substance, is less soluble in the cold solvent
than in the hot; hence the formation of crystals. There are salts, however, which are almost as soluble in cold water as in hot; to crystallize
these, the solvent must be removed in the evaporator, until for lack of it,
the salt drops out in crystal form. The graining pans for table salt function on the same principle. Sugar syrup in the strike pan is allowed to
form many small crystals, and the pan is then held at a certain temperature in order to permit the crystals to grow to the desired size. A similar
growth of nuclei is illustrated in the devices which follow.

CONTINUOUS CRYSTALLIZERS, KRYSTAL SYSTEM

Crystallizers which might function continuously, with continuous
feed and continuous discharge of crystals, without interruption, and requiring no labor for the handling of the crystals, have long been desired,
and are now available in the form of the Krystal installations.‡ Each
one of the several types of continuous crystallizers has a vaporizer and a
crystal container; the latter is filled with a suspension or slurry of crystals. The process is as follows:

The solution of the salt is treated in the vaporizer in order to give it a
moderate degree of supersaturation; it then passes to the bottom of the
crystallizer, wherein it is allowed to travel gently upward through the

---

* A flow sheet will be found on p. 635, *Ind. Eng. Chem.*, 32 (1940).

† "The formation and growth of crystals," by Professor W. E. Gibbs, *Trans. Inst.
Chem. Eng.* (London), 8, 38 (1930).

‡ The Struthers Wells Corporation, Warren, Pa.

slurry of crystals already formed. While in contact with the very large surface of crystal faces offered by the numerous crystals, the supersaturation of the solution is relieved by the deposition on the crystals of a certain amount of solid salt, so that the crystals grow in size. The supersaturation is not permitted to become extreme, for extreme supersaturation, the labile state, would form fresh nuclei and would not contribute to the growth of the crystals already present. The moderate degree of supersaturation maintains the solution leaving the vaporizer in the metastable state. The gentle flow upward produces *a classification of the crystals,** the largest ones at the bottom, the medium sized ones next, and the finest ones at the top. A portion of the slurry is drawn from the bottom of the crystal container, and passed to a centrifuge or filter for the separation

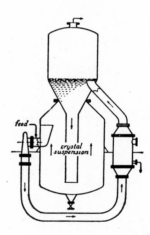

FIGURE 343.—Principle of the Krystal Evaporator-Crystallizer, for salts with small increase in solubility with temperature rise. The operation is c o n t i n u o u s. (Courtesy Struthers Wells, Warren, Pa.)

of the crystals from the mother liquor. The latter is returned to the system, specifically, to the circulating line, along with the feed. A portion of the liquor in the crystal container is fed to a pump and returned to the vaporizer; in other words, it is circulated.

Avoidance of extreme supersaturation also means that the formation of crusts is discouraged.

The Krystal Evaporator-Crystallizer operates at any pressure but chiefly at atmospheric pressure or above. Feed liquor, mixed with mother liquor, and a certain amount of liquor taken from the top layer of the crystal container suspension (which is thus circulated) are pumped through a tubular heater and thence to the vaporizer. The steam developed passes out at the top of the vaporizer to a condenser, while the liquor, now suitably and moderately supersaturated, travels down an inner tube to the crystal container, where crystal growth and classifica-

* " 'Krystal' classifying crystallizer," by Hans Swanoe, *Ind. Eng. Chem.*, **32**, 636 (1940).

tion take place. The process is controlled by the rate of pumping; by the amount of heat furnished; by changing the ratio between feed liquor, mother liquor, and circulated liquor; and by the rate of withdrawal of slurry.

In the Krystal Vacuum Crystallizer, which is a continuous crystallizer, the vaporizer is under vacuum, while the crystal suspension container is at atmospheric pressure; in fact, it is generally an open tank. The vacuum is produced by a steam jet ejector preceded by a condenser. In the simplest form of the vacuum continuous crystallizer, there is no heater. The heat introduced into the system is the sensible heat of the feed, and the heat of crystallization. The vacuum serves to vaporize

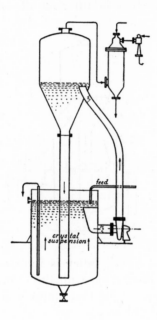

FIGURE 344.—Principle of operation of the Krystal Vacuum Crystallizer, with continuous operation, designed for salts with substantial increase in solubility with rise in temperature. (Courtesy Struthers Wells, Warren, Pa.)

water and to cool the solution to the temperature at which the proper degree of supersaturation is developed. The supersaturated solution passes from the vaporizer to the crystal container through a barometric leg. The yield of slurry is drawn from the bottom of the crystal container, as it is in the Evaporator-Crystallizer, and sent to a centrifuge. The crystals are collected separately, while the mother liquor is returned to the system. A circulating pump draws liquor from the top layer of the suspension in the crystal container and feeds it back to the vaporizer. The feed liquor, suitably heated, and the mother liquor, enter the system at the suction side of the pump.

The Krystal Vacuum Evaporator may be operated at temperatures lower than those utilized in the Evaporator-Crystallizer. For work at very low temperatures, a steam jet vacuum booster is used in addition to the customary steam jet ejector.

For the crystallization of salts showing a moderate increase in solubility with rise in temperature, a modified vacuum crystallizer is recommended. The modification consists of a tubular heater added to the normal equipment of the Vacuum Evaporator; it permits the vaporization of more water than the sensible heat of the feed and the heat of crystallization would account for.

There is also a cooling Krystal continuous crystallizer, in which the desired degree of supersaturation is produced by cooling. The mixture of mother liquor and feed is pumped through a specially designed shell and tube heat exchanger utilizing very small temperature differentials between the coolant and the mother liquor to prevent excessive supersaturation in the tubes. The cooling liquid may be water, brine, or some other liquid, for operation at subzero temperatures if necessary.

For large production, multiple-effect systems, comprising several crystallizers in series, are available.

The crystal size produced in the Krystal crystallizers may be selected, and may then be controlled so that the crystals are uniform in size. It is astonishing how uniform the crystals are, and free of undersizes without having been screened or otherwise graded in any way. A relatively large sized crystal requires a shorter centrifuge cycle and a shorter drying period. The attractiveness of uniform, well-developed, and well-formed crystals cannot be overemphasized.

FLAKERS

The flaker is a device for the production by chilling of flakes, chips, large crumbs, or crystals from a hot, concentrated solution or melted crystals. It consists of a hollow, cylindrical metal drum lying on its side; of trunnions which permit its rotation; of a sturdy, straight, adjustable knife; and of a shallow feed pan into which it dips. A large gear mounted on one trunnion is driven by a pinion actuated by motor or pulley. A cast-iron or welded steel frame furnishes the supports. The drum is cooled by water or brine introduced and wasted through the trunnions. A coating of liquid forms on the drum as it dips in the feed pan; as the drum turns, the film at once begins to cool, so that after traveling about three-fourths of the rotation, it is hard and solid. It meets the knife which scrapes it off, the coating breaking into flakes (calcium chloride), chips (sodium sulfide, 60 per cent), or other fragments characteristic of the material. The flakes drop into an apron from which they may be shoveled into shipping drums, or they may drop directly into a screw conveyor which moves them to a chute and packing boxes or barrels. The drum is usually made of a special grade of cast iron, with a very smooth surface, which may be chromium-plated. The drum is also made of stainless steel, nickel, or bronze.

The motion is generally a steady rotating one, but for certain products, it has been found better to move the drum in a series of short jerks. Successful application of the flaker or, as the machine with the ratchet motion is called, the chip machine, depends upon a low adhesion of the solidified material to the surface of the drum. Should the adhesion be too high, the knife will be unable to lift off the solid, and will ride on the material instead of on the drum. The serious strain which results can be borne only by stoutly constructed knives and holders. The adhesion of some troublesome materials is lessened by a wetting roll which leaves a film of mois-

FIGURE 345.—A flaker with chain and sprocket-wheel drive for flaking caustic soda. The drum is 48 inches in diameter and 40 inches wide. The scraper knife is placed low while the feed pan is masked by the frame. (Courtesy Buflovak Equipment Division Blaw-Knox Co.)

ture on the metal just before the coating is formed. It is avoided altogether by the addition of paraffin wax to the feed pan in small quantities, an addition which is not always permissible, however.

The great advantage of flaking caustic soda is that the product may be dissolved rapidly by the consumer, without any special apparatus, and without danger to workmen. Flakes of caustic soda are more common now than the solid form; magnesium chloride, phthalic anhydride, and trisodium phosphate are produced in flake form, as well as asphalt, pitch, waxes, and stearic acid. TNT is flaked.

Flakers are manufactured in various corrosion-resisting materials.

The flaker may be open, or it may be furnished with a hood for the removal of fumes; it also may have protective shields, or it may be fully enclosed for protection from dust and from toxic hazards.

FIGURE 346.—A flaker which illustrates the variety of corrosion-resisting materials embodied in chemical process equipment. A benzene hexachloride flaker using a 36-inch diameter by 54-inch face double shell, steel, chrome-plated drier roll. The agitator is solid nickel. The drip pan is fabricated of Lukens Nickel-Clad steel and jacketed for 100 psi steam pressure. The hood is light gauge solid stainless steel. The drive is a variable speed arrangement. (Courtesy Lukenweld Division, Lukens Steel Co., Coatesville, Pa.)

Buflovak flakers are made in six standard sizes, the drum ranging from 24 inches in diameter and 20 inches in width, to 60 inches in diameter and 72 inches in width.

Numerical Example

It is required to cool 42,000 gallons per 24 hours of a sulfuric acid solution containing, among other ingredients, ferrous sulfate to be removed by crystallization. The conditions are as follows: Feed solution, 50° Bé at 140°F. Cool to 50°F. Crystals 125,000 pounds of $FeSO_4.7H_2O$ per 24 hours, initial crystallization point, 90°F; boiling-point rise of feed solution, 11°F, boiling-point rise of final mother liquor, 15°F; specific heat of feed and mother liquor, 0.85, specific heat of crystals, 0.3; heat of crystallization, 29 Btu per pound of crystals; available cooling water at 80°F (summer maximum); available brine at 20°F; steam at 125 lbs pressure, dry and saturated.

	Mechanical Crystallizer	Vacuum Crystallizer
Type	Double pipes	Batch
Materials of construction	Steel and lead	Rubber-lined steel
Installation cost, exclusive of building and foundations	$30,000	$18,000
Cooling water at 80°F (gal/min)	180[a]	675
Refrigerated brine at 20°F (gal/min)	100	None
Brine refrigeration (tons/day)	85	None
Hp for refrigeration and brine pumping	160	None
Hp for agitation, drives, etc.	15	30[b]
Av. steam consumption (lb/hr)	None	2,000
Water evaporated (lb/day)	None	35,000
Approximate space (length, width, height) (ft)	30, 10, 10	20, 15, 55

[a] Cool part way with water; does not include cooling water for ammonia condensers.
[b] Includes power for pumping condenser water.

This example brings into consideration another factor. It requires cooling to a lower temperature than is directly possible with ordinary cooling water. In the past it has been customary to use mechanical refrigeration equipment with its ammonia compressor, condenser coils, brine system, pumps, etc., to obtain the low-temperature cooling medium for a mechanical crystallizer. The vacuum crystallizer, on the other hand, uses only a steam-jet thermocompressor or booster, which is much less expensive, even in acid-resistant construction, and occupies only a fraction of the space. Because there is no solid surface through which the heat must be transferred in a vacuum crystallizer, the vacuum crystallizer is naturally a smaller piece of equipment than the mechanical type.

OPERATING COSTS

	Mechanical Crystallizer	Vacuum Crystallizer
Annual[c] interest and depreciation at 15%	$ 4,500	$ 2,700
Cooling water at 1 cent per 1,000 gal	933	3,500
Refrigeration at 1.4 kw-hr/ton	8,225	.....
Power at 1 cent per kw-hr	1,450	2,160
Labor at 70 cents per man-hr	2,664	2,664
Maintenance at 10 and 3%, respectively	3,000	540
Steam at 30 cents per 1,000 lb	.....	5,184
Annual gross operating cost	$20,772	$16,748
Credit for evaporation figured as steam at 1.25 lb/lb water (single-effect economy)	.....	4,730
Annual net operating cost	$20,772	$12,018

c 360 days per year.

Reproduced from G. E. Seavoy and H. B. Caldwell, *Ind. Eng. Chem.*, **32**, 632, 635 (1940), where two additional Numerical Examples will be found.

Pertinent Patents

U. S. Patent 1,860,741, crystallization apparatus, to Finn Jeremiassen.
U. S. Patent 2,042,661, crystallization apparatus, to the same.

Reading References

"Theoretical and industrial aspects of crystallization," by H. B. Caldwell, *Chem. Met. Eng.*, **49**, 116 (1942).

"Heat transfer and crystallization," by W. L. Badger, published by Swenson Evaporator Company, Harvey, Ill., 1935.

"Vacuum and mechanical crystallizers, a comparison," by G. E. Seavoy and H. B. Caldwell, *Ind. Eng. Chem.*, **32**, 627 (1940).

" 'Krystal' classifying crystallizer," by Hans Svanoe, *Ind. Eng. Chem.*, **32**, 636 (1940).

"Crystallization," Review of unit operation, by C. S. Grove and J. B. Gray, *Ind. Eng. Chem.*, **42**, 26 (1950).

"Crystal growth," by H. E. Buckley, New York, John Wiley and Sons, Inc., 1951.

The operation of drying is a common one in the chemical industries, yet it is by no means limited to them. The vitreous coating of steel, all ceramic processes, the food dehydration industry which is growing by leaps and bounds, and others also require a formidable total of drying devices.

17. DRIERS*

The drying of products in the chemical and allied industries must not be thought of as a finishing touch, a final step presenting little difficulty, a mere detail, or perhaps, an afterthought. On the contrary, it is a major unit operation, as discussed in more detail further on. The procedure varies with the product—its physical qualities, degree of wetness, and value. With respect to the last, it may be observed that when the value is low, the closest kind of study will be required to determine how the undesirable adhering moisture may be removed at the lowest possible cost. If the product brings a high price, the need for economy in the drying processes will be less, and there will be correspondingly greater latitude in the selection of drying equipment. Certain materials may be treated directly with fire gases without damage; others are more delicate, and must be treated indirectly with heat or with warm air. Drying with a vacuum permits the maintenance of lower temperatures; but it is more costly than atmospheric drying.

Each group of materials has its own class of driers. Liquids containing dissolved solids and thin slurries carrying suspended matter are usually handled in drum or spray driers. Sludges and pastes may be mixed with dried materials until they crumble, and this mixture then dried as solids would be, or they may be diluted with water to form a slurry thin enough to be dried in the same manner as a liquid. Wet solids are frequently dried in rotary driers, which are cylinders lying lengthwise, through which a current of heated air or of flue gases travels. Compartment driers are closets or even rooms in which the material is spread on trays or in shallow pans; in the drying of dyes, for example, the same pan must be used for a given color exclusively. Separate pans are used for different colors, but the drier itself may be used for all. The operation is discontinuous; in order to make it continuous, the pans may be placed on trucks traveling on rails, and these pushed through a tunnel in which warm air circulates. The belt drier and the chain drier are efforts in the same direction.

* In collaboration with Mr. D. J. Van Marle, Engineer, Buflovak Equipment Division of Blaw-Knox Company.

TABLE 68. CLASSIFICATION OF DRIERS—PART I

Driers which Provide Direct Contact between Heating Medium and Material

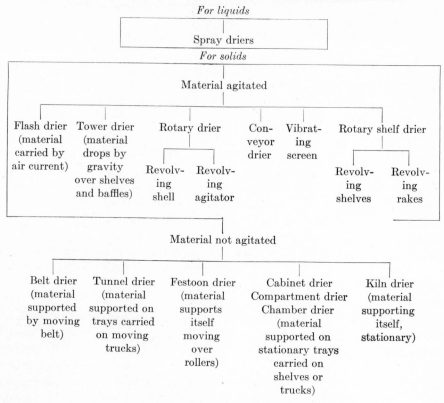

For liquids

Spray driers

For solids

Material agitated

Flash drier (material carried by air current)

Tower drier (material drops by gravity over shelves and baffles)

Rotary drier — Revolving shell, Revolving agitator

Conveyor drier

Vibrating screen

Rotary shelf drier — Revolving shelves, Revolving rakes

Material not agitated

Belt drier (material supported by moving belt)

Tunnel drier (material supported on trays carried on moving trucks)

Festoon drier (material supports itself moving over rollers)

Cabinet drier Compartment drier Chamber drier (material supported on stationary trays carried on shelves or trucks)

Kiln drier (material supporting itself, stationary)

The various devices which might meet the needs enumerated and fit other circumstances not yet specified are shown in Table 68.

The process of drying a substance is not simple. In drying a solid carrying 30 to 40 per cent water, for example, the rate of evaporation is constant and high as long as the surfaces exposed are wet. This is known as the constant rate period. After the surface is dry, the water in the interstices must make its way to the surface, a process of diffusion which is slower than evaporation from a wet surface; the rate will then drop. This second part of the process, the falling rate period, will be modified according to the ease with which the material crumbles as it dries, exposing new surfaces. The study of drying will be concerned with heat transfer and material transfer: heat transfer—such as latent heat of vaporization, and sensible heat to the vapor molecules, to the water in the pores, and to the solid; material transfer—mainly the transfer of water from the inner portions of the material to the surface.

TABLE 68. CLASSIFICATION OF DRIERS—PART II

Driers in which Material and Heating Medium Are Separated by a Wall

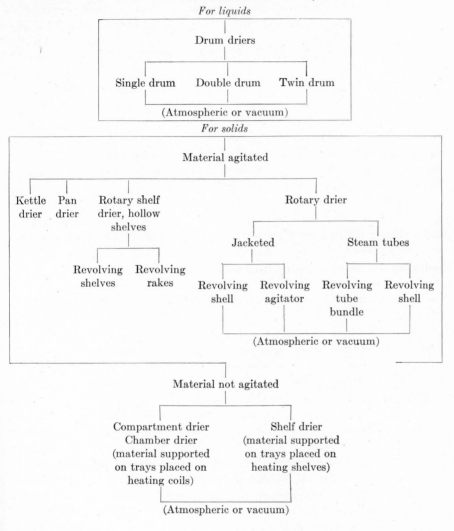

For liquids

Drum driers

Single drum   Double drum   Twin drum

(Atmospheric or vacuum)

For solids

Material agitated

Kettle   Pan   Rotary shelf   Rotary drier
drier   drier   drier, hollow
           shelves

                       Jacketed   Steam tubes

    Revolving   Revolving
    shelves   rakes   Revolving   Revolving   Revolving   Revolving
                       shell   agitator   tube   shell
                                          bundle

(Atmospheric or vacuum)

Material not agitated

Compartment drier   Shelf drier
Chamber drier   (material supported
(material supported   on trays placed on
on trays placed on   heating shelves)
heating coils)

(Atmospheric or vacuum)

The process of drying a thin layer is essentially one step: the vaporization of the water (or other liquid) into air (or gas) in motion. The vaporization is rapid since diffusion does not enter the picture. Air in motion is applied in order to carry away the vapor and avoid reaching the saturation point at which vaporization would. stop. The latter event occurs only rarely because the carrying capacity of the air or gas generally is much greater than the evaporative capacity, which is limited by the amount of heat the air can transfer to the material, and by the temperature at which the air is exhausted from the drier.

There must not be overlooked a means of drying which requires no apparatus, namely air-drying, which may be combined with draining. For example, crystals of ammonium sulfate may be discharged from the pickle onto a drainage board set at a slope so that the drainings run back to the main tank. As the draining takes place, there is evaporation to the air, causing the mass of crystals to dry over a period of 24 hours or so.

The draining may be accelerated by feeding the mass to a centrifugal basket in which the adhering mother liquor is whirled off, leaving merely moist crystals which may be delivered, after screening, to a lower floor where, on standing some hours, they dry by natural evaporation. Any crystalline chemical, such as sodium thiosulfate, $Na_2S_2O_3.5H_2O$, may be handled in this way, provided the quantities to be dried are not too large.

The drying of lumber piled in lumber yards is natural air-drying. It must be emphasized that "drying a substance" is a relative term; it sometimes does mean the removal of all moisture, leaving the material truly dry, as, for example, oxalic acid crystals. Generally, however, it means reducing the moisture content from the original value, such as 60, 50, or 10 per cent, to a specified low value, such as 4 per cent (in coal), 8 per cent (in casein), 0.5 per cent (in table salt), or 14 per cent (as in certain cheeses).

A further observation must not be left out: The removal of part of the water in a material by the application of pressure is a kind of drying; it is, moreover, a method to be recommended because it is cheaper to press out water mechanically than it is to vaporize it.

Classification. Driers may be divided into two main groups. The first comprises all driers in which the material is in direct contact with the heating medium, the second those in which material is separated from the heating medium by a wall. The heating medium for the first group may be hot air or flue gas; for the second group steam, hot water, or flue gas. Each group may be subdivided into driers for liquids and for solids, and those for solids into driers with and without agitation.

Let us consider for a moment the classification of drying as a unit operation. An analysis of drying problems reveals that in many respects drying is more often a combination of two unit operations. In many manufacturing processes drying is the final operation; for this reason, it is not merely a matter of removing moisture or drying proper, but also of the preservation of the physical appearance of the dry product. The latter point is frequently of great importance, and determines the drying method selected. Another feature which makes drying different from other unit operations is that the nature of the product is more of a controlling factor. For example, in drying food products the effect of the drying process on proteins, carbohydrates, fats, sugars, enzymes, or vitamins may be the deciding factor, rather than economy of heat or first cost of the equipment.

An entirely satisfactory definition of drying is almost impossible to formulate without overlapping the definitions of evaporation or distillation, or leaving some drying methods not covered by the definition.

Classification of the various types of drying equipment is equally difficult; the one which has been given is based on the method of transferring heat. Driers of similar design or of similar operation generally can be found in both main divisions. The classification in Table 68 does not serve as a guide in selecting a suitable drier for a specific product. An alternate classification is offered below which is based on the nature of the material handled; it has the merit of furnishing a better guide to the prospective buyer.

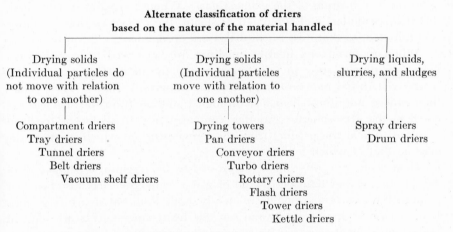

**Alternate classification of driers
based on the nature of the material handled**

Drying solids (Individual particles do not move with relation to one another)	Drying solids (Individual particles move with relation to one another)	Drying liquids, slurries, and sludges
Compartment driers	Drying towers	Spray driers
Tray driers	Pan driers	Drum driers
Tunnel driers	Conveyor driers	
Belt driers	Turbo driers	
Vacuum shelf driers	Rotary driers	
	Flash driers	
	Tower driers	
	Kettle driers	

In this alternate classification of driers, it may be observed that the first class of driers comprises those drying units in which solid materials are dried and the individual particles *do not* move in relation to one another. These driers are selected for drying materials whose physical shape must be preserved, or which must be dried under carefully controlled conditions for definite time intervals, such as vegetables, fruit, and many other food products; compartment, tray, tunnel, belt, and vacuum shelf driers are included in this class. The drying problem in these driers is largely one of air conditioning, temperature and humidity control, and air circulation.

In the second class of driers solid materials are also handled, but individual particles *do* move in relation to one another, that is, the material is continuously agitated. The problem in these driers is largely one of agitation and material handling. Included in this class are pan, conveyor, turbo, and rotary driers of various types with revolving shells, revolving agitators, or tube bundles.

The third class of driers is for drying liquids, slurries, and sludges sufficiently fluid to be pumped; drum driers and spray driers are included. The most important problem in this class is that of the dispersion or spreading of the liquid.

Sludges and pastes which cannot be pumped can be treated as liquids by adding water, or as solids by mixing them with a sufficient quantity of the dry product, as suggested in the introduction to the chapter.

Heat Economy. The main cost in drying operations is for heat. In all driers with direct contact between heating medium and material there is a considerable heat loss, namely, all the heat that was required to raise the gases from room temperature to the temperature at which they are discharged from the drier. Efforts to reduce this loss have led to recirculation and to reheating of the exhaust gas. When flue gases can be used, this loss is smaller, and compared to steam, the cost of raising the latter is eliminated, so that direct-heat driers are economical.

When material and heating medium are separated by a wall, heat losses are much lower in proportion to the useful heat employed, particularly if initial moisture content of the material is high. These losses then consist mainly of heat lost through radiation from the surfaces exposed to the atmosphere. Another comparatively small loss is the heat required to heat the product from the temperature at which it enters the drier to that at which it leaves.

Heat economy preferably is expressed as heat required per pound of dry product rather than per pound of water evaporated, because heat per pound of water evaporated is relatively high if initial moisture is low. In that case, radiation losses and sensible heat requirements are high in proportion to heat required for evaporation of moisture.

Spray Driers. Returning now to the apparatus employed in drying, the spray drier may be considered first. It consists of a closed chamber in which a liquid carrying dissolved solids or a thin slurry carrying solids in suspension is atomized. A current of hot air meets the droplets and travels with them or past them, simultaneously vaporizing the water, so that when the bottom, or the discharge point is reached, only a dry solid remains in fine suspension in an air laden with water vapor. The flow of air may be parallel to the flow of the droplets and downward, which permits complete drying of the material by the time it reaches the bottom. The dried particles are so light that they follow the air currents. The dried product accumulates in the bottom of an inverted cone, for example, and is pulled away by an exhauster (if not by the escaping air itself) which delivers it to a collector and bin. The air with all its moisture travels the same path and is discharged from the collector into the atmosphere. When the flow of air is counter to that of the material, it is essential that the air be made to traverse a curtain of atomized liquid in a wet scrubber, which then retains the entrained particles of dry matter.*

The spray drier, then, consists of a drying chamber, an atomizing device, and means for moving and heating the air (or other gases) and for recovering the product. The drying chamber may be 10 to 20 feet in diameter, and 15 to 30 feet in height; it may be in the form of a cone or of an upright cylinder. The air is heated by passing it over a nest of

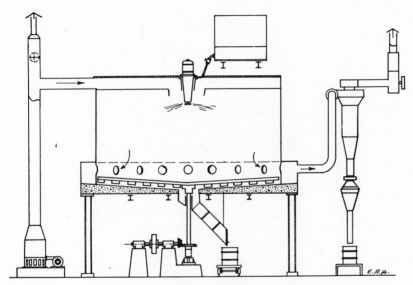

Figure 347.—A spray-drier assembly, including burner with air inlets for the flue gas-air mixture, the drying chamber with atomizer and feed tank, rake for sweeping the product into the discharge chute, dust collector, and exhauster. The spray chamber is circular and 20 feet in diameter. The flue gas-air mixture leaves the chamber by the annular enlargement at its base. (Courtesy Instant Drying Corp., New York, N. Y.)

finned or gilled tubes in which steam circulates. More and more generally, however, flue gases are used as a source of heat, with a similar arrangement of tubes, except that it is now flue gases which pass inside them (indirect application). It has been found feasible to go a step further and mix air with flue gases from an oil or gas burner (direct application). Steam tubes give an air temperature of 300°F or so; flue gases, indirectly or directly applied, give 500°F and higher, not infrequently as high as 1200°F; the temperature is regulated by the volume of

* Of the twelve best known commercial spray driers listed further on, two have counter-current flow (Ravo-Rapid and Rogers). The others have either parallel flow or parallel for part of the path, in the cyclone type of air movement, with a rising column in the center.

cold air admitted. It is desirable to have a high inlet temperature, because the amount of the applied heat transferred to the wet material is then greater, as already suggested under heat economy. For example, let us suppose that 60°F air is heated by tubes in which 150-pound steam circulates, and that the steam has a temperature of 366°F. The air will reach 320°F, let us say. If the outlet temperature is 175°F, in accord with general practice, the useful heat is 56 per cent of the total heat. With flue gases, directly or indirectly applied, 500°F air or air-flue gas mixture may be obtained. If the outlet temperature is the same as before, the heat applied usefully is 74 per cent of that put into the air. With 750°F gases, the corresponding figure is 83 per cent.

The direct use of flue gases is not only more economical, but it has the further merit of reducing the danger of dust explosions because of the lower oxygen content of the gases.

Electrical heating by means of resistance coils would seem well adapted for heating the air in spray drying. The heating unit is compact; air which is clean and fairly high in temperature is obtained, and its temperature is readily controlled automatically. Where the electric current is cheap, it would seem to be an ideal method for medium and low temperatures, at any rate.

The temperature which may be used depends upon the sensitivity of the material. If it scorches easily, a more moderate temperature will have to be selected. The danger is not quite as great as it may seem at first sight; in driers in which hot air travels parallel with the droplets, the very hot air comes in contact only with the very wet material, which is protected by its water. As evaporation proceeds, the temperature of the air falls, and it must also be remembered that the droplet is always cooler than the air surrounding it. As the droplet turns to a semisolid, then to a solid, the temperature of the air has dropped so far that there is little danger of scorching.

The total time the droplet spends in the system, from liquid to collected powder, is between 15 and 30 seconds. The period of active evaporation is probably 4 seconds. It is for these reasons that the spray drier, also called "the instantaneous drier," is particularly well adapted to drying heat-sensitive substances, such as milk, eggs, and blood.*

A few more words on the direction of the air current: Parallel and downward flow was mentioned in the opening paragraph; such was the earlier general custom. Increase in the velocity due to an effort to increase output causes the formation of eddy currents and, along the outer vertical walls, a return current which results in coatings on the walls. Parallel and downward flow requires larger chambers. In order to avoid

* See von Loesecke, "Drying and Dehydration of Foods," New York, Reinhold Publishing Corp., 1943.

eddy currents, the air current is made tangential, skirting the wall first and traveling inward toward the center bottom exit, for example, or toward peripheral outlets near the base. In the inverted, cone-shaped chamber, the air may enter tangentially, continue downward along the walls, which gradually approach each other, then turn about at the apex of the cone and spiral upward to the exit flue in the center top.

The reason the air is discharged at what may seem to be a needlessly high temperature and incompletely saturated with water vapor is that reabsorption of moisture must be avoided. It is essential that the air be kept well above its dew point; otherwise it might deposit water on the product. Another reason for a high outlet temperature is that, in parallel flow of product and air, the residual moisture in the dry product depends to some extent on the outlet temperature, and on the partial pressure of the vapor in outgoing air. It depends also on the temperature and the vapor pressure of the material in contact with this air. To make certain that this residual moisture will not be too high, the outlet temperature is not allowed to drop below a safe point. This temperature is generally well above the dew point. The volume of air required to provide the requisite heat for evaporation of the moisture then leaves the drier well before its saturation point has been reached. The resulting poor heat economy is remedied to some extent by installing economizers in which the incoming air is heated by the outgoing gases or by setting up scrubbers in which the outgoing gases meet the incoming liquid. In the scrubber, any fine particles carried by the air are deposited while at the same time some of the water is evaporated from the liquid. Another way to improve the economy is to recirculate and reheat part of the exhaust gas.

In dropping from 300 to 175°F, one pound of air will give up 29.8 Btu and evaporate 0.030 pound of water; from 500 to 175°F it will give up 77.4 Btu and evaporate 0.078 pound of water, and from 750 to 175°, 136.8 Btu which will evaporate 0.137 pound of water. Inasmuch as air which is saturated at 175°F is capable of carrying over 0.5 pound of water in vapor form for each pound of dry air, there will be little danger of condensation at this temperature. It may be well to emphasize that air-flue gas mixtures contain considerable amounts of moisture formed as a product of the combustion, a circumstance which must be given consideration.

For a well-designed unit with a 10-foot-diameter spray chamber, with air of 300°F inlet temperature, and liquor containing 33 per cent solids, preheated, there would be a production of 500 pounds of dry product (2 per cent residual moisture) per hour, or 6 tons a day. In the same unit, with the same liquor, but with an inlet temperature of 600°F, the production would be 1700 pounds per hour, depending on the type of auxiliary equipment.

There are three kinds of devices for atomizing the liquid: (1) the pressure nozzle (of special construction designed to impart a rotary motion to the liquid as it leaves the tip of the nozzle) to which the spray liquor is fed under pressures varying from 100 to 3000 pounds per square inch, and which delivers a cone-shaped rain of droplets; (2) the two-fluid type nozzle in which the liquor meets the atomizing steam (or air) under 100 pounds pressure (of the steam or air); (3) the centrifugal atomizer, a disk rotating as fast as 10,000 rpm. The last two are less easily clogged by dirt specks or by skins of crushed vegetables, and in that respect are superior to the simpler pressure nozzle.

The pressure nozzle and the atomizer are more generally installed than the two-fluid nozzle, as shown by a survey of the twelve more

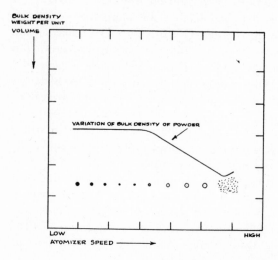

FIGURE 348.—Weight per unit volume against atomizer speed. [*Trans. Inst. Chem. Eng.*, **13**, 116 (1935).]

prominent American and European* spray driers, of which six have pressure nozzles and six employ revolving disks for atomizing the liquid. In addition, some of these firms offer either type for certain duties. A brief discussion of nozzles will be found in Chapter 9.

The product may be removed from the bottom of the chamber by a separate fan, or by the outgoing gases, whose velocity in the smaller flue provided is high enough to convey the solid to a cyclone separator, followed by a bag filter, a scavenging cyclone separator (Aerotec, Aerodyne), or a Cottrell precipitator. The product may also be removed by scraper arms which deliver it to a mechanical conveyor.

The heat input to the drier required for the evaporation of 1 pound of water from the spray liquid varies from 1800 to as high as 3500 Btu. As

* Swenson, Merrell-Soule, Peebles, Instant Drying Corp., Kestner, Ravo-Rapid, Bowen, Krause, Holliday-Dickerson, Rogers, Niro, Buflovak.

to capacity, the spray drier is built in sizes which will allow the production of 40 tons or more of dry product per day.

The spray drier does more than dry. It gives the product a powdery quality; certain materials on spray-drying form hollow spheres, which indicates that in some respects at least, "drying" is a unit process. The physical quality of the product is likely to determine whether spray-drying is to be adopted, irrespective of heat consumption. It should be remarked that the shape of the product is greatly influenced by the type of nozzle* and, with certain materials at least, by the speed of the atomizer.

Spray driers have been used to prepare a dry powder when other

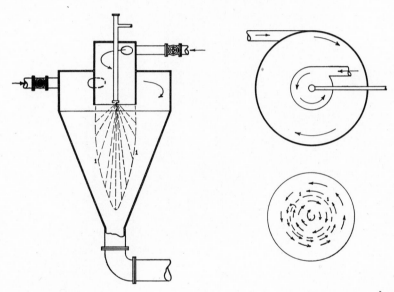

FIGURE 349.—A cross-sectional view of the double-vortex Peebles spray chamber; the dotted line 1-1 divides the two vortexes. Upper right, a top view showing the opposite directions of tangential flows; lower right, the supposed path of a particle.

methods, drying on shelf, for example, followed by pulverizing, failed to do so.

The advantages of spray drying are continuous operation; the short period of contact, which is well indicated by speaking of the spray drier as the instantaneous drier; and the safe handling of heat-sensitive materials.

The spray drier has its own difficulties, among which may be mentioned the tendency for the material to coat the walls of the drying chamber. There is furthermore the difficulty of complete recovery of the dry material, for a very small loss, of no moment from the point of view of

* B. B. Fogler and R. V. Kleinschmidt, *Ind. Eng. Chem.*, **30**, 1376 (1938).

economy, may create a serious nuisance when discharged into the atmosphere in a populated neighborhood. Two remedies have been proposed. One* consists of two currents of drying air, both tangential but opposite to each other, and one outside the other. A greater efficiency in air application is made possible: "The humidity of the gas leaving may be made

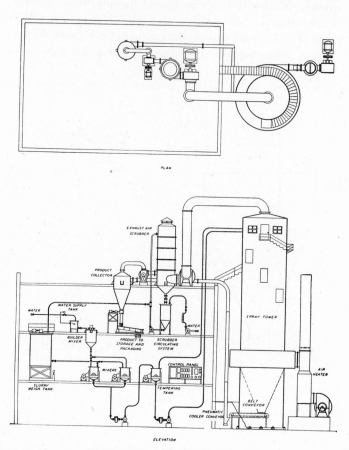

FIGURE 350.—Installation for drying a synthetic detergent by the continuous spray process. (Courtesy Wurster and Sanger, Inc., Chicago 15, Ill.)

greater than 50 per cent compared to about 5 per cent saturation obtained with desiccating apparatus employing a single vortex." Besides this, a reduction in the size of the spray chamber is possible: "An apparatus having two vortexes formed within a single chamber 6 feet in diameter has a desiccating capacity about equal to a single vortex apparatus having a chamber about 30 feet in diameter." Recent improvements include a

* U. S. Patents 1,914,895 and 1,830,174 to D. D. Peebles.

rotary brush which prevents solids from sticking to the inner walls of the chamber.

The second remedy is to introduce the air through vertical slots in two levels of the drying chamber, so placed and shaped that the air has a tangential movement which causes it to travel first around the vertical wall.* This also includes the introduction of a current of air over the atomizer, forming a cap over it. The two currents together then carry the droplets downward and inward. A sweeper on the bottom of the chamber may be equipped with nozzles fed with suitably conditioned air, and so arranged that the sweeper will rotate as the air escapes. The stream of air causes the product to be blown into a scroll manifold. Such a sweeper is termed a rotating-reaction air sweeper. Both these proposed remedies involve a reduction in the size of the spray chamber.

It is sometimes advisable to cool the particles rapidly to prevent their sticking together. This may be done by the introduction of a second but colder current of air near the bottom of the spray chamber.

Materials of Construction. The spray chamber, which is the essential part of the spray drier, may be built of any plate metal such as galvanized iron, stainless steel, "Monel" metal, and others. It may also be constructed of wood lined with stainless steel, "Monel" metal, brick, hollow tile, or other suitable material.

Spray Chilling. If under the heading of "drying" is included the transformation of liquid water to solid water fixed as water of crystallization, then spray chilling too is a form of drying. Spray chilling is the atomization of a solution of crystallizing strength which is liquid while hot, but has only as much water as is needed to form the solid crystal when cooled. The hot solution is atomized in a chamber which is essentially a spray drier, and meets a current of cold air, this time with parallel flow. The finely divided crystal product collects on the bottom and in a bag filter or similar auxiliary device.† The air generally carries off a small amount of residual moisture.

Flash Driers. The flash drier represents the application of the principle of the spray drier to materials which are solid or semisolid in the wet state. The wet material is dried while suspended in finely divided form in a current of heated air. This is accomplished by dropping the wet material into a high-temperature air stream which carries it to a hammer mill or high-speed agitator where the exposed surface is increased. The fine particles leave the mill through a duct small enough in area to maintain carrying velocities, and reach a cyclone separator. The flash drier is thus another example of parallel-flow operation. The particle takes

---

* U. S. Patents 2,081,909 and 1,946,566 to W. S. Bowen.

† "Soap Technology Meets Changed Markets," by O. H. Wurster, *Chem. Met. Eng.*, **38**, 215 (1931), U. S. Patents 1,732,454 and 1,740,759.

6 to 8 seconds to pass from the point of entry into the air stream to the collector. The air temperature drops from 1,200 to 600°F, for example, in 2 seconds, or from 1,200 to 350°F in 4 seconds. The time for drying is essentially 2 to 4 seconds; hence the term "flash."* The material itself is not raised in temperature by more than perhaps 100°F; thus materials which would burn at the temperature of the heating agents pass through unharmed.

Parallel flow demands a high enough discharge temperature to assure a low moisture content in the dry products; the result is a poor heat economy. The latter can be improved by reheating the air, feeding the wet product into this air, and then separating the partially dried product in a cyclone collector and dropping it into the stream of hot fresh air for final drying. The final dry product is separated in a second collector from its air; the air from the second stage is reheated for use in the first stage.

An initial moisture content of 80 per cent may be reduced to 5 or 6 per cent in the dried product.

In the Raymond Flash Drier, the wet solids are caught in a flow of high-velocity flue gases (3000 to 4000 feet per minute), travel through a special squirrel-cage disintegrator where the many new surfaces are constantly exposed to the hot gases, and thence to a cyclone separator. The dried solid is collected, and in many installations is mixed with the wet incoming solid so as to condition it and increase the wet surface area. A Gravity Cascade Flash Drier has been described briefly and illustrated.†

Drum Driers. In drum drying, a liquid containing dissolved solids or a slurry carrying suspended solids is spread on the surface of a large hollow drum mounted horizontally and heated internally. In the simplest arrangement, the drum dips in a pan underneath and there receives its coat. As the drum revolves, the liquid is gradually vaporized, so that after seven-eighths of a revolution, a dried deposit can be scraped off (sometimes loosening is sufficient) by a flexible, adjustable knife. The rotation of the drum is made slow enough so that all of the liquid portions are evaporated as the residual solid approaches the knife. The solid collects on an apron in front of the knife and rolls to a container or to a screw conveyor. The operation of the drum drier, called a film drier in England, is continuous.

The drum is rotated continuously by a gear driven by a pinion which receives its motion through a belt, a chain, or through a reduction gear from a direct-connected motor. The speed of the drum may be regulated

---

* For a table of 24 materials dried in a flash drier, with initial and final moisture content, see "Flash Drying for Materials of High Moisture Content" by Richard F. O'Mara, *Chem. Met. Eng.*, **43**, 186 (1936).

† *Ind. Chemist*, **16**, No. 183, 119 (1940).

by a variable-speed drive to adapt the speed to any slight variation in the liquid. If the material is dry quite a distance before the knife is reached, the speed should be increased; if the material is too wet at the knife, the speed must be decreased.

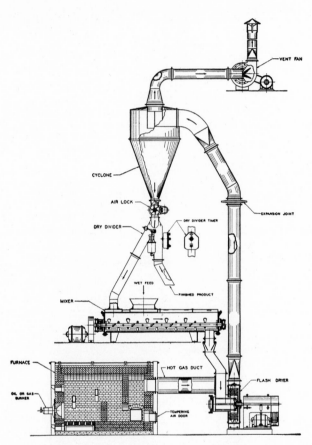

FIGURE 351.—One of the two types of Raymond flash drying system. Here provision is made for returning part of the dried product to mix with the wet feed; note the dry divider, and the mixer, the latter acting as feeder to the flash dryer. The cage disintegrator has three rotating cages which fit the two stationary ones. (Courtesy Raymond Pulverizer Division, Combustion Engineering-Superheater, Inc., Chicago 22, Illinois.)

The knife may be held just against the surface, or it may be forced against it by turning the adjusting wheels. In recent installations, the knife may be mounted in eccentric supports, so that the angle of the blade of the knife relative to the drum surface may be selected for the greatest shearing effect.

The drum drier is heated by steam which enters through the trunnion.

The condensate is discharged by means of a scoop or syphon through the second trunnion.

The rotation of the drum varies with its duty, but in general it will lie between 4 and 10 rpm. Occasionally, it is slower, and sometimes faster; the limits of from 1 to 20 rpm will cover all installations.

The drum for the *single atmospheric drum drier* is made of a single casting or plate. The face is turned true on a lathe and is then ground and polished. The materials generally are cast iron and bronze; they may also be, when advisable, steel, stainless steel, or nickel and may be chromium plated to provide a hard smooth surface. As for dimensions, a drum 5 feet in diameter and 12 feet long would be a large-sized one. The smallest commercial size is generally a 24-inch diameter drum, 24 to 36 inches long. The heat from the condensing steam passes through the

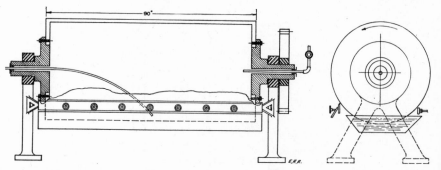

FIGURE 352.—An atmospheric single-drum drier with dip feed. Besides the knife, a spreader is shown which regularizes the coating. The sketch gives some of the details of construction which insure sturdiness; support for pan not shown.

condensate film, through the metal of the drum, and then to the coating on the drum. The maximum rate of evaporation for a dilute solution, which gives up its water more readily than a concentrated one, is as high as 18.5 pounds of water per hour per square foot of drum surface. This, however, only indicates that a high rate of evaporation may be obtained. As the purpose of drum drying is rather to produce a quantity of dry material, the true measure of efficiency is the number of pounds of finished product per unit heating surface. The rate of evaporation is determined by the concentration at which the material is fed to the drier, the thickness of the adhering film, the drum speed, and the steam pressure.

The capacity of a drum drier depends on its dimensions, the speed of rotation (the greater the speed, the greater the discharge, with the reservation expressed below), and on the initial concentration of the liquor or slurry; it will depend furthermore on the residual moisture allowable in the product, on the heat resistance of the liquor film, on the steam pressure; and on the thickness of the coat to the surface.

Some of the factors are interrelated; also the result is not always the one expected. For instance, with increased speed, which would lead us to expect a proportionally higher output, the coating is generally thinner, so that capacity does not increase in proportion. Again, increased steam pressure increases the available temperature difference and in most cases the adherence also; thus the capacity increases more than in proportion to the increased temperature difference. Greater concentration increases the thickness of the coating, but for many materials there is a critical

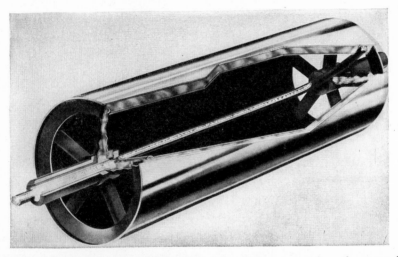

FIGURE 353.—Jacketed double-shell drier roll. Steam enters through rotary joint and journal, flowing through pipe spokes into annulus. Condensate is removed by separate pipe through journal and rotary joint. Originally used in paper and textile drying, but now also for chemical products in drum driers, for cellophane casting, for vinyl and "Celanese" plastics. These rolls are used in cooling as well as in heating service, as in flakers. (Courtesy Lukenweld Division, Lukens Steel Co., Coatesville, Pa.)

point beyond which the adhesion or the uniformity of the coating is adversely affected. Residual moisture increases with higher speed, lower steam temperature, greater thickness of the coating, and higher concentration.

As to the dimensions of the drum, the capacity is practically proportional to the surface area. It is slightly favored in the larger sizes because of better mechanical control of operating conditions.

The capacity for various products varies greatly, as adherence and liquid film resistance (to heat) vary over an extremely wide range. The amount of dry product may be from one to six pounds per square foot of surface per hour. The method of application of the liquid to the drum surface, briefly described further on, is very important in its effect on adhesion.

The size of the drum required for a given duty is decided on after trials on a small drum, by determining the output per square foot of surface. A drum is then chosen whose dimensions afford the number of square feet necessary. It is important to note that the time interval from dip to knife on the trial drum becomes the time interval on the larger drum. Peripheral speed has no relation to the results.

The *heat economy of drum driers* is very favorable because the heat of the condensing steam is transferred directly to the material. In addition to the theoretical amount required to heat the liquid to the boiling point,

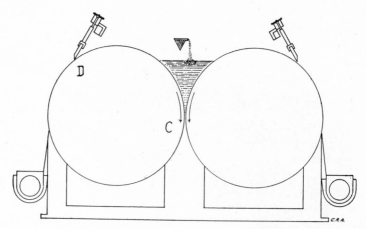

FIGURE 354.—An atmospheric double-drum drier, with center feed. The drums rotate at the rate of 4 rpm; the drum tops rotate toward each other. The dry material collects in the conveyors which run along the face of the drums. Driving gear and vapor hood not shown. End boards form the two end walls which confine the liquid or slurry.

evaporate the moisture, and compensate for any endothermic physical change, only enough heat has to be furnished to compensate for radiation loss. Heat economy should be calculated on the basis of a pound of dry material produced and not on the basis of a pound of water evaporated, for when computed on that basis, it will be greater for concentrated than for dilute solutions—a misleading index.

It may be desirable to avoid dipping the heated drum into the liquor to be dried in order to prevent boiling of the liquid or undue concentration. One way is to use a type of feed in which the liquor is splashed onto the drum from below by splash rolls. Another way is to use the *double-drum drier*. It consists of two drums set close together, revolving so that the drum tops move toward each other, and with only enough clearance to pass. The material is fed into the trough between the two drum tops and two end boards which confine the liquor (see Figure 354). Thin pastes may be applied in this way; thicker pastes also may be used with the aid of a special feeding trough with an agitator which delivers a definite amount to the V-space between the drums. Preferably these pastes should be diluted to a slurry and dried on a single or twin drum drier. The location of the discharging knife is shown in the illustration. Both drums are driven, either directly by a reduction gear or by means of a belt or chain. The advantage of this type of drier is that no residual liquor is left as is the case when a feed pan is provided. In many installations using a feed pan, the liquid must be circulated in order to maintain uniform concentration. With the double-drum drier there is no need for such circulation. Finally, if the liquid does concentrate in the space between the drums, it is generally an advantage because it tends to increase the thickness of the coating of the drums.

The coating thickness is governed by the clearance between the drums. The larger the clearance, the thicker the coating, and the higher the capacity of the drier. The clearance is adjusted by moving the bearings of one of the drums, by means of adjusting screws, to the maximum thickness which can be dried uniformly.

The *twin-drum drier* was developed from the double-drum drier to avoid the dropping of lumps and crusts between the drums which sometimes forced them apart, shearing the safety pins in the drum adjusting screws. In the twin-drum drier, the drums revolve in opposite directions; that is, the drum tops move away from each other. If the feed is by splash or by dip, the clearance between the two drums is greater than in the double-drum drier; it may be less, if the feed is from the V-shaped space between the drums, i.e., center feed. The latter is recommended for a product which should have a granular structure, and which may retain a considerable amount (as high as 25 per cent) of moisture. The dip feed is adopted for liquors of high concentration which adhere readily to the hot drum surface. The splash feed, as with the single-drum drier, overcomes the lack of adhesion of many materials to a heated surface. It should be noted that the splash feed liberates the part of the drum surface otherwise buried in the dip pan, so that evaporation takes place from a larger active surface. Finally, the splash feed reduces the amount of concentration of the liquor before its application as a coating. This is sometimes a major point, particularly if solubility of the product is limited and crystals separate out, or in the case of slurries which thicken too much.

The amount of product from double-drum or twin-drum driers varies from 1 to 10 pounds per square foot of surface per hour, depending almost entirely on the properties and the concentration of the material.

In order to prevent the deformation of the surface (which happens rarely, but still is a possibility), caused, for example, by a hard lump caught between drums or between knife and drum, a number of castings have been made with inner rings, running parallel to the heads of the drum. The rings are part of the casting. It is interesting to observe that the heat transfer through the face of the drum remains uniform, in spite of the greater thickness at the location of the reinforcing inner rings.

For the double-drum drier shown in Figure 354, the over-all heat transfer, under most favorable conditions, is about 360 Btu per hour per square foot of surface per °F difference in the area between the drums, and 220 Btu between C and D in the figure. On the steam side, the coefficients are 2,650 and 450; on the liquid side they are 1,500 and 1,800. The temperature drop through the metal (a thickness of $\frac{3}{4}$ inch) is 65 and 35°F.*

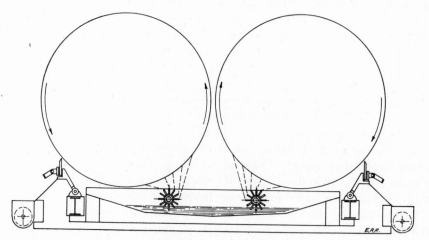

Figure 355.—An atmospheric twin-drum drier, with splash feed. The rotation of the drums is opposite to that in the double-drum drier.

In such cases, the steam-side coefficient and the heat transfer through the metal become the controlling factors. Uniformity in steam distribution, removal of noncondensable gases, and rapid removal of condensate are important, and are accomplished with the aid of baffles, syphons, and air vents. By these means also, the steam-side coefficient is increased.

The drum metal should be of minimum thickness and maximum conductivity compatible with safety. Unfortunately, most metals of high strength, such as stainless steel, or of high conductivity, such as copper, are comparatively soft; they are not used except in a few installations. On the other hand, modern cast iron has been so greaty improved in strength and uniformity that it may now be built in lighter sections. The strength of steel can now be made available by chromium-plating its surface, for in that way the required hardness is provided, together with resistance to cor-

* "Drum drying," by D. J. Van Marle, *Ind. Eng. Chem.*, **30**, 1007 (1938).

rosion. The drum drier may be equipped with a vapor hood and exhaust fan, pulling out the water vapor with fresh air. For a discussion of vacuum drum driers, see p. 476.

Rotary Driers. The rotary drier is a cylinder, slightly inclined to the horizontal; the entire cylinder may rotate as in the *revolving rotary drier*, or the shell may be stationary, within which an agitator revolves slowly. In either case, the wet material is fed in at the upper end, and the rotation (or agitation) advances it progressively to the lower end, where it is discharged. In the *direct-heat, revolving rotary drier*, warm air or a mixture of flue gases and air travels through the cylinder. The rate of feed, the speed of rotation or agitation, the volume of heated air or gases and their temperature, are so regulated that the solid is dried just before discharge.

The shell fits loosely into a stationary housing at each end. The material is brought to a chute which runs through the housing; the latter also carries the exhaust pipe (see Figure 357). The revolving shell runs

FIGURE 356.—A rotary-drier shell, made of steel, and glass lined. Made in one piece in length up to 40 feet; in sectional design, to any desired length. (Courtesy The Pfaudler Co., Rochester, N. Y.)

on two circular tires, and is turned by a gear which meshes with a driven pinion. The inclination is 1 in 16 for high capacities and 1 in 30 for low ones.

As the shell revolves, the solid is carried upward one-fourth of the circumference; it then rolls back to a lower level, exposing fresh surfaces to the action of the heat as it does so. This simplest of revolving rotary driers serves well enough when the fuel is cheap. The efficiency is greatly improved by placing longitudinal shelves 3 or 4 inches wide on the inside of the cylinder (itself, let us say, 5 feet in diameter.) The longitudinal shelves are called lifting flights. The shelves carry part of the solid halfway around the circumference and drop it through the whole of a diameter in the central part of the cylinder where the air is hottest and least laden with moisture. By bending the edge of the shelves slightly inward, some of the material is delivered only in the third quarter of the circle, producing a nearly uniform fall of the material throughout the cross section of the cylinder.   The heated air streams through a rain of particles.   This is the commonest form of revolving rotary cylinder.   It is well liked because it has a great capacity, is simple to operate, and is continuous.

To say that the air "streams" through the cylinder is an overstatement. For fine materials, which are powders when dry and which must be dried

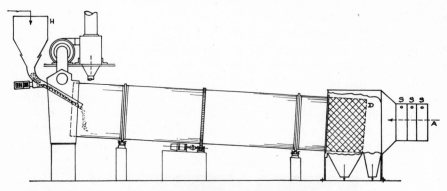

FIGURE 357.—A direct-heat rotary drier, 9 feet in diameter and 45 feet long.   The shell runs on two circular rails, carried by two sets of four idlers.   The girth gear and its driving motor and connection are at the center of the shell.   The wet material enters hopper H and the vibrating feeder; the dry material enters the delumper D, which retains the lumps, but permits the fines to drop to hopper below, which feeds a bucket elevator.   The combustion gases enter at A, with secondary air regulated by inlet-baffles S; the gases travel through the shell, and leave through the exhauster at upper left.

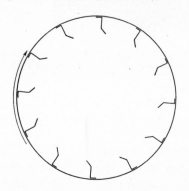

FIGURE 358.—Cross-sectional view of the direct-heat rotary drier, showing the lifting flights.

to a low moisture content, the air speed must not exceed 2 or 3 feet per second; for grains such as crystal salt (NaCl), it may be 4 feet.   These are the velocities in chemical driers.   It might, therefore, be better to say that the air "travels" through the cylinder.   For certain other purposes, such as the drying of lump coal, the velocity may be 12 or 15 feet per second.

The mass of material in the drier is 25 or 30 per cent of the volume of the shell; the air has a narrower channel than the full diameter of the shell, and for the same volume of air the velocity is higher.   Nevertheless, velocities are commonly computed on the basis of the whole shell space.

How greatly the limitation of air velocity influences the kind of installation is shown by the following example: A drier 10 feet in diameter and 50 feet long for a selected service would have an air exit velocity of 3.8 feet per second. The same duty may be performed by two driers 8 feet in diameter and 45 feet long with an air exit velocity of 2.99 feet per second. The second installation would cost about 80 per cent more than the first.

Division of the falling particles, which permits more intimate contact between the hot air or hot gases and the material, is further increased in the *cellular type* of *rotary drier* whose lifting flights have become cells fill-

FIGURE 359.—Rotary drier operating with steam-heated air, with feed end box removed. The lifts are serrated, and the serrations are at two different angles, one straight, one with a lip. The lifts are arranged in sections along the drum, and the sections are staggered. (Courtesy Geo. L. Squier Mfg. Co., Buffalo, N. Y.)

ing the interior of the shell. As the shell rotates, the material flows from one cell to another, thoroughly exposing the wet surfaces. The cellular drier produces less dust in the exit gases than does the rotary with lifting flights; it is more difficult to repair and higher in first cost.

The direction of air travel for the three examples of revolving rotary driers which have been described is generally countercurrent to the flow of the material; the hottest air enters at the lower end and leaves where the wettest material enters. Not infrequently, however, the hot air travels concurrently, entering at the upper or feed end and leaving at the lower or discharge end. When the material is sensitive to heat, this is obligatory, although the efficiency of heat utilization is somewhat lower. The main factor governing efficiency, however, is the temperature drop of the air or gases, so that here, as in the spray drier, the higher the inlet temperature (of the air or gases), the greater the efficiency. Thus, steam-heated air entering the drier at 200°F, for example, and leaving at 120°, using 60° air for the heater, would usefully apply 57 per cent of the heat. Based on the steam used in the heater, it is nearer 40 per cent. A *high-temperature, direct-heat, revolving rotary drier* with an inlet temperature of 700°F, for

FIGURE 360.—Interior view of the rotary drier in Figure 359 loaded selectively to show the action.

example, and direct application of the fuel heat may usefully apply 70 or 80 per cent of the heat. Limited to low temperatures by the susceptibility of the material, the lower efficiency will have to be borne unless an intermediate kind of drier is available.

Such an intermediate drier is the *double-shell drier* with *direct-indirect heat.* It consists of an inner cylinder through which the fire gases pass concurrently to the lower end of the cylinder, there to turn and travel in the open shell space counter to the material until they leave at the point where the wet material enters. The transfer of heat from the inner cylinder is through the metal wall by radiation and conduction. As the drum revolves, the wettest material falls on the hottest wall, there to remain for only one-half revolution. When the same portion falls again, it is drier, but, also, the wall is cooler. For many materials, the danger of damage is thus removed. The gases, on their return trip, transfer their heat directly to the material by convection. They are now much cooler and serve mainly to carry off the vapor. The double-shell drier has performed services in handling heat-sensitive materials which no other drier could have done as well. Example: The hot gases enter the inner shell at 1,100°F, turn about and enter the annular space at 400°F and are discharged with an exit temperature of 160°F.

The evaporative efficiency of the double-shell drier is 7 or 8 pounds of water per pound of fuel, such as coal of 12,600 Btu per pound; the single-

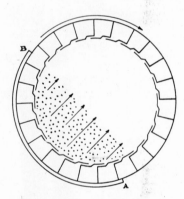

FIGURE 361.—A cross-sectional view of the Pehrson or Roto-Louvre drier showing the peripheral chamber through which the hot gases enter, and sweep through the material. Only the chambers facing the stationary hood A-B receive the hot-gas feed.

shell, revolving rotary drier has an efficiency of 4 or 4½ pounds of water evaporated per pound of similar fuel. The time spent by the material in the drier is 10, 15, or 20 minutes.

The double-shell drier becomes an indirect drier by placing flues along the inside of the outer shell through which the gases traveling countercurrent may pass on their way to the exit instead of in direct contact with the material.

A revolving rotary drier in which the air application is somewhat different is the *Roto-Louvre*, or *Pehrson drier*, which is extensively used in food dehydration.* Each of its lifting flights is mounted on a longitudinal chamber set on the inner face of the cylinder. Through these chambers the air is applied to the material itself through spaces left between the

* For complete discussion of food dehydrating principles and equipment see "Drying and Dehydration of Foods," by H. W. von Loesecke, New York, Reinhold Publishing Corp., 1943.

flights.   Hot air (or gases) traverses the material resting on the curved shelves and then continues the drying action in the usual way as it travels through the cylinder.   The circumferential chambers are tapered so that the interior surface made up of the lifting flights is a section of a cone. The outer shell may be made truly horizontal, and as the cylinder revolves the material fed in at the narrower end of the cone travels toward the wider end.   The interior cone surface takes the place of the inclination. The taper in the several chambers permits the application of air at higher velocity at the wet end (where the cone is narrower) and of air at lower

FIGURE 362.—A screw conveyor, inclined, feeding a rotary drier.   (Courtesy Link-Belt Co., Chicago, Ill.)

velocity at the drier end (where it is wider).   The air is applied only to the compartments which are overlaid by the wet material by means of a stationary inlet piece which covers only 8 out of 20 compartments, or 10 out of 24 (see Figure 361).   The vapor-laden air is removed by an exhauster with an extension piece from a point half way in the cylinder, thus insuring the advantages of both concurrent and countercurrent air travel.   The rotation of the drum is in the direction which avoids clogging of the slits.

The more thorough the exposure of wet surfaces to the air or gases, that is, the better the contact, the shorter the drier need be; consequently, the less the first cost.

Another form of indirect-heat rotary drier has a number of flues parallel to the axis of the cylinder and terminating in a grid chamber with central entry into which a stationary pipe fits. For high temperature, air-flue gas mixtures are sent through the flues; for low-temperature driers, steam-heated air is used. The heat transfer is by radiation and conduction. There is a further modification which has an agitator and a stationary shell. It is somewhat difficult to operate because part of the wet material may be advanced too rapidly, and the agitator distributes the material unevenly over the whole cross section of the drier.

The *steam-tube drier* has a revolving shell, and the material drops through a bundle of steam tubes, which run the full length of the drier parallel to the shell axis. They are mounted at one end in a steam distributing head, generally in two concentric rows; at the other end, they are loosely supported in a plate, free to expand and vented to remove permanent gases. The tubes may also be mounted on a floating head. Lifting flights are provided, if necessary. This drier was originally developed for drying waste grain in breweries and distilleries, but it is now used for a great variety of materials (See frontispiece).

Still another design of this same general type has a stationary shell and revolving bundle of tubes. There are a number of other modifications and combinations serving special purposes. A rotary drier with indirect heat is built to receive the heat of a fire placed under the shell, the transfer of heat being through the shell wall. A portion of the flue gases may be diverted through the cylinder to carry off the vapors.

The rotary drier is a high-capacity machine. For example, a direct-heat revolving rotary drier 5 feet in diameter and 40 feet long (single shell) delivers 6 tons per hour of material with the moisture content reduced from 12 to 1 per cent. Per pound of fuel of 12,600 Btu per pound, $4\frac{1}{2}$ pounds of water are evaporated. In another instance, a double-shell drier 5 feet in diameter and 30 feet long delivers $8\frac{1}{2}$ tons of dry material per hour, with the same moisture reduction as before, and in this drier, 7 pounds of water are evaporated per pound of fuel.

Rotary driers are playing an increasingly important role in the national economy, as for example, in the dehydration of foods.

The *screw conveyor drier* is similar in operation to the rotary drier with revolving agitator; it is also known as a desolventizer on account of its use in oil extraction plants to recover solvent used in the extraction from the residue. It consists of a steam-jacketed, covered, conveyor trough through which the material is moved by means of a screw conveyor, or paddle type agitator. A number of units may be placed in series, one above the other, and each of these may be heated to a different temperature. Thus this drier provides continuous operation with a long drying path, and is well adapted to drying materials slowly. A gentle current of air may be passed countercurrent through the drier in order to assist in the removal of water vapor without creating dust. Other gases may be used if the material is liable to decompose or oxidize in contact with air.

The *tower drier* differs from other driers in which the material is agitated in that the material moves by gravity, dropping down a tower in which it meets an ascending current of hot air. Inclined baffles are placed in the path of the descending stream of material, and are so arranged that the stream is deflected from one to another. As a result, the path of the material is a cascade. A typical use for this type is for drying grain before storage.

For granular materials from which only a small amount of moisture must be removed, a *vibrating screen* may be used for forwarding the material. Warm air is blown through the screen and the material.

Drying Rooms. For drying materials which cannot be agitated, the drying room and the tray drier, of which there are many varieties, are largely used. In the former, the material may be spread on pans and these stacked in a rack, which leaves a space between the trays for air circulation. The room has loosely fitted side walls of plaster board, or similar material, or even canvas, and contains a steam radiator. The natural circulation of the warm air removes the moisture. The drying period is generally long, for example, one or two days. A ventilator may be placed over the central part of the room to carry away the air and vapor. Such is the simple drying room, which may be home-made, and may be small or large. In some potteries, a large portion of the floor is so enclosed; this serves as a drying room, with shelves on which the ware is placed to dry slowly.

Tray, Truck, and Tunnel Driers. In order to accelerate drying, the closet is factory-built with tight walls of plain or enameled steel. It forms a box, and the air is passed by means of a fan over a radiator or over finned tubes, and then over the trays. A portion of the air escapes at the discharge opening; the remainder is reheated and recirculated. An amount of new air equivalent to the volume discharged is admitted at the fan. Secondary heating tubes are placed in the path of the air to restore their temperature and heat content.

In the *tray drier*, shallow pans 2 feet $\times$ 3 feet $\times$ 2 inches deep, for example, are placed on a rack, forming part of the drier.

In the *truck drier*, the rack is on wheels, and the whole may be wheeled in and out of the drier. There may be one or several trucks to each drier, and each truck may have 12, 16, or more levels for trays.

A number of tray or truck driers may be set up side by side and air passed through them countercurrent with respect to the ware. The regulation is by means of conduits, by-passes, and dampers. This arrangement is known as a *compartment drier*.

The drying kiln for lumber is a form of compartment drier, the lumber being stacked on cars and these spaced to provide passage for the air.

The *tunnel drier* is a natural extension of the truck drier. It is a long chamber holding a number of trucks which travel in one direction; as a fresh truck is pushed in at one end, by hand or by machinery, the truck with the longest period in the tunnel at the other end is pulled out. The warm air is introduced at the dry end and leaves at or near the wet end. The tunnel drier, then, is composed of a long chamber, let us say 40 feet, with doors at both ends; a low-pressure fan; a set of heating tubes or a source of fire gases; and a number of trucks with racks for the trays.

FIGURE 363.—A small tunnel drier, holding three trucks. The door receives the air and delivers it in portions through the louvres to each section over the trays; no stratification is possible. The fan and the heater are not shown. (Courtesy Geo. L. Squier Mfg. Co., Buffalo, N. Y.)

There are a number of modifications of such installations, many of them of the greatest value to the special need they serve.

These driers are frequently employed for drying materials which tend to warp and check. When such materials are treated, the drying rate at all times must be carefully controlled by regulating the temperature and humidity of the air as the drying proceeds. Recirculation and reheating are practiced and are automatically controlled. This increases the economy of the drying process, which otherwise is poor on account of the low temperature generally maintained.

Of great interest are the driers which use infrared lamps as the source of heat. Such driers serve, for example, for the baking of enamels (paint type), and the drying of automobile bodies. The latter are mounted on low carriers which run on rails laid in a tunnel-like chamber, with lamps over the whole surface of the side walls and ceiling. The use of radiant heat from infrared lamps is expensive and therefore is used only when small amounts of moisture or solvents have to be removed quickly. Gas as a source of radiant heat is more economical.

Belt Driers. A belt drier consists of a set of hinged shelves between two endless chains. As the "belt" so formed travels, on large sprocket wheels, its path lies within a chamber in which warm gases circulate.

FIGURE 364.—A conveyor drier, with belt 5 feet wide and 80 feet long (80 feet between sprockets). The temperature is maintained at 325°F by means of 200-pound steam. There are four passes of the air; the same air travels through all four fans, and some of final air is fed to the first one for recirculation. The drier is covered with 2½-inch magnesia insulation panels which are quickly removable. (Courtesy Geo. L. Squier Mfg. Co., Buffalo, N. Y.)

The belt is long enough to keep the product within the heated chamber for a number of minutes, perhaps an hour, after which time it is carried to the serving point again. The pieces to be dried, if large, are placed on the shelves one by one; if small, a removable pan or tray is placed on the traveling shelves. At the discharge point, the dried piece (or pan) is removed and replaced by a fresh one. The rate of travel is slow. The purpose of the belt drier is to allow placing the pieces in and taking them out of the drier with a minimum of labor.

A belt conveyor drier is a belt drier with the belt made up of stout links with hooks, for example. The belt travels overhead, and the product, let us say flat pieces of plasticized rubber just out of a bath of talc suspension, reaches a long compartment or tunnel in which warm air is circulated. As the belt moves, the suspended rubber slab approaches the point of discharge, and the time is so computed that it arrives there dry.

The material itself also may form a belt, as is done with cloth and with yarn, which is made to travel over rollers through a tunnel-like chamber countercurrent to the air. This type is known as a *festoon·drier* and is used, for example, in making coated paper.

The belt may be made of coarse-mesh chain and the material pressed into it in paste form. The belt is made to travel up and down the length of the drying chamber, festoon fashion.

Belt conveyor-type driers in which the material may be spread directly on the belt are finding increasing use because their cost is comparable to that of a rotary drier, their thermal efficiency is reasonably high, and their operation is continuous. They consist of a belt made of woven wire of suitable mesh, on which the material is spread; the drying air passes through the bed of material and through the meshes. The belt

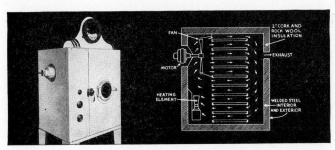

FIGURE 365.—A laboratory shelf drier, with circulated air, electrically reheated. (Courtesy Proctor and Schwartz, Inc., Philadelphia 20, Pa.)

travels on a chain, or is simply stretched over two large pulleys; the whole assembly is generally enclosed in a cabinet. The belts are made of steel wire or of any corrosion-resisting metal obtainable in wire form. The manufacturers of this special belting have also developed a belt with side guards woven into the main belt to confine the material. In order to save space, instead of one very long belt, a series of belts may be arranged one on top of another in a multi-pass arrangement.

With this type of drier the material may be subjected to stages of varying heat and humidity to accomplish continuously what would otherwise take two or three steps. As an example, a material which tends to caseharden may be subjected to a zone of high humidity and high heat to draw moisture out of the center; then the humidity may be lowered in the next zone to dry it thoroughly. The first two zones can be supplemented by a cooling zone to prepare the material for packaging. The zones are separated by light-gauge dividing walls. The belt conveyor-type drier lends itself very nicely to recirculation of part of the air after it has been reheated.

Shelf Driers. The shelf drier has hollow shelves, usually of welded steel, with connections for incoming steam and outgoing drips to each shelf; a number of shelves are superimposed in a square or rectangular box. The material is spread on the shelves directly, or on trays which are placed on the shelves, and the heating is through the metal wall of the shelf. In the atmospheric shelf drier, an exhauster may be connected to the top of the shelf.

The *rotary shelf drier* has stationary, horizontal circular shelves, and a rotating vertical central shaft with arms carrying paddles or ploughs. The shelves are hollow, and usually of steel, with steam and drip pipe connections; they have alternating central and circumferential openings, through which the material makes its way downward, traveling over the whole width of each shelf. The ploughs are set to sweep inward or outward, as the shelf may require. At the lowest shelf, the material is discharged at the circumference into barrels or a conveyor. A light steel casing fits around the shelves and permits the removal of gases which may develop, by an exhauster connected to the top compartment. Rotary shelf driers are built in all sizes; a medium-sized one may be 6 feet in diameter, with eight shelves 6 inches apart. It is comparatively inexpensive both to purchase and to operate, and in many ways is extremely satisfactory. It is best adapted to a wet crystalline powder just whizzed in centrifugals. For example, such a drier has given excellent service in the drying of anhydrous bisulfite of soda.

A turbo drier is a kind of a shelf drier. An example follows.

The *turbo drier** about to be described is an improved automatic shelf drier. It is of the continuous, vertical, transfer type, and is built in a number of sizes and variations. It includes a rotating structure carrying annular tray assemblies superimposed upon each other to form a number of levels, such as 12 to 45. The structure rotates about a central well in which a central shaft (vertical) carries a number of multiblade fans, such as 2 to 7. The tray assembly at each level consists of a number of segments between which the material may be dropped down from one level to the next lower one, by means of a stationary scraper (see Figure 366). The action of the fans is to draw air over the charge, inward toward the central axis of the drier, and also, over different trays, to push air outwardly toward the housing. Heating elements erected inside the housing reheat the air as it turns to re-enter the space between the shelves. It is the lively air circulation which gives the drier its name. The wet feed enters at the top, reaching first the uppermost tray or shelf. The charge is leveled by means of a stationary leveler, and then, after the trays have made a full turn, it is scraped (by a stationary scraper arm)

* The Vertical Turbo Dryer, transfer type, Wyssmont Company, 31–04 Northern Boulevard, Long Island City 1, N. Y.

from the shelf to the one beneath. The leveling and transferring to the next lower shelf is repeated several times (at each transfer exposing new surfaces), until, upon reaching the lowest shelf, a wiper pushes the charge of material, now dry, into the discharge hopper, which in turns delivers

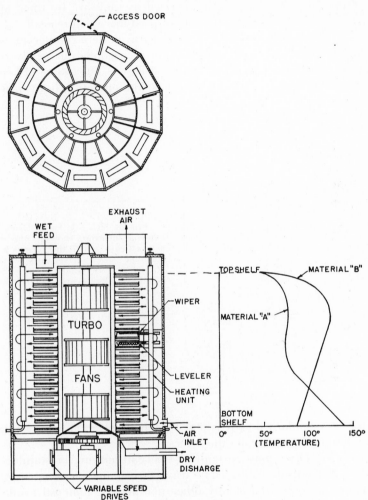

FIGURE 366.—A Turbo Drier of standard construction, with internal heating elements. Feed, shelves, wiper, leveler, dry discharge, and turbo fans are all well shown. New air enters near the bottom; exhaust air leaves at the top. Note insulated polygonal shell, insulated roof and bottom. (Courtesy Wyssmont Co., 31–04 Northern Boulevard, Long Island City 1, N. Y.)

it to a conveyor. An air inlet at the bottom of the housing, and a stack at the top, with suitable gates and valves, permit the regulation of the volume of new air admitted. The travel of the air, it might be noted, is counter to the travel of the charge. The rate of rotation of the shelves controls the rate of travel and final discharge of the material to be dried; the volume of air and the temperatures employed are regulated for each duty. The rotation of the rotating structure carrying the trays is slow, as for example 1 to 20 minutes per revolution. The fans on the other hand rotate fast (60 to 300 rpm), carried as they are by their separate sleeve shaft. For each shaft, a variable speed drive is provided.

The air travel with respect to material travel, here countercurrent and once through, may be made parallel, and recirculated, or partly recirculated, with counterflow, parallel, or mixed flow. The source of heat may be steam, "Dowtherm," electricity, or gas; the operating limit in temper-

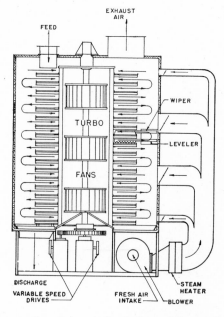

FIGURE 367.—A Turbo Drier with external heating, showing the delivery of heated air to the various levels. Variable speed drives are provided. (Courtesy Wyssmont Co., 31–04 Northern Boulevard, Long Island City 1, N. Y.)

ature for the standard design is 300°F. In a variation, the heating elements may be placed outside the drier.

The Turbo Drier may be built of steel, aluminum, or stainless steel, with insulated outside walls. The trays proper may also be constructed of "Chemstone," transite, or any other nonmetallic material available in sheet form.

For small production and for pilot plant operation, the smaller units, 6 feet or 9 feet in diameter, and from 6 to 12 feet in height, with 12, 18 or 24 shelves, are shipped all assembled and ready to be set up. Larger sizes are shipped knocked down, to be erected indoors, or, for the larger ones, outdoors. One such large unit, 35 feet in diameter and 60 feet in height, capable of evaporating 25,000 pounds of moisture per hour, cost $200,000 (March 1951). One of the smaller units, 6 feet in diameter and

6 feet high, delivering 40 to 70 pounds of material dried from 30 per cent moisture to 5 per cent final moisture, cost, including the heating system, $10,000 (March 1951). Intermediate sizes would be proportionately priced.

It should be borne in mind that the capacity of a unit will vary widely depending upon the physical characteristics of the material being handled and the operating conditions.

The Turbo Drier is available in two designs, standard and sealed. With cooling coils instead of heating elements, the standard drier becomes a cooler; equipped with purifying filter, condenser, preheater and heating elements, it becomes a sublimer. The continuous removal and recovery of a solvent from the material to be dried is done in a Turbo Drier of special, sealed construction.

Pan Driers. The atmospheric pan drier has a jacketed round pan in which a stirrer or paddle revolves slowly, driven from below. The stirrer exposes fresh surfaces and thereby raises the rate of evaporation, and hence of drying. The dried material is discharged by opening a gate in the side of the pan. The pan drier is a batch machine and is limited to small batches.

The pan drier may be used first to evaporate a solution to crystallizing strength and then as a crystallizer by sending cold water instead of steam into the jacket. The effect of the stirrer during crystallization is to prevent the growth of large crystals and to promote, on the contrary, the formation of small, uniform crystals. The mother liquor is then drained off and the crystals dried in the same apparatus. For the production of "hypo" (sodium thiosulfate) in rice size, for example, the pan drier transformed into a crystallizer gives excellent results. Similarly, it can be used for carrying out a number of operations in succession without transfer of material.

Vacuum Driers. Vacuum driers possess several advantages over atmospheric driers. One is that any danger of contamination by dirt in the drying air is avoided. Another is the avoidance of a chemical change in the substance by the oxygen of the air; still another is the easy recovery of a valuable vapor such as that of an organic solvent. A fourth advantage is the lower working temperature secured. The latter is the controlling factor for certain pharmaceuticals, extracts, and similar substances which are entering the market in increasing number and variety.

The disadvantages of vacuum drying are the greater first cost of the apparatus, the greater operating cost, and the limited production. It is not surprising, therefore, that the vacuum drier is seldom used if any other drier will do. When the product is heat-sensitive even to steam temperatures, and when the solvent must be recovered, first-cost considerations and efficiency of heat application are overlooked.

For all vacuum driers, it is true that as long as sufficient moisture is present to wet the surface of the material completely, the temperature will be low and will be controlled by the vacuum in the chamber. As soon as the moisture drops below the critical point, the temperature of the material begins to increase. Finally, when the material is dry throughout, the temperature closely approaches that of the heating medium and the latter therefore must be kept below the critical temperature.

The drum drier can be made into a useful *vacuum drum drier* by setting it inside a casing with air-tight joints and connections. The drum is heated internally by steam, as usual; the low pressure inside the casing, 27 to 29.5 inches of mercury, for example, allows the development of vapor at 115°F, or less. The dry material scraped off by the knife falls into a conveyor which feeds one of two receivers, accessible from the outside. When one receiver is filled, the other receives the product; the first one may be opened and emptied without breaking the vacuum in the main chamber. The vapors and with them any air which leaked in, are pulled out by a suction pump, preceded by a condenser.

The vacuum drum drier has been successfully applied to the manufacture of malted milk powder, skim milk powder, dried albumen, and similar heat-sensitive substances.

The *vacuum double drum drier* has its own characteristics. The feed is center feed, that is, above and between the drums (as in all double drum driers), and is uniformly distributed by the pendulum feed (U. S. Patent 2,129,329). The amount of material applied to the drums is a minimum —only as much as lies between them. All of the material is used (dried) very quickly, and none is recirculated, so that the danger of contamination is also a minimum.

It is only recently that successful installations of the double drum vacuum drier have been made in America. Defects and shortcomings in earlier installations had to be remedied. The present design permits moving one drum horizontally with respect to the other without opening the drier, without breaking the vacuum, and without interrupting the process. The movement is necessary in order to adjust the spacing between the drum, which now may be done at any time, but is especially important at the start of the drying operation. The spacing governs the moisture left in the film of dried material. If too dry, the spacing is increased; if too wet, it is decreased. Among other advantages, the double drum vacuum drier has this one, that only a minimum of material need be in process, just enough to form and maintain the relatively small pocket of material between the drums. Thick materials are fed uniformly along the whole of the pocket by the pendulum feed.

The shelf drier is readily converted into a *vacuum shelf drier* by fitting the hollow steam-heated shelves into a heavy square or rectangular casing reinforced by outside ribs. The door is swung on a hinged yoke, and fits against a rubber gasket when closed. It is held in place by eyebolts. The shelves receive steam from a vertical manifold; the drips are removed from the shelves by drip pipes ending in a manifold. The material is placed on the shelves either directly or in trays set on the shelves. The vapor passes through a connecting pipe to a condenser and any uncondensed vapor and gases go to a suction pump. The temperature may be kept low and may be regulated by altering the vacuum. Moreover, the temperature may be set higher or lower during the first part of the drying operation and lower or higher during the latter part, by manipulating the steam pressure.

Vacuum shelf driers have found extensive use in the freeze-drying or drying by sublimation of high-priced pharmaceuticals and antibiotics. The solution to be dried is frozen, often in the glass containers in which

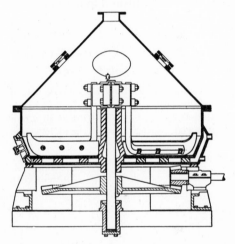

FIGURE 368.—Sectional view of a vacuum pan drier with welded construction.

the product will be shipped. The containers are placed on the shelves and dried under a very high vacuum, such as fractions of a millimeter, and at such low temperature that the ice does not melt. After drying, the containers are sealed.

The rotary drier may be transformed into a *rotary vacuum drier* by closing its ends air-tight, by jacketing the shell for heat application (steam), and by installing a shaft with paddles or scrapers. The shell is held stationary; the material is mixed by the agitator. Such vacuum rotary driers have been constructed of stainless steel. For additional heat, the shaft may be made hollow and steam circulated through it.

The *vacuum pan drier* consists of a round pan surmounted by an air-tight hood and fitted with a slow-moving stirrer driven from below (see Figure 368). The pan is jacketed and is strong enough to take steam under pressures as high as 100 pounds. For drying a wet solid, the vapor would be pulled out by a suction pump, condensed, and saved if desired.

The stirring is important because the drying is promoted by the exposure of fresh surfaces by the stirrer. There is a discharge door at the side of the drier.

Jacketed kettles with double motion agitators like the Dopp kettle may also be used for drying solids. The outside agitator has scrapers which keep the wall clean; horizontal arms move in a direction opposite to a set of paddle arms, thus causing the material to break up more readily and mix more thoroughly without forming large lumps. Such kettles used in this way become *kettle driers.*

Drying can also be accomplished by means of *dielectric* heat, which is the only source of heat which will completely penetrate the material and does not require diffusion of the moisture to the surface. Dielectric heat is quite costly and the equipment expensive; as a result, the method has so far found little application.

Numerical Example

Countercurrent Rotary Drier

A comparison of costs for three types of rotary driers performing the same duty

Capacity required: 20 tons dry material per day of 24 hours, to be reduced from 70% to 12% moisture.

Wet Material:	4890 lb/hr at 70% moisture		Total moisture 3423 lb/hr
Dry Material:	1667 lb/hr at 12% moisture		Bone-dry solids 1467 lb/hr

Evaporation of water: 3223 lb/hr

TEMPERATURES (°F)

Type drier	Direct Heat	Steam Heat	Tubular
Heating medium	Flue Gas	Hot Air	Steam, 80 lb
Gas enters	500	300	. . .
leaves	220	160	160
Material enters	70	70	70
leaves	250	200	200
Average temperature of evaporation	200	160	170
Latent heat (Btu/lb)	978	1002	996

HEAT BALANCE (BTU/HR)

	Direct Heat	Steam Heat	Tubular
Evaporation 3223 lb	3,152,000	3,229,000	3,210,000
Heating evaporated moisture to average evaporation temperature 3223 lb	419,000	290,000	322,000
Heating residual moisture to temperature of material leaving 200 lb	36,000	26,000	26,000
Superheating vapors from evaporation temperature to temperature gas leaves 3223 lb, sp.h., 0.5	32,000	. . . .	−16,000
Heating bone-dry solids to temperature material leaves 1467 lb, sp.h., 0.45	119,000	86,000	86,000
Total heat required (Btu/hr)	3,758,000	3,631,000	3,628,000

Numerical Example. *(Continued)*

Volumes, preliminary

Heat available per lb heating medium, sp.h.			
0.238 Btu	66.6	33.3	.....
Heating medium required (lb/hr)	56,500	109,000	.....
Cu ft/lb at exit temperature	17.1	15.6	.....
CFM at exit temperature	16,100	28,400	.....
Vapor CFM at exit temperature	1,500	1,300	.....
Exhaust CFM at exit temperature	17,600	29,700	.....

Volume of vapor is determined by taking specific volume of steam at 212°F, which is 26.8 cu ft/lb and assuming that the vapor follows the gas laws.

Drier Size

Assuming a permissible exit velocity of the exhaust gases of 4 ft/sec, the diameter of the drier can be determined.

Area required (sq ft)	73.3	124	.....
Diameter of drier (ft)	2–7	2–9	.....
Actual area (sq ft)	77	127	.....
Length of drier (ft)	45	45	.....

The capacity of the tubular drier is determined on the basis of heating surface and a heat transfer coefficient of 10 Btu/hr/sq ft/°F. With steam at 80 lb gauge in the heating tubes, temperature of the steam is 324°F.

> Temperature of material entering, 70°F; leaving, 200°F
> Temperature difference: entrance, 254°F; exit, 124°F
> Average temperature difference, 189°F
> Heating surface required, 1910 sq ft
> Size drier required, 6 x 40 ft

Radiation Loss

With the size of drier determined, radiation loss can be found on the basis of 0.5 Btu/hr/sq ft/°F for a well-insulated drier.

Average gas temperature (°F)	380	230	180
Average temperature difference with the atmosphere (°F)	310	160	110
Drier surface (sq ft)	1,980	2,540	755
Radiation loss, Btu/hr	307,000	203,000	42,000

Total Heat and Volume

Total heat to be supplied (Btu/hr)	4,065,000	3,834,000	3,670,000
Heating medium required, lb/hr	61,000	115,000	....
CFM at exit temperature	17,400	29,900	....
Exhaust CFM at exit temperature	18,900	31,200	....
Actual exit velocity (ft/sec)	4.1	4.1	....

Numerical Example. (*Continued*)

FUEL CONSUMPTION

Source of heat	Oil	Steam, 100 lb	Steam, 80 lb
Heat available (Btu/lb)	. . . . .	880	891
Heat required to heat air, sp.h. 0.238 from			
70°F to entrance temperature (Btu/hr)	. . . .	6,300,000	. . . . .
Flue gas, cu ft/lb fuel at exit temperature	2,300	. . . .	. . . . .
Fuel required (lb/hr)	454	7,160	4,120

HORSEPOWER

Driers	32	48	12
Fans, 3-inch static pressure	10	20	. .
Total HP	42	68	12
KW	31.5	51	9

OPERATING COST (1950)

Oil 1.2¢/lb	$5.45	. . . .	. . . .
Steam 75¢/1000 lb	. . . .	5.37	3.09
Power 2.5¢/KWhr	0.78	1.27	0.23
Labor $1.50/hr, 0.2 hour	0.32	0.30	0.30
Operating cost per hour	6.55	6.94	3.62
Cost of drier	$20,700	41,500	13,500
Freight and erection 20%	4,140	8,300	2,700
Total cost erected	24,840	49,800	16,200
Depreciation and interest (14%)	$3,480	6,970	2,280
Insurance, taxes, and maintenance (8%)	1,985	3,980	1,295
Overhead charges, per year	5,465	10,950	3,575
Overhead charges, per hour	0.76	1.52	0.50
Total cost per hour	7.31	8.46	4.12
Total cost per ton dry material	8.78	10.15	4.95

Although more expensive, the steam-heated, hot-air rotary drier (second column) is used when the temperatures have to be kept low and no direct contact with heating surface is permitted. The steam tube drier (third column) will be preferred for general work on account of its lower cost and more economical operation, provided steam is available and the material does not form a coating on the tubes or pack between the tubes.

Calculation of amount of flue gas per lb of fuel proceeds as follows: Per lb of oil the amount of furnace gas, based on chemical analysis of the oil and using 50% excess air, is 22.5 lb. On the basis of a calorific value of 18,400 Btu per lb of oil, and allowing for moisture formed in combustion and 5% furnace radiation, the temperature of this gas will be approximately 2620°F. To reduce this temperature to 500°F, at which the gas enters the drier, requires 113.6 lb = 1510 cu ft of secondary air at 70°F. After cooling to the exit temperature of 220°F the diluted flue gas will take up a space of 2300 cu ft per lb of fuel, which permits one to calculate the amount of fuel required from the total amount of flue gas needed in the drier.

Selection of a Drier. In selecting the most suitable drier for a given product, a preliminary selection can be made from the classifications given early in the chapter. To make an intelligent selection from the several driers available it is necessary to determine which specific type produces the best quality of material most economically. Quality of the finished product and size of the drier can only be determined definitely from previous experience or tests on a pilot plant scale. Once these are established, economy of operation can be estimated quite closely.

Continuous driers are well suited to large production over long periods; they do not lend themselves well for short working hours. Direct contact driers require considerable time to warm up and come to equilibrium conditions with a corresponding waste of heat. Spray and flash driers are better in this respect than rotary driers and others in which the hold-up time between feed and discharge is longer. Batch-type driers are properly considered for limited production, intermittent operation, and versatility in the drying of a variety of products.

Size of the direct-contact driers is determined by the flow of air required both in volume and linear velocity. The amount can be calculated as soon as entrance and exit temperatures have been established in accordance with the nature of the product handled. In countercurrent operation, entrance temperature will be chosen as high as possible without danger of overheating the material. Exit temperature is limited by the dew-point of the outgoing air; it must be high enough to prevent condensation of water vapor in contact with the incoming wet material. In concurrent operation the inlet temperature can be high, even when heat-sensitive products are handed, because it drops rapidly in contact with the wet material and the latter's temperature is kept low by rapid evaporation of surface moisture. Exit temperature in this case must be carefully selected because it must be high enough to reduce final moisture in the outgoing product to the desired point; the vapor pressure in the outgoing air must remain low enough to accomplish this.

Direct-contact drier installations consist essentially of the drier proper, a heater or furnace, one or more fans, and a dust collector to separate entrained product from the exit gases. With the volume of gas calculated as shown in the "Numerical Example" on pp. 478–480, steam or fuel consumption can be estimated closely. Data for pressure drop through the equipment and for power requirements for the fans, and for the rotation of the drier shell, are readily available.

The size of "Heated Wall" driers depends entirely on the heat-transfer coefficient* through the wall to the material, and this in turn is controlled

---

* Heat-transfer coefficients are very difficult to determine because they vary in different parts of a continuous drier or at different times in a batch drier as the moisture content changes. Average temperature difference also is hard to calculate in view of

largely by the coefficient between the outside of the wall and the bulk of the material. Variation of this over-all coefficient is so great that its prediction is extremely hazardous. Wherever possible, capacity is based on heat transfer per unit area of effective heating surface in actual contact with the material. Steam or fuel consumption can be calculated as shown in the "Numerical Example." Power is required for the drier only.

Vacuum driers are the only driers which require the use of cooling water for condensation of the vapors, and this involves a simple condenser calculation. In addition, power or steam is required for a vacuum pump or steam air ejector and for the removal of the condensate from the system.

Labor requirements of continuous driers are only incidental. For batch driers they are generally limited to charging and discharging of the material. Labor cost does become important if material is handled in pans or trays which must be filled and dumped. Material loaders and dumpers are available for this purpose.

Reading References

"Die Trockentechnik-Grundlagen, Berechnung, Ausführung und Betrieb der Trockeneinrichtungen," by M. Hirsch, Berlin, Julius Springer, 1927.

"Das Trocknen und die Trockner," by O. Marr, 4th ed., revised by Karl Reyscher, Munich, R. Oldenbourg, 1923.

"The development of spray drying," by T. B. Philip, *Trans. Inst. Chem. Eng.*, **13**, 107–120 (1935).

"Spray drying," by W. S. Bowen, *Ind. Eng. Chem.*, **30**, 1001 (1938).

"Spray drying," by B. B. Fogler and R. V. Kleinschmidt, *Ind. Eng. Chem.*, **30**, 1372–1384 (1938).

"Spray dryer," Advances in Food Research, vol. 2, pp. 399–515, New York, Academic Press, 1949.

"Principles of spray drying," Part I: Fundamentals of spray-dryer operation, by W. R. Marshall, Jr. and Edward Seltzer, *Chem. Eng. Progress*, **46**, 501–508 (1950); Part II: Elements of spray-dryer design, *ibid.*, 575–584.

"Typical dryer calculations," by O. A. Hougen, *Chem. Met. Eng.*, **47**, 15 (1940).

"Approximate diffusion calculations for the falling-rate phase of drying," by W. B. Van Arsdel, *Trans. Am. Inst. Chem. Eng.*, **43**, 13–21 (1947).

"Through-drying of porous media," by Joseph Allerton, Lloyd E. Brownell, and Donald L. Katz, *Chem. Eng. Progress*, **45**, 619–635 (1949) [drying of filter cakes].

"Flash drying for materials of high moisture content," by R. O'Mara, *Chem. Met. Eng.*, **43**, 186 (1936).

"Flash drying," by Charles W. Gordon, *Chem. Eng. Progress*, **45**, 477 (1949).

"Factors influencing the performance of rotary dryers," by C. F. Prutton, C. O. Miller, and W. H. Schuette, *Trans. Am. Inst. Chem. Eng.*, **38**, 123–141, 251–257, 841–864 (1942).

"Studies in rotary drying," by S. J. Friedman and W. R. Marshall, Jr., Part I: Holdup and dusting, *Chem. Eng. Progress*, **45**, 482–493 (1949); Part II: Heat and mass transfer, 573–588.

---

the comparatively constant temperature of the material during the steady rate period, the continual change in temperature during the falling rate period, and the difference in length of these periods for various materials.

"Rotary dryers," by B. A. Smith, *Ind. Eng. Chem.*, **30**, 993 (1938).

"Roto-Louvre dryer," by John L. Erisman, *Ind. Eng. Chem.*, **30**, 996 (1938).

"Rotary steam-tube dryer," by C. E. Bill, *Ind. Eng. Chem.*, **30**, 997 (1938).

"Blower and heat requirements of rotary vacuum filter dryers," by L. E. Brownell and H. E. Crosier, *Chem. Eng.*, pp. 124, 170 (Oct. 1949).

"Blower requirements of rotary-drum vacuum filters," by L. E. Brownell and G. B. Gudz, *Chem. Eng.*, p. 112 (Sept. 1949).

"Vertical Turbodryers," by A. Weisselberg, *Ind. Eng. Chem.*, **30**, 999 (1938).

"Fundamentals of drying and air-conditioning," by E. R. Gilliland, *Ind. Eng. Chem.*, **30**, 506 (1938).

"Aeroform dryer," by A. O. Hurxthal, *Ind. Eng. Chem.*, **30**, 1004 (1938).

"Drying machinery," by F. Kershaw, *Ind. Eng. Chem.*, **30**, 1115 (1938).

"Filter drying," by D. F. Irvin, *Ind. Eng. Chem.*, **30**, 1002 (1938).

"Drum drying," by D. J. Van Marle, *Ind. Eng. Chem.*, **30**, 1006 (1938).

"Effective drum drying by present-day methods," by G. N. Harcourt, *Chem. Met. Eng.*, **45**, 179 (1938).

"Rotary vacuum drying," by L. H. Bailey, *Ind. Eng. Chem.*, **30**, 1008 (1938).

"Drying commercial solids," R. C. Ernst, D. B. Arden, O. K. Schmied and F. M. Tiller, *Ind. Eng. Chem.*, **30**, 1119 (1938).

"Practical vacuum drying," R. C. Ernst, J. W. Ridgway and F. M. Tiller, *Ind. Eng. Chem.*, **30**, 1122 (1938).

"The drying of granular solids," by N. H. Ceaglske and O. A. Hougen, *Trans. Am. Inst. Chem. Eng.*, **33**, 283 (1937).

"Data on evaporation and drying in a jacketed kettle," by H. G. Laughlin, *Trans. Am. Inst. Chem. Eng.*, **36**, 345 (1940).

"Principles and practice in drying of solids," by A. Weisselberg and T. R. Olive, *Chem. Met. Eng.*, **49**, 93 (1942).

"Outlines of Food Technology," by H. W. Loesecke, New York, Reinhold Publ. Corp., 2nd ed., 1949.

"Dehydration of heat-sensitive materials," by H. W. Schwarz, *Ind. Eng. Chem.*, **40**, 2028–2033 (1948) [vacuum dehydration from the liquid state].

"Freeze-drying" [drying by sublimation], by Earl W. Flosdorf, New York, Reinhold Publishing Corp., 1949.

"Low temperature vacuum dehydration," by A. L. Schroeder and H. W. Schwarz, *Chem. Eng. Progress*, **45**, 370–376 (1949).

"Mechanism and rate of drying by near infra-red radiation," by L. E. Stout, K. J. Kaplan, and W. G. Baird, *Trans. Am. Inst. Chem. Eng.*, **41**, 283–314 (1945).

"Mechanism of dielectric drying," by C. A. Mann, N. H. Ceaglske, and A. C. Olson, *Ind. Eng. Chem.*, **41**, 1684–1694 (1949).

"Infrared Radiant Heating," by H. J. Garber and F. M. Tiller, *Ind. Eng. Chem.*, **42**, 456–463 (1950).

"Freeze drying with radiant energy," by W. H. Zamzow and W. R. Marshall, Jr., *Chem. Eng. Progress*, **48**, 21 (1952).

"Vacuum freeze drying," by H. H. Chambers, *Trans. Inst. Chem. Engrs. (London)*, **27**, 19 (1949).

"Drying machinery and its development," by E. F. Mactaggart, *Trans. Inst. Chem. Engrs. (London)*, **27**, 23 (1949).

"Radio frequency drying," by R. L. Stephens, **27**, 37 *Trans. Inst. Chem. Engrs. (London)*, **27**, 37 (1949).

"The mechanism of the drying of solids," by J. F. Pearse, T. R. Oliver, and D. M. Newitt, *Trans. Inst. Chem. Engrs. (London)*, **27**, 1–18, 39–41, 44–45 (1949).

Distillation is a unit operation; without this designation, it has been a standard operation for centuries. The alchemists practiced distillation, and developed it considerably. Likening the rise of the invisible volatile constituent to the human spirit, they called the distillate "spirits"; hence we have spirits of nitre, spirits of hartshorn, and alcoholic spirits.

18. DISTILLING AND FRACTIONATING EQUIPMENT*

Definition. Distillation is a separation process based on the relative volatility of the materials to be separated and on a change in phase of part of the original mixture. In the simplest example, a volatile component of a liquid mixture is vaporized by the application of heat leaving a relatively nonvolatile component as a liquid residue. With slight exception, distillation differs from evaporation and drying in the means provided for saving the volatile component, in the degree of difficulty of separation, and in the complexity of the operation when more than one volatile component is to be separated, each from the other. Generally, distillation applies to liquid mixtures, the notable exceptions being the destructive distillation of wood and coal where liquid fractions are separated from a solid.

Distillation may be applied for the purpose of obtaining a valuable vaporizable portion (overhead), a valuable nonvolatile portion (bottoms or residue), or both. In an alcohol distillery the volatile alcohol is the valuable product; water is discarded. In the making of alkyd resins, water is distilled overhead and discarded, the bottoms being the valuable product. In petroleum refining, crude oil is distilled into overheads, sidedraw cuts, and bottoms, all of which are valuable.

The modern science of chemical engineering treats distillation as a unit operation to which several principles and design methods can be applied, regardless of the materials to be handled or the industry involved. The trend in equipment is away from special or peculiar designs for different industries and toward designs fitted to the needs of the process.

Scope. Distillation equipment is built in many types, arrangements, and sizes to meet the conditions of the particular mixture to be handled and the products to be made. Selection of the type to be used is based on the physical properties of the material to be distilled, the degree of the separation to be effected, and the magnitude of the operation. The size of the component parts of the distillation system that is chosen is a matter of engineering design based on well-developed methods as given in handbooks and textbooks, but tempered by the extensive experience of manufacturers

---

* In close collaboration with Dr. Hal B. Coats, Research Director, Chemical Plants Division, Blaw-Knox Construction Company, Pittsburgh 22, Pa.

of distillation equipment. This chapter is intended to guide the choice of equipment by type and arrangement but purposely omits the lengthy treatise that would be required for instruction in detailed design.

Theory. The theory of distillation is, for industrial purposes, based on the physical chemistry of a two-phase system (gaseous and liquidous) and the types of operation that are employed for the distillation process. These types are:

(1) Simple distillation wherein the liquid is heated until vapor is formed, and the vapor is condensed and collected. The condensed overhead can be collected as one "fraction" or in successive fractions.

(2) Flash distillation is a slight variation of simple distillation in that the vapor is formed as one equilibrium fraction. This is usually accomplished in a continuous manner by "flashing off" a vapor fraction in equilibrium with all the liquid.

(3) Multiple distillation can effect further separation by successively redistilling the overhead. Extensive multiple distillation would be inefficient and would indicate the need for fractionation.

(4) Fractional distillation is a countercurrent multiple distillation in which rising vapor makes many contacts with descending liquid, the vapor being enriched in the more volatile component as it rises and the liquid being enriched in the less volatile component.

(5) Steam distillation is any of the previous procedures in which open steam is admitted to the still.

(6) For difficult separations a third component may be added to alter the volatility relationship so as to favor the desired separation. Where the added component appears in the vapor, the process is termed "azeotropic distillation"; where it appears in the liquid it is "extractive distillation." These processes are usually conducted as continuous fractional distillation.

Distillation calculations for determining the degree of separation and the size of equipment are based on vapor-liquid equilibrium data, heat and material balances, allowable vapor velocities, disengaging rates, and heat transfer rates. The calculations are simplest for batch distillation of one volatile constituent from a nonvolatile residue. They become increasingly complicated as the number of constituents becomes greater, whether a batch or a continuous process is used. The case of simple distillation is well presented by Rayleigh in the Philosophical Magazine of 1902.* Many authors have presented methods that tend to minimize the complications of the multicomponent system but the basic approach is given

* "Distillation of binary mixtures," by Lord Rayleigh, *Phil. Mag.*, **4**, 521–537 (1902).

by McCabe and Thiele,* for binary systems, and Lewis and Matheson,† for a higher number of components.‡

Although it is assumed that the reader is not seeking detailed instruction in design of equipment, it is well that he be aware of the information required to make a complete design. The first requirement is the physical data on each component over the range of temperature and pressure of the operation as follows:

(1) Specific gravity of liquid.
(2) Specific volume of vapors.
(3) Solubility of each component in the other and in water if open steam is used.
(4) Specific heat of liquid and vapor.
(5) Latent heat of liquid.
(6) Viscosity of liquid and vapor.
(7) Surface tension (at least approximate values for estimating entrainment).
(8) Thermal conductivity of liquid and vapor (for heat transfer calculations).
(9) Foaming characteristics.
(10) Corrosion rates on probable materials of construction.

Similar physical data on the various compositions of the mixture are desirable but can often be approximated from the data on the individual components. The data on the mixture that must be known are:

(1) Vapor-liquid equilibrium compositions at operating conditions. Direct experimental data are best, but, lacking these, approximate rules such as Raoult's Law, Henry's Law, and other thermodynamic generalizations can be used.
(2) Boiling points of mixtures.

* "Graphical design of fractionating columns," by W. L. McCabe and E. W. Thiele, *Ind. Eng. Chem.*, **17**, 605 (1925).

† "Studies in distillation-design of rectifying columns for natural and refinery gasoline," by W. K. Lewis and G. L. Matheson, *Ind. Eng. Chem.*, **24**, 494 (1932).

‡ Selected from an extensive literature on the subject, an adequate library for accomplishing the detailed design for most distillation systems would be:
1. This book for determining the type of equipment, the arrangement, and instruments required.
2. "Process Heat Transfer," by D. Q. Kern, for sizing heat transfer equipment.
3. "Chemical Engineer's Handbook" by Perry, and "Unit Operations" by G. G. Brown for fundamental data and methods of calculation.
4. "Chemical Engineering Costs," by Lavine and Zimmerman, for cost data.
5. "Bubble Trays—Design and Layout," by James A. Davies, *Petroleum Refiner,* **29**, p. 93 (Aug. 1950), and p. 121 (Sept. 1950), for an organized method of design of bubble cap trays.

Classification of Distillation Equipment. Distillation equipment can be classified broadly into equipment for batch operation and equipment for continuous operation. The characteristics of the equipment in either case are influenced mainly by the difficulty of the separation to be accomplished. Easy separation is accomplished by "simple distillation," difficult separation by "fractionation." A classification of distillation equipment is shown in Table 68a. A further differentiation is whether the distillation is conducted with (wet) or without (dry) the injection of open steam into the still pot or into the base of a column.

The conditions for which distillation equipment is built vary over a wide range. Temperatures may range from liquid nitrogen (low-temperature gas separation) to 700–800°F for some separations in petroleum refining. Pressures vary from low vacuum to 1000 psi and throughout may range from a few gallons to 50,000 gallons per hour. Separations may vary from the easy separation of hexane from practically nonvolatile vegetable oil to the difficult separation of heavy water from normal water (difference in boiling point of 2.5°F).

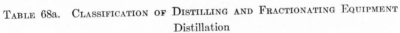

TABLE 68a. CLASSIFICATION OF DISTILLING AND FRACTIONATING EQUIPMENT

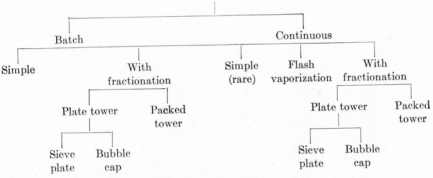

Batch Distillation Equipment. The simplest and yet the most useful piece of distillation equipment is the "batch" still. In operation, a batch or charge is fed to a pot, heat is applied, and the vapor is condensed and collected in a receiver (Figure 369).

A very satisfactory pot still for low-pressure operation is a horizontal cylinder of welded steel construction. Alloy steels are used for corrosive conditions. For large stills of thin metal such as copper, stills are often made as vertical cylinders for structural reasons. Cast-iron still bodies are usually made as vertical cylinders and with flanged ends. The still body is fitted with some means for heating such as direct fire, a jacket for steam or "Dowtherm," an internal coil, or, in some cases, a sparger for open steam. Less usual means of heating are electrical immersion heaters, electrical clamp-on heaters, induction heating, and the circulation of hot oil through jacket or coil.

For pressure operation the pot still is usually a heavy walled vertical cylinder and is essentially an autoclave. Accessories may include an agitator and an internal heating coil (Figure 370).

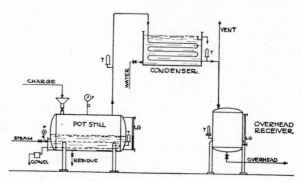

FIGURE 369.—A batch still for simple distillation at atmospheric pressure. (Courtesy Chemical Plants Division, Blaw-Knox Co., Pittsburgh 30, Pa.)

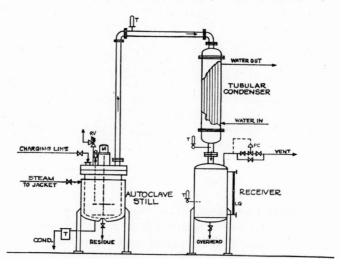

FIGURE 370.—Batch still for simple distillation, with pressure operation. (Courtesy Chemical Plants Division, Blaw-Knox Co., Pittsburgh 30, Pa.)

A direct fired autoclave arranged for simple distillation under vacuum is shown in Figure 371.

The pot still is fitted with charging inlet, discharge line, level indicator, thermometer, pressure gage, and, if solids are involved, a clean-out door.

The simplest form of condenser is a continuous pipe coil (or worm), either as a single coil or many coils in parallel, submerged in a water tank

(Figure 388). Such condensers, using cast-iron section with extended surface on the water side, are commonly used in the petroleum industry. This type of condenser is particularly suited for condensing high melting point liquids where the water bath can be readily maintained at a high enough temperature to assure a liquid condensate. The "fly wheel" effect (the steadying effect) of the water bath indicates where the water supply is irregular.

The most common tubular condensers are shown in Figures 389, 390, and 391. In the vertical condensers the vapors pass downward through the tubes and water is passed around the tubes. For very large units, particularly in the petroleum industry, horizontal units of relatively high (4

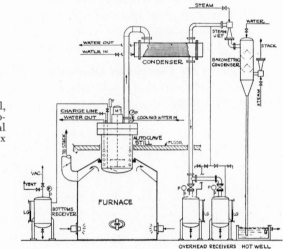

Figure 371.—Batch still, direct fired, with vacuum operation. (Courtesy Chemical Plants Division, Blaw-Knox Co., Pittsburgh 30, Pa.)

to 10) length-to-diameter ratio are used, the water passing through the tubes in multi-pass arrangement and the vapor around the tubes. This arrangement is indicated where water is of poor quality and tube cleaning is required.

Tubes are made of many materials to meet the particular conditions of corrosion. A very common size for vertical condensers is 1 inch O.D. 16 gauge 8 to 10 feet long. Horizontal condensers are frequently fitted with tubes ¾ inch O.D. 18 gauge 16 to 20 feet long.

The usual means of producing vacuum is the steam jet using steam at 100 psi gauge. For operation at 100 mm Hg absolute a single-stage jet is adequate; a 10 to 100 mm pressure uses a two-stage jet and a 2 to 10 mm range a three-stage jet. Two- and three-stage jets require inter-condensers between stages which are either tubular condensers or direct contact barometric condensers. Operations below 2 mm Hg absolute are outside the range of common industrial distillation but approach the field of molecular distillation which is considered later in the chapter.

Receivers are generally simple tankage, except vacuum receivers which, in addition to being tight and designed for vacuum, must have the required connections for evacuating, venting, and switching (Figures 371 and 392). For small capacity, receivers are used in parallel and switched alternately. Larger installations use a single receiver with a pump operating on level control (Figure 375) and pumping to other receivers at atmospheric pressure.

Simple batch distillation is indicated in general for:

(1) Easy separations, i.e., separations of a very volatile material from a relatively nonvolatile material.

(2) The separation of overheads into several cuts or fractions of decreasing volatility and without sharp separation between cuts.

(3) All-purpose unit for several feed materials and products.

Equipment for Continuous Distillation. Continuous simple distillation is comparatively rare but could be accomplished in the same equipment used for batch distillation by charging continuously, operating the still at

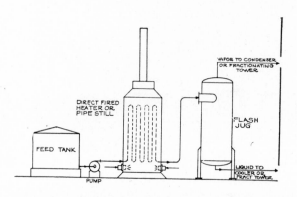

FIGURE 372.—Continuous flash vaporizer, direct fired. (Courtesy Chemical Plants Division, Blaw-Knox Co., Pittsburgh 30, Pa.)

a fixed temperature corresponding to the desired residue composition, and discharging continuously from a fixed level in the still pot. A fairly common operating procedure that is not truly continuous but which might be termed "continuous-batch" involves a continuous charge to the still, the bottoms being accumulated, or boiled down (or "batched down") to desired composition after all feed is in, and withdrawn as a final batch. This procedure also uses the same equipment as simple batch distillation with the additional requirement of some means of maintaining the still-pot level within bounds. Such means can be a gauge glass, a float indicator or controller, or simply a material balance accounting from charge tank and overhead received.

Continuous simple distillation would be indicated for processing a large volume of a mixture containing a volatile component in a relatively non-volatile residue where complete purity of neither overhead nor residue is required. The requirement is better met by a continuous distillation procedure termed "flash vaporization" which is commonly employed in the petroleum industry. The feed is usually pumped through a heater and discharged into a disengaging chamber from which emerge a vapor and a liquid that are essentially in equilibrium. The term "flash" comes from the common practice of superheating the liquid under a back pressure, either purposely provided by a back pressure valve or by the resistance in the heating coil, or both, above the equilibrium temperature corresponding to the pressure in the flash jug. The excess heat is converted into

FIGURE 373.—A plate tower in process of assembly, built of stainless steel. The sections to the right will fit on top of those to the left. The plates are built for radial flow of liquor. (Courtesy Vulcan Copper and Supply Co., Cincinnati, Ohio.)

latent heat constituting a "flash" of a portion of the liquid into vapor. Such a system, illustrated in Figure 372, may serve a useful purpose in itself, or, as in the topping operation in petroleum, the system may be the means of providing the feed to a continuous fractionating tower for further refinement of the vapor and liquid into relatively pure products.

Fractionation. Fractionation is a method of multiple distillation for effecting the separation of two or more volatile components. Although such separation can be accomplished by successive batch distillations, special equipment known as a fractionating column (or tower) has long been in use for this purpose. The essential characteritics of a fractionating tower are an upward flow of vapor counter current to a downflow of liquid with a multiplicity of intimate contacts, a return of a portion of the condensed overhead as reflux to the top of the column, and a return of vapor to the base of the column. The return of reflux to the top of the column is a necessary feature of fractionation, and the higher the ratio of reflux to product (reflux ratio) the greater the degree of separation.

Fractionation is indicated for separations of close-boiling components into relatively pure fractions. Although it is not possible to make pure products by distillation alone, the approach of absolute purity is close for modern multiplate fractionating columns. The degree of purification increases with an increase in the proportion of the overhead vapor that is condensed and returned to the top of the column, i.e., reflux, and with the number of contacts of vapor and liquid from top to bottom of the column (number of plates).

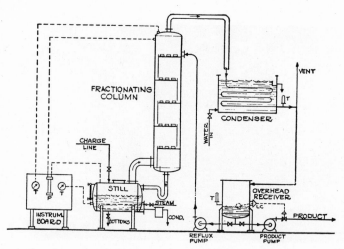

FIGURE 374.—Batch rectifier, with atmospheric operation. (Courtesy Chemical Plants Division, Blaw-Knox Co., Pittsburgh 30, Pa.)

Equipment for Batch Fractionation. When the operation is conducted batch-wise with the vapors rising from the still pot through a fractionating tower, it is called "rectification." Equipment for batch fractionation is essentially the same as that shown in Figure 369, with the insertion of a fractionating tower between the still pot and condenser and with provision made for the return of reflux at the top of the tower. Figure 374 illustrates batch fractionation at atmospheric pressure. A batch rectifier arranged for vacuum operation is shown in Figure 375.

Such a system is used for separating binary mixture, i.e., the making of cologne spirits, and for separating products from a reaction mixture. In the latter case, a series of fractions, or "cuts," may be made in succession, and each cut rerun to improve the degree of separation. Although theoretically an absolutely pure product cannot be made by distillation alone, the approach to purity can be very close and adequate for commercial purposes. In this operation, the reflux ratio (i.e., ratio of the quantity of liquid returned to the top of the column to the quantity sent to product) must be changed over the run, often being total reflux between cuts to sharpen the separation.

A batch fractionating system is indicated for the requirement of running many different mixtures, no one of great value, and for making

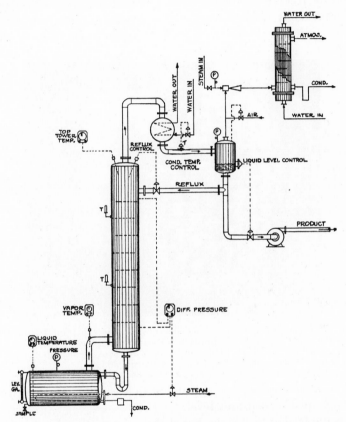

FIGURE 375.—Instrumentation in vacuum batch rectification. (Courtesy Chemical Plants Division, Blaw-Knox Co., Pittsburgh 30, Pa.)

sharp separation of several overhead fractions. The flexibility of such a system makes it a general purpose unit.

Equipment for Continuous Fractionation. The art and science of distillation has reached its highest degree in the form of continuous fractionation. Certainly the greatest bulk and value of products are produced by continuous fractionation by virtue of the extensive use of this process in the alcohol and petroleum industries alone.

The characteristics of continuous fractionation are the continuous feed at the half height point, or at the top of a fractionating column, continuous withdrawal of denuded residue at the bottom, and continuous removal of product from the top. The operation can be conducted at atmospheric pressure, several atmospheres of pressure, or under vacuum. Vegetable oils are deodorized in a vacuum fractionating tower operating at 5 mm Hg absolute pressure. The light hydrocarbons of petroleum are continuously separated by fractionation under several hundred pounds pressure.

All continuous fractionating towers require a source of heat at the base of the column. This may be open steam as in the case of alcohol

FIGURE 376.—Looking onto the upper side of a bubble cap tray, 4 feet in diameter, of stainless steel, for the alcohol column of an acetic acid plant. The pressed stainless-steel bubble caps are 4 inches in diameter, and are spot welded to tray. (Courtesy Chemical Plants Division, Blaw-Knox Co., Pittsburgh 30, Pa.)

distillation, a steam coil, or a reboiler which is the equivalent of the pot still but operated at constant level.

When the feed enters at the top of the column, the object is to remove a volatile constituent from the residue, and the operation is called "stripping." Thus, alcohol is stripped from "beer" in a distillery, and the volatile solvent is removed from the extracted soybean oil in a solvent extraction plant. In a straight stripping operation no reflux is returned to the top of the column. The degree of stripping increases with the number of liquid-vapor contacts (plates in a plate column) and with the ratio of vapor flow to liquid feed.

When the feed enters at or near the half height of the column, the action above the feed entry is termed "rectification," the action below the

eed entry "stripping." This form of distillation allows the ultimate
distillation technique in that "side cuts" and heat exchange can be used as
illustrated in a large-scale distillery and in some phases of petroleum
distillation. Such a system is shown in Figure 378.

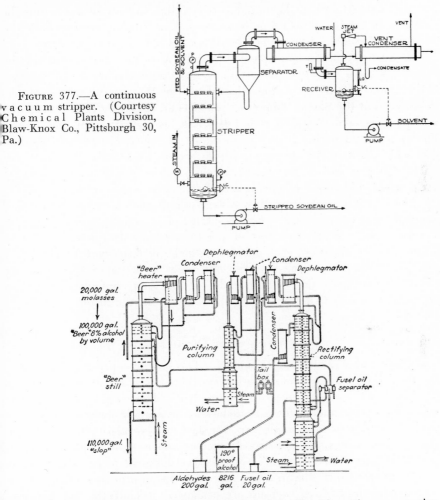

FIGURE 377.—A continuous
v a c u u m stripper. (Courtesy
C h e m i c a l Plants Division,
Blaw-Knox Co., Pittsburgh 30,
Pa.)

FIGURE 378.—The Barbet or Guillaume ethyl alcohol still, with continuous operation.
The steam consumption is 35 to 37 pounds per gallon of 190 proof alcohol. [*Chem.
Met. Eng.*, **36**, 716 (1929).]

A few more words about the reflux. In fractionation, there must be
reflux, as already stated, for if there were no reflux, there would be no enrichment of the vapor from the feed tray on up. Total reflux, the return
of all the condensate to the column, would give the highest composition to

the more volatile compound in the overhead; it would however leave no product. No reflux at all would mean that the vapor composition would be in equilibrium with the liquid on the feed tray; in other words, nothing would have been accomplished by the plates above the feed plate. For a given enrichment to lead to a final product composition (overhead), there is a relation which can be found between the number of trays and the amount of reflux. The reflux may be hot or cold; there is no fundamental difference in the effect produced. Cold reflux will make more liquid by its condensation action, but will cause the loss of some of the effectiveness of the top trays. Hot reflux, produced by a partial condenser, adds to the separating effectiveness of the column. It might be observed that the partial condenser presents an easy way of getting reflux at its boiling point, and that it takes less heat away from the column operation as a whole. If instead of water, the partial condenser receives the feed liquor as condensing liquid, no heat at all is lost. Hot reflux in batch columns makes the operation more even. There are times, however, when cold reflux is more convenient.

The continuous fractionating system is indicated for large volumes of uniform feed material and where fractions of reasonably good separation are required. Many fractions of good separation can be obtained by using columns in series, each one fed with the bottom from the preceding one. Also side draws can be taken and used "as is" or sent to a stripper for additional separation of light ends. This system provides separations at the lowest cost and find application mainly in the alcohol distilleries and the petroleum industry.

EQUIPMENT DETAILS

Bubble Cap Fractionating Columns. The bubble cap column is one of the most useful pieces of distillation equipment. The essential elements of such a column are given in Figure 379. The column itself can be made in any diameter from 6 inches to 30 feet or even larger. The smallest would have a single cap, the largest several hundred caps per plate. Caps are made of many diameters and designs to meet the particular requirements. In all cases they are designed to provide intimate vapor-liquid contact and, in many cases, for the least pressure drop. Columns operating at high vacuum are designed especially for low pressure drop. The cap shape most commonly used is the round type, but other shapes are in use. Round caps are available in many diameters, and the most widely used sizes are 3, 4, and 6 inches. Plate layout for proper distribution is an important feature for which one common arrangement is shown in Figure 379.

The bubble cap plate provides sure contact between vapor and liquid over fairly wide ranges of operating rates. Large columns, above 20

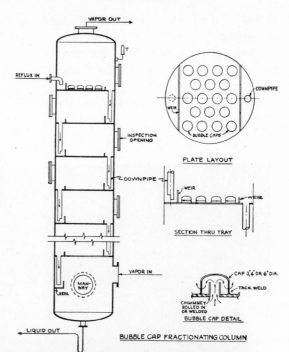

FIGURE 379.—The essential elements of a bubble cap fractionating column. (Courtesy Chemical Plants Division, Blaw-Knox Co., Pittsburgh 30, Pa.)

FIGURE 380.—A Glitsch 10-foot 6-inch diameter bubble cap tray, with double pass. The tray shown has side downcomers; the tray above it would have central downcomer. All tray parts are designed to pass through the tower manhole for installation, and later, removability, if necessary. (Courtesy Fritz W. Glitsch & Sons, Dallas, Texas.)

inches in diameter, are usually bubble cap columns although there are exceptions.

Among the newer developments in the matter of equipment details for fractionating columns, the Glitsch* "Truss-Type" bubble trays and caps should be mentioned.   The tray itself is fabricated of relatively thin metal sheets, and supported on trapezoidal, channel-shaped, or other trusses.   The tray sections are held in place by means of friction washers; in the event of an explosion or serious bump or surge, they slip from

FIGURE 381.—Construction details of cap and riser assembly, with set-on riser, snap-in frog, and bubble cap.   The snap-in frog is so designed that it is operable from the top side of the tray floor.   (Courtesy Fritz W. Glitsch & Sons, Dallas, Texas.)

under their clamps, thus quickly affording relief.   In case of some bending or warping of trusses, sections, or caps, it is generally possible to restore alignment.   The frictional washers also provide for thermal expansion and contraction of the trays while in service.   Details of cap construction, of a bubble cap tray assembly, and of rectangular cap assembly are indicated in Figures 381 and 382.   The Glitsch fabricated trays are about 75 per cent lighter than cast trays of the same dimensions; fewer men are needed to lift them into place.   The trays are fabricated of

* Fritz W. Glitsch and Sons, Inc., 4800 Singleton Boulevard, Dallas, Texas.

carbon steel, any of the stainless steels, or of any other corrosion-resisting metal, as specified.

Sieve Plate Fractionating Columns. The sieve plate column substitutes, for the bubble caps, a perforated plate as the contacting means, but is otherwise similar to the bubble cap column. The essential features are illustrated on Figure 383. Sieve plates are indicated where solids in the liquid would constitute a fouling problem and where a minimum holdup on a plate is important. Sieve plates do not have the range of operability

FIGURE 382.—A Glitsch rectangular cap tray, 9 feet in diameter, single pass, complete with circular pipe type downcomer. The tray is of the typical light weight Glitsch "truss-type" design with all tray parts designed to pass through the tower manhole. (Courtesy Fritz W. Glitsch & Sons, Dallas, Texas.)

of bubble cap plates, and the plate liquid drains slowly through the plate at low flow rate and at shutdown.

Packed Fractionating Columns. In the packed column, small pieces of various shapes, usually in random distribution in the column, serve as the contacting medium for vapor and liquid. Many materials such as coke, gravel, lathe turnings, chain, staples, and wire helices have been used. For many applications, cost and availability determine the choice. Special shapes such as illustrated in Figure 384 have been developed where optimum performance is required. Packed columns are indicated when low column holdup is desirable in cases where relatively **few**

"theoretical plates" are required.* In sizes of commercial importance the height of a packed column will exceed that of a bubble cap column. Packed columns are most commonly used in sizes below 20 inches diameter. Larger diameters require the use of devices for redistribution and at best are subject to irregular performance, probably due to channeling.

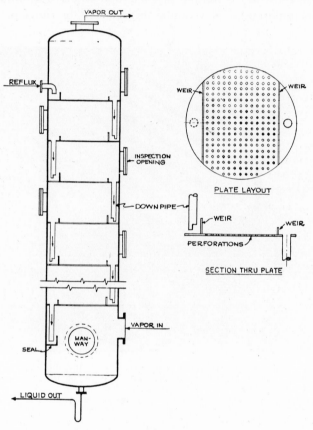

Figure 383.—The sieve plate column. (Courtesy Chemical Plants Division, Blaw-Knox Co., Pittsburgh 30, Pa.)

Still Bodies. Still bodies as illustrated in Figures 386 and 387 are characteristic of batch stills, with or without fractionating columns. The most common still body is the horizontal shell, supported on legs and steam heated. Rounded ends are required for vacuum or pressure operation but are commonly used also for atmospheric pressure.

* A theoretical plate is defined as one in which the vapor leaving is in equilibrium with the liquid on the plate.

Cast iron jacketed bodies are commonly used as combination reaction vessels and still bodies, frequently at reduced or elevated pressure. Reaction vessels for high pressure and high temperature are thick-walled steel autoclaves which also serve as still bodies. The design in Figure 387 marked "Autoclave" is arranged for direct firing. The Dopp kettle, to the left in Figure 387, has an integral steam jacket with cast-in steam coil.

Condensers. Condensers serve to convert the vapor product into a liquid by a cooling means that is usually water. Air or other medium can be used. The heat is usually transferred through a surface, such as

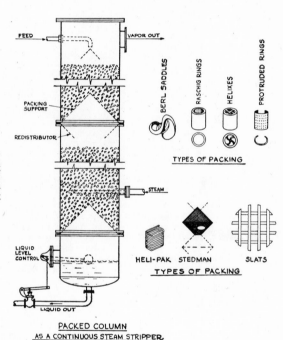

FIGURE 384.—Packed column, as a continuous steam stripper. Note the types of packing. (Courtesy Chemical Plants Division, Blaw-Knox Co., Pittsburgh 30, Pa.)

tubes, but a direct-contact condenser such as is commonly used with evaporators may be employed.

Condensers are made in a variety of shapes dependent partly on size of the unit and partly on function. Small units frequently use a simple coil in a tank or a jacketed pipe (Figure 388).

Multitubular condensers are disposed either horizontally or vertically. The choice may be made on head room considerations or according to the path of the vapor. Where water is of good quality so that scaling is no problem, the vapor can be run through the tubes as in Figure 389 (right). This is a relatively low-cost design, especially with long tubes (i.e., 20 feet). The vertical design is often used for a vent condenser where the

FIGURE 385.—L.P.G. (Liquefied Petroleum Gases) recovery plant. A gasoline stripping plant for stripping natural gas of its gasoline values. Note that the plant is
mounted on skids, so that it may be moved to a new location. Note also the water-
cooling tower, provided so that the water may be used again, which must be done in
areas scarce in water; and the gasoline motor-driven pumps at right of picture. The
tall column is the absorber, a packed tower. At the right is the stripper, in which the
oil is stripped of its gasoline. The stripper is a bubble cap tower.

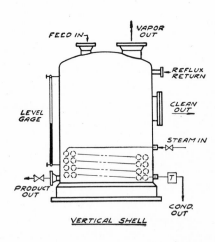

FIGURE 386.—Still bodies may be
of the vertical shell type, shown here;
or of the horizontal shell, shown as
pot still in Figure 369.

object is to produce the coldest vent and the water stream is in series with the full water stream to the main condenser (Figure 390A).

When water is passed through the tubes and the vapor is condensed on them, it is more common to dispose the unit horizontally (Figure 390B).

The reflux condenser (Figure 389, center) is especially suitable for dirty vapors in that the condensate provides a washing of the tubes, or for

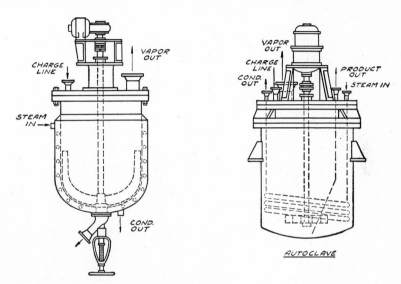

FIGURE 387.—Left, a Dopp kettle with a cast-in steam coil; right, a kettle designed for direct firing.

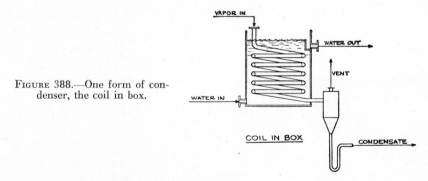

FIGURE 388.—One form of condenser, the coil in box.

producing a hot condensate. Conversely, the condenser with vapor in the tubes and with downward travel (Figure 389, right) is especially suited for producing cooled condensate.

Partial Condensers. Partial condensers are arranged in series with the final condenser, the vapor first passing through the partial condenser and then the final condenser, and are used to produce hot reflux. Although

Figure 391 shows water cooling, in continuous distillation systems the feed is often run through the tubes to produce the condensate and to pre-heat the feed. For small columns a portion of the vapor pipe can be jacketed. A coil in box unit would also be most likely chosen for a small

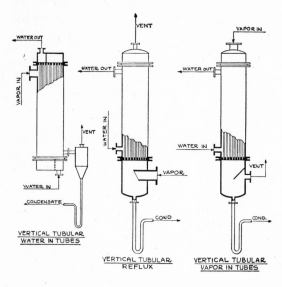

FIGURE 389.—Vertical tubu-lar condenser with various ar-rangements, as noted in the sketch. (Courtesy Chemical Plants Division, Blaw-Knox Co., Pittsburgh 30, Pa.)

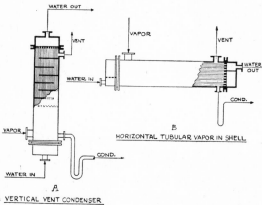

FIGURE 390.—Vent conden-sers, as noted in the sketch. Both have the cooling water in the tubes, the vapor in the shell. (Courtesy Chemical Plants Division, Blaw-Knox Co., Pittsburgh 30, Pa.)

still. Larger installations would use tubular devices essentially the same as condensers except for the greater outflow of vapors.

Receivers. Receivers for overheads from distillation conducted at at-mospheric pressure are simple tankage, usually with a thermometer and means for observing level (Figure 392A). The tanks may be either horizontal or vertical but are usually vertical for ready determination of quantity by measurement of level. Receivers for overheads distilled

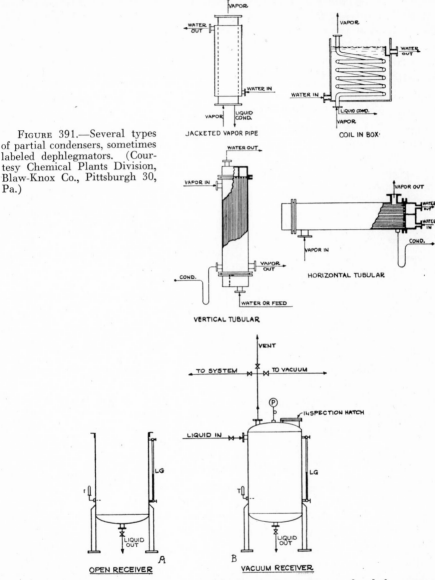

Figure 391.—Several types of partial condensers, sometimes labeled dephlegmators. (Courtesy Chemical Plants Division, Blaw-Knox Co., Pittsburgh 30, Pa.)

Figure 392.—Receivers, open for atmospheric pressure systems, closed for vacuum systems.

under vacuum are usually vertical cylinders with rounded ends and are fitted with the required connections for evacuating and venting (Figure 392B).

Reflux Arrangements. The handling of reflux to the column is subject to many variations depending upon the instrumentation chosen and whether the operation is batch or continuous. For continuous operation, the reflux ratio is fixed and can readily be controlled by a fixed split of the overhead as in Figure 393B. Where the product can be instantaneously analyzed as in an alcohol distillation, product draw can be regulated in accordance with product quality, and the remainder of the overhead returns as reflux (Figure 393D). Reflux can be returned at a controlled rate based on tower temperature, which is in turn related to overhead quality, either by gravity or by being pumped through a control valve (Figure 393, A and C). Another means, not illustrated, is the use of partial condensers with controlled flow of coolant through the tubes.

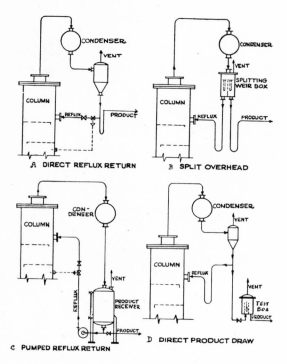

FIGURE 393.—Four different reflux arrangements, as noted on the sketch.

Instrumentation. Instrumentation is a very important item in the operation of a distillation system. However, the instrumentation to be used is based on so many variables that no simple treatment of the subject is adequate. The instrumentation shown in Figure 369 is adequate for a simple batch still. However, it will be noted that all operations are controlled by hand. A greater degree of automatic instrumentation is illustrated for a batch rectifier in Figure 375. Although the reflux return is under automatic control, it is assumed that the operator changes the set point in accord with the successive cuts to be produced. In the continuous distillation system there is greater need for automatic control. The system indicated in Figure 394 shows a normal amount of instrumentation and also illustrates the opportunity for heat saving by heat exchange in the continuous system.

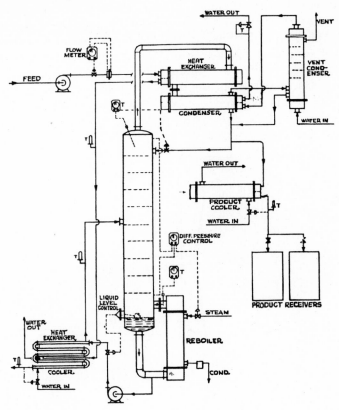

Figure 394.—Instrumentation and heat exchange in continuous fractionation. (Courtesy Chemical Plants Division, Blaw-Knox Co., Pittsburgh 30, Pa.)

MOLECULAR DISTILLATION

"The process of free transfer under a high vacuum from evaporator to condenser is known as unobstructed-path distillation; when the distance of transfer is comparable to the mean free path of the vapor molecules in the residual gas, it is known as molecular distillation."* Another definition, somewhat simpler, but which would represent an ideal process, is that "in molecular distillation, the molecules leave the surface of the liquid to assume the vapor state, and reach the condensing surface without collision with any other molecule while in transit." Still another represents the large-scale operations of industry: "Molecular distillation is known in the chemical and industrial field as a unit operation for purify-

* *Chem. Revs.*, **34**, 53 (1944).

ing or separating high-boiling organic liquids of molecular weight above 250."* Such "undistillables" of yesterday which are today distilled by the tank car are vegetable oils, fish oils, animal oils, certain petroleum residues, and vitamins A and E.

The high vacuum required and maintained is secured by oil ejector vacuum pumps, backed by mechanical vacuum pumps, with or without refrigerated traps between the two. A well-adapted pump is the combination diffusion and booster pump, type KS-100 (Distillation Products Industries) which will pump 100 liters per second of noncondensables at a pressure of 10 microns and as low as 0.02 micron Hg pressure (using

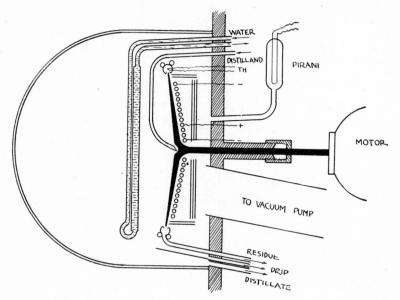

Figure 395.—Diagrammatic vertical section of centrifugal still. Reproduced from Figure 11, page 65, *Chem. Rev.*, **34** (1944).

Myvane 20). The limiting forepressure is 0.800 mm Hg. At 1 micron to 4 microns Hg pressure, its speed is 140 liters per second. Oil ejector vacuum pumps are further described and illustrated in Chapter 19. The ultimate vacuum which may be reached with type KS-100 is 0.01 micron Hg at 25°C.

In molecular distillation or unobstructed-path distillation, the conditions for the vaporization are made as favorable as possible. The liquid is spread in a thin film on the surface of a rotating, shallow, cone-shaped vaporizer, mounted with its axis horizontal. The condensing surface is placed close to it, so that the distance to be traversed by the vaporized molecule is short (see Figure 395). An important modification in the

* Private communication from Distillation Products Industries, May 1952.

purification and separation of liquids is the removal at the edge of the cone of the nonvaporized residue.

In metallizing glass and other surfaces, a high vacuum is similarly necessary; such metallizing is a form of distillation, or at least sublimation, from the solid metal through monomolecular vapor to the thin film deposited. Well-known examples are the Ray-Ban sunglasses.

Reading References

"Fractional distillation. I. Methods for determining the number of equilibrium plates," by G. G. Brown and M. Souders, Jr., *Trans. Am. Inst. Chem. Eng.*, **30**, 438 (1934); "II. Theoretical comparison of methods of calculation," by G. G. Brown, M. Souders, Jr., and W. W. Hesler, *Ibid.*, 457; "III. Application of theoretical method of calculation to commercial gasoline stabilizer data," by E. G. Ragatz, H. V. Nyland, M. Souders, Jr., and G. G. Brown, *Ibid.*, 477, with a list of 80 references.

"Batch fractionation; calculation of theoretical plates required for separation of two normal liquids," by A. Rose, *Ind. Eng. Chem.*, **33**, 594 (1941).

"Efficiency and design of rectifying columns for binary mixtures," by W. K. Lewis, *Ind. Eng. Chem.*, **14**, 492–7 (1922).

"Chemical engineering developments in grain distillery," by A. Herman, E. M. Stallings, and H. F. Willkie, *Trans. Am. Inst. Chem. Eng.*, **38**, 791 (1942).

"Getting more alcohol from present facilities," by G. T. Reich, *Chem. Met. Eng.* **49**, 129 (1942).

"Plate efficiencies in rectification of binary mixtures," by J. S. Carey, J. Griswold, W. K. Lewis and W. H. McAdams, *Trans. Am. Inst. Chem. Eng.*, **30**, 504 (1934).

"Distillation practices and methods of calculation," by D. F. Othmer, *Chem. Met. Eng.*, **49**, 84 (1942).

"Liquid holdup and flooding in packed towers," by J. C. Elgin and F. B. Weiss, *Ind. Eng. Chem.*, **39**, 435 (1939).

"The practical testing of a continuous petroleum still," by A. H. Goodliffe, *Trans. Inst. Chem. Eng.*, **12**, 107 (1934).

"Cost of pressure vessels and pressure fractionating columns," by F. C. Fowler and G. G. Brown, *Trans. Am. Inst. Chem. Eng.*, **39**, 241 (1943).

"The elements of fractional distillation," by C. S. Robinson and E. R. Gilliland, New York, McGraw-Hill Book Co., 1950.

"Multicomponent fractionation," by J. J. Hogan, *Ind. Eng. Chem.*, **33**, 1132 (1941).

"Vapor re-use process; separation of mixtures of volatile liquids," by D. F. Othmer, *Ind. Eng. Chem.*, **28**, 1435 (1936).

"Absolute alcohol, an economical method for its manufacture," by D. F. Othmer and T. O. Wentworth, *Ind. Eng. Chem.*, **32**, 1588 (1940).

"Fibrous glass as a packing material for packed column distillation," by G. W. Minard, J. H. Koffolt and J. R. Withrow, *Trans. Am. Inst. Chem. Eng.*, **39**, 813 (1943).

"Unit Operations," by George G. Brown, New York, John Wiley and Sons, 1950.

"Process Heat Transfer," by Donald Q. Kern, New York, McGraw-Hill Book Co., 1950.

"Chemical Engineers Handbook," by J. H. Perry, New York, McGraw-Hill Book Co., 1950.

"Chemical Engineering Costs," by O. T. Zimmerman and Irvin Lavine, Dover, N. H., Industrial Research Service, 1950.

It is desirable to produce a vacuum in process vessels for several reasons. Of paramount interest to the chemical engineer is the lowering of the boiling temperature which always takes place when the pressure is decreased. Thanks to this, substances may be distilled, or their solutions concentrated, with minimum decomposition. Permanent gases evolved during the process must be removed constantly, if the vacuum is to be maintained.

19. VACUUM-PRODUCING DEVICES: CONDENSERS, STEAM JET EJECTORS, MECHANICAL PUMPS*

In many processes in the chemical and food industries, it is necessary to remove a vapor, as for example in evaporating, distilling, drying, and cooling. It may be desirable, furthermore, to condense the vapor, which is generally water vapor. Frequently, moreover, it is desirable to remove the vapor at as low a temperature as possible. By operating under a vacuum, the boiling temperature of the liquid is lowered, with beneficial results. At the lower boiling temperature, decomposition is less likely; or if it does take place, it is less in amount. In food preparations, the maximum flavor, of high quality, is preserved.

When condensing a vapor, noncondensable gases, usually air, are always present. Air enters the system through leakage at gaskets and joints; it may enter in the form of dissolved gases in injection water, if such is used in the condenser. As the vapor, usually steam, is condensed to a liquid, a vacuum is produced; to maintain the vacuum, and to keep the noncondensable gases from accumulating, they must be removed as soon as formed by a vacuum pump or a steam jet ejector.

The change of vapor or steam to water takes place in the condenser, and is accompanied by a considerable decrease in volume. For saturated steam at atmospheric pressure, the decrease is from 1,640 volumes to 1; for steam under the low absolute pressure of the evacuated vessel, the decrease may be from 20,000 volumes to 1. The drop in pressure in the condenser is rapidly communicated to all parts of the system.

There are two main classes of condensers: (1) the direct-contact condenser, wherein the vapors are cooled and condensed by contact with the condensing liquid; (2) the surface condenser, in which the vapors condense against a cold metal wall, generally pipes in which cold water circulates. In both classes of condensers, it is necessary to remove the noncondensable gases to maintain the vacuum. The open or direct-contact

---

* In collaboration with Mr. Eugene D. Murphy, Mechanical Engineer, Schutte & Koerting Company, Cornwells Heights, Bucks County, Pa.

TABLE 69. CLASSIFICATION OF DEVICES FOR PRODUCING VACUUM

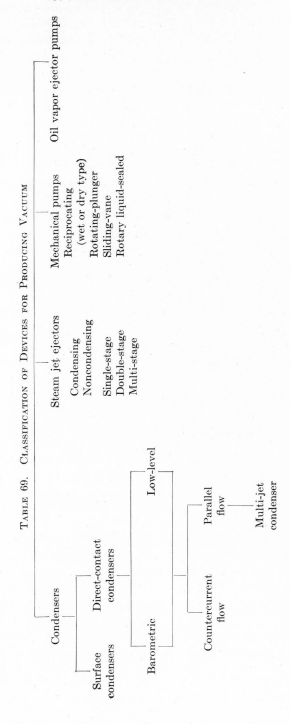

condenser produces a vacuum down to the vapor pressure of the condensing liquid, at the temperature prevailing in the condenser. The non-condensables are removed by either a steam jet ejector or a mechanical vacuum pump.

The initial cost of the direct-contact condenser is much lower than that of the surface condenser; it is partly for this reason that the surface condenser is used only when the condensate must be collected separately from the condensing medium, and uncontaminated by it.

The advantages of operating with vacuum are many, as previously indicated; they differ with the nature of the operation. As an example, the application of vacuum to evaporators, with a consequent lowering of the boiling point, may be considered more closely. Thus with steam pressure at 80 pounds gauge the steam temperature is 312°F. The boiling temperature of the liquid, at atmospheric pressure is, let us say, 212°F; at 28 inches vacuum (barometer 30 inches), the boiling point is 101.14°F, about 110° lower. Furthermore, the differential between steam chest and boiling liquid is now 210° instead of 100°. Two advantages result: (1) less damage by heat is suffered by a delicate material at the lower boiling temperature and (2) evaporation takes place more than twice as fast, so that the capacity of the unit is doubled (or the same capacity may be obtained with steam in the steam chest at much lower pressure).

Application of the vacuum to closed kettles, pressure vessels, aging tanks, or resting tanks may have the important result of disengaging bubbles of air which then rise to the top and are removed by the vacuum device. Trapped air must be removed while such materials are still hot and comparatively free-flowing.

In vacuum crystallizers, the application of vacuum makes it possible to cool the material and remove the heat of crystallization; in steam power plants, the use of vacuum extends the pressure range over which the steam expands.

CONDENSERS

Direct-contact Condensers. Direct-contact condensers may be arranged at barometric height or low level. In the *barometric arrangement* there must be a tail pipe 34 feet long, sufficient to balance the atmospheric pressure, between the condenser discharge flange and the level of the water in the hot well which acts as a sump to seal the discharge of the condenser. In the *low-level arrangement*, a removal pump is connected to a shorter tail pipe to remove the condensate. Generally speaking, the barometric arrangement is far more satisfactory, because the barometric leg provides a seal which requires no adjustment while the condensate removal pump in the low-level arrangement must have a liquid level controller maintaining a level at the outlet of the condenser, regulating the water valve to prevent either the flooding or the pumping dry of the condenser by the removal pump.

A direct-contact condenser may be of the countercurrent or parallel-flow type. In the *countercurrent* type, the vapors enter the lower part of the condenser, the water enters at the top, and the two fluids travel countercurrently, the water carrying the condensed vapor out of the condenser. In the *parallel-flow* condenser, both the vapors and water enter at the top of the condenser and the two fluids flow in parallel towards the bottom of the condenser. The countercurrent condenser is generally of the tray or baffle type, with the water passing from one tray to another, forming curtains of water through which the vapors must pass. In another design, a water spray nozzle is used which forms three water cones through which

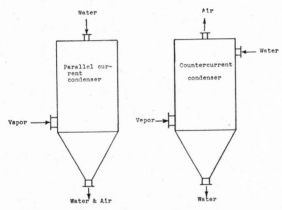

FIGURE 396.—Left, the parallel-flow principle in condensers; vapor and water both travel downward. Right, countercurrent flow principle.

the vapors similarly must pass. The vapors entering the lower part of the condenser are cooled and condensed by contact with the curtains of water. The noncondensables rise to the top and are usually taken off through a connection near the top of the condenser. The countercurrent condenser operates on a 5° terminal difference which means that the temperature of the water in the tail pipe can be maintained within 5° of the temperature prevailing in the body of the condenser; the latter is the temperature corresponding to the vacuum being maintained.

As an example of the operation of the countercurrent condenser, if it be assumed that the vapor load is 10,000 pounds per hour, with condensing water at 70°F maintaining a vacuum of 28 inches Hg, the temperature in the body of the condenser would be about 100°F which corresponds to the 28 inches of vacuum. The temperature of the water in the tail pipe would then be 95°F. The temperature rise of the water passing through the condenser would be 25°F (95° minus 70°). The amount of cooling water would then be:

$$\frac{10{,}000 \text{ pounds vapor per hour} \times 1{,}000 \text{ Btu's per pound}}{25°\text{-temperature rise} \times 8\frac{1}{3} \text{ pounds per gal.} \times 60 \text{ min.}} = 800 \text{ gpm}$$

In the parallel-flow condenser with the vapors and water entering at the upper part of the condenser and falling together to the outlet, the downward flow of the water creates a suction in addition to the reduced pressure brought about by the condensation. The water passes by gravity

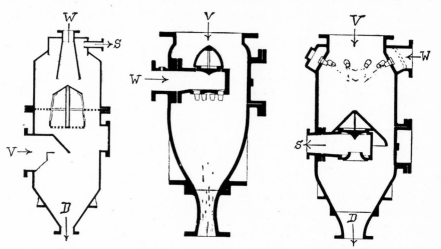

FIGURE 397.—Three direct condensers, each one representing a type. At left, a countercurrent condenser; the vapors *V* rise against the descending and cascading water *W*; noncondensables leave at upper right to suction (*S*). The central condenser is a multi-jet type parallel-flow condenser so designed that the discharge water carries with it the noncondensables; no vacuum pump nor steam jet ejector is used. The vapor *V* enters at the top; the water *W* comes in near the top. The condenser at the right is a multi-spray type parallel-flow condenser; the vapors *V* enter at the top, the water *W* near the top. The noncondensables are drawn off by the suction line under the conical baffle which keeps the spray out of the line. The multi-spray condenser is used where cooling water supply is limited, its temperature rather high, or where a large volume of noncondensables must be removed. *D* = discharge. (Courtesy Schutte and Koerting Co., Cornwells Heights, Pa.)

to the outlet. The noncondensables are drawn off through an air chamber to the gas take-off. Usually spray nozzles, arranged annularly around the periphery of the condenser, give a good intimate mixture between the water and the vapors. The parallel-flow condenser also operates on a 5° terminal difference and the example given above would also apply to this condenser. There are some advantages to the parallel-flow condenser: (1) its design prevents flooding, (2) because of the absence of trays or baffles there is no chance for foreign material to collect inside the condenser and disturb its operation, and (3) there is practically no pressure drop.

Another design of the parallel-flow condenser is the *multi-jet condenser* in which the vapors enter either at the top or at the side near the top. The water passes through jets which converge on a venturi-type combining tube at the condenser outlet, compressing the noncondensables and discharging them into the tail pipe. With this type of condenser, a vacuum pump is not necessary inasmuch as both the condensables and noncondensables are discharged into the vertical 34-foot discharge pipe. Because of the extra work done by this condenser in removing the noncondensables, it operates on a higher terminal difference and requires more water. The terminal difference may vary from 10 to 20°F depending upon the operating conditions. When condensing 10,000 pounds per hour of vapors (in the multi-jet condenser), maintaining a vacuum of 28 inches Hg with 70°F water, approximately 1,000 gpm of water would be required, an amount 25 per cent greater than that required by either the countercurrent or the spray-type parallel-flow condensers. At lower vacua the additional water consumption would not be as great and might be as low as 12 per cent. Therefore where restriction of water consumption is of prime importance, a condenser operating on a 5° terminal difference with a steam jet ejector or a vacuum pump should be used.

For resisting the corrosive effect of vapors, condensers may be made of cast iron, welded steel plate, steel plate with rubber lining, any of the bronze alloys, stainless steel, steel plate with glass lining, "Haveg," or "Karbate." The latter two materials are phenolic resin plastics with high resistance to corrosion.

As mentioned previously, to maintain a vacuum in a condenser, the noncondensables must be removed to prevent the development of a back pressure. The noncondensable gases leaving the condenser will be saturated at the pressure being maintained in the body of the condenser and at a temperature about 5° higher than the temperature of the injection water entering the condenser. The degree of saturation is determined by Dalton's Law. The removal pump may be either a mechanical pump or a steam jet "pump." The choice between the two would be determined by the cost of steam for the jet "pump" versus the cost of power for the mechanical pump; in general for the lower vacua, let us say up to 26 inches, the operating cost of a mechanical pump is lower. Above this point the relative costs should be investigated.

The initial cost of a mechanical vacuum pump is much higher than that of a steam jet "pump" and the cost of maintenance of a mechanical pump is also greater owing to the fact that it has moving parts, while the jet "pump" has none. Also where corrosive gases must be handled, the mechanical pump must be protected by scrubbing or neutralizing devices which the jet does not require. Such devices, moreover, introduce a pressure drop in the system. On the other hand, to the further advantage of the jet, steam jets may be constructed of corrosion-resistant materials at a moderate cost; under conditions of severe corrosion, the steam jet is the only practical method of creating vacuum.

Another fundamental difference between the steam jet ejector and the mechanical vacuum pump is that the former is a velocity entrainment device; the entrainment depends upon velocity impact. The mechanical pump is a displacement device, limited by the re-expansion of the clearance volume. In the steam jet, as the density of the gas being handled

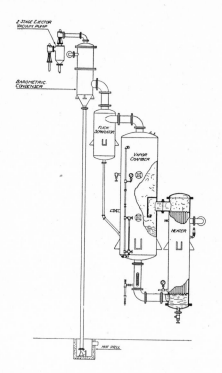

Figure 398.—A barometric condenser, with a two-stage steam jet ejector serving a sweet-water evaporator working under vacuum. Note the hot well. The vapors and gases travel from the lower right, to the upper left.

decreases as the result of either a higher vacuum or a lower molecular weight, the steam jet's relative effectiveness increases. As the vacuum in the body of the jet increases, the actuating steam emerging from the expanding nozzle tip increases in velocity owing to the increased expansion. This causes greater impact. With the mechanical vacuum pump the reverse occurs. Furthermore, steam jets handle gases on a weight basis while the mechanical pump handles gases on a volume basis.

Barometric Condenser. The barometric condenser, to repeat once more, is a direct-contact condenser with countercurrent flow in the condenser head. The warm condenser water is removed from the condensing chamber through a tail pipe 34 feet in vertical length; this is done so that when the tail pipe is filled with flowing water, the solid water column balances the atmospheric pressure. Discharge takes place without any pump. The tail pipe ends in a hot well, from which the water is run off to the sewer. Inasmuch as the condenser proper must be elevated some 34 feet, the over-all height of a barometric condenser may well be 44 or 50 feet. The construction costs involved may be reduced by making the tail pipe carry the condenser. From the condenser head, the noncondensables are removed by a vacuum pump or a steam jet ejector, so that the gases leave at the coldest part of the condenser, in contact with the coolest water.

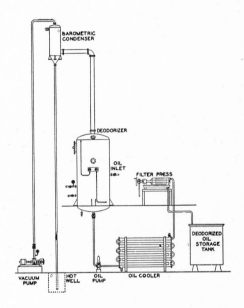

FIGURE 399.—A barometric condenser with a mechanical vacuum pump removing the noncondensables from the condenser head, operating on an oil refining system.

The condenser proper has special nozzles for separating the condensing water into a spray or into thin curtains of liquid. The Disk-Flow method of water distribution is of the disk and doughnut type; a thin, uniform water curtain is formed between the steps even when the water flow is reduced to one-fourth the normal rating. There are a number of different dispositions within the condenser which bring about the intimate mixing of vapors and condensing water.

In the operation of this condenser the steam enters near the base and meets the warmer water, while the noncondensable gases, warm and rich in vapor, are devaporized and cooled by the coldest water, which enters the condenser near the top. As already stated, the noncondensables are removed from the top of the chamber by a steam jet ejector or a vacuum pump. The former is frequently two-stage. It should be remembered that the rate of travel of the gases in the upper part of the condenser is greatly reduced, and the time of contact correspondingly increased.

The vapors leave the condenser as condensate, with the warm water. For this condenser, the water must be pumped to near the top of the condenser, but the reduced pressure in the condenser lightens the power load.

The condensation of steam in direct-contact condensers is rapid—one might say immediate—yet not instantaneous. A finite period of time is required. Furthermore, intimate contact means that large bubbles should not be able to form and rise in the condenser, nor large drops descend; both the bubbles and drops should be small. Only an approach is made to equalizing the temperatures of the outgoing gases and the incoming water. The differential, which is known as the "approach," may be 10°F; with good construction and proper operation, it may be reduced to 5°. The difference in temperature between the entering mixture and the outlet water (now warm) is called the "terminal difference." These two values—approach and terminal difference—are interdependent.

TABLE 70. EXAMPLES OF PERFORMANCE OF BAROMETRIC CONDENSERS*
(INGERSOLL-RAND DISC-FLOW BAROMETRIC CONDENSERS)†

Type of Service	Absolute Pressure Mercury (in)	Equivalent Vacuum (basis 30-inch) (in)	Saturated Steam Temperature T_s (°F)	—Water Temp.— (°F) In T_1	Out T_2	Air Vapor Outlet T_a(°F)	"Approach" $T_a - T_1$	"Terminal Diff." $T_s - T_2$
Brine evaporator	1.60	28.4	93.7	74	90	78	4	3.7
Petroleum distillation	1.42	28.58	89.9	75	86	79	4	3.9
Steam turbine	1.00	29.00	79.0	55	74	56	1	5.0
Grain drier	.80	29.2	72.3	54	67.5	58	4	4.8
Vacuum refrigeration	1.23	28.77	85.3	70.8	82.2	74	3.2	3.1
Milk evaporator	3.85	26.15	123.9	70	122	75.9	5.9	1.9

* Actual performance readings shown in the table were obtained with air or noncondensable loads ranging from 5 to over 200 lbs/hr depending on type of service.
† Data supplied by Ingersoll-Rand, New York, N. Y.; second column, equivalent vacuum, added by the author.

The barometric condenser head, formerly of cast iron, is now usually made of welded steel; the reduction in weight is 50 per cent or more (from 12,000 to 5,000 pounds); there results a great saving in supporting structures. Condensers are also built of wrought iron, "Everdur," stainless steel, or any other suitable metal.

A barometric condenser with parallel flow, the multi-jet condenser, has already been mentioned as desirable when water is plentiful, because no vacuum pump, nor mechanical pump for the removal of noncondensables, need be provided. By means of the cold water entering through jets, the steam is condensed, and the noncondensables are compressed and entrained, the bubbles traveling down the cone and tail pipe.

Another such simplified condenser is the *injector-jet barometric con-*

denser, suitable if the noncondensables are not excessive, such as 20 to 40 pounds per hour (vacuum pans, evaporators). While on the one hand this condenser does not require a separate vacuum pump, on the other, it does not produce such a high vacuum, because the gases leave at a higher temperature, and the vapor pressure at the tail pipe temperature is higher than in a countercurrent condenser. The injector-jet barometric condenser is rather slow in evacuating the system at the start of operation; it is well to provide a single-stage steam jet exhauster (ejector) specifically designed for this purpose.

Low-level Condenser. In the low-level direct-contact condensers, the condenser body surmounts a tail pipe which is short. The discharge of the condenser water may be accomplished by means of a removal pump, as already stated in the introductory paragraphs, or by a vacuum pump which accepts water as well as gases. A third method utilizes the kinetic energy of water jets directed into the nozzle case; upon emerging from the nozzles, the jets are united in the tail diffuser tube. "Due to the combined effect of the external water pressure, the vacuum existing in the condenser, and gravity, the water jets attain a velocity sufficient to entrain the condensed steam, air, and noncondensable gases, and to discharge them into the hot well against the pressure of the atmosphere."* The pressure on the water for the jets should be 9 pounds or over.

Surface Condensers. The second type of condenser for vapors, especially for steam, is the surface condenser, in which a metal wall separates the vapors from the cooling medium. In constructional features, surface condensers resemble shell-and-tube heat interchangers; the steam is the shell fluid, the cooling water the tube fluid. The shell is extended in length to provide high water velocity through the tubes. The passages to the tubes and the baffles, or protecting grids, have been the subject of minute study by steam engineers.

The great advantage of the surface condenser is that the condensate may be kept separate from the cooling water. The surface condenser may act as a partial condenser, and be followed by other condensing devices. For example, in a petroleum refinery, a unit may consist of a vacuum fractionating tower, delivering to a surface condenser, which is followed by a barometric condenser and a two-stage steam jet ejector. The surface condenser handles the oil vapors having little or no steam; the barometric condenser handles the steam having little or no oil; the gases are pulled out by the steam jet ejectors. Such a unit may work with an absolute pressure of 4 inches of mercury.

The surface condenser has another advantage. It does not introduce into the system the permanent gases dissolved in the cooling water, which are introduced by the barometric condenser and must then be pulled or

---

* From the literature of Schutte and Koerting Company, Philadelphia 22, Pa.

pumped out. Such gases are usually estimated at 3 per cent of the volume of the cooling water.

The construction of surface condensers in all-welded steel and other metals has made great progress, practically displacing the cast-iron construction.*

The S-bend condenser could have been mentioned here, but since it is primarily a cooler, for gases as well as for vapors, it has been included among the gas coolers. It may function, however, as a condenser pure and simple; for example, in ammonia refrigeration systems, the compressed, hot ammonia gas travels in double-thickness steel tubing connected with suitable fittings to resist the pressure, perhaps 300 pounds. The tubes are cooled on their outer side by a trickle of water; within the tubes, the ammonia forms a liquid which runs off to a receiver.

Steam Jet Ejectors

The steam jet ejector consists of (1) a steam chest, (2) a steam nozzle, (3) a vapor chamber, (4) a diffuser tube, and (5) in the condensing type, a condenser. The diffuser tube is a convergent-divergent tube accurately machined, and shown in some detail in Figure 400. Between the

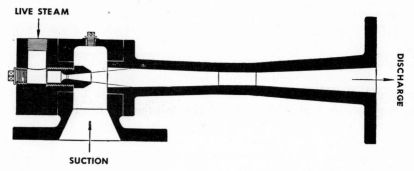

FIGURE 400.—A single-stage steam jet ejector or vacuum pump. Note the nozzle, the vapor inlet, the convergent-divergent tube, also called the diffuser.

steam nozzle and the entry to the diffuser tube is a gap, so that as the expanding boiler steam issues from the nozzle, it must travel through the vapor chamber, where it entrains the surrounding vapor or gases by impact. The expanded steam travels at a high velocity, corresponding to its greater volume and lower pressure; thus for example, it may be at a pressure of 1 inch of mercury, instead of at its original pressure of 100 pounds. Further changes in velocity and pressure take place as the steam enters the diffuser. The velocity at the point of entry is high; it is still high at the throat of the tube, its narrowest portion. After passing the

* Ross Heater and Mfg. Co., Buffalo, N. Y.

throat, the velocity diminishes, but at the same time, the pressure rises. The divergent portion of the diffuser tube converts velocity energy into pressure; the net result of its action is to deliver a volume of the entrained vapor mixed with steam at a pressure higher than the pressure in the

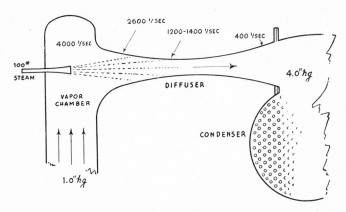

FIGURE 401.—Velocities and pressures in a diffuser tube. Boiler steam at 100-pounds pressure enters nozzle *1*, entering vapor-chamber *2* with velocity of 4000 ft per second, then travels into *3*, the diffuser, with velocity of 2600 ft, at the throat, 1200 ft. At the end of the divergent part, the velocity is 400 ft per second. The pressure of the vapors has been raised from 1.0 to 4.0 inches mercury.

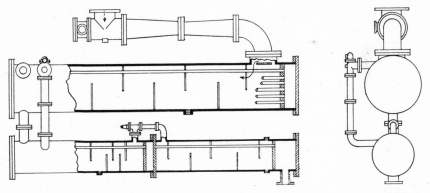

FIGURE 402.—Steam-jet ejector delivering to a triple-surface condenser which permits the collection of the condensate uncontaminated by the condensing medium. (Courtesy Ross Heater and Mfg. Co., Inc., Buffalo, N. Y.)

vapor chamber, to a pipe or vessel connection covering the exit from the diffuser. The diffuser may properly be described as a compressor. Approximate examples of pressures and velocities are shown in Figure 401.

Steam jet ejectors may be single-stage or multi-stage. The former has a single diffuser tube and discharges into the atmosphere; the degree of compression must be sufficient to raise the pressure above atmospheric. Generally, the steam consumption will be less if the compression is distributed among several stages. In the two-stage steam jet ejector, the first stage compresses to an intermediate pressure. The load on the second ejector is lightened by sending the partly compressed vapors from the first ejector to a condenser, so that the condensables are removed; only the noncondensables, saturated with vapor, need be compressed further in the second stage, which discharges them into the atmosphere. The second stage is usually considerably smaller than the first.

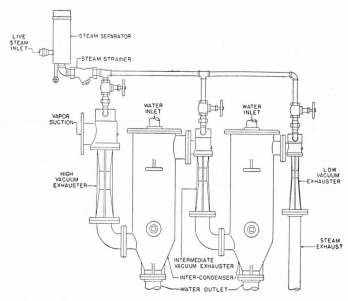

FIGURE 403.—A three-stage condensing steam jet ejector unit, barometric installation. The primary stage discharges into an inter-condenser of the jet type. The intermediate vacuum exhauster (the second stage) discharges into a second condenser of the jet type, while the third stage discharges into the atmosphere. Designed for manufacturing processes from which a large quantity of noncondensable gases must be withdrawn at high vacuum. (Courtesy Schutte and Koerting Co., Cornwells Heights, Pa.)

Three-, four-, and even five-stage ejectors are in use for the production and maintenance of a vacuum of 29 inches and over. The three-stage ejector may have two intercondensers, one after the first diffuser tube and another after the second. In the first intercondenser, the vapors travel countercurrent to the water; in the second they sometimes are concurrent with it, merely for convenience in design. It is interesting to note that the compression in the second (and later) stage raises the condensing point of the steam, so that with the same cooling water, the terminal difference is greater, and reasonably good condensation correspondingly easier. There may be a condenser following the third compression; this would be called the aftercondenser. The latter adds nothing to the economy of the ejector; in rare instances, it serves to recover the thermal values in the steam, and it may be useful, in very special installations, in collecting a valuable condensate. The main function of the aftercondenser is to prevent a double nuisance, the discharge of steam into the open, and the ear-splitting roar (it serves as a muffler).

The steam jet ejector may work with a surface condenser instead of the barometric condenser, as shown in Figure 402.

In the chemical industries, it is steam from evaporators, from a drier, and from other devices, which very generally requires condensation, and

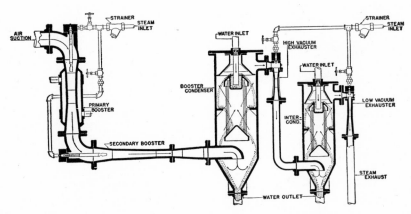

FIGURE 404.—A four-stage condensing steam jet ejector unit designed for noncorrosive service (standard materials), barometric installation. Two steam jet boosters operate in series and discharge into a booster condenser which, with barometric tail pipe (not shown) removes operating steam and condensable gases. The condensers have countercurrent flow. The primary booster has a steam jacket around the diffuser throat to prevent ice formation at extreme vacua. The unit is designed to produce very high vacua, from 3 mm Hg to less than 1 millimeter Hg absolute. (Courtesy Schutte and Koerting Co., Cornwells Heights, Pa.)

the open or direct condenser is suitable. The surface condenser as intercondenser or aftercondenser, however, may be selected for those special installations in which the condensate is valuable and must be collected separately.

Steam jet ejectors which are noncondensing are also in use; they serve well when the capacity is small, the vacuum to be maintained is high, and the steam cheap. It should be noted that the second stage must be larger than the first, since now the propelling steam as well as the original vapors must be handled. One interesting feature is that since no condenser is involved, the noncondensing steam jet ejector may be placed anywhere, at any level.

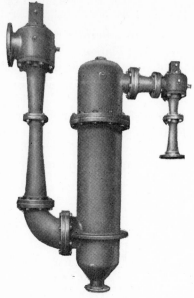

FIGURE 405.—Outside view of the two-stage steam jet ejector shown in the cross-sectional sketch which follows. (Courtesy The Elliott Co., Jeannette, Pa.)

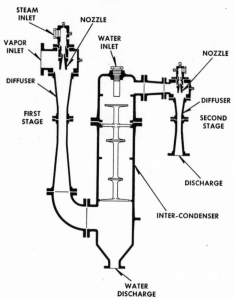

FIGURE 406.—A two-stage steam jet ejector, with intercondenser, cross-sectional sketch, to show principle of operation and construction features. The condenser has countercurrent flow. (Courtesy The Elliott Co., Jeannette, Pa.)

The vacuum produced increases progressively as the number of stages are increased, as indicated in Table 71.

The steam jet ejector is made in all sizes, from one small enough to cover with the hand, to large ones, 23 feet in length and with a 30-inch suction opening. The steam capacity varies; for a large, single-stage

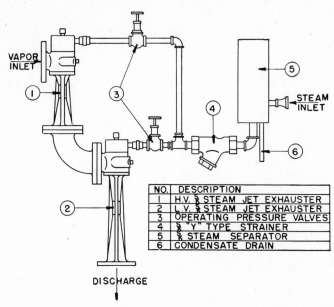

NO.	DESCRIPTION
1	H.V. STEAM JET EXHAUSTER
2	L.V. STEAM JET EXHAUSTER
3	OPERATING PRESSURE VALVES
4	"Y" TYPE STRAINER
5	STEAM SEPARATOR
6	CONDENSATE DRAIN

FIGURE 407.—A two-stage noncondensing steam jet ejector unit, which may be used when cooling water is not available, steam consumption relatively unimportant, or space limited. (Courtesy Schutte and Koerting Co., Cornwells Heights, Pa.)

ejector it runs from 2000 to 3000 pounds per hour. Small ejectors may require 75 pounds of steam per hour.

TABLE 71. CONDENSING STEAM JET EJECTORS*

No. of Stages	Absolute Pressure (in of Hg)	Equivalent "Vacuum" on Basis of 30 Inches Atmospheric Pressure (in)
Single	4 or 3	26 or 27
Two	4.5 to 0.75	25.5 to 29.25
Three	1.0 to 0.1	29 to 29.9

* Data supplied by the Elliott Co., Jeannette, Pa.

TABLE 72. COST FIGURES FOR MODERATE-SIZE STEAM JET EJECTORS* (SUBJECT TO CHANGE WITHOUT NOTICE) (1951)

Single-stage ejector	$400
Two-stage ejector, noncondensing	800
Two-stage ejector with barometric intercondenser	1200
Three-stage ejector with barometric intercondenser	2000
Four-stage ejector with barometric intercondenser	3500
Five-stage ejector with barometric intercondenser	6000

* Figures supplied by the Elliott Co., Jeannette, Pa.

Booster. The pressure maintained in the vessels may be so low (i.e., the vacuum be so high) that steam at that pressure would not condense with the cooling water available. The remedy is to compress by means of a steam jet ejector to a higher pressure, with the correspondingly higher condensing point, within reach of the cooling water. Thus raising the pressure of the steam from 0.50 to 3.00 inches of mercury absolute raises the condensing point from 58.80 to 115.06°F. Condensing water in the United States averages 75°F, and such water would readily condense the 3-inch pressure steam. Such a steam ejector is called a "booster," and is very generally the first stage of a three-stage steam jet ejector. It might be emphasized that the booster is not preceded by a condenser, but draws vapor directly from the containing vessel. It is the booster ejector which is made in the large sizes, such as the 23-foot one mentioned above. Some pressures and corresponding condensing points for steam follow:

Steam Pressure	Condensing Point
1 inch mercury, absolute	79.03°F
0.75 inch mercury, absolute	70.43
0.50 inch mercury, absolute	58.80
0.25 inch mercury, absolute	40.02

When there is variation in the volume of vapors to be removed, and the volume is large, a multiple steam jet ejector is recommended. It has a number of diffuser tubes in parallel. For maximum volume removal all are placed in service; for lesser volumes, one or more are turned off, the remaining ones being sufficient. The multiple ejector is often single-stage.

Diffuser tubes are not made in quantities, but one at a time. Each is tailored for the special duty it is to perform, that is, for the actual volumes and velocities necessary to accommodate the required kinetic energy at the various points along its length. Turbulence in the vapor stream is held down to a minimum.

An efficiency figure may be misleading, mainly because it is subject to many interpretations. What is important is that the diffuser perform its duty exactly as expected, with boiler steam at the designated pressure. A distinction should be made between kinetic energy and momentum. "If one considers a steam jet discharged from a nozzle at velocity v and entraining an equal weight of stationary vapours, the velocity of the mixture with 100 per cent conservation of momentum will be $v/2$. The kinetic energy of the mixture, however, will be only $2 \times (v/2)^2$, that is, 50 per cent of the original value. A 100 per cent efficient steam ejector gives 100 per cent conservation of momentum, but the conservation of kinetic energy can never be 100 per cent and depends on the entrainment ratio as well as on the efficiency of the ejector."[*] The success of the

* Quoted from a private communication from Mr. Chas. R. Colley, Surbiton, Surrey, England, dated December 4, 1950.

ube and its rating depend upon the weight of the vapor or gas it removes
rom the vapor chamber per pound of steam at the nozzle. Diffuser tubes
ire generally sold with a guaranteed steam consumption. Compared
vith the steam-driven mechanical pump with respect to steam consump-
ion for a given duty, the jet ejector is not far behind, and in some in-
tances is ahead.

Each nozzle must be supplied with steam at the pressure for which
t was designed. The general experience is that 100-pound steam is
deal. Lower pressures may be used; but since the energy available in
he expansion of lower pressure steam to atmospheric pressure is small, a
iigher consumption results. Steam at higher pressures than that for
vhich the nozzle is designed also causes greater steam consumption.
Pressures ranging from 2 to 50 pounds are used successfully, but for a
single-stage ejector, or for the last stage of a multi-stage one, the steam
should be at least 50 pounds. On the high side, the pressure should not
exceed 400 pounds, because the nozzle serving it would require a very
small opening, difficult to machine.

The steam pressure should not fluctuate. The quality of the steam
should be 100; in other words, it should be dry. Wet steam will cause
irregular operation, especially in the smaller sizes. Furthermore, the
droplets will wear the nozzle at its throat, as well as any unprotected
tube in a surface condenser where that type condenser is used. Superheat is of no special advantage, except insofar as it helps maintain high
quality.

For chemical processes the high vacuum is of no particular interest.
For multiple-effect evaporators, for example, a vacuum of 26 inches is
frequently chosen; there are installations in which 27 inches, 28 inches,
or even better are the practice. The pressure can never be reduced,
with normal supply of heat to the chests, below the vapor pressure of the
liquid, which may average 2 inches; hence the vacuum would be at best
28 inches on the basis of a 30-inch barometer. A certain amount of air
leaks in, varying with circumstances. For example, a raw-sugar plant
in the tropics is likely to consider a 26-inch vacuum (with normal
barometer) as good, while a sugar refinery on the Atlantic Seaboard
might run with a 28-inch vacuum. The controlling factor is the temperature of the cooling water. In the tropics, 100°F water is average,
whereas in continental United States 75°F is common, and the pressure
produced by these two waters differs by over an inch. Dissolved air and,
still worse, permanent gases formed by decomposition and side reactions
contribute to lower the vacuum (i.e., raise the absolute pressure).

A high vacuum may be obtained in other operations, such as in a
deaerating plant for clay, or in an oil-deodorizing plant in which the oil
has essentially no vapor pressure and only the injected steam is to be

removed.   When a closed chamber containing only air or other noncondensable gas is to be evacuated, the lowest pressure which the ejector
can produce may be reached, barring leaks.

The molecular weight of the gas or vapor entrained affects the performance of the ejector; the higher the molecular weight, the greater
the weight of vapor pulled out by the ejector.*

Figure 408.—A three-stage porcelain steam-jet ejector with intercondenser between the
second and third stages.   (Courtesy Worthington Corp., Harrison, N. J.)

In chemical plants, it may be necessary to preserve the heat values
in the steam issuing from the last stage of an ejector set, instead of allowing it to pass into the atmosphere or feeding it to an aftercondenser.
This is done by sending it to a steam chest in an evaporator, or to the
shell of a tubular heat exchanger, through the tubes of which runs a
solution or liquid to be heated.   Generally, it is a question whether the
installation cost and continual care of piping and fittings do not outweigh
the fuel saving.

* Performance of ejectors as a function of the molecular weight of vapors," by L. T.
Work and V. W. Haedrich, *Ind. Eng. Chem.*, **31**, 464 (1939).

In handling explosive mixtures of gases, and in explosives plants, the steam jet ejector presents no explosive hazard from a spark, which is another point in its favor.

The steam jet ejector is recommended for the uninterrupted removal of large volumes of vapors and gases, with the simultaneous maintenance of a vacuum of 28 or 29 inches of mercury (absolute pressures of 2 inches and 1 inch) on the system. It has the advantages of simplicity, ease of operation and regulation, small space, and a minimum of repairs; it handles high-temperature steam easily, and also vapors which are contaminated with sticky matter or dusts. As it has no moving parts,

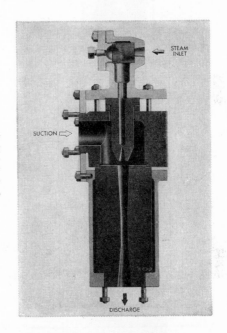

FIGURE 409.—Cross-sectional view of a steam-jet ejector for handling corrosive vapors. The steam chamber, the nozzle and even the diffuser tube are made of "Karbate." (Courtesy Worthington Corp., Harrison, N. J.)

it is subject to little wear, with the exceptions which have been noted. The diffuser tube and other parts are generally built of cast iron, a material which has good corrosion and erosion resistance. For especially corrosive vapors, or other unusual circumstances, the tube may be built of stainless steel, "Everdur," leaded bronzes, or carbon steel. There is also available a steam jet injector with the steam nozzle made of "Karbate" and the diffuser tube of porcelain, which will handle the most corrosive gases with impunity. If preferred, both the nozzle and the diffuser tube may be of "Karbate." Such ejectors are made single-stage, two-stage, or multi-stage, condensing or noncondensing. The barometric condenser or intercondenser for the condensing installations should be of porcelain (see Figures 408, 409, and 410). "Karbate" is carbon or graphite, as may be selected, into which a synthetic resin has been formed *in situ*, so that porosity is close to zero.*

For batch operations, the mechanical pump is generally preferred, and there are installations in which the steam jet ejector is used to ad-

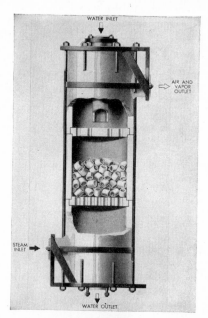

FIGURE 410.—A new corrosion-proof scrubber-type barometric condenser made entirely of porcelain. The same construction is available of "Karbate." (Courtesy Worthington Corp., Harrison, N. J.)

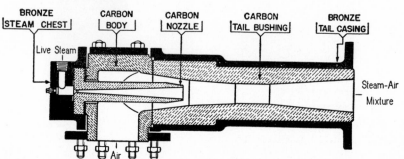

FIGURE 411.—A corrosion-resisting steam jet ejector, single stage, with all inner parts made of "Karbate," a nonporous graphite product.

vantage in combination with a vacuum pump. For example, a two-stage ejector with intercondenser may be followed by a vacuum pump as the third stage in a cyclical process; the vacuum pump serves to evacuate air quickly from the vessel at the beginning of each cycle.

In volumetric capacity, the steam jet ejector has the advantage over

* "Carbon, graphite and Karbate as materials of construction," by L. C. Werking, Trans. Amer. Inst. Chem. Eng., **35**, 489 (1939).

he mechanical pump, for its capacity may be made very large. The rdinary range is between 10 and 20,000 cubic feet per minute, and a jet andling 53,800 cubic feet of vapor per minute, under high-vacuum onditions, has recently been built. A single one could be built which vould handle 100,000 cubic feet per minute, with a vapor line 20 inches r so in diameter, depending on the vacuum. The volumetric capacity of nechanical pumps is of the order of 1000 cubic feet in the larger sizes. ome further comments on the relative merits of the several types of levices will be made in the next section.

Refrigeration by means of the steam jet ejector is presented in Chapter 21. The steam jet ejector is used as a thermal compressor, as described in Chapter 15.

Mechanical Vacuum Pumps

A distinction is made between wet and dry vacuum pumps. The wet vacuum pump handles mixtures of water and vapors; the latter may be partly noncondensable. The dry vacuum pump should be protected by a cooler or separator, so that only gaseous material reaches it. A number of dry vacuum pumps, however, can accommodate a certain amount of condensate. The volumetric capacities of the rotary-plunger pump, and of the sliding-vane pump are in general of the order of 1000 cubic feet per minute, while the largest reciprocating pump handles some 2800 cubic feet per minute per cylinder. As explained in the preceding section, the volumetric capacity of the steam jet is far greater; yet in spite of their smaller volumetric capacities, mechanical pumps are still selected in at least a fair proportion of new installations which require a vacuum.

One controlling factor is the relative cost of steam and of electric current. When power is cheap and steam expensive, an electrically driven (belt) mechanical pump is indicated.

Reciprocating Wet Vacuum Pumps. The reciprocating, steam-driven wet vacuum pump has large clearances and disk valves which seat automatically; it is single-stage and has no flywheel. The practical limit on the vacuum side is 26 inches, while on the discharge side the pressure is 15 pounds gauge. The high discharge pressure is provided because the pump serves chiefly for the removal of mixtures of condensed steam and vapors from radiators, which may have to be delivered some distance away to an elevated point; in general, it is suitable for all those installations which require the removal of slugs of water mixed with air and steam. It is comparatively inexpensive. A number of sizes are available, the largest handling 2700 gallons per minute.

Nash Hytor Vacuum Pump. The Nash Hytor vacuum pump, which operates on the same principle as the Nash Compressor, is of the wet type, especially adapted to the removal of mixtures of air and water, or any gas or vapor mixed with liquid. When the pump casing contains water as the sealing liquid, the entering slugs of water join it, and an equivalent amount of sealing water is discharged; there is no disturbance whatever of the functioning of the pump, for a certain amount of sealing water is discharged in normal running. By selecting a suitable sealing liquid, a mixture of any liquid and vapor may be handled. The single-stage pump produces a vacuum of 27 inches; the two-stage pump develops a vacuum of 29 inches (barometer 30 inches). In general service, the Nash vacuum pump finds application where the air is wet or contaminated with wet chemicals. It is recommended for use in the priming of centrifugal pumps, for operating the suction flat boxes under

Figure 412.—A horizontal, duplex, tandem, four-cylinder, double-acting synchronous motor-driven vacuum pump employed in chemical processing service. (Courtesy of Worthington Corp., Harrison, N. J.)

the "wires" of papermaking machines, in vacuum filtration, and for removal of noncondensables from barometric condensers. The principle of operation is described and illustrated in Chapter 8.

Reciprocating Dry Vacuum Pumps. The rotative reciprocating dry vacuum pump may be motor- or steam-driven; if the latter, the power end is of conventional steam-engine design. Both constructions provide a flywheel. Dry vacuum reciprocating pumps have been made more efficient by reducing clearances to a minimum, and by using feather valves—strips of very light ribbon steel—covering a slightly smaller slot. The strip rests in the valve seat, and is housed in a guard; it responds to a minimum of differential pressure, and seats tight. One pump of this type is the Worthington horizontal dry vacuum pump, both single-stage and two-stage. The two stages of the latter pump are achieved in a single cylinder by an arrangement of valves, ports, and connections. The single-stage produces a vacuum up to 28 inches of mercury, the two-stage pump one of better than 29 inches, on the basis of a 30-inch barometer. The pump cylinder is jacketed for the circulation of cold water. The single-cylinder, single-stage pump is made in eight sizes, the largest having a capacity of 2832 cubic feet per minute; the largest two-stage pump has a capacity about half of that. For larger capacities, duplex machines using two or four cylinders are obtainable.

The Worthington vertical dry vacuum pump is motor-driven and is made in sizes with capacities running from 3 to 250 cubic feet per minute, single-stage and two-stage. It is used in industries requiring high vacuums, particularly in the canning industry.

The Connersville vacuum pump is a 2-lobe pump which produces the proper vacuum for suction rolls and flat boxes of papermaking ma-

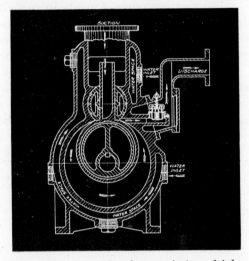

FIGURE 413.—Cross section through the Kinney vacuum pump with poppet valve. As shown, the slide arm is in its highest position, and is ready to slip down; the air now in the cylinder will be compressed and forced out through the valve, while new air enters through the port in the arm, to be compressed in the next revolution. The slide pin turns slightly as the hollow arm moves up and down. (Courtesy Kinney Mfg. Co., Boston, Mass.)

chines. It may be obtained in the combination flat box unit in which a separator tank separates the air and water; the pump removes the air, discharging it into the atmosphere, while a centrifugal pump on the same shaft removes the water. The vacuum for this purpose varies from 14 to 20 inches, depending upon the kind of sheet being formed.

Rotating-plunger Vacuum Pumps. The Kinney dry high-vacuum pump is of the rotating-plunger type. The pumping element, called the piston, is circular in cross section and has mounted upon it a vertical hollow arm with a side port. The hollow arm fits into the slide pin which turns through a part of the circle. The arm moves up and down while the plunger moves along the wall of the circular casing, driven by an internal eccentric mounted on a shaft. The plunger forces the air or other gas ahead of it along the casing wall to a port leading to a feather or poppet valve, to the separator, and thence to the open air or a receiver. By this motion a vacuum is created on the other side of the plunger; to this more air or gas from the space to be evacuated is admitted through the port in the hollow slide. This air in turn is trapped, compressed, and discharged. The plunger does not rotate.* In addition to the simplex pump, which has one plunger, such as has been described, there are duplex models. The latter have two plungers, each with its vertical hollow slide, and run by two eccentrics on the same shaft but set 180° apart. A wall separates the working chambers, but both chambers have suction and discharge openings which converge into common pipe connections. A small amount of sealing oil which at the same time lubricates, is always present in the pump. An excess oil is discharged along with the air and passes through a separator, where any condensed liquid is removed; the clean oil is used over again. The drive is generally by V-belt.

The vacuum pump is made in capacities from 10 to 700 cubic feet of free air per minute and produces a vacuum of 2 to 10 microns (0.002 to 0.010 mm) of mercury. In the compound type, the pump produces pressures well under 1 micron (0.001 mm).

The smallest Kinney vacuum pump has feather valves and is air-cooled. Three medium sizes are made in either feather or poppet valve construction; the four larger sizes are made only in the latter. The five larger pumps are water-cooled, the three smaller pumps in the standard form air-cooled. The former are duplex, the latter simplex.

TABLE 73.   EXAMPLES OF SINGLE-STAGE KINNEY VACUUM PUMPS

	Speed (rpm)	Theoretical Displacement (cu ft per min) (free air)	—Pipe Connections— Suction (in)	Discharge · (in)
556	430	12.47	1¼	1
8810	430	105.20	2	1¼
14918	350	303	3	1⅞
181420	350	682	8	3

The Kinney pump serves in the manufacture of lamps, radio-tubes, vacuum electric furnaces, vacuum driers, and vacuum distillation equipment, especially for delicate oils and pharmaceuticals. The poppet valve construction, with its large port areas, is capable of handling considerable condensate, and is made of noncorrosive materials, as ordered.

The VSM 556 single-stage Kinney pump without motor is priced $344, while the Kinney CVM high-vacuum pump, mechanical, oil-sealed, is priced at $612 (April 1951; subject to change). The CVM pump has two plungers in series.

A *formula* for determining *vacuum pump size* for taking care of a known amount of leakage, expressed in pounds, is

$$V_1 = \frac{B \times T \times W}{P \times E},$$ (1)

* In order to understand the motion, make a paper cut-out of the plunger and hollow arm, and move it over the cross section shown, remembering that the slide pin turns slightly.

in which V_1 is the pump displacement in cubic feet per minute required to take care of the leakage; P is absolute pressure in pounds per square inch; W is pounds of gas leaking into the system per minute (at 70°F, 1 cubic foot of free air weighs 0.075 pound); B is a gas factor taken from Table 74; T is the temperature in degrees Rankine, or absolute Fahrenheit (add 459.6 to the °F reading); and E is volumetric efficiency read off a set of curves* (at 30 mm absolute pressure, $E = 81.5$ per cent; at 3 mm, 73 per cent).

TABLE 74. GAS FACTORS

Gas	B	Gas	B
Air	0.370	Hydrogen chloride	0.294
Argon	0.268	Methane	0.669
Ammonia	0.628	Methyl chloride	0.212
Acetylene	0.412	Nitric oxide	0.357
Carbon dioxide	0.243	Nitrogen	0.382
Carbon monoxide	0.383	Oxygen	0.335
Ethylene	0.382	Nitrous oxide	0.243
Helium	2.68	Sulfur dioxide	0.167
Hydrogen	5.31		

Other valuable formulas are given under Numerical Examples.

In pumping from a hot system, a condenser or cooler should precede the pump, so that the condensable vapors may be eliminated, thus lightening the load on the pump. A second beneficial result is the cooling of the noncondensables, which lowers their volume and again lightens the load, decreasing the volume to be handled by the pump.

The Stokes high-vacuum pump is made in five sizes—of 225, 100, 50, 28, and 10 cubic feet of free air per minute capacity. It is of the rotary-plunger type. The gases enter through a vertical hollow arm and leave by a chamber which has a reservoir for oil. Oil is constantly lifted into the pump by vacuum, and delivered to the reservoir, whence it flows to a built-in high-speed centrifugal clarifier, which removes the condensed water and returns cleaned oil to the pump.

The Beach-Russ high-vacuum pump is a dry pump with sliding vanes. In a slightly elliptical casing rotates an element on a shaft which is set eccentric with respect to the casing. The element has slots into which fit four blades or gates, for the pumps in Series SS, each pair of opposing blades forming together a straight, rigid system, so that the rotating element carries two slide valves, at right angles to each other. As the rotor revolves, spaces are formed which grow as the gates pass the suction inlet, and diminish as they near the discharge port, until just opposite the port, none is left. Figure 415 will make the play clear. Oil is admitted to the pump, so that there is at all times an oil-film seal be-

* Kinney Mfg. Co., Boston, Mass.

FIGURE 414.—Stokes combined vacuum shelf drier, center, and impregnator, left, with high vacuum pump. Note the vertical-surface condenser, on the same block as the vacuum pump and just in front of it. (Courtesy F. J. Stokes Machine Co., Philadelphia, Pa.)

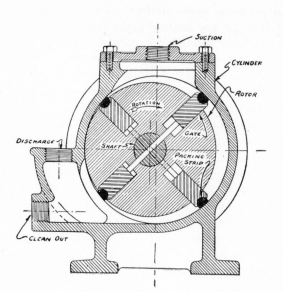

FIGURE 415.—A cross-sectional view of the Beach-Russ high-vacuum sliding vane rotary pump, Type SS, single stage, with four gates. (Courtesy Beach-Russ Co., Brooklyn, N. Y.)

tween gate and casing. The single-stage units maintain a vacuum of 5 mm absolute. The small pump has a capacity of 8 cubic feet per minute of free air, and will pump out an 8-cubic-foot vessel from atmospheric pressure to the low pressure in 2 minutes. Under proper conditions, an absolute pressure of 2½ microns may be reached in 20 minutes.

In Type RP, the rotor carries one slide valve. The inlet ports are in the hollow slide valve itself, and the discharge is past an automatic double-exhaust valve, submerged in oil. Type RP maintains a vacuum of 10 microns (mercury, absolute pressure) on blank flange tests; in factory practice, 1 mm absolute is reached.

A wet vacuum may be handled without additional parts, for the pump has an oil separator, and an oil reservoir from which any con-

FIGURE 416.—A single-stage Beach-Russ vacuum pump on a pug mill used to produce de-aerated clay for ceramic purposes. (Courtesy Beach-Russ Co., Brooklyn, N. Y.)

densed water may be run off. Type RP pumps are made in nine sizes, the largest with a capacity of 750 cubic feet per minute; a special size of 1100 cubic feet per minute is also made.

There are numerous other vacuum pumps, as will be clear from the statement that any compressor connected in reverse is a vacuum pump.

OIL EJECTOR VACUUM PUMPS

There has been developed a special type of oil ejector vacuum pump which can be used over a wide range of required vacua, from 0.01 mm to several millimeters mercury pressure. They are built in all sizes, from small laboratory models to large-scale industrial units. The oil ejector pump is usually backed by a mechanical pump, but may be backed by three-stage steam jet ejectors.

The oil ejector vacuum pump depends for it action upon a blast of oil vapor directed from the nozzle which delivers it, to a diffuser tube, not unlike the action of the steam in the steam jet ejector described earlier in the chapter. An example is the KB-150 Exhaust Unit,* shown in Figure 417. The principle of the oil ejector pump may be illustrated by means of a cross-sectional line drawing (Figure 418). The KB-150 Exhaust Unit consists of a water-cooled diffuser tube, here a vertical, convergent (downward) tube with a large flange (11 inches O.D.). The diffuser tube runs into the horizontal condenser with forepressure flange (7½ inches O.D.) to the right and only partly visible. In the condenser,

FIGURE 417.—An oil ejector vacuum pump, of steel, type KB-150. (Courtesy Distillation Products Industries, Rochester 3, N. Y.)

the oil vapor liquefies and passes, by gravity, to the boiler below, which latter is the horizontal cylindrical vessel on the floor. In the boiler, the oil is vaporized by electrical resistance heat; pressures ranging from 6.8 to 9.5 inches oil are developed in the KB-150. The blast of oil vapor travels upward through the vertical riser and return bend to reach a nozzle (not visible in the Figure) which delivers it to the vapor chamber at the entrance of the diffuser. The high-velocity vapor entrains vapors and gases coming from the process through pipe connections at the 11-inch flange. After traveling through the diffuser tube, the oil vapor condenses to a liquid, as already said, in the condenser. The condensables mix or dissolve in the oil, while the noncondensables are removed by the forepump whose suction line is attached to the 7½-inch condenser flange. The inexpensive oil seldom needs replacing as the

* Built by Distillation Products Industries, Rochester 3, N. Y.

volatile portions are ejected into the forevacuum and the other con-
taminants are collected in the sump.

The small diameter tubing wound around diffuser and condenser is a
cold water cooling coil. The oil ejector vacuum pump KB-150 is operated with a Kinney DVD-8810 mechanical pump as a forepump. A
"roughing line" from the high vacuum to the mechanical pump, by-
passing the oil ejector pump, permits rapid pumping down from atmospheric to low pressures.

The great merit of the oil ejector pump is that it has no moving
mechanical parts. Furthermore it provides extremely low-cost operation

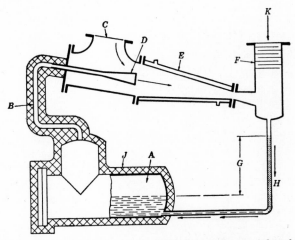

FIGURE 418.—A cross-sectional sketch exhibiting the principle of the oil ejector
vacuum pump. Side elevation of high-speed oil-vapor ejector pump. *A*, boiler; *C*,
entry of vapors from the process; *D*, nozzle for the oil vapor; *E*, the water-cooled diffuser; *K*, connection to the suction side of the forepump; *F*, baffles to retain oil droplets; *H*, return of liquid oil to the boiler; *G*, working head. Electrical immersion heating elements for *A* not shown. (Reproduced from "Scientific foundations of vacuum
technique," by Saul Dushman, New York, John Wiley and Sons, 1949, page 236, by
permission.)

where large volumes of gas are continuously handled and the vacuum
is to be maintained in the range of 1 to 100 microns Hg. The maximum
speed of the KB-150, expressed in volume of gas pumped, varies from
100 to 300 liters per second, depending upon the pump fluid and the
boiler pressure. The speed varies also with the vacuum, but maximum
speed can be obtained at any pressure in the range of 10 to 100 microns
by adjusting the heater input. The volumes stated are for air at room
temperature measured at the intake pressure. The limiting forepressure
is in the range of 0.400 to 0.250 mm Hg. The ultimate vacuum lies
between 0.5 micron Hg pressure and 2 microns, depending on pump
fluid and heater input. The amount of pump fluid required is 2.5 gallons (9.5 liters) (Myvane 20).

In another model by the same company, the KB-300 Exhaust Unit, high pumping speeds in the pressure range of 50 to 500 microns are provided. The allowable forepressure is high, 1.5 to 2.5 mm Hg, which permits the forepump to do more work, and is permissible because the KB-300 delivers its noncondensables at a higher pressure. In the KB-300 oil ejector vacuum pump, the diffuser tube is a Venturi tube, surmounted by the condenser which delivers its condensate to the boiler below, as depicted in Figure 419. The vapors from the process enter a connection to the horizontal flange (11 inches O.D.), while the forepump is connected to the 8½-inch O.D. flange at the right end of the condenser. The volume pumped is 350 to 450 liters per second meas-

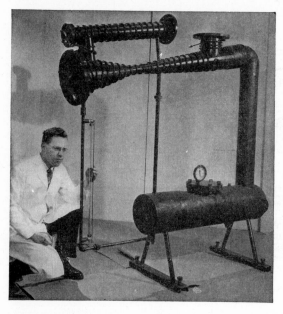

FIGURE 419.—An oil ejector vacuum booster pump, type KB-300, steel construction. (Courtesy Distillation Products Industries, Rochester 3, N. Y.)

ured at the intake pressure. The KB-300 offers the same general advantages as the KB-150.

The *diffusion pump* differs from the oil ejector pump in that its vapor is delivered to the nozzle at pressures of less than 2 mm Hg ($= 1$ inch oil) and expands laterally on leaving the nozzle until the boundary between the vapor and gas on the high-vacuum side is so nebulous that gas molecules can diffuse from the high-vacuum region into the forwardmoving part of the vapor jet before becoming entrained in the vapor stream. In other words, the mean free path of the gas molecules through the vapor is greater than the distance between the nozzle and the casing, until the gas molecule has penetrated the diverging vapor jet to a position in front of the plane of the nozzle exit. In *ejector pumps* the gas is entrained by contact with the forward-moving boundary layer of the vapor jet.

For distillation at high vacua, for short-path distillation, and for molecular distillation, see Chapter 18.

Numerical Examples and Problems

Example 1. Performance of a Worthington 6-inch, single-element, two-stage steam jet ejector, with a barometric intercondenser. A barometric condenser precedes the ejectors.

Noncondensable vapors to be handled	81 lb/hr
Water vapor to be handled	69 lb/hr
Total weight of mixture to be handled	150 lb/hr
Absolute pressure at suction	1.0 inch Hg
Temperature of vapors at suction	63°F
Back pressure at exhaust	1 lb ga
Steam pressure at throttle	125 lb ga
Steam consumption: 1st stage	330 lb/hr
2nd stage	290 lb/hr
Total	620 lb/hr
Condensing water temperature	58°F
Condensing water consumption	35 gpm

This ejector is used to remove air and vapors from the barometric condenser operating on the fourth effect of a four-effect sodium chloride saturator.

For the same duty, under the same conditions of operation, a study was made of the equipment and steam necessary to remove the 150 pounds of mixture of vapors per hour. There would be needed two RDV steam-driven mechanical suction pumps, each of the size 11 x 26 x 11 inches HBV-2 single horizontal, two-stage. The machines would have the following approximate performance:

	Each Machine	Total
Piston displacement (cfm)	965	1930
Speed (rpm)	285	
Suction pressure (Hg abs) (inches)	1	
Discharge pressure (psi ga)	1	
Volumetric efficiency (%)	68	
Actual capacity (cfm measured at suction conditions)	656	
Equivalent capacity (lb mixture/hr)	78	156
Steam, indicated horsepower	27	
Steam consumption, lb steam IHP/hr, basis, steam conditions of 135 lb ga dry saturated at throttle and 1 lb back-pressure	37	
Peak steam (IHP)	57	
Steam consumption (lb/hr)	1000	2000

The steam consumption is 2,000 lb/hr, compared to 625 for the steam jet ejector. Also the price for the pumps is much higher than for the steam jet ejector. In this instance there is no comparison whatsoever in price or performance between mechanical suction pumps (RDV Worthington) and steam jet ejectors.

The comparison would be less unfavorable if the system were not evacuated to such a low pressure. Also, as stated in the text, there will be conditions which make the choice of the mechanical pump, run by electric motor, the proper one under any conditions.

Example 2.

CAPACITY REQUIRED TO PUMP DOWN

(assuming a perfectly tight and dry system)

Let $V_2 =$ pump displacement in cubic feet per minute to pump down.

$C\ =$ capacity of system in cubic feet.

$F\ =$ constant depending on vacuum required and obtained from Table 75.

$K\ =$ factor depending on heat transfer conditions of the system (may vary between 0.90 and 1.30).

$M\ =$ time allowable to pump down in minutes.

Then

$$V_2 = \frac{CF}{KM} \tag{2}$$

TOTAL CAPACITY REQUIRED FOR ANY DRY SYSTEM

Let $V\ =$ total capacity required.

$V_1 =$ capacity to take care of leakage.

$V_2 =$ capacity to pump down.

Then

$$V = V_1 \times V_2 \tag{3}$$

The determination of V_1 has been described in the text. To take care of leaks and other unknown contingencies it is recommended that the capacity of the pump be at least 20 per cent in excess of that indicated by the above formula.

HORSEPOWER REQUIRED

The actual horsepower required for any specific operating vacuum is equal to the pump displacement in cubic feet per minute multiplied by the power constant obtained from Table 75. But in every case the motor or other power source must be capable of delivery, for short periods, the maximum horsepower specified in Table 21* in order to drive the pump over the period of peak load which occurs when the vacuum is between 13 and 26 inches mercury and which reaches its maximum at approximately 22 inches.

Problem

What size vacuum pump is necessary to maintain a vacuum to within 0.1 inch mercury absolute (29.9 inches when referred to a 30-inch barometer) on a given system with 0.05 pound of free air leaking in per minute, system temperature 70°F?

B (for air) $= 0.370$ (Table 74)

$P = 0.049$ (Table 75)

$T = 459.6 + 70 = 529.6$

$W = 0.05$

$E = 65\%$

than from formula (1)

$$V_1 = \frac{BTW}{P \times E} \text{ or } V_1 = \frac{0.370 \times 529.6 \times 0.05}{0.049 \times 0.65} = 308$$

* In Bulletin 18, Kinney Mfg. Co., Boston, Mass.

TABLE 75. VALUES OF CONSTANTS AT VARIOUS VACUUMS (SELECTED ITEMS)

Vacuum (in)	$P*$	F	Power Constant V. S. D. Pump	Power Constant D. V. D. Pump
5	12.25	0.19	0.0200	0.0261
10	9.80	0.43	.0255	.0364
15	7.35	0.75	.0289	.0414
18	5.88	1.01	.0306	.0436
21	4.41	1.35	.0321	.0455
22	3.92	1.49	.0325	.0455
24	2.94	1.84	.0302	.0448
25	2.45	2.06	.0279	.0439
26	1.96	2.33	.0258	.0425
27	1.47	2.68	.0238	.040
28	0.98	3.18	.0219	.035
29	0.490	4.02	.0190	.0287
29.5	0.245	4.89	.0130	.0247
29.7	0.147	5.54	.0115	.023
29.8	0.098	6.06	.0105	.022
29.9	0.049	6.96	.0097	.0208
29.95	0.0245	8.00	.0097	.0208
29.99	0.0049	10.70	.0097	.0208

* P is pounds per square inch equivalent to the "vacuum" in inches of mercury.

Now let us assume that the cubical contents of the gas space in the above system is 200 cubic feet and it is desired to pump the system down to operating pressure in 20 minutes, then, from Formula (2), capacity to pump down:

$$V_2 = \frac{CF}{KM} \text{ or } V_2 = \frac{200 \times 6.96}{0.9 \times 20} = 77$$

Total pump displacement required from Formula (3) is

$$V = V_1 + V_2 \text{ or } V = 308 + 77 = 385 \text{ cu ft, plus } 20\% = 461 \text{ cu ft}$$

Pump size from Table 21* would be DVD14 × 14.

Example 3. A barometric condenser calculation with graphs and tables will be found in *Chem. Met. Eng.*, **43**, 194 (1936).

Reading References

"Vacuum-producing equipment for chemical plant use," by C. T. Chave, *Chem. Met. Eng.*, **43**, 190–195 (1936).

"Performance of ejectors as a function of the molecular weights of vapors," by L. T. Work and V. W. Haedrich, *Ind. Chem. Eng.*, **31**, 464 (1939).

"Selection and use of ejectors," D. H. Jackson, *Chem. Eng. Progress*, **44**, 347 (1948).

"Scientific Foundation of Vacuum Technique," by Saul Dushman, New York, John Wiley and Sons, 1949.

"High-vacuum short-path distillation," by K. C. D. Hickman, *Chem. Rev.*, **34**, 51 (1944).

"Performance of diffusion pumps," by K. C. D. Hickman, *Nature*, **156**, 635 (1945).

"The Design of High Vacuum Systems," by Dr. C. M. Van Atta, a 44-page book published by Kinney Manufacturing Company, Boston 30, Massachusetts (1950).

* In Bulletin 18, Kinney Mfg. Co., Boston, Mass.

Our knowledge of heat transfer is quite extensive: of all the unit operations, heat transfer is the one about which we know most. There are two reasons for this. One is that it has been studied most energetically by many engineers because of its economic importance; the other is that it lends itself to exact study—to mathematical formulations which can be tested by experimentation. As long as operations are conducted at elevated temperatures, and as long as new heat must be bought, so long will heat-transfer studies, which after all aim at heat conservation, remain in the forefront.

20. HEAT EXCHANGERS*

A heat exchanger, in the narrow sense, is a vessel in which an outgoing, processed, hot liquid transfers some of its heat to an incoming cold liquid about to be processed. An alternative term is heat interchanger. The amount of heat so transferred is not lost to the process but is used over again; its equivalent need not be supplied by new fuel; it may be considered as cycled heat. The heat exchanger is the valve which prevents its leaving. Hot gases and vapors similarly may be enabled to pass part of their heat to the incoming cold liquid. A heat exchanger, still in the narrow sense, may also transfer in the opposite direction, for example, in an interchanger in which an outgoing cold gas takes up the heat of the incoming warmer gas, as in a liquid-air plant. In the widest sense, a heat exchanger is any device at all which makes possible a heat transfer from one fluid to another through a containing wall.

For the moment, let us consider the heat exchanger in which an outgoing hot liquid transfers its heat to an incoming cold one. One type which is widely used, largely because of its compactness, is the "shell-and-tube" type, consisting of a cylindrical shell within which lies a bundle of tubes, either straight or coiled in the form of U-tubes. Another type is the multitube type, containing numerous (perhaps 40) separate tubes, within each of which an inner tube carries the cold liquid.

Shell-and-Tube Heat Exchangers. For the shell-and-tube exchanger, there is no rule governing which liquid should travel through the shell and which through the tubes. In general, the hot liquid should travel through the shell and the cold liquid in the tubes. A wide variety of considerations will govern the final selection. Thus, in an exchanger for a caustic solution which is to be built partly of nickel and partly of steel, the tube side would be selected for the travel of the caustic solution, because less nickel would be required on that side to provide all-nickel

* In collaboration with Mr. J. W. Connolly, of the Griscom-Russell Company, 285 Madison Avenue, New York 17, N. Y.

passages. Another example is that of a dirty fluid to be treated with a clean liquid. The dirty liquid would be sent through the tubes, irrespective of temperatures, for the tubes may be cleaned on their inner side comparatively easily.

The exchanger may be on its side, that is, the long axis may be horizontal; less frequently, when floor space is lacking, it is made vertical. The ratio tube length to shell diameter for liquid-liquid interchangers may be as low as 4 to 1 and as high as 7 or 8 to 1. An average of all the standard installations in the chemical industries would be perhaps 6 to 1. For gas-to-gas interchangers, the ratio may be even less than 4 to 1.

The tubes vary in number, but for the majority of installations which might be called standard, the number is high; one exchanger, for example, which has been described* has 380. Another one has 86.† In

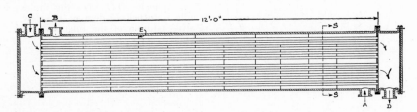

Figure 420.—Shell-and-tube heat exchanger, of the rigid-tube sheet type. The shell is usually welded steel; the tube sheet, header, and shell are welded together; the end plates are removable. The tubes are made of a metal chosen to suit the particular liquid. The hot liquid enters at *A*, travels to outlet *B* over cross-baffles *E*. The colder liquid enters at *C*, and leaves at *D*. This exchanger represents true countercurrent conditions; no correction in the computed "log mean temperature difference" is necessary.

diameter, the tubes are small, e.g., ⅝, ¾, and 1 inch in outside diameter; and also ¾ and 1½ inches pipe size. There are a few instances in which the tubes were selected as large as 2 inches in outside diameter to accommodate a heavy deposit without becoming choked. Tubes may be bare or may have extended surface; in the last five or six years, the use of the finned tube has gained markedly in favor.

The tubes are said to be "square-pitched" when they lie in a straight line, the centers of four neighboring tubes forming a square. Tubes are square-pitched if it is desired to reach between them with a brush or other cleaning tool. The "triangular pitch" allows more tubes to be installed per unit volume in the shell. In this arrangement the tubes are set so that the centers of any three form an isosceles triangle. When the square pitch is used, the bundle may be cocked 45° so that the liquid in cross flow will be forced to take a zigzag path on its way to the outlet (Figure 421).

* *Ind. Eng. Chem.*, **28**, 543 (1936).

† *Ind. Eng. Chem.*, **30**, 1352 (1938).

Rigid Tube Sheet Type. In the simplest type of exchanger construction, the tubes are rolled (expanded) into the holes in the tube sheets, which themselves are held rigidly against the shell, if not welded into it. It is called the "rigid tube sheet" type. By providing removable end plates, the interior of the tubes is accessible for cleaning, but the tube bundle is not removable. The straight-tube type is suitable for small temperature differences; it may be used for larger temperature differ-

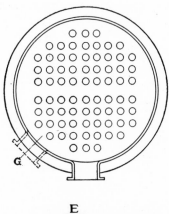

FIGURE 421.—Cross-sectional view S-S of the rigid-tube, sheet-type exchanger in the preceding figure; 74 tubes, 1-inch O.D. If the tube bundle is turned 45 degrees, the new relative position of the inlet will be as shown at *G.*

FIGURE 422.—A two-pass shell and tube-heat interchanger, with internal floating head for expansion of tube bundle. The floating head fits into a wider portion of the shell casing, and the tube bundle generally is not constructed removable; by a slight change in construction, using a split ring, the tube bundle may be made removable. The tube liquid enters at *A*, travels to chamber *B*, where it turns, and leaves finally at *C*. Shell liquid enters at *D*, passes cross baffles, and leaves at *E*. This would be a left to left exchanger; the flow of the two liquids is not purely countercurrent, and a correction to the "log mean temperature difference" would be necessary.

ences in certain installations in which the tube metal is held at about the same temperature as the shell so that the two expand at about the same rate. An example is a fuel-oil heater in which oil travels within the tubes while steam passes through the shell. The oil is heated from 100 to 250°F with 250-pound steam. The heat transfer from tube metal to oil is low enough to allow the tubes to be at about the same temperature as the steam, and hence as the shell, even though the oil on the interior part of the tubes is still relatively unheated. As a result, no considerable strains develop, and the straight-tube type of interchanger is a proper choice.

Floating-head Type. Unequal expansion of tube bundle and shell produces a strain which may tear loose the tubes and thus destroy the apparatus. This can be prevented in three ways: (1) by means of a floating head, i.e., one tube sheet remaining unanchored and free to move, while the other is fixed; (2) by providing the shell with an annular bulge which will allow a certain amount of contraction and expansion of the shell; and (3) by using U-bends for the tubes in which

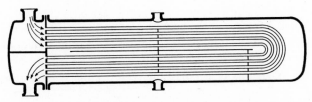

FIGURE 423.—A shell and tube-heat exchanger with tubes in the form of U bends. The shell liquid has cross flow, and must spread out because of the deflecting plate. This "center baffle" has two support plates which are fastened by tie rods to the tube sheet. A rear support plate permits the bundle to ride when pulled out, and to rest when in place. The supporting plates are provided with numerous openings for the passage of the liquid.

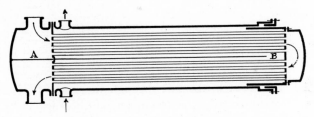

FIGURE 424.—A shell and tube-heat exchanger with floating head, longitudinal baffle, and with all pipe connections close together and to one side. Note outside packed stuffing box which allows movement of the tube bundle. The partition plate A makes this a two-pass exchanger. The shell liquid travels countercurrent to the tube liquid, from left to right, then turns at B. The tube bundle is removable.

expansion and contraction of the latter may take place without affecting the shell. The tubes in the form of U-bends cannot be cleaned mechanically; instead, they are cleaned chemically. In fact, there is a Chemical Cleaning Service Company which specializes in this work. U-tube exchangers are widely used today, particularly in power-plant heaters wherein good quality water (boiler feed) is circulated, and where consequently the cleaning of tubes is at a minimum.

Thus, the prospective buyer of a heat exchanger will be concerned with several questions: Is the interior of the tubes accessible? Is the tube bundle removable for repair or replacement? Is there a provision for rendering unequal expansion of tube bundle and shell harmless?

A removable bundle which has square-pitched tubes will permit ready cleaning, outside the tube as well as inside, as has already been mentioned.

The floating-head exchanger may have a stuffing box on the outside where it is accessible and where a leak may readily be detected. In an alternative construction, the floating head may be placed within the shell, avoiding leaks to the outside but leaving interchamber leaks unrevealed. Still another means of providing for differences in expansion, adapted for low pressures, is the metal bellows sold under such trade names as "FlexoDisc" and "Sylphon."

One-pass and Multi-pass Exchangers. The rigid tube sheet exchanger, shown in Figure 420, is "one-pass," that is, the liquid enters all the tubes at the left and leaves all the tubes at the right. This may be modified in a simple way by means of a partition plate in the head at the right; the

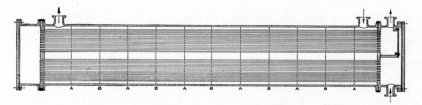

FIGURE 425.—Shell and tube-style heat exchanger designed for liquids under pressure of 600 psi and over. The separator plate may be thin because the pressures on its two sides essentially balance each other. Baffles *A* have openings near their base, baffles *B* near their top (see Figure 427.)

inner liquid is thus sent to the left through the lower half of the tubes and returned through the tubes in the upper half. It leaves by a suitably placed outlet. This is then a "two-pass" exchanger. By placing two partition plates at the right and one at the left, a "four-pass" exchanger is provided. The number of "passes" may be 6, 8, or more. When a floating head is used, which is generally the case, uneven heat distribution may cause it to crack. This difficulty is met by dividing the floating head into two or more segments. It is best that the partition plate be welded to the annular part of the head which carries inlet and outlet, and that the chamber be closed by a circular removable head plate; the partition plate bears against a horizontal gasket strip integral with the circular gasket for the head plate and tube sheet joint.

For high-pressure installations, a modified partition plate construction is available which permits the entering liquid to exert pressure on all sides, thus allowing a thinner plate to be used. The only pressure it must then withstand is the differential between the pressures at inlet and outlet to the tube bundle.

It may become advisable to use several heat exchangers set up in series, and connected so that the two fluids, as for example, two gases, flow countercurrent to each other. Such an installation is shown in Figure 426.

Baffles. Besides shell and tubes and floating heads and partition plates, baffles usually are provided to regulate the flow of the shell liquid and cause it to flush the surface of the tube walls for most of their length. The kind of baffles chosen depends upon the disposition of inlet and outlet pieces and upon whether one desires cross flow, with travel at approximately right angles to the tube wall, or longitudinal flow along the tube wall. In the illustrations, there will be found examples of cross baffles, longitudinal baffles, deflecting plates for cross flow, disk and doughnut baffles. There are at least two more types which might be mentioned:

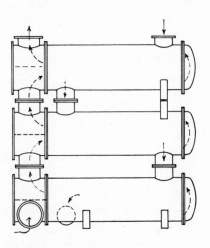

FIGURE 426.—Three heat exchangers in series, for transfer of heat from outgoing gas to incoming gas in a catalytic process. Note the wide conduit connections to both shell and tube sides. The hot gas is in the shell.

circular plates at right angles to the tubes, provided with two triangular openings alternately in the upper and lower half of the circle; and circular baffles with a segment cut off, alternately on one side and the other. Both these types produce a flow along the tubes, causing but little pressure drop as compared to the cross-flow baffles. The motion of the liquid might be described as undulating.

The velocity of the liquids varies between 2 and 8 or 9 feet per second. The slower the velocity, the lower the rate of heat transfer, because the stagnant film of liquid will be thicker; the higher the velocity, the thinner the stagnant or clinging film and the higher the rate of transfer, but the greater the pressure drop. A few explanatory remarks regarding the "stagnant film" will be found further on in this treatment of exchangers.

The pressure drop for the shell side liquid is the one which is affected by the type of baffles and by their pitch (number and spacing). The drop is usually divided, for study purposes, into three parts, one due to entry, one to travel, and the third to exit. It is the part due to travel which can be modified by judicious choice of baffles. As generally designed and installed, the disk and doughnut type and the circular baffles with triangular openings bring about a good rate of heat transfer without contributing much to the drop in pressure.

On the tube side, the fewer the tubes and the smaller the bore of the tubes for a given volume per hour, the greater the velocity. The pressure drop is less for a one-pass exchanger, greater for a two-pass vessel, and correspondingly more for additional passes within given diameter limits. The drop at each entry is made less by belling each tube (flaring).

The amount of heat transferred will depend upon (a) the difference in temperature between the two liquids—the greater this difference, the greater the heat transferred; (b) the tube or transfer area provided for the

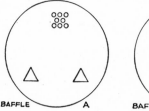 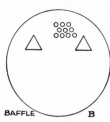

FIGURE 427.—Baffle *A* has its openings as shown, in its lower half; baffle *B* in its upper half. With *A* and *B* alternating in a heat exchanger, the shell liquid strikes many of the tubes at approximately right angles, and thus approaches maximum heat exchange. (See Figure 425.)

exchange—the greater the transfer area, the greater the transfer; and (c) the resistance to heat conductivity of the wall through which the transfer must be made.

In order to increase the area, the tubes may be made longer, which necessitates making the shell longer, or the number of tubes must be increased, if that is possible. Otherwise a second exchanger must be installed in series with the first (Figure 426). It will receive on the tube side the liquid leaving the tubes of the first exchanger and, on the shell side, the shell liquor leaving the first exchanger. In this way, additional surface is provided for continuation of the heat transfer. The total pressure drop will be greater, and the power at the pump will have to be increased. Should the volume of liquids be greater than that accommodated by the exchanger, a second one may be placed next to it, but this time connected in parallel. The two exchangers then function independently. Exchangers connected in series or in parallel are common.

Installation Cost versus Operation Cost. The complete exchanger plant consists of a pump and the exchanger proper. There is often a temptation to save on the installation cost, and leave it to be discovered later (or not at all) that the operation cost may be equal to, or several times greater than the saving. An exchanger accommodating too small a volume of liquids will require operation at higher velocities. The higher velocity is desirable in order to disturb and renew the clinging films constantly; but the pressure drop is then greater, requiring a more powerful pump (a first-cost item) and more power for operating the pump. As the weeks go on, the additional power will run to a sizable total. On the other hand, a somewhat larger exchanger will accommodate the same volume of liquid more slowly, but still at a sufficient velocity to disturb the clinging films. The pressure drop, the size of the pump required, the running cost of power, and the heat transfer rate will all be less. The heat transferred will be the same, because the greater surface area presented will counterbalance the somewhat lower rate of transfer because of the lesser disturbance of the clinging films. By designing a larger exchanger and paying a little more in first cost, the interest of economy will best be served.

Calculations of Length of Tubes and Amount of Heat Transferred. A few words on the calculation of the rate of transfer and of the proper size of a shell-and-tube heat exchanger may be welcomed at this point.

The function of a heat exchanger, it should be remembered, is to allow the passage of a predetermined heat from the hot side of the tube wall to the cold side. The heat must pass, not merely through the metal of the tube wall, but also through the film of liquid which coats the outer wall, as well as through the second film which coats the inner wall (in liquid-to-liquid exchangers). The conductivity of this triple wall depends very largely upon that of these films, and usually only to a lesser degree upon the conductivity of the metal. The conductivity of the film, in turn, depends upon the thermal conductivity of the fluid and upon its viscosity. The higher the viscosity, the thicker the stagnant film, and, therefore, the greater its resistance to the transfer of heat. Resistance due to mud deposits, scale formation, or crystal deposition on the tube walls may reduce the over-all conductivity to a very low value. This is called "the dirt factor." Its consideration must be left for each individual installation. One of the great debts we owe to modern chemical engineering is the correct understanding of the nature and conductivity of the triple wall.

The amount of heat per hour, Q, transferred in an exchanger, will depend upon the extent of the wall, the area called A. The greater the area, the greater the amount transferred, as already stated. Q depends also upon the temperature gradient, i.e., the difference in the temperatures. There are four temperatures involved; it is necessary to find what is called their logarithmic mean value. The finding of the logarithmic mean may best be shown by means of examples.

Given the set of temperatures shown in the sketch below in which the flows are countercurrent, the logarithmic mean would be $(220 - 180)$

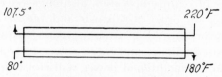

less $(107.5 - 80)$, divided by the natural logarithm of the ratio of the differences, $40 \div 27.5$, or

$$\frac{(220 - 180) - (107.5 - 80)}{\ln \dfrac{40}{27.5}} = 33.7$$

In another example, one with concurrent flow,

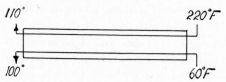

the differences would be $(220 - 60)$ and $(110 - 100)$, and their difference should be divided by the natural logarithm of the ratio $160 \div 10$, to give

$$\frac{(220 - 60) - (110 - 100)}{\ln \dfrac{160}{10}} = 54.2$$

It will be noted that the two temperatures at one end are taken for one difference, and the two at the other end for the other difference, irrespective of the direction of flow. Once the differences are set down, the lesser difference is deducted from the greater.

The logarithmic mean temperature is always used in designing the exchanger. Frequently, however, an approximation is all that is needed; in such cases, the arithmetic mean, within certain limitations, may be used. To find the arithmetic mean, add the temperatures for one fluid and divide by two; then add the two temperatures for the other fluid and divide by two. The difference between the two numbers so obtained is the arithmetic mean. In the first example given, it would be 33.8, a close agreement. In the second example, it would be 85, an altogether different value; in this case, the differences are too unlike. In general, when the ratio for the two differences is less than 4, the arithmetic mean will lead to an error not greater than 12 per cent; for larger ratios, only the logarithmic mean should be considered.

The amount of heat transferred depends, in the third place, upon the conductivity of the triple wall, for which a conductivity coefficient called

U is determined by experiment or from plant observations. These several values are related by the expression

$$Q = U \times A \times \Delta t$$

which reads that the number of Btu per hour transferred is equal to the product of the over-all temperature coefficient, multiplied by the area, multiplied by the temperature gradient. The quantity Q may be viewed as the heat which would be passed through a long tube with wall area A, with coefficient of transfer U, when the temperature gradient is definite and equal to Δt.

The amount of heat transferred should be obtained in another way, namely, by computing the heat gained by the cold liquid in its passage through the exchanger. In this computation, the volume in pounds per hour multiplied by the specific heat and by the rise in its temperature will be the total Btu per hour sought.

$$Q = \text{pounds per hour} \times \text{specific heat} \times \text{temperature rise}$$

The question will then arise, Of what use is the formula which says that $Q = U \times A \times \Delta t$? The answer is that the latter formula, called the efficiency formula for the heat exchanger, permits the computation of the area A when the other quantities are settled. Since A consists of the circumference of the tube times the length (both in feet), one can find the length of the tube (single tube, divided into appropriate lengths subsequently) for a selected diameter. If Q and A are known and are kept the same in several experiments, the value of U for a certain pair of liquids may be determined. Its most common function, however, is the determination of the tube length and, from that, of the dimensions of the exchanger.

The logarithmic mean temperature difference is satisfactory when the heat exchanger has true countercurrent flow. The single-pass shell with single-pass tube has such flow. In multi-pass heat exchangers the flow is not strictly countercurrent, and the proper logarithmic mean temperature difference is less than the calculated value. The latter must be corrected by multiplying it by a factor which is a function of the two thermal temperature ratios. The factor may be most conveniently read on charts 8 to 13 in the "Standards of the Tubular Exchanger Manufacturers Association,"* which is based on numerous previous studies. The "Standards" contains much additional and valuable information regarding thermal conductivities and specific heats.

Materials of Construction. The shell-and-tube exchanger is generally built of steel: welded steel (electric) for the shell and ferrous or nonfer-

---

* "Standards of Tubular Exchanger Manufacturers Association," published by Tubular Exchange Manufacturers Association, Inc., 366 Madison Avenue, New York, 1941.

rous metal, bare or expanded, for the tubes. The welding of large pieces, such as these shells, has been improved so much that, for example, the longitudinal weld in the shell is made free from "lip" or "gob," as a result of the introduction of a special flux. In the past, the lip had to be ground away with grinding wheels. The strength of the weld is greater than that of the steel. Instead of steel, other metals may be employed for their resistivity to corrosion by the liquids to be treated, or for other reasons. Such metals are: Admiralty metal, copper, cupro-nickel, nickel, other

FIGURE 428.—A cooler made of "Durichlor" pipe and return bends laid in a steel jacket. Brine is circulated around the tubes to remove heat from the chlorine-containing solution circulating through the tubes. (Courtesy Duriron Co., Dayton, Ohio.)

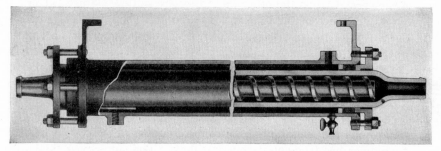

FIGURE 429.—Duriron heat exchanger for heating or cooling corrosive liquids. (Courtesy Duriron Co., Dayton, Ohio.)

nickel alloys, "Monel," aluminum, stainless steel, chrome-vanadium steel, other steel alloys, "Duriron," "Durichlor," and others. A shell-and-tube exchanger for handling fatty acids, with "Inconel" tubes and "Monel" tube sheets and header boxes has been described.*

As regards costs, the general statement may be made that, depending on structure and materials, prices will vary from \$3.00 to \$15.00 per square foot of transfer surface (A in the equation $Q = U \times A \times \Delta t$).

Much has been said about the length of the tubes and something about the kind of metal. There remains the duty of calling attention to the surface of the metal. Clean, smooth tubes hold the film less firmly than

* *Ind. Eng. Chem.*, 30, 1352 (1938).

rough or dirty tubes; hence the importance of cleaning both inside and outside the tubes. Actual deposits on either side of the wall will decrease the coefficient of heat transfer, as suggested in the discussion of the dirt factor.

Extended Surface. The surface presented to the hot liquid outside of the metal tube may be made six to fourteen times as great by forcing metallic fins into the outer wall, thus extending its surface. There are two main types of fins: the straight fins, set lengthwise along the tube,

FIGURE 430.—The Squier juice heater, a form of heat exchanger, in the cane sugar factory at Iberia, Louisiana. (Courtesy Geo. L. Squier Co., Buffalo 5, N. Y.)

parallel to the latter's axis, suitable for longitudinal flow; and the helical fins, suitable for cross-flow of the shell fluid in shell-and-tube exchangers. The straight-finned tube is generally the inner tube of a double-wall tube heat exchanger (see multiple-type exchangers just below). An improved form of the double-wall heat exchanger is the Twin G-Fin section consisting of two horizontal tubes combined in one unit with pipe connections at one end while the other end is free to expand or contract with changes in temperature. At the floating end, the return member for the G-Fin element is a U-bend, while the return member for the shell liquid is a special shell cover. Several sections may be connected one above the other into a vertical bank. There are other applications of the longitudinal-finned tube.

The helical fins are successfully applied to shell-and-tube exchangers. For a given heat transfer duty, fewer tubes are required, and their spacing will be wider. Of great interest is this consideration: the extended surface compensates for unequal heat transfer rates of two liquids. The liquid with the lower specific heat, and therefore lower heat transfer rate, is placed on the shell side, in contact with the finned surface, while the liquid with the greater specific heat, hence greater heat transfer rate, flows on the inner side of the tube, thus establishing the compensation.

Returning for a moment to the structure of finned tubes, it may be remarked that the fins are secured to the outer wall of the tube in such a way that metal-to-metal contact is established. Heat will flow from the fin to the tube as unimpeded as it flows along the tube wall itself, at all temperatures. Helical-finned tubes of various tube diameters and having fins of various diameters and pitch are available.

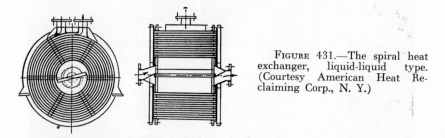

FIGURE 431.—The spiral heat exchanger, liquid-liquid type. (Courtesy American Heat Reclaiming Corp., N. Y.)

Multiple-type Exchangers. Another type of heat exchanger for liquids is the multitube type, in which each inner tube with its outer tube forms a separate unit, and many units (as many as 40) are combined. The flow of the liquids through all the tubes is truly countercurrent. The advantage of this type is that each unit acquires a definite temperature essentially uniform for the single unit, so that once the apparatus is operating, the strains are constant. The multitube exchanger is not adapted to the handling of large volumes of liquids.

In the *Spiral Heat Exchanger*, the heating surfaces consist of plates instead of tubes. Two plate spirals are placed one inside the other, so that two narrow passages are formed through which the liquids flow; the end walls of the passages are formed by U-shaped packing strips of rubber, kept in position by means of steel bars rolled to fit the passages, or by means of flat steel covers. The hot liquid enters at the center of the apparatus, flows through the inner passage, and leaves at the periphery; the cold liquid enters at the periphery, flows through the outer passage, absorbs heat from the hot liquid through the spiral plates, and leaves the apparatus at the center. The construction and operation of this novel exchanger will be clearer after examining Figure 431. Many advantages are listed, two among them being high efficiency and small space requirement. The exchanger is built in three main types, a liquid-liquid exchanger, a surface condenser with crossflow principle, and a surface condenser working on the contra-flow principle.

Still another type adapted to high pressures and to installations in which there must be no possibility of either liquid leaking into the stream of the other, is the Tubeflo type, which transmits heat through an intermediate plate of metal crimped tight to each tube, or for high-pressure work, with the plates pressed close together. The metal wall in contact with the hot liquid is not bathed on its other side by the second liquid. The transfer of heat is less direct (Figure 432). The heat passes from the walls of the hot liquid through the disk metal to the walls of the cold liquid. There are four tubes set in the disks for each section: two for the

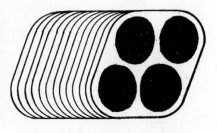

FIGURE 432.—Cross section of a part of the Tubeflo-heat interchanger. The metal vane is pressed into the several tubes, making metallic contact. Numerous metal vanes are pressed against each other, forming an almost solid piece. Hot liquid flows through the lower left and upper right tubes, colder liquid through the other two tubes. Leakage from one system to the other is impossible.

hot liquid, and two for the cold. A number of such four-tube sections form an installation. Return bends, with machined-tapered surfaces, are held tightly in place by bolts and nuts and permit ready cleaning.

In the *plate type heat exchanger* a number of polished, die-pressed, stainless-steel plates are assembled and connected in such a manner that the spaces between the plates form alternately chambers for the hot liquid and chambers for the cold liquid. The two liquids travel in countercurrent directions, and the heat transfer is through the plate itself. The grooves provided in the plates bring about turbulence in the traveling liquids which favors heat transfer. The Paraflow, mainly a wort and beer cooler, functions according to this principle. In general outward appearance, the Paraflow resembles a plate filter press.

Condensers, Surface Condensers. The heat exchangers described are used for exchange of heat between two liquids. They are adapted also for the exchange of heat between a gas and a liquid or condensable vapors against liquids. In these adaptations, wide ports for entry of vapors or steam are provided in the shell; the gases or vapors enter the shell, and the cold liquid travels in the tubes. Still another form is a vertical one in which the vapors enter through a wide port and travel in the tubes. The condensate runs down the tubes by gravity and is collected in a receiver space (Figure 433).

If steam is fed to such an exchanger, and if cold water is circulated in the shell, the device is a surface condenser, used in many steam-power

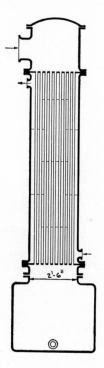

FIGURE 433.—A shell and tube-heat exchanger of the vertical type, for the condensation of vapors. The vapors enter through the wide inlet at the top, while the condensate collects in the receiver below the tubes. The shell liquid enters as shown, and is deflected for better contact by the disk and doughnut-type of baffles. The interior of the tubes is accessible for cleaning, and the tube section may be dismounted. A "surface condenser" for powerhouse operation is essentially like this.

plants in which it is desired to condense the steam in order to use the condensate over again, uncontaminated by cooling water.

In general, the heat exchanger may be termed a cooler if the cold liquid is water, which is then wasted or cooled in a spray or other cooler. Frequently, a true exchanger is followed by a "cooler" so that the still warm, outgoing liquid may be made to lose the remainder of its heat above ordinary temperature and be ready for shipment.

Reading References

"Studies in heat transmission, particularly as applied to tubular gas condensers," by A. P. Colburn and O. A. Hougen, Bulletin of the University of Wisconsin, Engineering Experiment Station Series No. 70, 158 pages, 1930.

"Heat exchangers for crude fractionating unit," by G. K. Hickin, the winning solution of the students' contest problem, *Trans. Am. Chem. Eng.*, **38**, 288 (1932).

"The drop-wise condensation of steam," by W. M. Nagle and T. B. Drew, *Trans. Am. Inst. Chem. Eng.*, **30**, 217–255 (1933–34).

"Heat transfer and pressure drop data for an oil in a copper tube," by J. F. Downie Smith, *Trans. Am. Inst. Chem. Eng.*, **31**, 83–111 (1935).

"Tube temperature variations in a double-pipe heat exchanger," by J. F. Downie Smith, *Trans. Am. Inst. Chem. Eng.*, **31**, 588 (1935).

"Mean temperature differences in multipass heat exchangers," by W. M. Nagle, *Ind. Eng. Chem.*, **25**, 604–609 (1933).

"Mean temperature difference correction in multipass exchangers," R. A. Bowman, *Ind. Eng. Chem.*, **28**, 541 (1936).

"How thermal conductivity of metals affects equipment transfer rates," by F. L. LaQue and C. Rolle, *Chem. Met. Eng.*, **44**, 438 (1937).

"Mean temperature difference correction in multipass exchangers," by F. K. Fisher, *Ind. Eng. Chem.*, **30**, 377 (1938).

"Film coefficients: Condensation of mixed vapors," by J. L. Wallace and A. W. Davison, *Ind. Eng. Chem.*, **30**, 948 (1938).

"Multipass exchanger calculations," by H. Ten Broeck, *Ind. Eng. Chem.*, **30**, 1041 (1938).

A heat exchanger with Inconel tubes, headers and header boxes of Monel metal for handling fatty acids at high temperatures is shown in *Ind. Eng. Chem.*, **30**, 1352 (1938).

"Heat transfer to boiling liquids," by F. H. Rhodes and C. H. Bridges, *Ind. Eng. Chem.*, **30**, 1401 (1938).

"Mean temperature difference in unbalanced-pass exchangers," by K. A. Gardner, *Ind. Eng. Chem.*, **33**, 1215 (1941).

"Heat transfer of condensing organic vapors," by A. H. Cooper, R. H. Morrison and H. E. Henderson, *Ind. Eng. Chem.*, **34**, 79 (1942).

"Mean temperature difference in multipass exchangers," correction factors with shell fluid unmixed, by K. A. Gardner, *Ind. Eng. Chem.*, **33**, 1495 (1941).

"The effect of pulsations on heat transfer-turbulent flow of water inside tubes," by F. B. West and A. T. Taylor, *Chem. Eng. Progress*, **48**, 39 (1952).

Chemistry is the science of changes in matter, by which is meant changes in its composition. Most substances in contact are inert, or comparatively so. But when they are heated, still in contact, profound changes in composition can be effected, to the advantage of mankind. Such heating is done in kettles, and their active part in the scheme of chemical engineering operations may be easily pictured.

21. DEVICES FOR HEATING AND COOLING*

Devices for the application of heat comprise all installations which facilitate the inflow of heat into a system; conversely, those for cooling include all installations which permit the removal of heat from a system. The former may be divided into two groups: those with direct heat, and those with indirect. In the first are included the devices which take heat directly from an open flame, such as a pot still or a caustic pot over a gas burner, oil burner, or other fire. The reverberatory furnace, the open-hearth furnace, the cement kiln, lime kiln, the tunnel kiln for firing ceramic ware, all fall into the first class, as do also some of the sulfuric acid concentrators, and the direct-fire magnesium chloride concentrator at Freeport, Texas. Methods involving the injection of live steam belong here. Electric furnaces in which electricity is the source of heat also belong to this class. In the arc furnace, the current generates heat as arcing takes place; the electric resistance furnace generates its heat by the resistance either of the charge itself (direct-resistance furnace), or by the resistance of a separate material introduced for that purpose (indirect-resistance furnace). In the second class fall all the devices which take their heat from an intermediate agent, such as steam in a jacket or coil. This group includes jacketed kettles and kettles with heating coils, as well as evaporators with steam chests.

For cooling, devices which fit in both classes are used. The introduction of ice into a vessel would be an example of direct application of cold, and would fall into the first class. The devices in the second class are numerous; generally the cooling agent is water in a pipe or jacket, which may itself be refrigerated by a vacuum system, by refrigerants, or in a spray pond.

In a heat exchanger for liquid-liquid interchange, there is heating and cooling; the cold liquid is being heated, while the hot liquid is being cooled. In general, however, in chemical·plants the term "cooling" is associated with the removal of so much heat that the temperature of the

* Reviewed by Mr. Guy Harcourt, Vice-President in charge of Engineering, Buflovak Equipment Division, Blaw-Knox Company.

560

TABLE 76. CLASSIFICATION OF DEVICES FOR APPLICATION OF HEAT

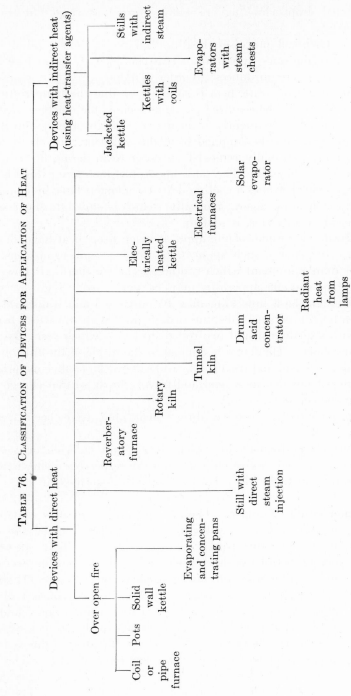

Heat-transfer agents: steam, hot water, "Dowtherm," mercury, HTS, hot oil.

system treated drops close to, or below, normal average temperature (60°F [15.6°C]).

In many chemical processes, heating and cooling must follow each other rapidly in the same apparatus. This characteristic procedure rests upon the following circumstances: in order to induce a reaction to proceed at a certain satisfactory rate, heat is supplied, so that the temperature of the system may reach the required point; as soon as the reaction starts, if it is exothermic, as it frequently is, heat is evolved by the system itself, and no more heat need be supplied from the jacket or coil; on the contrary, heat must be rapidly removed, in order to moderate the reaction and keep it within bounds. The same apparatus, therefore, which began as a heating device becomes a cooling device a moment later by changing the agent: the heating agent, generally steam, is shut off; the cooling agent, generally cold water, is sent in.

Direct Heat. Examples of the application of direct heat have already been given. In general, such applications involve engineering constructions rather than equipment which can be purchased; there are, however, instances when suitable apparatus may be purchased. Thus a rotary kiln, which might be a lime kiln, may be purchased and transported; it consists of a horizontal steel tube, unlined, or lined with refractory bricks, provided with a girth gear and two rolled-steel tires which carry the kiln and run on rollers. The flame is applied to the inside of the tube at the lower or discharge end and travels up, while the rock or other material to be fired enters from the upper end and travels down, so that charge and fire gases move countercurrently.

Direct rotary driers receive direct heat, and have been treated elsewhere.

The electrolytic furnace in which magnesium chloride or sodium chloride is decomposed to give chlorine and the respective metal, is a device with direct heat; the electrical current is transformed, in part, into heat.

Oil Heater or Pipe Furnace. The "oil heater," or as it is sometimes called, the pipe furnace, is an elaborate and carefully designed and constructed furnace with tube banks, heated with direct fire. It serves mainly for heating petroleum oils for topping, thermal cracking, reforming, polyforming, polymerization, and hydrogenation. Figure 434 shows the Lummus single-combustion chamber oil heater; it consists of the convection tube section, to the right, and the combustion chamber proper, equipped for firing either from the hearth, with gas fuel, or from the end walls, with either oil or gas fuel. The tube banks in the roof and sidewalls of the combustion chamber are the radiant tubes. The fire gases pass out of the chamber through the roof rows of tubes, then down through the convection tube section, and thence to the stack. The tubes

ıre of special metal, and are carried by special brackets and support
ıangers (roof tubes); special shaped baffles are used, and the 10-inch
ıvalls in the radiant chamber are made up of 9 inches of high refractory-
ınsulating brick and 1 inch of block insulation encased in steel. The
standard 9-inch refractory-insulating brick weighs approximately 2
pounds compared with the standard refractory of the same size which
weighs 7½ pounds.

FIGURE 434.—An oil heater with single-combustion chamber setting which may be
fired either from the hearth with gas fuel, or from the end walls with oil. (Courtesy
Lummus Co., New York, N. Y.)

The distinctive feature of the Lummus oil heater is the method of
evacuating the combustion products from the firing chamber. By means
of a diffusion baffle tile arrangement and the provision of a properly proportioned plenum chamber above the roof tubes, the gases are positively guided and uniformly discharged over the entire ceiling area of the
combustion chamber. After passing through the arcuate and vertical
slots in the roof baffle, the gases merge and flow over the convection tubes.

In general service the flow of oil is normally as follows: first, through
the convection tube bank; next, through the upper roof row; then through

the lower roof row; thence through the first side-wall bank, and finally through and out of the second side-wall bank. For thermal cracking, a larger combustion chamber may be divided by a low wall into two separate firing zones, the heating zone, followed by the soaking zone. Multi-chambers are available, and a number of variations are offered.

The heat transfer in the various radiant-tube banks differs. If the heater is being fired for an average transfer rate of 10,000 Btu per square foot per hour to the single-row radiant tubes of the side-wall banks, then the lower roof row will be absorbing at approximately 9750 Btu per square foot per hour, by radiation and convection combined, and the upper roof row at approximately 6630 Btu per square foot per hour, also by radiation and convection combined. The average corresponding absorption rate in the convection section would be in the neighborhood of 3000 to 3300 Btu per square foot per hour, depending, among other variables, upon the width of the convection section and consequent velocity of the mass of the gas, and upon the temperature of the entering oil.

Indirect Heat (using heating agents). Heat applications with the use of intermediate substances are very general in the chemical industries; the advantages are that the heat supplied is more moderate, both in quantity and intensity, and can be closely controlled. The intermediate substances are called "heat-transfer agents." The transfer agent picks up heat from an oil burner, gas burner, or furnace, and then reaches a jacket or coil through whose walls its heat is transferred to the liquid or the reacting system in the vessel. The major heating agent is still steam; others with certain special merits are "Dowtherm" and mercury; still others are hot oil, hot water, HTS, flue gas, and heated air. Steam, "Dowtherm," and mercury travel as vapors and furnish their heat of condensation as well as their sensible heat; hot oil, hot water, HTS, and flue gas furnish sensible heat only. It may be noted that the quantity of heat furnished by the latter group depends upon the specific heat of the agent as well as upon its temperature. The choice of the agent depends primarily upon the temperature at which it can maintain the reaction, or other, vessel. The temperature reached by the heating agents which condense may be controlled, within limits, by the pressure under which they are made to boil; the higher the pressure, the higher the temperature.

The temperatures obtainable by means of heat-transfer agents in indirect heating and cooling are shown in Table 77.

To summarize briefly: for temperature as high as 400°F, steam may be the agent; from 400 or even 300 to 600°F, circulating oil may be the choice. From 500 to 725°F, "Dowtherm A" is now available; circulating HTS will give temperatures up to 1000°F.

Steam is still the great heat-transfer agent, and it has a certain flexibility which enlarges its range. If the available steam gives somewhat

TABLE 77. HEAT-TRANSFER AGENTS FOR INDIRECT HEATING AND COOLING*

	Usual Temperature Limits (°F)	Pressure
Steam or water	32– 460	0–450 psi gauge
Oil	30– 550	0
"Dowtherm A"	54– 700	0–135
Mercury	−37–1000 or higher	0–180 or higher
HTS	290–1000	0
Flue gas or air		
in iron ducts	up to 800	0
in special alloys	up to 1600	0

* *Trans. Am. Inst. Chem. Eng.*, **36**, 373 (1940).

too low a temperature, it may be compressed mechanically to a higher pressure and hence higher temperature. Thus, if the available boiler steam is 175 pounds saturated, giving a temperature of 377°F, compressing it in a mechanical compressor to 225 pounds gives a temperature of 397°F.

Sensible Heat and Latent Heat. Heat has two factors; the heat capacity factor and the intensity factor. The heat capacity is expressed as specific heat, which is the heat required to raise one gram (or one pound) of the substance or mixture one degree (centigrade or Fahrenheit); it varies with temperature. The intensity factor is the temperature. The heat transferred by sensible heat is equal to the weight of the substance times its specific heat (in the proper unit), times the gain in temperature.

$$Q \text{ (Btu)} = \text{pounds} \times \text{specific heat} \times \text{rise in temperature (°F)}$$

In general, the heat furnished by a condensing vapor, i.e., its latent heat, is many times greater than the sensible heat in an equal weight of the substance as liquid or as gas or vapor over a moderate number of degrees in temperature. Not infrequently, a vapor is superheated, in which case it combines the two functions; it gives up sensible heat to the condensing point, then gives up, at this lower temperature, its latent heat. The condensed liquid may furthermore still contribute to the heat transfer by giving up some of its sensible heat when temperature relations permit.

The temperature which saturated steam reaches under various pressures is shown below.

TABLE 78. STEAM PRESSURES AND TEMPERATURES

Pressure on the Steam		Temper-	Latent Heat of	Heat of the Liquid
Absolute	Excess over Atmospheric*	ature (°F)	the Steam per Pound (Btu)	Water Formed, Compared to 32°F Water (Btu)
14.7	0	212	970.4	180
40	25.3	267.3	933.3	236.1
100	85.3	327.8	888.0	298.3
250	235.3	401.1	826.3	375.2
450	435.3	456.5	774	435

* Gauge pressure.

Under ordinary circumstances, the chemical plant operator is satisfied with saturated steam, that is, steam without superheat.

A few words on the several heat-transfer agents other than steam must precede the description of kettles.

"**Dowtherm.**" Various organic substances have been proposed as heating agents, among others diphenyl and mixtures of diphenyl and diphenyl oxide under the trade name of "Dowtherm." Thus "Dowtherm A" is a heating agent for the temperature range of 500 to 725°F; it is a eutectic mixture of 26.5 per cent diphenyl and 73.5 per cent diphenyl

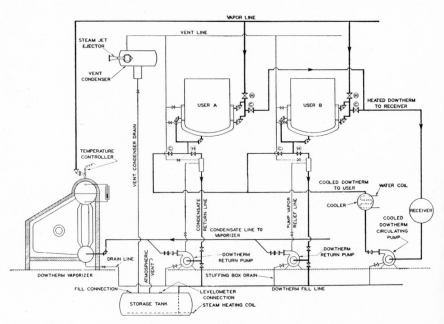

Figure 435.—A "Dowtherm" vapor system in which rapid cooling is required after the heating period. The kettle jackets receive "Dowtherm" vapor for heating; a special receiver and pump supply cooled liquid "Dowtherm" to the jackets for rapid cooling. (Courtesy Foster Wheeler Corp., N. Y.)

oxide. In fact, its range is even larger, for "Dowtherm" under vacuum is used for temperatures below 500°F. The heating with "Dowtherm" (or diphenyl) is just like heating with low-pressure steam; the liquid is heated in a boiler, the vapor is sent to the jacket where its heat of vaporization is transferred to the substance, with the usual heat-transfer resistances, while the "Dowtherm" liquefies and is run back to the boiler. When boiled under atmospheric pressure, its vapor produces a temperature of 500°F; under higher pressures, the boiling point is raised. For example, 90-pound gauge pressure means 700°F, while 100-pound pressure gives the top line at 725°F. Beyond that temperature, the mate-

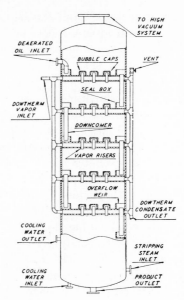

FIGURE 436.—Method of heating the plates in a bubble cap plate tower with "Dowtherm." The tower shown is for the deodorization of oils. The same method of heating serves in the simple distillation of fatty acids. (Courtesy Wurster and Sanger, Inc., Chicago 15, Ill.)

rial decomposes. Dowtherm is noncorrosive and nonpoisonous, but it is flammable. Below 54°F, it is a solid. "Dowtherm B" contains naphthalene.

"Dowtherm" boiled at atmospheric or very moderate pressures offers temperatures which could not be reached with steam without using very high pressures.

TABLE 79. PROPERTIES OF DOWTHERM COMPARED TO WATER

	Water	"Dowtherm A"
Boiling point (atm. pressure) (°F)	212	500
Specific gravity at 212°F	0.9584	0.9950
Melting point (°F)	32.0	53.6
Specific heat of liquid at respective boiling points (Btu/lb)	1.005	0.63
Heat of vaporization at respective boiling points (Btu/lb)	970.2	123

(Steam is nearly eight times as efficient a heat carrier as "Dowtherm" at the boiling point)

Kettles heated by "Dowtherm" vapor may need to be cooled rapidly after a certain stage in a reaction is reached. The cooling may be done by circulating, not water, but cooled liquid "Dowtherm" through the jacket.

HTS. A heat-transfer fluid for high-temperature transfer has been developed and perfected so that it is now in service in batches of one million pounds and over.[*] The mixture consists of salts, hence the name

[*] A new heat transfer medium for high temperatures," by W. R. Kirst, W. M. Nagle, and J. B. Castner, *Trans. Am. Inst. Chem. Eng.*, **36**, 371 (1940). The reading should include the discussion which follows the article.

"heat-transfer salts," and the designation HTS. The composition is 40 per cent sodium nitrite, 7 per cent sodium nitrate, and 53 per cent potassium nitrate, producing a mixture which melts at 290°F. The recommended range for HTS is 300 to 1000°F, but its special field of usefulness lies between the high for "Dowtherm" (725°F) and 1000°F, an interval in temperature which otherwise is not covered by any commercial fluid. Its main application hitherto is to the catalyst cases in the Houdry process, which the fluid HTS cools and maintains at a temperature within the range of 850 to 900°F. The fluid gives up part of its heat to a cold oil in a special heat exchanger with solid disks (see Chapter 20), and is then returned to the catalyst case.

Circulating Hot Liquid. Hot water and hot oil are circulated as heating media. Hot water may be heated to 340°F (171°C) under a pressure of 100 pounds gauge; it has been used under pressures as high as 600 pounds gauge, with correspondingly higher temperatures. For the range of temperature between 300 and 600°F, hot oil is suitable also, especially because the oil is not under any excess pressure over atmospheric.

In the Merrill process system, a special mineral oil, "Merprolene," is heated to a temperature about 50°F higher than the temperature to be maintained in the kettle. The oil is circulated by a positive rotary pump, such as a gear pump, at a fair velocity, to an oil heater where it picks up heat, and thence to the jacket or coil where the oil gives up heat. From the jacket the oil returns to the pump. The piping system includes an expansion tank. The specific heat of "Merprolene" is 0.5 calorie per gram (water = 1.0).

Circulating hot oil is a transfer agent suitable for use in asphalt-dipping tanks, in deodorizers, in jacketed pressure vessels, in jacketed cast-iron kettles, and in jacketed glass-lined tanks, where it is especially welcome because these are difficult to stay-bolt, and hence to make pressure-proof.

Mercury as a heat-transfer agent has been studied and several installations designed.[*] Mercury is a temperature regulator and a heat remover; hence it is used as a cooling agent, for instance around a catalyst case in which naphthalene is oxidized with air; the temperature cannot rise appreciably above the boiling point of the mercury, 674.6°F (357°C).

KETTLES

Kettles are containers for material which is to be heated. Heating may be for the purpose of carrying out distillation, bringing about a reaction, or raising the temperature for any other purpose, including the cooking of foodstuffs. Kettles may be either open or closed. Open ket-

---

[*] "Mercury vapor as applied to process industries," by C. A. Hulsart, *Trans. Am. Inst. Chem. Eng.*, **30**, 402 (1934).

tles may have no cover at all, or merely a loose-fitting, flat cover which prevents escape of fumes into the room, or prevents spatter into the working space. The closed kettle has a built-in cover, which may have openings suitable for the feed line, for a sight glass, for a vent line, or for vapor line. Kettles are made with and without covers, stirrers, and scrapers. Those having built-in covers may withstand some pressure. When that pressure is moderate, the vessel is still a kettle; but when it is high, 100 or 200 pounds per square inch and over,* the kettle becomes a "pressure vessel." Like the kettle, the pressure vessel may or may not have a stirrer. It may or may not be subjected to heat from the outside; in the latter case it is an "unfired pressure vessel." In shape, kettles are generally round pots, with dished or hemispherical bottoms.

Figure 437.—A glass-lined jacketed-steel evaporating pan, with bottom outlet (optional). It is made in capacities of 12, 60, and 150 gallons. (Courtesy The Pfaudler Co., Rochester, N. Y.)

The unfired pressure vessel may be a tall cylinder, or a very low, broad one; there is no definite shape associated with the term.

Heat is applied to the unjacketed kettle, referred to as the "solid metal" kettle, by means of an open fire. The successful operation of many such kettles depends upon the continued functioning of an agitator which directs toward the bottom a flow of less highly heated liquid or melt, to prevent overheating. Other open-fire kettles or pots require no agitation.

Heat may also be applied by means of a jacket which may receive steam, circulating hot oil, "Dowtherm," mercury vapor, HTS, or other heat-transfer agent. Instead of the jacket, a coil may be laid in the pot and steam passed through it, or the coil may be cast in the wall of the kettle assuming that the latter is made of cast iron. The cast-in coil may be sectioned, so that only a certain number of turns, matching the level of the charge, need be supplied with the heating agent.

* Any vessel with pressure over 15 pounds is according to the A.S.M.E. code a "pressure vessel."

FIGURE 438.—An ultra-modern jacketed closed kettle, with agitator and individual overhead motor. Note that the supports do not interfere with the jacket, so that heating from the whole jacket takes place. Note also that insulation of the whole jacket is feasible. (Courtesy Buflovak Equipment Division, Blaw-Knox Co., Buffalo 11, N. Y.)

FIGURE 439.—A jacketed-steel reaction kettle lined with acid-resistant glass, with the special Pfaudler 3-blade impeller agitator also glass enameled, and the glass-enameled adjustable baffle. The agitator operates at a speed of 140 rpm. (Courtesy The Pfaudler Co., Rochester, N. Y.)

The third way of applying heat is by electricity—a method which is constantly gaining favor, partly because of the compactness of the installation. The heat may be developed by induction, or by heating elements set around the kettle body and enclosed in a mantle. In the strict sense, the electrical kettle has no jacket, but the mantle may be made water-tight, and by enclosing the heating elements in half tubing welded to the wall, water for cooling may be introduced after the heating period.

Materials. Kettles were originally made of cast iron, and this is still the major material of construction, for it has good corrosion resistance, good thermal conductivity, excellent machining properties, and produces kettles free from seams. Kettles may be cast of nickel-chromium-iron alloys, of silicon iron, and of other casting metals. In recent years, the improvements in welding have made fabricated seamless steel kettles possible; this permits a reduction in the weight of the kettle. Many addi-

FIGURE 440.—A Dopp kettle with cast-in jacket, cast-in coils, equipped with combination sweeper agitator and paddle. (Buflovak Equipment Division, Blaw-Knox Co., Buffalo, N. Y.)

tional materials are now available for building kettles, and they are selected to suit the particular duty. For example, the choice may hinge on the pressure to be sustained. Aluminum and stainless steel are both corrosion-resistant. Aluminum is lighter and hence less expensive per square foot in sheets of equal thickness, but stainless steel is stronger, so that for a pressure vessel, stainless steel would be selected over aluminum. If, however, the kettle is to work under no pressure, aluminum will be the choice. Other metals in the form of plates which may be fabricated are copper, nickel, tantalum, "Everdur," and "Hastelloy"; in addition, a number of clad steels, such as nickel-clad and stainless-steel clad steel, are available.

FIGURE 441.—A Buflokast
Kettle with cast-in coils for
processing resins; the capacity
is 1600 gallons.

FIGURE 442.—Cast-iron jacketed reaction kettles, with a special cover to accommodate a motor-driven agitator. Size 6 feet in diameter by 6 feet deep. Note the height
of jacket. (Courtesy Buflovak Equipment Division, Blaw-Knox Co., Buffalo 11, N. Y.)

In addition to metals, there are available glass-lined steel kettles which
combine the strength of steel with the inertness of glass. They are made
in all styles, and consist of the fabricated low-carbon steel shell lined with
a borosilicate glass of high resistance to acids. Several glass formulas
are available.

A jacketed steel reaction kettle lined with very acid-resistant glass, with a special glass-enameled propeller, is shown in Figure 439. The polymerization kettles in several synthetic rubber plants (GR-S) financed by the government were glass-lined. It should be remarked that glass

FIGURE 443.—Two sulfonators, with cast-iron body and welded sheet steel jacket, equipped with power-driven agitator. (Courtesy Buflovak Equipment Division, Blaw-Knox Co., Buffalo 11, N. Y.)

FIGURE 444.—A positively-scraped kettle or still with type "J" agitator for the polymerization and dehydration of a synthetic resin. (Courtesy Buflovak Equipment Division, Blaw-Knox Co., Buffalo 11, N. Y.)

linings will tolerate an exceptional amount of rough handling and sudden temperature differences to as great as 200°F, without danger of breakage.

Kettles are made in all sizes, from ½ to 3,000 gallons and larger. The simplest type is the caustic pot, which consists of the pot itself, with a hemispherical bottom cast in one piece, without outlets and without stirrer. An average pot will weigh 24,000 pounds, and the cost may be estimated at nine cents a pound.

A jacketed kettle with cover and agitator, of 1,600-gallon capacity, might weigh 36,000 pounds; the weight will vary with pressure requirements among other factors, as already indicated. The cost may be estimated at 16 to 20 cents a pound (1951).

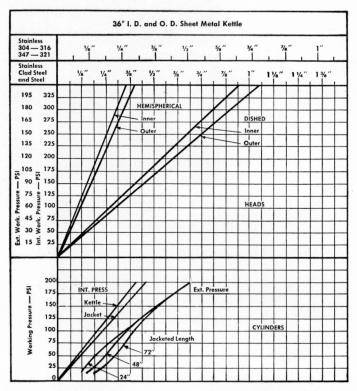

FIGURE 445.—Metal thickness chart for various pressures for 36-inch diameter kettles, recalculated to fit the 1949 ASME code. (Courtesy Buflovak Equipment Division, Blaw-Knox Co., Buffalo 11, N. Y.)

Design. Some jacketed kettles have removable jackets; the design provides circular flanges which are bolted together. The jacket may extend part way up the body, such as half or three-quarters of the way, or it may be a full-length jacket. Proper design of jacketed kettles is particularly difficult because the kettle may be heated at one time and cooled at another; it may be under pressure for part of a cycle, and under vacuum for another. The kettle proper, therefore, will be at a temperature which is sometimes different from that of the jacket; in this way, strains due to unequal expansion are set up. The shape of the head and of the bottom will affect the design. It may be well to note that the designer can effect economies in the use of materials by making variations in the proportions of the kettle, suiting it at the same time to the process requirements. By giving a certain leeway to the manufacturer, a satisfactory piece of equipment can be furnished with savings in the fabricating and materials costs.

The jacket and body may be made of the same metal, such as cast iron, or the jacket may be made of one metal, the body of another. A frequent combination is a cast-iron kettle with a carbon-steel jacket. Or, a stain-

FIGURE 446.—The core for a Buflovak-Dopp one-piece, Jacketed Cast Kettle. The holes in the core form the staybolts which become an integral part of the body casting.

less-steel body may be combined with a carbon-steel jacket; when this is done, it is recommended that the weld be made so that the weld metal is in compression.* The jacket space should be limited to ¾ inch for steam, and such a moderate width will be right for the application of water as well, for the narrower jacket increases the velocity of flow along the wall, for a given volume of flow, and thereby improves the heat transfer. The upper ring flange will be smaller, which is also an advantage, because it can be made thinner.

The thickness of the wall for various pressures and lengths may be found conveniently from charts prepared for a variety of metals. Each

* *Ind. Eng. Chem.*, **33**, 1116 (1941).

chart applies to a designated diameter. Two of these valuable charts have been selected for reproduction herewith; they cover three metals: stainless steel, 20 per cent stainless steel-clad steel, and ordinary carbon steel.

Besides those with removable jackets, kettles which have body and jacket in one piece are manufactured. The complete kettle is cast of the same metal, which may be cast iron or any similar metal; one such design has internal staybolts connecting jacket and body walls, stiffening both. The one-piece fabricated kettle has the jacket welded to the body.

Figure 447.—Heavy duty steam-jacketed stainless-steel kettle for mixing heavy materials, model TA. The twin shaft agitator turns the sweeper at the rate of 30 to 35 rpm; the secondary mixer has a mixing paddle turning at the rate of 80 to 100 rpm. Quickly demountable; bottom outlet; provided with removable cover. (Courtesy Groen Manufacturing Co., 4535 W. Armitage Ave., Chicago 39, Ill.)

Stainless-steel kettles are the proper selection whenever the least contamination has to be avoided; they have become very important. A number of designs are on the market. Stainless-steel, open-top, stationary, jacketed kettles are available, in one model (N) in twelve capacities, ranging from 20 to 300 gallons. The over-all height varies from 41½ to 69 inches. The small, open kettles may have a movable or portable propeller-type stirrer, set at an angle and fastened at the edge of the kettle. Kettles of the open type, especially the smaller ones, are often mounted on trunnions so that they may be tilted, and are also provided with a pouring lip.

Stainless-steel jacketed kettles may be provided with hinged or other covers, and may be designed for heavy mixing. They may be fitted with an agitator, generally of the sweep type, and also with a mixing or blending paddle (see Figure 447). Capacities and prices are indicated in Table 80.

TABLE 80. STAINLESS-STEEL INDUSTRIAL KETTLES WITH AGITATORS*
(SELECTED ITEMS)

Gallon Capacity	"SA" Model Single Motion	"TA" Mode Twin Shaft, Double Motion
40	$980	$1,500
60	1,075	1,590
80	1,180	1,750
100	1,320	2,030
125	1,420	—
150	1,580	2,350
200	1,820	2,860
250	2,050	—
300	2,210	3,420

(March 1951. All prices are subject to change without notice)
* Courtesy Groen Manufacturing Co., Chicago 39, Ill.

Of late, the Rota-therm steam jacket design has become standard equipment in these stainless-steel jacketed kettles, insuring more rapid cooking. The Rota-therm provides for multiple steam inlets (two or more), with a baffle-nozzle assembly installed at each inlet to give, in the jacket now made oversize, a high-velocity, all-encircling sweep of steam completely surrounding the kettle contour.

Large, closed kettles have built-in agitators, which may be of the slow-moving paddle type, with or without a scraper or sweep, or of the propeller or turbine type, entering from the top or from the side. For the glass-lined kettles, vertical glass-enameled steel agitators are available. The built-in high-speed stirrers may be direct-connected to an overhead motor. A bevel gear driven through a flat pulley serves for medium and low speeds, and when head-room for an overhead motor is lacking. Motors may act through reducers, and may then be mounted to the side.

A number of other types of kettles are exhibited in the illustrations which follow, and also in other sections (see Chapter 10 for example); they show the manifold duties which these vessels perform.

Figure 444 shows a positively-scraped kettle for the polymerization and dehydration of a synthetic resin. The scraper is a Dopp style "J," illustrated in Chapter 11. The kettle extends through the floor and is discharged from the floor below. Behind the kettle is an inclined surface condenser used for refluxing during polymerization and for the condensation of the dehydration water. Valves and instruments of control are

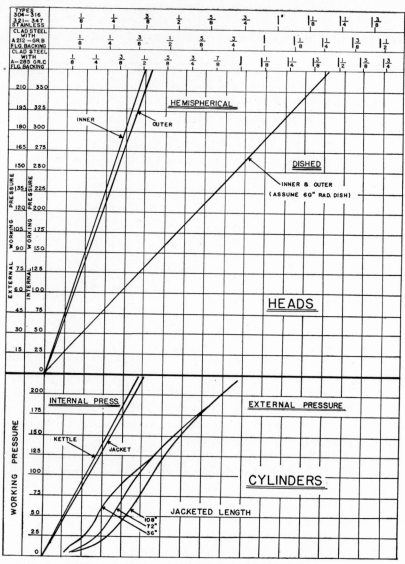

FIGURE 448.—Plate thickness chart for 1950 ASME code, for 60-inch I.D. and O.D. steel plate kettles. Instructions for using Plate Thickness Chart: The chart covers temperatures as follows: For steel, and for all clad steels, −20 to +650°F; for stainless steel, −20 to 700°F. The thickness may be read off three different scales on the abscissa. The upper scale refers to the types of stainless steel indicated; the second scale applies to clad steel, with A 212 grade B carbon steel flanged backing. The lower of the three scales refers to clad steel with A 285 grade C carbon steel flanged backing. Dished heads are seamless (joint efficiency = 100%) and their thickness depends upon the radius of dish, not on diameter (ASME code section VIII). Hemispherical heads are sectional (joint efficiency 80%). Where inner and outer heads or cylindrical shells are indicated, a jacket space of 1½ inches has been allowed for. Clad steel heads and cylinders are of the same thickness as the type steel used for backing material. All allowable stresses used for stainless steel, and steel, are based on a factor of safety of 4 (1950 ASME code Section VIII). (Courtesy Lukens Steel Co., Coatesville, Pa.)

578

brought to a convenient central point, only a step away from the still, so that the operator can be guided by his instruments and also observe the progress of the reaction through one of the observation glasses in the cover. The instruments give steam pressure, temperature, vacuum, agitator horsepower, and other information.

Figure 449 shows a 650-gallon seamless jacketed kettle with cover for vacuum and the special positive-scraping double-motion agitator, Dopp style "D," with four-speed motor drive. It serves for making shaving cream in large batches, each one sufficient to fill 19,000 tubes. The cream is compounded hot, and is cooled in the kettle while under vacuum, in

FIGURE 449.—A 650-gallon seamless-jacketed kettle equipped with cover for vacuum, and with double-motion, positive-scraping agitator with four-speed motor, for the manufacture of shaving cream and similar products. (Courtesy Buflovak Equipment Division, Blaw-Knox Co., Buffalo 11, N. Y.)

order to prevent the incorporation of air which necessitates an additional manufacturing step. The agitator used is shown in Chapter 11.

Kettles over Open Fire. So much has been said regarding jackets and heat-transfer agents that it may seem to the reader that the single-wall kettle is no longer of importance. Such an impression would be incorrect. Single-wall kettles exposed to the heat of a gas, oil, or other burner are in use for melting pitch, for performing alkaline fusions in the manufacture of dye intermediates, and for other purposes which call for a temperature higher than that afforded by ordinary steam. The open-fire kettle requires a brick setting, and the construction may provide a multiplicity of burners set to one side of a refractory wall which has openings at regular intervals, through which the fire gases may enter the space immediately below the kettle. By this means, the kettle wall is protected from radiation and from the danger of a hot spot. Open-fire kettles generally have agitators which contribute to the equalization of the temperature between various portions of the wall and promote heat transfer from the wall to the charge.

Electrically Heated Kettles. Kettles may be heated electrically by strip heaters, by coils of electrically resistant wire, by radiant heaters set close to the kettle wall, by resistance heating in which the wall itself contributes resistance, and by inductive heating. Strip heaters are mica-insulated

FIGURE 450.—A Patterson electric-process kettle equipped with Flasheat electric heating elements, turbine stirrer with Unipower speed-reducing drive. (Courtesy Patterson Foundry and Machine Co., East Liverpool, Ohio.)

strips and ribbons of resistance metal fastened to the wall of the kettle. An insulating mantle fits around the heaters, enclosing the whole unit.

The Flasheat electric heating element is a modified form of ribbon element with the side flanged to gain more mechanical strength. Porcelain beads are strung on "Nichrome" wire and inserted between the turns of the elements to keep them well spaced and to keep the element itself properly located with respect to the various enclosing walls. In order to apply the Flasheat element to kettles, ducts or half circles (half tubings) are welded around the kettle, and the element is slid into place within. All connections are brought out to a central point so as to be accessible for external wiring. The heat is radiated in part directly to the kettle wall, in part to the inner wall of the duct which delivers it by thermal conduction to the kettle wall. The element is left free to expand and contract. Repairs are easily made by simply disconnecting the ends of the elements and drawing them out, replacing them with others without disturbing any other part of the unit. The kettle is water-cooled most satisfactorily. A water-tight mantle is fitted over the kettle through which water may be circulated, cooling the kettle wall and the sealed-in ducts, without reaching the heating elements. The electric kettle is used generally for

FIGURE 451.—Standard 15 gallons stainless-steel Electro-Vapor heated resin pilot plant. (Courtesy Blaw-Knox Co., Pittsburgh, Pa.)

temperatures higher than that of steam. The kettle shown in Figure 450 has a gross capacity of 1000 gallons, and is usually used for 600- or 700-gallon batches, at temperatures of 550 to 600°F. For agitation, a turbine stirrer is provided, driven by the special Unipower speed reducer at any selected rate between 21 and 432 rpm. These kettles are built in a variety of sizes, of carbon steel, stainless steel, aluminum, "Monel" metal, nickel, copper, and other metals.

The Electric Process Kettle may be made of stainless steel or of plain steel, with proper insulation on the outside. If it is made of plain steel, or is equipped with fewer heating elements, the price is much less. Another advantage of this particular line of kettles is that the heat-up and cooling are rapid, so that a shorter cycle of operation is probable. Each bank of heating elements may have an individual push button, and current may be turned on or off in as many banks as desired.

Heating by the inductive electric method has been described;* it is a method which is simple and offers many advantages, not the least of these being the small space required, compared to the oil burner. The principle of inductive heating is that of the step-down transformer, except that here

FIGURE 452.—General view of a 2,000-gallon Blaw-Knox Electro-Vapor kettle, built for a paint and varnish works. Note the motor drive for the stirrer, the condenser overhead, the instrument panel. (By permission.)

the second coil is omitted. The primary coil is wound around the outside of the kettle wall, and the latter then becomes a combined core and one-turn secondary coil. Alternating current, for example 25-cycle, 220-volt single phase, is applied to the primary; there is set up in the walls a magnetic flux which induces eddy currents, and it is the latter which do the heating. The voltage of the induced current is 3 or 4 volts. The method is applicable to iron and steel only. It should be remembered that

* "Inductive electric heating in chemical plants," by R. D. Center, *Chem. Met. Eng.*, 39, 617 (1932).

"The inductive heating of process equipment," by R. D. Center, *Trans. Am. Inst. Chem. Eng.*, 31, 44 (1935).

all the parts affected by the alternating current will have a current generated within them.

Electro-Vapor Kettles. A new development are the Electro-Vapor kettles, self-contained units which combine the advantages of electrical heating and "Dowtherm" heating. Electric immersion heaters reach into a wide jacket [at the lower part of the kettle] which contains the "Dow-

FIGURE 453.—A five-gallon laboratory kettle with body in a lowered position, showing the double motion agitator. An almost infinite variety in speeds of rotation may be obtained by means of change gears. The stand may be moved about on castors. (Buflovak.)

FIGURE 454.—A laboratory kettle fitted with a Glas-Col electric resistance heater. The mantle may be lowered when the heating period is over. (Buflovak.)

therm." The temperature may be set anywhere between 100 and 700°F, and controlled accurately. The internal pressure in the kettle may be 15 psi down to a vacuum. The Electro-Vapor kettle is built in all sizes, as large as 3,000 gallons capacity.

Glas-Col. A new combination of heating, insulation, and cooling has been developed, called the Glas-Col. It is a glass-fiber mantle shaped to fit over the unjacketed kettle (or flask), and containing the electric heating elements. After fitting it to the kettle and making it tight with a zipper belt, the current is turned on and the heating proceeds. At the end of the heating period, the current is turned off; the mantle will prevent rapid cooling. If the cooling is to be rapid, the glass fiber mantle is dropped and the kettle (or flask) cooled by a spray of water issuing from a circular pipe set just under the flange of the kettle. The Glas-Col is available for the smaller kettles only, laboratory sizes.

Kettle Discharge. The discharge valves for kettles are of the flush type, that is, they are flush with the inner wall of the kettle, and do not reach inside of it. They have a Y construction. In the fabricated kettles, the valve is set in the center of bottom, with the agitator step, if any, resting on a yoke which permits free passage to the discharge. In the cast-iron kettles, the step is cast in the center of bottom, and the discharge valve is mounted to the side.

The valve may be of three types: (1) the telescoping type, in which a screw moves a sleeve bearing the closure surface, and which is operated by hand gear or by hand wheel; (2) the standard type, which resembles a globe valve; or (3) the extended stem type, with a yoke to steady the stem. All valves have clean-out hand holes.

Agitator Drives. Drives for the agitators in kettles may be "fabricated number 1" drives, for double motion and requiring four gears. One drive shaft carries the two pinion gears which engage (above), a bevel gear set on the agitator shaft, and (below) a second bevel gear. The lower gear faces upward, so that its rotation is in the opposite direction to that of the upper gear, which faces downward. The lower gear turns a sleeve which carries the agitator, while the shaft carries the sweep and scrapers. The load of the agitator is taken by a thrust bearing, so that the step in the bottom of kettle is merely a guide, and not a bearing. It is interesting to note that in a pressure kettle, the effect of the pressure is to force the agitator upward and out; in order to take up the upward thrust, a bearing over the agitator shaft must be provided.

The agitator and sweep may also be driven from both sides, right and left, with two extended stems to provide the drive shaft bearings.

Unfired pressure vessels are tanks built of flange or firebox steel and otherwise in conformity with the official code. They are generally upright cylinders, provided with covers, but they may be horizontal cylinders as well. Heating if required may be provided by steam jackets or electric strip heaters, covered with adequate insulation.

When a process is on a production basis, it is important that the time for opening and closing the pressure vessel be short, for during such period the equipment is idle. For vessels operated at pressures under 200 psi, there is available a *Quick Operating Cover and Lock** which permits lifting the cover out of the way by moving it upward on an upright member erected

---

* Jackson and Church Company, Saginaw, Michigan.

at the side of the tank. The heavy cast-steel locking ring is centered and maintained in proper position by a series of roller bearings. The time required for opening the pressure vessel equipped with a Quick Opening Cover is one minute or less. Vessels operated at pressures higher than 200 psi are built with the conventional bolted-type cover.

Unfired pressure vessels serve for the impregnation of wood, wood products, presswood, plywood, electrical coil windings, magnesium alloy and other castings, graphite products, and other materials. They may be operated under a vacuum, as well as under pressures above atmospheric. Pressure polymerizing and immersion polymerizing are performed in such

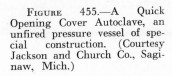

FIGURE 455.—A Quick Opening Cover Autoclave, an unfired pressure vessel of special construction. (Courtesy Jackson and Church Co., Saginaw, Mich.)

vessels; for these purposes the polymerizing or boiling tank is usually heated electrically to as high as 475 to 500°F.

Horizontal autoclaves are 78 inches in diameter, and as long as required up to 112 feet. They serve well for curing and hardening materials such as sand lime bricks, concrete bricks and blocks, graphite or carbon briquettes and blocks, and insulators. The horizontal autoclave is heated by direct steam. It is equipped with Quick Opening Doors at one or at both ends, if desired.

Bayonet-type Heater. A bayonet-type heat exchanger with the heater of tantalum is available for heating hydrochloric acid and other acids (Figure 456). The outer jacket through which the acid circulates may be rubber-lined steel, stoneware, fused silica, or synthetic plastics. The heating element reaches throughout the length of the exchanger; it receives steam through an inner tube, while the condensate can drain off from the outer space. The heat transfer of tantalum is high, 4000 Btu/sq ft/°F/hr. Another way to apply bayonet heaters is to place a number of them in the wall of a larger container, in a horizontal plane, so that they extend finger-like toward the center in contact with the liquid to be heated.

A similar heating service for corrosive solutions is performed by "Duriron" immersion tubes, especially suited to heat small deep tanks or

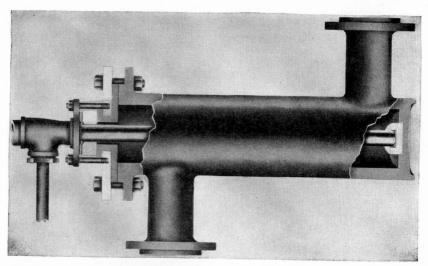

FIGURE 456.—A tantalum bayonet-type heat exchanger, for heating hydrochloric acid. The exchanger may be set up horizontal or vertical. (Courtesy Fansteel Metallurgical Corp., North Chicago, Ill.)

comparatively wide, shallow tanks. They are made in diameters of 1, 1½, 2, and 3 inches, and in lengths up to 5 feet. The straight bayonet type is used single; the "ell" type may be manifolded, as shown in Figure 457.

Coils. Heat may be applied by coils as well as jackets; these may be placed in round, square or rectangular tanks as well as in pots and kettles. Lead coils are much used, with chemical lead or antimonial lead for steam pressures up to 45 pounds, and lead-covered copper tubes or high-silicon iron tubes for pressures up to 150 pounds. Some statements on the various types of lead will be found in Chapter 5.

Atomic Energy. The application of atomic energy to useful purposes has been sought in various directions. Atomic energy is the heat released when nuclear changes take place. In an atomic reactor, uranium 238 is changed to uranium 239 by the addition of a neutron to the nucleus, after which uranium 239 may become neptunium by the loss of an electron and neptunium becomes plutonium, also by the loss of an electron; the plutonium on bombardment by neutrons fissions into smaller fragments with a loss of weight which is converted into an enormous amount of energy as heat. Heat produced by such nuclear changes could be used to generate steam which could in turn be used to run turbines as boiler steam is used at present. It must be possible to retard or even stop the action of the atomic material, so that too much heat will not be emitted; this could be accomplished by inserting cadmium rods and sleeves which will accept neutrons and thus interrupt or greatly reduce the chain reaction.

How valuable atomic energy will be may be seen from its application to the submarine. In a reactor there is placed uranium 235 with uranium

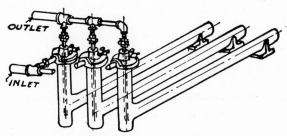

FIGURE 457.—A group of three "Duriron" immersion tubes of the bayonet type. (Courtesy Duriron Co., Inc., Dayton, Ohio.)

238, and the action is allowed to proceed. It may be moderated by means of hydrogen, carbon as graphite, or heavy water. The atomic heat will be accepted by water (Westinghouse project), or by sodium (General Electric project). In a heat exchanger, the sodium will pass its heat to water which will turn into steam and be available for driving turbines and electric generators. A submarine so equipped would not need to surface in order to recharge batteries by means of internal combustion engines; it could run indefinitely under water, except for the endurance of the personnel, and the exhaustion of the uranium supply.

On land the same procedure may be adopted for generation of heat energy and its useful application, but here the ordinary fuels would be competitive. The atomic reactor must be shielded in order to protect personnel from x-ray and other radiation, a task which is by no means simple. Furthermore, for a long time uranium and other atomic material will be monopolized for government enterprises; should these be over, there will remain the comparative scarcity of the fissionable material to limit its uses by civilians.

COOLING

Taken in its widest sense, any withdrawal of heat is "cooling." Pumping cold water into the jacket of a kettle, and circulating liquid "Dowtherm" or the fluid HTS for the purpose of abstracting heat from a system, have already been described. The fluid heat-transfer agents may work both ways, i.e., as either warming or cooling agents; in the first case, the agent is at a higher temperature than the system, in the second, at a lower temperature. The fluid heat-transfer agents furnish or remove heat in the form of sensible heat. The heat-transfer agents which function as heating agents by supplying their latent heat may also act as cooling agents, by absorbing the equivalent amount of heat in their vaporization. Thus, heat may be abstracted from a hot gas by bringing it in contact with water tubes, causing vaporization of the water, as in waste-heat boilers.

In the narrow sense, "cooling" is cooling to room temperature, and to temperatures near and below the freezing point of water. If the river, sea, or well water available for use in coolers employing water as the cooling agent is not cold enough, its temperature may be reduced in several ways, one of which involves the use of a vacuum (Decalorator, Chill-Vactor). The compressible gases, such as anhydrous ammonia, methyl chloride, "Freon," and sulfur dioxide, produce low temperatures upon vaporizing. Heat may be abstracted directly by vaporizing the liquefied gas in a tube bathed by the liquid to be cooled (Baudelot cooler); or a secondary cooling agent, generally a solution of calcium chloride, may be cooled and then circulated through a system. Cooling by means of "Dry Ice" is now large-scale practice, as in the manufacture of butyl rubber.

Several cooling devices have been described elsewhere; some of the remaining ones are presented in the following pages.

The commercial ton of refrigeration is the rate of abstracting heat in the amount of 288,000 Btu per day, equivalent to 12,000 Btu per hour, or 200 Btu per minute. The value per day is equal to the latent heat of one ton of ice (2000 $\times$ 144 Btu).

Water Refrigeration. The steam jet ejector is valuable in the study of water refrigeration because it may serve, indirectly, for such refrigeration. The ejector produces a vacuum which causes water to vaporize with a corresponding removal of heat. By a proper disposition of equipment, the heat may be removed from the water which is to be cooled. Refrigerated water may serve as a cooling liquid in a chemical plant when certain definite and perhaps rather low temperatures must be reached and maintained. The procedure for obtaining such refrigerated water is as follows. The incoming, warmer water is fed to the flash chamber where a vacuum is maintained by means of a booster ejector (see Chapter 19);

a certain amount of the water vaporizes and consumes heat. The heat so consumed is taken from the body of the water itself, reducing its temperature. The water remaining in the flash chamber is the cooled or refrigerated water; it leaves the chamber by a tail pipe and is pumped to the coolers. A certain amount of water is consumed by the vaporization and carried out through the ejector; an equivalent amount of new, liquid water must be fed in. In a modification of the method, the water from the coolers is returned to the flash chamber with the heat it has gained, gives up its extra heat, and then goes through the cycle again.

Such a water refrigeration plant may be used seasonally. For example: the water in the Niagara River rises to 73°F in the summer. In a certain plant along the river, water at 45°F is needed for the coolers. The steam ejector vacuum system lowers the temperature of the water in summer, while during the winter the system is shut down because the river water itself is well below 45°F and may be used direct. The river water is suitable for use in the condensers of the ejector system in all seasons. The "Ross Decalorator" (Figure 458) is such a refrigeration plant. It consists of a flash chamber with spray nozzles, of a primary booster ejector, surface condenser, second-stage ejector, a smaller surface condenser, third-stage ejector, and a final surface condenser delivering to the atmosphere.

Vacuum refrigeration may cool water 10°F, 40°F, or a differential between these two. For a given volume of water and a given differential, an installation of the proper size will require a calculated amount of steam. If the differential is raised, the initial temperature remaining the same, a greater amount of steam will be required and thus a larger booster ejector, or else the volume of water must be reduced, the apparatus and steam quantity remaining unchanged.

The efficiency of the ejector is maintained only by using the designated amount of steam. When the load fluctuates, it is best to install three or more units so that one whole unit or perhaps two, may be shut off at times.

Absorption Refrigeration. An important absorption refrigeration cycle involves lithium bromide and water, in which lithium bromide and its concentrated solution are the absorbent, and water is the refrigerant. The cooling effect comes about by the vaporization of water in a vacuum; the water vapor is absorbed by the lithium bromide solution. This type of absorption refrigeration may be applied to the cooling of a stream of air, which is discussed in the next chapter; or it may be applied to the cooling, or "chilling" of a volume of water, generally flowing water. In order to avoid confusion, a specific device will be described.

The 25-ton Servel water chiller is an hermetically sealed, air-evacuated, absorption refrigeration system; it has no moving parts. Water is its

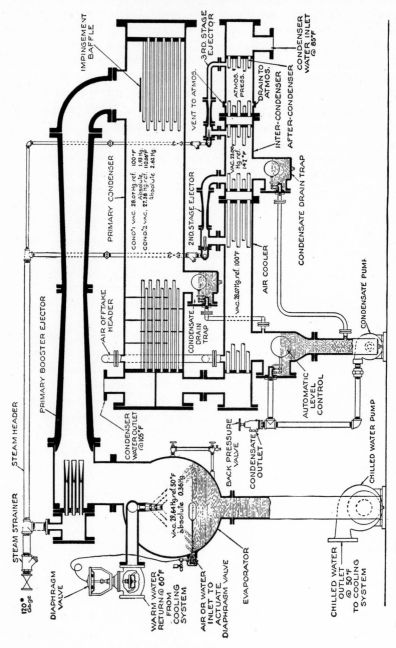

FIGURE 458.—The Ross Decalorator, exhibiting the application of the steam-jet ejector booster to the refrigeration of water. The figures for temperatures and vacuums are taken from an actual installation in the Buffalo-Niagara Falls area. (Courtesy Ross Heater and Mfg. Co., Buffalo, N. Y.)

refrigerant; lithium bromide its absorbent; steam its source of energy. The entire unit operates under a vacuum at all times. The chilled water circuit, however, is under pump pressure, and is not a part of the vacuum system. A flow of cooling and condensing water similarly is separate and outside the system.

A simplified flowsheet is shown in Figure 459. Heat (steam) around the generator (boiler) tubes drives out part of the water from the dilute lithium bromide solution. The vapor lift action so created drives liquor and vapor upward to the separator; the vapor continues upward, to the condenser, while the lithium bromide solution, now warm, flows to the heat exchanger and thence, now cool, to the absorber. The condensed

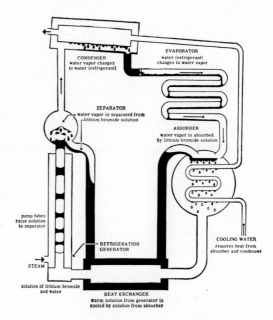

FIGURE 459.—A simplified flowsheet of the 25-ton Servel water chiller, exemplifying absorption refrigeration. Water is the refrigerant, lithium bromide the absorbant. (Courtesy of Servel, Inc., Evansville 20, Ind.)

water vapor flows into the evaporator through an orifice plate which regulates the degree of vacuum in the several sections of the system. In the evaporator, under a high vacuum, water turns to vapor, absorbing heat from the water surrounding it. The water to be chilled is not shown in the sketch. The vaporized water is removed by the cold, concentrated lithium bromide solution in the absorber. The heat of dilution is removed by an outside cooling water stream, the same one which later cools the condenser. The dilute lithium bromide solution, still cold, now enters a heat exchanger where it takes up heat from the warm concentrated solution leaving the generator and separator, and travels thence to the tubular boiler, where the cycle begins again.

Water is capable of refrigeration because of the vacuum maintained in the unit, which lowers the temperatures of rapid vaporization considerably. The working pressure on the low side of the Servel unit is normally 7 to 10 mm mercury, at which pressure water will boil in the neighborhood of 40 to 45°F. On the high side, the pressure is 50 to 60 mm mercury (generator and condenser).

In the 25-ton Servel water chiller model DUT, water entering at 50°F, for example, leaves at 40°F, at the rate of 60 gpm. In pumping the water to be chilled through the unit, there is a pressure drop of 13 pounds.

In the corresponding air conditioner unit, the tubes in which the water refrigerant evaporates are finned, and the air to be cooled is made to flow past the tubes at a predetermined rate. The cooling may be sufficient to cause liquefaction of its water, which may then be removed by baffles and traps (dehumidification).

In a new development of the lithium bromide-water absorption refrigeration system, the water is cooled by flashing a small part of it. Furthermore, absorber and evaporator are combined into one common shell, and the condenser and generator into another one, giving a compact as well as simple unit.*

This latter system is the Carrier system. Comparing the two, it may be said that the Carrier water chiller units are of large tonnage, and use a solution pump; the Servel units are smaller and use no pump, in fact, they have no moving parts. The Servel units operate on atmospheric steam, while the Carrier system requires steam at approximately 12 pounds pressure.

Another unit made in capacities of 12 and 35 tons refrigeration for producing chilled water is the Williams Oil-O-Matic which employs methylene chloride as the refrigerant and dimethyl ether of triethylene glycol as the absorbent.*

The well-known Servel domestic refrigerator requires only a gas flame for source of energy; it requires no compressor, unlike the refrigerants discussed further on. It operates on the principle of absorption refrigeration. The gas flame evaporates ammonia gas from an aqueous solution; the ammonia is led to the condenser, where it passes through finned, air-cooled tubes, gives up its heat, and condenses. The liquid ammonia now passes to the evaporator where it evaporates into an atmosphere of hydrogen, thus absorbing heat from the refrigerator cooling coils. Hydrogen and ammonia gas pass to the absorber where the ammonia dissolves, while the hydrogen is unchanged and free to recirculate. The ammonia solution is then returned to the generator and the process begins again.

Spray Pond. In order to cool water which has just come off the coolers with a temperature of 120 or 100°F, it may be fed by a pump to nozzles

* "Absorption refrigeration, a modern development using water vapor," by A. A. Berestneff, *Mech. Eng.*, March 1950, p. 216. See also U. S. Patent 2,565,943.

set upright in a shallow basin or pond. The spray formed favors vaporization of part of the water, and produces a cooling of the remainder. Towers, usually made of wood, are widely and successfully used instead of ponds. Cooling in spray ponds or towers depends among other conditions upon "wet bulb" air temperature.

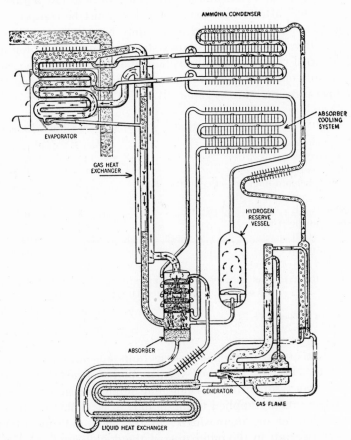

FIGURE 460.—Sketch showing the construction and working principle of the household Servel refrigerator. It has no moving parts, and operates on a gas or oil flame.

Cold *high-velocity air* directed against furnace walls (such as those of a glass furnace) lengthens the life of the furnace, and represents an application of cold which differs from any of the preceding ones. In one well-known system* a number of streams of cold air issue from large cast-aluminum nozzles mounted on nozzle risers; the air streams are so directed and distributed that the whole of a given wall area is cooled.

* Kirk and Blum Mfg. Co., Cincinnati, O.

REFRIGERANTS

For general refrigerating purposes, substances known as refrigerants are used. They are gases which are readily compressed to liquids, which in turn are readily vaporized under the proper conditions. During vaporization, these agents absorb heat, and since they work at low temperatures, they "refrigerate," after which expansion they must be compressed by a mechanical compressor, and cooled moderately by common cooling water or air, when they resume their liquid state and are ready for another cycle. Instead of compression, absorption in a solvent may be employed. The temperature obtained depends upon the compressible gas selected, and upon the operating pressure. (Tables 81 and 81a.)

TABLE 81. BOILING POINTS AT ATMOSPHERIC PRESSURE OF VARIOUS REFRIGERANTS

Ethyl chloride (C_2H_5Cl)	+ 55°F	+ 12.5°C
Sulfur dioxide (SO_2)	+ 14	− 10
Methyl chloride (CH_3Cl)	− 11	− 23.9
"Freon," dichloro-difluoromethane (CCl_2F_2)	− 21.6	− 29.8
Anhydrous ammonia (NH_3)	− 28	− 33.3
Propane (C_3H_8)	− 49	− 45
Carbon dioxide (CO_2)	−108.8	− 78.2
Ethylene (C_2H_4)	−151.6	−102
Liquid nitrogen (N_2)	−320.6	−195.8

TABLE 81a. RELATION OF PRESSURE AND TEMPERATURE FOR THE REFRIGERANTS AMMONIA AND CARBON DIOXIDE

Boiling Temp.	Pounds per Square Inch Gauge Pressure	
	Ammonia	Carbon Dioxide
−28°F	0	167

The most frequently employed refrigerants are anhydrous ammonia, carbon dioxide, "Freon," sulfur dioxide, methyl chloride, ethyl chloride, and propane; less frequently, ethylene and liquid nitrogen are used.

The refrigerants are applied to the liquids to be cooled in the double-pipe heat exchanger or, increasingly, in the shell-and-tube exchanger. The liquid refrigerant in the outer pipe of the double-pipe vaporizes, and consumes heat, which is drawn through the walls directly from the liquid to be cooled. For the shell-and-tube exchanger, there are two ways to apply the refrigerant. In one, the anhydrous ammonia, let us say, is the liquid in the shell, and is allowed to boil, the vapor formed (it is this process of vapor formation which removes the heat) being drawn off by a compressor which delivers the compressed gas to a cooler (water), where it liquefies and is returned to the shell. In the other system, the refrigerant is sprayed over the tubes in the exchanger; the liquid which reaches the bottom of the shell is recirculated to the sprays, and a compressor draws the vapor and returns it in the liquid form. The spray system is used particularly with "Freon." Applied in any one of these three ways, the agent would be a direct refrigerant.

There are also secondary refrigerants, chief among which is 28 per cent calcium chloride brine which is itself cooled by the refrigerant, and is then circulated through the liquid (or space) to be refrigerated. The refrigeration of the brine by means of ammonia was originally performed in double-walled tubes, or "double pipes," set up, for example, in sections of 14 pipes in height, and of suitable length, about 20 feet being the maximum. Thus a 3-inch outside pipe would receive the ammonia to be vaporized, and a 2-inch inner pipe would carry the brine. Such double

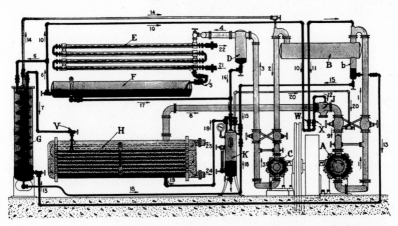

Figure 461.—A refrigerating plant designed especially for producing very low temperature, employing a horizontal two-stage ammonia compressor. Brine is cooled, and the cold brine circulated by pumps to storage or other rooms. *A*, first-stage cylinder; *C*, second-stage cylinder of compressor; *B*, intercooler; *E*, double-pipe ammonia condenser; *F*, liquid ammonia receiver; *G*, liquid precooler where high-pressure liquid ammonia is cooled by the evaporation of intermediate pressure ammonia; *H*, brine cooler, shell and tube-type, with the refrigerant in the shell, the brine in the tubes; *23*, brine entering, *24*, brine leaving, cooler; *21*, cooling water entering, *22*, leaving, condenser; *V*, main-expansion valve; *8*, ammonia-vapor suction line leading to scale-trap *J*, and then to compressor *A*. *17* and *19*, oil drains to separator *K*.

pipe systems are still in use, but they are being displaced by double-pass or multipass shell-and-tube exchangers. An installation in which the shell-and-tube exchanger is used is shown in Figure 461.

Direct refrigeration is performed in the Baudelot cooler (Figure 462) in which the upper turns have water as inner cooling agent, the lower ones the refrigerant. The liquid to be cooled trickles over the outside of the pipes. Chlorine is liquefied in a double-pipe condenser, in the outer pipe of which liquid carbon dioxide is vaporized. Another interesting example of direct refrigeration is the application of liquefied ethylene to the liquefaction of natural gas, in which three refrigerants were made to function in succession: anhydrous ammonia, liquefied ethylene, and a portion of

FIGURE 462.—Hot liquids to be cooled are allowed to flow over the outside of cooling pipes in the Baudelot cooler. Water is circulated through the upper 18 pipes, ammonia through the lower 5; the cooled liquid collects in the pan underneath the cooler. (Courtesy Atlas Copper and Brass Mfg. Co., Chicago 14, Ill.)

the liquefied natural gas itself. The plant described in the reference below is no longer in operation.*

Reading References

"Industrial developments in heat transfer with organic compounds," by R. L. Heindel, Jr., *Trans. Am. Inst. Chem. Eng.*, **30**, 378 (1934).

"Mercury vapor as applied to process industries," by C. A. Hulsart, *Trans. Am. Inst. Chem. Eng.*, **30**, 402 (1934).

"Heat transmission through bare and insulated furnace walls," by R. H. Heilman, *Trans. Am. Inst. Chem. Eng.*, **31**, 378 (1934).

"Application of Dowtherm vapor heating," by D. K. Dean, *Ind. Eng. Chem.*, **31**, 797 (1939).

"Notes on the design and operation of a high-temperature Dowtherm system," by R. E. Hulme, *Chem. Met. Eng.*, **47**, 685 (1940).

"Data on evaporation and drying in a jacketed kettle," by H. G. Laughlin, *Trans. Am. Inst. Chem. Eng.*, **36**, 345 (1940).

"Designing efficient equipment," by Guy N. Harcourt, *Ind. Eng. Chem.*, **33**, 1112 (1941), presenting the design of kettles especially, with illustrations.

"Water vapor refrigeration," by P. Bancel, *Trans. Am. Inst. Chem. Eng.*, **30**, 136 (1933–34).

"Refrigeration A-B-C's for Chemical Engineers," by F. L. Kallam, *Chem. Met. Eng.*, **41**, 190 (1934), and a criticism by Benjamin Miller, p. 373, same volume.

"Application of refrigeration to the manufacture of natural gasoline," by F. L. Kallam, *Chem. Met. Eng.* **41**, 355 (1934).

"Combination process coolers reduce operating costs," by C. C. Christensen, *Chem. Met. Eng.* **41**, 122 (1934).

"Pebble heater—new transfer unit for industry," by C. L. Norton, Jr., *Chem. Met. Eng.* **53**, July 1946, p. 116.

"Absorption refrigeration, a modern development using water vapor," by A. A. Berestneff, *Mech. Eng.*, March 1950, p. 216.

"Refrigeration in the refining industry," by Tyler G. Hicks, *Petroleum Refiner*, **30**, March, p. 88; June, p. 145; July, p. 147(1951).

"Atomic Energy," an interview with Lawrence R. Hafstad, *Chem. Eng. News*, **30**, 3808 (Sept. 15, 1952).

* "Liquefying natural gas for peak load supply," by R. W. Miller and J. A. Clark, *Chem. Met. Eng.*, **48**, 74 (1941).

Air conditioning means the creation of an artificial atmosphere by rob-bing the air of its water vapor, or by adding to it; by raising its tempera-ture, or by lowering it. Gas conditioning is similar, but the demand is generally more severe. The total removal of water is not infrequently the task. The devices to be used must function continuously in many processes; they must be scientifically exact.

22. GAS CONDITIONING

Gas conditioning means removing from a gas suspended nongaseous particles or droplets, as well as foreign gases and vapors, and adjusting its water-vapor content and temperature to predetermined levels. The most important gas is air, and its conditioning has been studied exhaustively because it contributes to comfort and health, as well as to success in industrial operations. In dwellings, public halls, and workrooms, air conditioning for bodily comfort undertakes to keep the water-vapor content and the temperature within rather narrow limits. For industrial air conditioning, the requirements vary. Thus in a pharmaceutical establishment in central New York, four kinds of "air" are necessary, all of them involving conditioning: hot and dry air must be furnished to the pill-coating department; hot and moist air to the compounding department; cold and dry air to the department for packaging ointments into jars; and cold and moist air to the room where suppositories are manufactured. To give two more extremes: in the country's largest yeast plant a cool, damp atmosphere is required; and in a world-famous candy-manufacturing house the air must be hot and dry.

Installations for general air conditioning vary with the service they are to render. A very simple type performing a light duty is shown in Figure 463. Outside air mixed with an adjustable volume of recirculated air passes over cooling coils to reach the fan, which then delivers the cooled air to the room. This system is recommended for the treatment of air in office buildings, where the main duty is the removal of sensible heat, and where there is very little moisture to be eliminated. The cooling coils are part of an ammonia system, but they may also be cooled by water or brine. The controlled volume system just described is supplemented by the automatic by-pass system (Frick).

In another, more elaborate system, the incoming air is cooled by water, then mixed with a certain volume of recirculated air, and both passed over cooling coils which lower the temperature to below the dew point. The water separating out is caught against the eliminator baffles, and the air is warmed to the desired temperature by reheating coils. The water in the coils which cool the incoming outside air may serve to warm the dehumidi fied air. This system is recommended when the moisture load is large

For all-year service in the temperate zones, with hot summers and cold winters, complete air conditioning must include summer cooling and de humidifying and winter heating and humidifying, besides year-round cleaning. A part of the air from the building is recirculated, generally by-passing the apparatus preceding the fan. In winter the incoming out side air passes a dry filter, a steam coil, a rich spray of water which satu rates it, eliminators (baffles), and a cooling coil which may be inoperative and reaches the fan together with the by-passed air. In summer, the steam coil is inoperative, and perhaps the water spray also; but the cooling

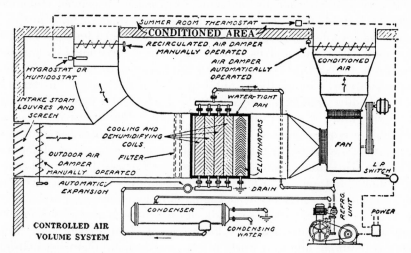

FIGURE 463.—The controlled air volume system, for use where little moisture is to be removed. Outside air mixed with recirculated air is pulled by the fan through the cooling coils, followed by the eliminator baffles. Air volume may be varied between 70 and 100 per cent of fan capacity. (Courtesy Frick Co., Waynesboro, Pa.)

coil functions. It is generally fed with cold water, but better with ex panding ammonia or brine. Here too the treated air mixes with a portion of by-passed air.

The comfort zone is from 63° to 71°F and between 35 and 55 relative humidity.

A number of portable, self-contained conditioning "units" are avail able. The "Buffalo" cabinets are obtainable either with a washer section, ("PCW" type), or without ("PC" type) for horizontal operation, and in two vertical types ("VPC" and "VPCW"). The cabinets with washers have spray nozzles, spray piping, eliminator plates, close-couples pump, cooling coils, and heating coils. The cooling coils may be direct-expan sion coils (40°F), or may be water-cooled (45° and higher).

Air filters have been described in Chapter 9.

For the production and maintenance of special combination of water-vapor content and temperature, such as were mentioned in the opening paragraph of this chapter, apparatus similar to that described, but arranged purposefully, is employed.

Basic to air conditioning is the study of the properties of air, dry air, saturated air, and air with intermediate amounts of water vapor. The percentage of water vapor which air can hold at saturation varies greatly; it is higher for warm air than for cold air. The degree of saturation at any one temperature is ascertained by means of a double thermometer, one with its bulb wetted by a moistened cotton stocking or wrapping, the other with its bulb dry. Placing the double thermometer in the room to be tested, or better, swinging it for a short period (sling psychrometer) gives two temperatures, and also a differential. The differential is the measure of the water-vapor content of the air at the temperature of the dry bulb. Its value in grains per cubic foot, or per pound, is found by consulting the psychrometer tables; the greater the differential, the lower the amount of water vapor.

Industrial Gas and Air Conditioning. The requirements for the conditioning of gases and air in the industries are generally quite different from those in air conditioning for comfort.

For process use, air may be partially dried by cooling, by means of water or a refrigerant; the proportion of water vapor left in the air is the saturation value at the lowest temperature reached. This proportion is comparatively small, but for many chemical purposes it is much too high; further drying may be brought about by an adsorbent, such as activated silica gel, activated alumina, activated carbon, "Drierite," and others, which are solids, and glycerin, polyglycol, diethylene glycol, phosphoric acid, or sulfuric acid, which are liquids. Air saturated with water vapor at 87°F (30°C) contains 13.6 grains of water vapor per cubic foot, equivalent to 0.855 gram. If this air is passed through a bed of activated alumina, at the same temperature (87°F), its water content will be reduced to less than 0.0000008 gram per liter, or 0.000022 gram per cubic foot, equivalent to 0.00035 grain. In order to reach the same low value by refrigeration alone, it would be necessary to reduce the temperature to —105°F (—76°C).

Other gases require drying under certain conditions. Hydrogen, oxygen, and other permanent gases must be dried before bottling; the drying of natural gas prevents the formation of hydrates, and raises the carrying capacity of the line. Foreign vapors other than water vapor are removed by the same treatments which remove the latter, and hydrogen for catalytic hydrogenation, inert gases for use in handling solvents, and gases for bright annealing, are successfully conditioned.

In the following pages, equipment in which gases may be "dried" are

presented. It may be well to remember that "dried" and "dry" are relative terms; a quantitative value is introduced by saying that the residual
water vapor content is 0.00035 grain per cubic foot, for example.

Silica Gel Adsorbers. Among the several different kinds of devices
which employ activated silica gel as the solid adsorbent are the Kemp Silica
Gel Adsorptive Dryers, manufactured in a number of models. The drier
may have a single adsorber and operate intermittently, or a dual adsorber,
which permits continuous delivery of dry gas. During the adsorption of
vapors, heat is evolved. To remove the heat, a number of models have
special interposed coolers, while others rely on self-cooling. The latter
are satisfactory when the initial water-vapor concentrations are not ex-

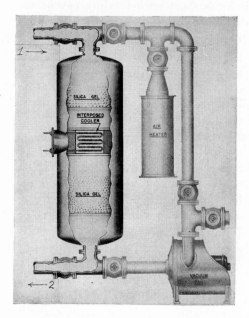

FIGURE 464.—A cut-open
silica gel adsorptive drier,
shown as in active operation.
At *1*, the wet gas enters; it
travels downward through the
desiccant and leaves at lower
left, 2. Heater, vacuum fan,
and connection for revivifying
the gel are included in the
drawing. (Courtesy The C. M.
Kemp Mfg. Co., Baltimore 2,
Md.)

cessive, especially when a severe degree of drying is not necessary; usually
such driers operate under pressure.

The operation of a water-cooled adsorber is as follows: The gas to be
dried enters the top of the tower and meets first the primary bed of silica
gel granules to which it gives up much of its water vapor. As it does so,
the temperature rises. The heat is removed by passing the warm air or
gas over extended surfaces of a heat exchanger, in which cold water circulates. The cooled air now diffuses through the granules of the secondary
bed, where the remainder of its moisture is removed; this stage is accompanied by only a slight temperature rise. After a time, the adsorptive
mass becomes saturated, and its effectiveness must be restored. The flow
of air is interrupted, or shifted to the second adsorber if the model is of the

dual type, and heated air is pulled downward through the adsorber by the fan, now connected to function as an exhauster. The air is heated to 300 or 350°F by steam, gas, or electricity; during this period the flow of cooling water is interrupted. After a definite period, the mass is dry; it is then cooled by restoring the flow of water in the heat-exchanging coils and circulating one volume of air through the tower, the fan now acting as a circulating agent.

Air is dried for many purposes. One which may not come to mind at once is the need for dried air in the operation of instruments of control

FIGURE 465.—A 10,000 scfm wind tunnel drier with silica gel as desiccant. Operating pressure, 45 psi; entering temperature 40°F; effluent dewpoint, —70°F. Reactivation is based on external heating and cooling. (Courtesy The C. M. Kemp Mfg. Co., Baltimore 2, Md.)

in the chemical factory. Another is the feeding of dried air to drying cabinets, to driers in general. Other gases which are currently dried by means of Silica Gel driers are ammonia, carbon dioxide, carbon monoxide, ethylene, helium, hydrogen as already stated, inert gases other than helium, nitrogen, natural gas, and oxygen.

The silica gel granules are 3 to 8 mesh and 6 to 16 mesh in size. Silica gel resembles crushed quartz, or coarse clear sand, and can adsorb up to 43 per cent of its weight of water and still remain apparently dry. It is an inert solid, and is reasonably strong. It will adsorb large quantities of other liquids having boiling points over 50°F and release them when heated to about 300°F.

One cubic foot of commercial silica gel varies in weight from 40 to 45 pounds, depending upon the mesh size. Where only moderate drying is required, such as in comfort air conditioning, the ratio of air treated to silica gel is often in excess of 10 cubic feet per minute per pound of gel; in chemical process work, the ratio may be considerably less than one cubic foot per minute per pound.

Silica Gel Adsorptive Dryers are built in single and dual types, for high pressures and for low; they are both portable and stationary, and are used for special as well as for general purposes. There is also a continuous rotary type.

FIGURE 466.—A silica gel drier used for rocket experimentation, working at pressures as high as 3,500 psi. Reactivation is based on imbedded electric heating elements. (Courtesy The C. M. Kemp Mfg. Co., Baltimore 2, Md.)

In addition to the applications of dynamic adsorption which have been listed, those for static adsorption deserve study. For static adsorption, silica gel of selected fineness is placed, for example, in the spaces between the multi-paned windows of railroad cars and aeroplanes to prevent fogging.

Silica Gel is used to a considerable extent to dehydrate compounds in the liquid state, e.g., refrigerants.

Lectrodryer. The Lectrodryer is a device for drying air and gases; it employs activated alumina as the adsorbent and therefore belongs in the group which makes use of solid adsorbents. The single self-cooled Lectrodryer has one cylindrical adsorbing chamber containing the alumina; the gas to be dried is passed through the drier for a period of hours, after which the mass is saturated and is no longer effective. For intermittent operation, the Lectrodryer is so proportioned that the desired volume of dry gas is obtained before the adsorptive power drops off markedly. The mass is then revivified by blowing through it air heated by electrical heating elements imbedded in the mass, whereby the adsorbed water is removed and voided in vapor form. After about 4 hours, the alumina is reactivated; it must be allowed to cool to room temperature for another 4 hours, and is then ready for another cycle.

FIGURE 467.—The Standard Oriad type drier, to provide a source of dried air in moderate quantities. It provides dried compressed air for tools, valves, and instruments, but is also used for other gases. Arranged for imbedded steam coil reactivation and semi-automatic operation. (Courtesy The C. M. Kemp Mfg. Co., Baltimore 2, Md.)

Whenever a steady flow of dry gas or air is required, the dual Lectrodryer is selected; it has two adsorbers. While one functions over a period of about 8 hours, the other is reactivated by the heated air, and cooled. The spent adsorber can be cut out of service and onto reactivation, and a fresh adsorber cut into the drying circuit by shifting a single lever.

Adsorption of water vapor is accompanied by heat evolution; rapid removal of this heat is assured in the water-cooled Lectrodryers by placing finned coils within the mass of adsorbent. The same coils offer a second advantage, namely, reactivation by steam, which is performed by passing 100- or 150-pound steam through them. Electrical heating remains optional. The four standard sizes listed below provide a flow of dried gas at rates ranging from 2500 to 30,000 cubic feet per hour. Larger capacities are available. For drying large quantities of gas or air to very low dew points continuously, the dual-adsorber, water-cooled Lectrodryer is recommended. Single-adsorber, water-cooled units are also furnished.

The dual-adsorber, self-cooled Lectrodryer is made in four sizes capable of handling flows up to 5,000 cubic feet per hour, with approximate water capacities (—40° dew point) of 1.5, 3, 6, and 18 pounds per day, respectively.

FIGURE 468.—A dual-adsorber water-cooled Lectrodryer for drying gases in large volumes. The particular unit photographed is for handling acetylene gas. (Courtesy Pittsburgh Lectrodryer Corp., Pittsburgh 30, Pa.)

In high-pressure equipment, a small quantity of any adsorbent will dry a large volume of gas. Lectrodryers are available for operation with air or gases at pressures of 600, 860, and up to 5,000 pounds per square inch.

As oil vapors reduce the rate of adsorption of the solid adsorbents, it is desirable to protect a Lectrodryer. The Lectrofilter is a small upright cylindrical vessel containing a removable filter basket filled with adsorbent, designed to retain the oil vapors. The basket is cleaned periodically and used over and over.

FIGURE 469.—A dual-adsorber, high-pressure Lectrodryer for operation on pressures as high as 5,000 psi. (Courtesy Pittsburgh Lectrodryer Corp., Pittsburgh 30, Pa.)

TABLE 82. DUAL-ADSORBER WATER-COOLED LECTRODRYERS WITH STEAM OR ELECTRICAL OPERATION. DATA FOR WORKING PRESSURE 15 PSI. ALL MODELS ARE OBTAINABLE FOR WORKING PRESSURES OF 100, 150, AND 300 PSI AS WELL. (1952)

Model Designation BWC	250	500	750	1500	2500	3500
Pounds H_2O adsorbed per 24 hours based on $-40°$ dew pt.	32	64	96	190	315	445
Cooling water gpm	3	4	5	8	12	18
KWH per reactivation electric unit	24	32	40	72	140	190
Steam per reactivation steam unit (pounds)	90	150	225	450	800	1000
Over-all length (inches)	66	80	90	115	110	127
Over-all width	42	53	57	71	73	81
Over-all height	56	64	76	83	128	168

Nonregenerative Calorider. The nonregenerative Calorider* employs cubical lumps of calcium chloride for the dehumidification of air. Its present form has been described† and also the process for producing the uniform, nonporous, strong cubical lumps, with 72 per cent calcium chloride which contain powdered activated carbon added as a deodorant.‡

* Air conditioning, non-regenerative "Calorider" performance," by C. R. Downs and J. W. Spiselman, *Ind. Eng. Chem.*, **31**, 681 (1939).

† *Ibid.*, p. 682.

‡ "Production of "Caloride," *Ind. Eng. Chem.*, **31**, 691 (1939).

Placed in a perforated container with a reservoir for collecting the liquefied material, a quantity of lumps serve well for the partial dehumidification of a closed space, such as an air-raid shelter for civilians. The nonregenerative Calorider is a more elaborate unit containing a large supply of cubes, a certain quantity of calcium chloride solution, fan and ducts. The air to be dried is mixed with atomized solution, drawn over the finned tubes of a radiator through which cold water circulates. Its partial drying is continued and essentially completed by drawing it through a bed of Caloride lumps. The cold water removes the heat of dilution of the calcium chloride solution (the heat of absorption is 1,150 Btu per pound of moisture).

Regenerative Calorider. The regenerative Calorider employs a hygroscopic solution to dry the air (in the Absorber); in the process, the solution becomes dilute, and the dilute solution is brought back to its original effectiveness by concentrating it (the Concentrator). The cycle is continuous; the diluted solution is circulated to the Concentrator, and the concentrated solution is pumped to the top of the Absorber where it issues from nozzles in spray form and travels concurrently with the flow of air.* The hygroscopic liquid may be triethylene glycol.

The moisture contained in air which is to be introduced into a chemical process, and that contained in certain gases about to be processed, may be removed by allowing the air or other gas to travel up a *packed tower,* down which sulfuric acid, for example, is flowing slowly.

Electrical Precipitation. The electrical precipitator for removing suspended matter from gases may be the sole cleaning device, or it may follow preliminary dust catchers and washers. An example for the latter sequence is the blast furnace installation shown in Figure 470, in which the blast furnace gas, destined to serve as fuel in gas engines, is cleaned of its last traces of dusts by electrical precipitation by the Cottrell process.

The principle of electrical precipitation is shown in the schematic wiring diagram of a Cottrell (Figure 471). A high-tension current, ranging from 7500 to 100,000 volts, is applied to one electrode in the form of a wire, while the other electrode, a flat surface, is grounded. The current is direct, mechanically rectified; best results are obtained when the ionizing electrode, here the wire, is made negative in polarity. The suspended matter acquires a charge, partly from high-speed electrons from the current, partly from ionized gas, which precipitates it at the extended, grounded surface. Droplets so precipitated unite to form a stream of liquid; solids form a coating which must be rapped off to a collecting box below at intervals. The electrical precipitators, it should be noted, introduce practically no back pressure.

* "The regenerative "Calorider," by C. R. Downs and J. W. Spiselman, *Ind. Eng. Chem.,* **31,** 692 (1939).

The pipe-type Cottrell consists of vertical pipes 3 to 12 inches in diameter and from 5 to 15 feet long, in which a small wire is suspended axially. A number of units are nested in a shell with connections that permit the gas to enter at the bottom and emerge clean at the top.

The plate type has a series of parallel plates in a casing which forms the channels through which the gas flows. The discharge electrodes are

FIGURE 470.—A blast furnace installation of Cottrell precipitators for cleaning the gas. The two Cottrell precipitators are shown in the center foreground, with three stoves behind them, and to the left, a gas washer preceded by a dust catcher. The furnace itself is partly hidden by the gas washer. (Courtesy Western Precipitation Corp., Los Angeles, Calif.)

suspended between the plates from an insulated framework. The flow of gas between the plates may be horizontal or vertical. There are five different types of construction: solid steel plates, concrete with conductors imbedded in the center, rod curtain, perforated plate, and pocket type.

Complete self-contained Cottrell precipitators are available for small gas plants with capacities ranging from 500,000 to 4,000,000 cubic feet of gas per day. These units are shipped completely assembled ready to be installed.

Sterilization of Air. Large quantities of sterile air are required for the production of antibiotics, riboflavin, and other substances involving aerobic processes. The most common method of sterilization is the use of filters, alone or in combination with other techniques. An example would be electronic precipitation followed by filtration through columns of carbon or glass wool.*

Deodorization of Air. Air may be deodorized in a number of ways: by oxidation of the odoriferous component, as with ozone; by adsorption, as with activated carbon, activated alumina, or silica gel; by reaction with formaldehyde; by washing; by chemical combination; and indirectly by

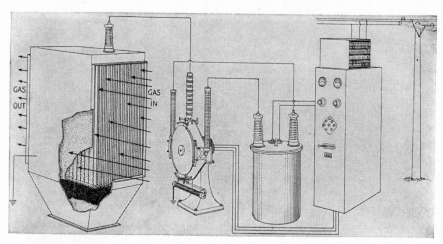

Figure 471.—Schematic diagram of the equipment used in the Cottrell electrical precipitator. From left to right, precipitator, rotary rectifier, transformer, switchboard. The precipitator is shown operating on a solid. (Courtesy Western Precipitation Corp., Los Angeles, Calif.)

electrostatic precipitation. The air to be deodorized may be passed over or through the agent, as an adjunct to air cooling or heating, or exposed to the agent or mixed with it in measured amounts. For deodorizing air in confined spaces as in the rooms of a dwelling, the active agent may be emitted from a wick, as in the familiar deodorizing bottle. Reodorization is frequently successful; in the main it is the masking of an unpleasant odor by a pleasant one, purposely added or generated.

A number of statements regarding air and gas conditioning will be found in the preceding chapter, incidental to absorption refrigeration.

Reading References

"Heat insulation on cylindrical surfaces," Channing Turner, *Ind. Eng. Chem.*, **32**, 904 (1940).

* *Ind. Eng. Chem.*, **42**, 1789 (1950).

"The development of air-conditioning in industrial, residential and public buildings; its effect on human beings; the factors which enter into its design," by P. L. Davidson, *Trans. Am. Inst. Chem. Eng.*, **30**, 50–121 (1933–34), 18 photographs, 13 sets of curves, 7 tables and diagrams, and 53 references.

"Practical air-conditioning," by A. J. Rummel and L. O. Vogelsang, New York, John Wiley and Sons, Inc., 1941.

"Heating and air conditioning," 5th ed., by J. R. Allen and J. H. Walker, New York, McGraw-Hill Book Co., 1940.

"Unit air conditioner, new model," *Chem. Met. Eng.*, **44**, 334 (1937).

"Air-conditioning equipment," by M. Ingels, *Ind. Eng. Chem.*, **30**, 980 (1938).

"Fundamentals of air conditioning," by V. P. Victor, *Drug and Cosmetic Industry*, **42**, 716 (1938).

"Recent advances in our knowledge of the problems of air conditioning," by C. E. A. Winslow, *Am. J. Public Health*, **27**, 767 (1937).

"A new electrostatic precipitator," by G. W. Penney, *Electr. Eng.*, **56**, 159 (1937).

"Report on conditioning of gases and air," a collection of 20 articles on various phases of the subject, including also "Air-solvent vapor psychrometric charts" by E. J. Barta and H. J. Garber, *Chem. Met. Eng.*, **47**, 286–332 (1940).

"Air conditioning in rayon plants and textile mills," *Rayon* **21**, 242, 639 (1940).

"Air conditioning, nonregenerative 'Calorider' performance, production of 'Caloride,'" by C. R. Downs, *Ind. Eng. Chem.*, **31**, 134, 681 (1939).

"Moisture removal from blast furnace air," by L. L. Lewis, *Refrig. Eng.*, **39**, 89, 157 (1940).

"Desirable temperature and humidities for industrial processing: tabulation," *Factory Management*, **98**, 100 (1940).

"Comparative efficiency of various dehydrating agents used for drying gases (a survey of the commercial drying agents)," by J. H. Bower, *Bureau Standards J. Res.* R P 649, 12, 241 (1934).

"Fan Engineering," Buffalo Forge Co., Buffalo, N. Y.

"Choice in dehydrating methods," by J. C. Patterson, *Chem. Met. Eng.*, **47**, 312 (1940).

"Drying air with phosphoric acid in a packed tower," by M. M. Striplin, Jr., *Ind. Eng. Chem.*, **33**, 910 (1941).

"Moisture control by a new process," by R. S. McBride, *Chem. Met. Eng.*, **45**, 520 (1938) (the Guardite process).

"Chemical dehumidification of air, by adsorption and absorption," by A. Weisselberg, *Chem. Met. Eng.*, **45**, 418 (1938).

"Adsorption, refrigeration and compression for the drying of gases," by J. H. Perry and H. C. Duus, *Chem. Met. Eng.*, **41**, 127 (1934).

"Silica Gel, its use as a dehydrating agent," by F. C. Dehler, distributed by the Davison Chemical Corporation, Baltimore, Md., 1941.

"Vapor barriers for dehumidification," by Elmer R. Queer and E. R. McLaughlin, Pittsburgh Lectrodryer Corporation, Pittsburgh, Pa., 1950 (the third in a series of three bulletins).

"Sterile air for industrial fermentations," by W. H. Stark and G. M. Pohler, *Ind. Eng. Chem.*, **42**, 1789 (1950).

"The fume and dust problem in industry," by Harry V. Welch, *Metals Transactions*, **185**, 934–947 (Dec. 1949).

Almost three centuries ago, the brilliant young French physicist, Blaise Pascal, made the statement: "If a vessel full of water, and closed on all sides, has two openings, the one a hundred times as large as the other, and if each be supplied with a piston that fits it exactly, then a man pushing the small piston will exert a force which will equilibrate that of one hundred men pushing the large piston, and will overcome that of ninety-nine." It is on this statement that the present-day applications of hydraulic pressure rest. Practical applications had to wait for Joseph Brahmah's invention of cup packing to make the "fit."

23. HYDRAULIC PRESSURE EQUIPMENT

Hydraulic power is power which may be transmitted and applied by means of water under pressure; it should be contrasted to mechanical power, pneumatic power, and springs. It is a convenient form of power for the operation of slow-moving machinery with straight-line or reciprocating motions, actuated by high pressures. Hydraulic power finds application in the compression or compacting of loose or plastic materials, the shearing, drawing, forging, and forming of metal, and the moving of heavy objects. In the chemical field, the molding of synthetic plastics, the expression of oil from nuts or seeds, and certain filtering operations may be performed to advantage with the aid of hydraulic power.

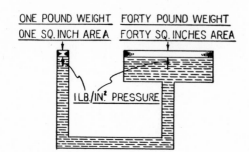

FIGURE 472.—Sketch illustrating the multiplying effect of hydraulic force. The one-pound force on the one square inch area piston balances the forty-pound force on the forty square inch area piston.

The science of hydraulics rests upon the principle that pressure of one pound per square inch applied to a confined body of fluid is transmitted undiminished in all directions. Figure 472 illustrates this. In practical applications, as for instance in the hydraulic press, the pump furnishes a pressure of 50 pounds per square inch (psi) which, exerted on a tight-fitting but movable platen 100 inches in area, produces a force of 5,000 pounds. Pressures as high as 13,000 psi are in general use. The pressure produced by hydraulic power has a resilience not possessed by metal-to-metal pressure. Water was the fluid originally used, and is still in favor for many applications; oil is being used more and more, especially in high-speed presses.

In addition to the applications just mentioned the hydraulic press is a valuable vulcanizing press for rubber products; in the manufacture of rubber belting, it is supplemented by hydraulic stretchers which hold the belt under uniform tension during vulcanization. Blocks of salt, of "Dry Ice," and similar materials are formed by hydraulic pressure.

The application of hydraulic power requires a cylinder in which is fitted a piston or ram which passes through a packing and a gland. The ram carries a platen (or plate) which engages the work to be compressed; opposite the ram there is a fixed platen against which the work rests during compression. The cylinder has one orifice with a pipe connection to

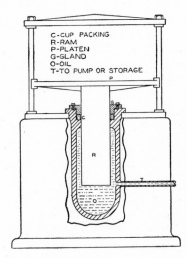

C-CUP PACKING
R-RAM
P-PLATEN
G-GLAND
O-OIL
T-TO PUMP OR STORAGE

FIGURE 473.—A sketch illustrating the application of hydraulic pressure.

the pump, and another leading to an oil tank. The ram may move upward, downward, or horizontally on its power stroke. In the simpler construction, the ram moves upward, the return stroke taking place by gravity. In presses with a downward power stroke, which has certain advantages, the ram must be lifted again by auxiliary cylinders, called push-back rams. To make the ram move on its power stroke, oil under pressure is admitted behind it; for the return stroke, a valve must be opened permitting the oil to escape to the small tank in which it is stored. The actions mentioned up to this point are those of a single-acting ram; for the operation of a double-acting ram, oil under pressure is fed alternately to one side and to the other side of a piston, which carries the ram rod ending in the ram proper.

The hydraulic machine may be self-contained, or it may be one of a number in a battery served by an accumulator. The self-contained machine has the hydraulic press and the hydraulic pumping equipment in a single unit, independent of any other devices; only connections for the electric current and for water to cool the hydraulic oil are required. Presses for molding thermosetting resins are usually operated from an accumulator, while the newer injection-molding presses for thermoplastic resins are self-contained.   An accumulator plant has a motor, a pressure pump such as, for example, a motor-driven triplex plunger pump, and a tank with a ram suitably weighted.   As the pump forces oil into the tank, the ram rises; oil under pressure is admitted to the press from the accumulated oil under pressure in the tank.

Recent developments have favored the self-contained hydraulic machine.   There are four types of pumps available for this service: the plunger pump, the gear pump, the vane pump, and the rotary radial piston pump.   The last has a reversible and infinitely variable discharge;

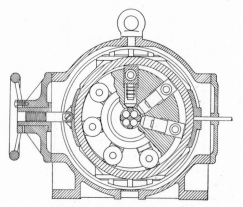

Figure 474.—A section through the rotary-radial piston pump, with infinitely variable and reversible discharge, the pumping unit which serves the high-pressure, high-speed hydraulic press. Note the floating ring, and hand wheel for its operation.

it is the device which has made the high-pressure, high-speed press of today possible.

The rotary radial piston pump is direct-connected to the motor, and consists essentially of a cylinder body fitted with radial plungers, a floating ring, and the housing.   The cylinder body is free to rotate—carrying the plungers with it—within the floating ring; the latter is capable of moving from right to left and from left to right.   The distance by which the floating ring is off the center of rotation of the cylinder body is called the "stroke" of the pump.   If the ring is on the same center, the pump is on "neutral," and a minimum discharge of oil results.   Increasing the stroke, that is, increasing the distance from the center of the cylinder body to the center of the floating ring, increases the volumetric discharge of the pump.   Shifting the floating ring past the center of the cylinder body to the other side of the vertical center line reverses the suction and discharge.   Thus a variable discharge rate is obtained from a constant-speed motor drive.

HYDRAULIC PRESSES

Hydraulic pressure is usefully applied to plows for unloading centrifugal baskets, to stretchers during the vulcanization of rubber belts, to jacks, and to other tools and machines. For the chemical and allied industries, presses are the most outstanding application; several examples will be presented.

Vertical-plate Type Hydraulic Press. The vertical-plate type hydraulic press is a self-contained, upward-acting platen press. The platen is of the saucer type, and a number of plates are provided. Oil-bearing seeds suitably prepared and confined by a filter mat or cloth are placed warm on

FIGURE 475.—Vertical-plate type hydraulic press for pressing tallow stock, oil-bearing seeds, and the like. It is a self-contained unit. (Courtesy Hydraulic Press Mfg. Co., Mount Gilead, Ohio.)

the plates. The oil is expressed as the ram moves upward, and runs down to the platen and thence to a weigh tank. Pin bars and pins are provided for holding the plates in the upper part of the press after pressure has been applied. The plates are lowered one by one, unloaded, and reloaded, without removing them from the press. Figure 475 shows this press; the model is designated as the "25-ton H-P-M Hydro-Power Oleo Press, vertical, upward-acting with flexible steel division plates." The platen is actuated by one double-acting main ram. This type of press serves for expelling oil from oil-bearing nuts as well as seeds, for expelling fruit juices, and for cold-pressing tallow stock and other materials. Pump and motor are mounted on the hydraulic oil reservoir.

Figure 476 shows the curb type dehydrating press, used for extracting water from fruits, vegetables, fats, herbs, chemicals and other raw materials.   In the model shown, all parts coming into contact with the material pressed are of stainless steel; the stainless-steel curb is 28 inches diameter by 60 inches in height.   The material to be pressed is fed into the curb through a cored hole in the head of the press.   The ram head is actuated by one double-acting main ram.   There are also 4 curb-lifting rams, 24 stainless-steel division plates, and 48 pieces of 28-inch diameter "Monel" cloth.

FIGURE   476.—A   dehydrating press of the curb type, H-P-M Hydro-Power Curb Press, vertical, upward acting, two-rod, top-ejecting type. All parts coming in contact with the material pressed are of stainless steel.   A self-contained unit. (Courtesy Hydraulic Press Mfg. Co., Mount Gilead, Ohio.)

Horizontal-plate Type.   The horizontal-plate type of hydraulic press is exemplified by the cellulose steeping press shown in Figure 477.   It is a self-contained, horizontal-acting press in which the platen traverses a rectangular open-top steeping tank; the ram is of the double-acting type. Sheets of cellulose pulp are steeped in caustic soda solution for a period, then (after running off the solution remaining) pressed to as nearly a dry condition as possible by the action of the ram on movable vertical plates which divide the steeping tank into compartments and hold the cellulose sheets on edge.   The oil-storage tank carrying the motor and the single radial pump are mounted as shown, with the controls conveniently located to permit the operator to regulate at will both speed of pressing and pressure applied to the pulp to give uniform results.   The press is made in seven sizes; the largest one has a ram travel of 168 inches.

The press selected for the illustration has a pressure head of 32 by 20½ inches, and a maximum ram travel of 108 inches.

Carver Five-pot Cocoa Press. An example of the application of hydraulic presses to filtering purposes in the chemical industries is the cocoa press, one model of which is vertical, with five pots above another. Each pot has below it a heavy hollow guide frame, through whose channels steam is passed, so that in all there are ten movable members. Four main round vertical posts rest on a heavy base and carry the sturdy stationary top piece, and furthermore act as guide rods for the five movable guide frames. Two auxiliary vertical supporting racks at the front of the press

FIGURE 477.—A 63-ton H-P-M Hydro-Power steeping press with rectangular open top tank, in which cellulose sheets, after steeping in caustic solution, are dehydrated by the pressure of the hydraulic ram. (Courtesy Hydraulic Press Mfg. Co., Mount Gilead, Ohio.)

take the load of the pots when the press is opened. In this press the brown cocoa "liquor," produced by grinding warm cocoa nibs, is separated into the clear oil, which on cooling hardens to cocoa butter, and the solids, which form a brown cake. This is done by squeezing the brown cocoa "liquor," held between two woven wire filter cloths, by a cylindrical projection on the heavy guide frame rising from below, while the upper surface cloth bears against the next higher guide frame, which holds the cloth stationary with respect to the pot. The lower filter cloth rests on a stout follower which has vertical passages and horizontal grooves; the clear oil passing through the lower cloth runs to the sides of the projecting cylindrical piece and from there into the gutters provided on each guide frame. Each gutter delivers to the next lower one by dripping, until the lowest one is reached, which delivers to a weigh tank. The clear product oil passing through the stationary upper cloth runs along grooves provided in its steel top piece, reaching a circular groove in the upper face of the pot, and traveling from there through vertical passages drilled through the pot wall to the next lower gutter. The solids remain in the pot cavity until ejection time.

The ten movable members move up under the pressure of the hydraulic ram which rises from below the upper edge of the pots, sealing tight against the filter plate above by pressure of springs. When the

FIGURE 478.—A battery of the new Carver 5-pot cocoa presses, with hydraulic operation. (Courtesy Fred S. Carver, New York, N. Y.)

hydraulic pressure is released, and the ram moves downward, the press opens by the weight of the parts and the force of the springs. On the rise, the ram must overcome the resistance of the springs, as well as perform its filtering task. The pressure is gradually transmitted from the ram to frame and pot; one might say that the cylindrical projections on the several frames become auxiliary rams.

The five pots are the filtering chambers, with filter plates; they are made of heavy steel castings and shaped outside as shown in the illustrations; the inside of the chamber is cylindrical, and is bounded at top and bottom by the woven wire filter cloths. The top filter cloth with its stiffening top piece remains in the same position with respect to the pot, but the lower cloth moves inward (and upward) as the pressing progresses and the clear product oil is evacuated. The auxiliary ram on the next lower frame engages the filter cloth-faced follower plate, forcing it up; it is machined to fit the pot cavity with small clearance, but has a number of vertical grooves which permit the oil to run off.

To follow a cycle all the way, let us assume that one pressing is over and the pressure has been released, allowing the pots to return to their normal levels. The pots are pulled forward, sliding along grooves visible in the illustration, until each comes to rest above an ejector, a steel member with an upper projection a little smaller than the filtering chamber.

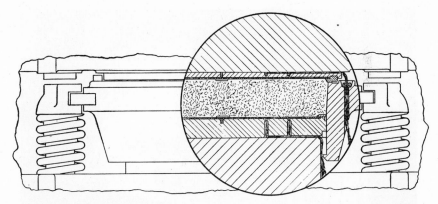

Figure 479.—The cocoa pot from the Carver 5-pot cocoa press shown in detail. At the stage depicted in the sketch, the follower carrying the lower filter cloth has been raised almost half the depth of the pot. The grooves and passageways which permit the clear pressed oil to run off from both the top filter cloth and the bottom one, are well shown. (Courtesy Fred S. Carver, New York, N. Y.)

The pot, it will be remembered, is uncovered, for its top filter leaf is integral with the guide frame above it; the cake is flush with the top. The ejector ram is set in motion, and at each level the ejector arm rises, forcing the lower filter leaf and follower to rise; thus the cake is pushed out of the cavity until the operator can lift it down. Next the ejector is lowered, and the lower filter plate returns to its starting position, on a shoulder at the base of the filtering cavity. The pots are now ready to receive the next charge. Rotatable filling valves deliver a downward stream of brown "liquor" into each pot from their slot-like openings; the horizontal delivery piece of the valves is visible to the right of each press in Figure 478. The filled pot is pushed gently into its rear position, over the main ram, and over or under the auxiliary rams. The main ram is set in motion, and rises; the lowest frame is lifted; it engages the lowest pot, entering its filtering chamber. The pot rises and lifts the next frame, which rises and in turn enters the filtering chamber of the second pot; at the same time, clear product oil flows from top and bottom filter plates. Gradually all the pots are engaged and lifted, the topmost last. Product oil flows steadily down the side of the pot and through its vertical passages, to collect finally in the weigh tank.

The distance through which the lowest frame is lifted is the greatest, about 14 inches; that through which the upper frame is lifted the least, about 2 inches. The others are lifted through intermediate distances, progressively smaller as one measures upward.

After the full weight of product oil has been expressed and collected, the hydraulic oil under pressure is shut off, and connection made with the

FIGURE 480.—The large size horizontal plastics injection molding press, completely hydraulic, self-contained, for molding thermoplastic resins, with a maximum capacity per cycle of 60 oz of plastics material. Feed hopper at right. (Courtesy The Hydraulic Press Manufacturing Co., Mount Gilead, Ohio.)

return oil tank. As the ram descends, by gravity, it forces the hydraulic oil into the tank, where it is stored until the next cycle. The guide frames and pots descend also, forced down by the four springs which act on each frame. The press is now open, the pots are about to be pulled forward, and the cakes are ejected. The period may be 35 minutes, or longer; the charge is 250 pounds of cocoa "liquor." The oil may weigh 100 pounds, or more, and the cakes the balance.

The hydraulic oil is pumped from the small storage tank forming part of the pump to the cylinder by a triplex plunger pump, motor-driven by the usual gears; the pressure attained is 5000 psi, sometimes more.

The price for the five-pot cocoa hydraulic press with all the recent improvements is at this time $30,000.00 (May 1952), without feeding pumps for the liquor. The press is adaptable for the separation of solids from liquids in semisolid masses other than cocoa "liquor."

The Carver Hydraulic Filter Press is a further development of filter plates and mechanical features in the pot press. The filter press and its hydraulic ram are horizontal; the latter applies pressure to the series of cakes, compressing them to a volume smaller than that of the filter chambers. The press has a capacity of 700 pounds per charge, in terms of chocolate liquor; it acts on the cakes with pressures up to 6000 psi, and after pressing, drops them automatically onto conveyors. It is hydraulically operated throughout, and therefore requires no manual labor. Such a press sells for $80,000.00 per unit (May 1952), and is being used not only on chocolate for cocoa butter but for other products in the chemical industries.

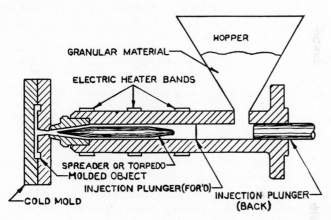

FIGURE 481.—The operation of injection molding. (*From Ind. & Eng. Chem.*, **33**, 564, 1941.)

Horizontal Injection-molding Hydraulic Press. In molding synthetic plastics, a distinction is made between compression molding and injection molding. Compression molding is the older method, and is applicable to the thermosetting resins. Generally the procedure is as follows: A preformed pellet is fed to the hot mold which is then closed, pressed, and opened, and the object knocked out or otherwise removed; the mold is part of a hydraulic platen press. The injection molding process is quite different; it is adapted to the thermoplastic resin plastics, which soften on heating—an essential property for this process. The thermosetting resins, it will be remembered, harden on heating. Examples of thermoplastic resins are cellulose acetate, ethylcellulose, acrylic resins, and vinylite. The procedure is as follows: In the injection molding press (Figure 480) the plastics are fed in the form of preheated granules to the cylinder, which is kept hot. The granules are compacted by the ram, then extruded into the mold which may be kept cold by circulating water, or maintained at any desired temperature. A moment later the mold opens and allows the molded piece to drop out automatically.

The period for the complete cycle of operations depends upon the properties of the particular plastic worked, and upon the thickness of the article. The following figure will serve as guide: the latest machines have as many as 12 cycles per minute, and the capacity for each molding is as high as 60 ounces.

The press shown has two major hydraulic members: a straight-line hydraulic clamp for opening, closing, and sealing the mold halves; and an injection plunger for transferring the plastic from the heating chamber into the mold. The granular plastic is force-fed into the heating chamber.

Both the clamp and injection actions require individual pressure generators with independent operating controls. The press is a self-contained unit, its press system being actually two separate units timed and synchronized for automatic operation.

TABLE 83. HORIZONTAL INJECTION MOLDING HYDRAULIC PRESS*

Model No.	250-H-9	350-H-16	600-H-32	1200-H-60-A
Mold clamp capacity (tons-max.)	250	350	600	1200
Material injected per cycle (oz-max.)	9	16	32	60
Injection pressure on material (psi)	20,000	20,000	20,000	20,000
Mold space, full platen vertically (inches)	17½ × 26	20 × 32½	43 × 25½	48 × 60

* Hydraulic Press Manufacturing Co., Mount Gilead, Ohio.

There are injection-molding presses in which the movement of the plunger is due to mechanical or pneumatic power instead of hydraulic; some presses have a combination of these methods. Injection-molding presses are generally horizontal, but there are also vertical units with larger capacities.

The sales prices of the four different models of conventional plastics injection-molding machines, completely hydraulic, are (January, 1953):

250-H-9-A or 9 oz capacity	$18,700
350-H-16-A or 16 oz capacity	27,600
600-H-32 or 32 oz capacity	42,000
1200-H-60-A or 60 oz capacity	71,000

New inventions and developments are following one another rapidly in the field of plastics, and the new forms of apparatus may be expected to be correspondingly varied and numerous. The distinction between the fields of application of injection molding and compression molding is in process of being reduced and even erased by new techniques, with corresponding changes in the construction and operation of the presses. Injection molding has been applied successfully to thermosetting resins by two novel procedures. In the first, the regular compacting chamber of the injection machine has a heating coil at its outlet to the mold space (Klem Shaw).   In the other, the transfer-mold method, high compression brings the uncured or partly cured resin to the fluid stage and forces it into the mold, where it sets (Frank Shaw).   The state of the resin, the time interval, and the temperatures as well as the pressure are fixed.

Compression molding of thermosetting resins is benefiting from another new development, namely, electronics.   The period in the mold is being reduced sufficiently by the "heatronic" treatment so that it approximates the short period which suffices in standard injection molding.

A unique development caused by wartime shortages has been the blowing and pressing of injection-molded plastics while retaining the injection

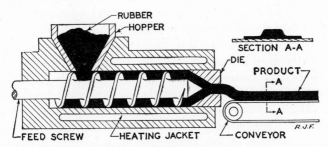

FIGURE 482.—Sketch showing the working principle of the extrusion machine.

heat.   Undoubtedly the future will see an extension of this practice in the form of fully automatic machines for injection and blowing of plastics containers, perfume bottles, oil cans, tableware, and all types of hollow products hitherto closed to thermoplastics.

Of constantly increasing importance is the extrusion process for shaping plastics, mainly because it is a continuous process.   Figure 482 shows the extrusion of rubber while in the plastic stage.   The application of extrusion methods in the thermoplastic resin industry has made rapid progress (see reading references).

Reading References

"Injection molding," by M. L. Macht, W. E. Rahm and H. W. Paine, *Ind. Eng. Chem.*, **33**, 565 (1941).

"Hydraulic power and its applications to modern industry," by W. L. Tann, *Modern Machine Shop*, March, April, May and June issues (1937).

"Extrusion of plastics, rubber and metals," by Herbert R. Simonds, Archie J. Weith, and William Schack, New York, Reinhold Publishing Corporation, 1952.

Just as in the middle of the past century the generation and application of steam at pressures appreciably above atmospheric had to wait for the development of large carbon-steel plates for the fabrication of a strong boiler shell, so present-day, newer industries which work with high pressures became realities only after the development of new materials and perfection of new fabrication methods. These developments are still in progress.

24. HIGH-PRESSURE EQUIPMENT. LININGS

Within the last twenty-five years chemical and allied operations have been extended into new regions of pressure and temperature. Some of the catalytic hydrogenation and petroleum-refining processes, and the use of liquefied gases as solvents on a tremendous scale, are cases in point, and the direct synthesis of ammonia must be counted in. Large-scale operations in these fields became possible only after materials for wall construction and methods of fabrication had themselves been developed in new directions. High pressure must be withstood not only at ordinary temperatures, but at high temperatures, a much more stringent requirement, and for other processes at low temperatures, a field until recently unexplored for large-scale construction. Not only must extreme temperature and pressure conditions be withstood, but the corrosive effect must be either resisted or allowed for, to permit reasonable life of the equipment. Better carbon steel, aluminum, and since 1926, chromium steel, chrome nickel steel, and other low-alloy and high-alloy steels, all supplemented by multilayer wall construction, lined or unlined, have been and continue to be suitable wall materials. The development of welding, especially fusion welding, has provided additional fabrication methods; x-ray examination of the welded joints detects the defective ones, which are then repaired or replaced.

It is well to discuss high-pressure equipment and corrosion-resistant linings separately, for linings of every type about to be mentioned are applied to low-pressure vessels as well as to medium- and high-pressure ones. Low-pressure vessels are those which can withstand pressures up to 300 psi; medium-pressure vessels, from 300 to 2,500 psi; and high-pressure vessels, above 2,500 psi. A number of devices suitable for low, medium, and high pressures have been presented in other chapters: storage tanks for pressures up to 100 psi in Chapter 5, a hydraulic pump for 3,000 psi in Chapter 6, and others. Two additional examples of storage tanks for liquids under pressure are shown in Figures 483 and 484.

At low temperatures it is advisable to distinguish between subzero service at low pressure, and subzero service at higher pressures. Table

622

86 indicates that −150°F is the minimum service temperature for the steel indicated, under stresses to be computed as 25 per cent of minimum tensile strength for low temperatures. In the medium-pressure range, there have been built several vessels of 18-8 nickel chrome stainless-steel

Figure 483.—Various size horizontal bullets for the storage of oil under pressure. Note the steel-on-concrete cradles. (Courtesy Chicago Bridge and Iron Co., Chicago, Ill.)

Figure 484.—Horizontal welded pressure vessel for storing and handling propane, 106 inches in diameter and 63 feet 3 inches long. (Courtesy Chicago Bridge and Iron Co., Chicago, Ill.)

for −300°F and 700 psi for the storage of liquid oxygen (A. O. Smith). It is held in other quarters that vessels of suitable material may be operated safely at −320°F, presumable at low or moderate pressures.

Welded Solid-Wall Pressure Vessel

Welded solid-wall pressure vessels are built from carbon steel plates and low-alloy steel plates. These vessels are used for temperatures from −150°F to 1,000°F. The most commonly used materials are shown in Table 84.

Plates are formed hot or cold, depending upon the gauge, type of equipment available, and class of material under consideration. Plates are

TABLE 84. CARBON AND LOW-ALLOY STEELS USED FOR PRESSURE VESSELS

Specification Number	Type of Steel Plate
SA-285	Carbon steel
SA-201	Carbon-silicon steel
SA-203	Nickel steel
SA-204	Molybdenum steel
SA-212	Carbon-silicon steel
SA-301	Chromium-molybdenum steel

joined by fusion welding, after which the vessel may be stress-relieved; it may furthermore be x-rayed in order to reach higher allowable joint efficiencies.

Table 85 gives the maximum allowable working stress for certain carbon and low-alloy steels. It is to be noted that in temperatures up to 650°F, alloy steel SA-212, Grade B, with its higher tensile strength, is the most economical when consideration is given to both allowable tensile strengths and cost of material. Above this temperature, materials such as SA-204, Grade B, and SA-301, are again more economical for the same considerations.

TABLE 85. MAXIMUM ALLOWABLE WORKING STRESS FOR CARBON AND LOW-ALLOY STEELS*

Specification Number	For Metal Temperatures Not Exceeding:		
	−20 to 650°F	800°F	1000°F
SA-285, Grade B	12,500 psi	9,400 psi	1,700 psi
SA-201, Grade B	15,000	11,400	2,500
SA-203, Grade B	17,500	12,500	2,500
SA-204, Grade B	17,500	16,900	6,250
SA-212, Grade B	17,500	12,500	2,500
SA-301	17,500	16,900	6,250

* From Table UG-23 of the ASME Boiler Code, Section VIII-Unfired Pressure Vessels.

For temperatures below −20°F, materials with certain impact resistance are required. The commonly used materials are given in Table 86 with their minimum service temperature. Below −150°F, which is the minimum temperature at which nickel steel may be used, materials such as austenitic stainless steels, copper, and aluminum are generally used.

TABLE 86. STEEL PLATE FOR USE AT SUBZERO TEMPERATURES*

Specification Number	Minimum Service Temperature
SA-201, SA-212	−50°F
SA-203, Grades A & B Firebox	−75
SA-203, Grade D Firebox	−150

* See ASME specification SA-300 for full requirements. Design stresses are based on 25 per cent of the minimum tensile strength for low temperature and on 100 per cent of the stress required to produce a creep rate of 1/100 per cent per 1,000 hours.

The chemical composition of the more important corrosion-resistant alloys has been given in Chapter 6.

The term *low-alloy steels* stands for carbon steels containing a low percentage of an alloying element, such 1½ per cent. The alloying element may be as high as 3 or even 4 per cent in special applications. In the low-alloy steels, the alloying element is added in order to make the steel stronger, not to make it more resistant to corrosion. The alloying elements are manganese, nickel, chromium, molybdenum, silicon, vanadium, tungsten, aluminum, columbium, and titanium. In the simple low-alloy steels, a single alloying element is dominant; in the complex low-alloy steels a combination of two or more alloying elements is introduced.

A list of various kinds of pressure vessels is given on page 633; the illustrations shown also are meant to exemplify the types of vessels which are built for high-pressure work.

The problem of corrosion has been met in different ways. For mild corrosive service, one method consists in using plain carbon steel, in spite of its ready response to corrosive agents, to determine the rate of corrosion and to allow for it in increased thickness over the design requirement. Other methods are: to line the towers with refractory materials; to apply a metal spray; to plate, as for example with chromium, and to use alloy lining materials such as a chromium, chromium-nickel steel, or other special alloy. The alloy lining may consist of a sheet or plate of the special alloy, applied to the wall of the vessel and held in place by spot welding or other welding, or it may be bonded to the steel to give a "clad" steel. In using the lined steel, the alloy side becomes the inner wall, unaffected by the corrosive influence exerted by petroleum crudes as well as by most other materials. The corrosion problem is met in the multilayer carbon steel vessel by providing a leakproof inner liner of chromium or chromium nickel steel or clad steel.

Clad Steel Plate. The clad steel plate is made as follows: A relatively thick plate of corrosion-resistant material is applied to the specially prepared surface of a carbon-steel slab. For stainless-steel or "Inconel" cladding, the carbon-steel surface is not only cleaned, but nickel-plated electrolytically. The carbon steel slab and the cladding material are placed on a table, and then a second similarly prepared assembly of steel and cladding material is placed upside down on top of the first, with an infusible parting compound between them. The two cladding plates are the inner layers, the carbon steel slabs the outermost layers of the resulting "sandwich." The steel backing plates are made slightly longer and wider than the cladding plates so that the sandwich has a groove running around the four sides of the assembly. The groove is filled with steel bars and then welded in place, after removing the air in the sandwich by the application of a vacuum. The welding seals the pack, preventing contamination and movement of the components during the subsequent heating and rolling. For these, the pack is heated in a soaking pit to

Figure 485.—Knocked-down sections of a 16½ feet diameter by 125 feet long oil fractionating column to be assembled by welding in the field. The sections shown are Smithlined with "Monel," that is, the "Monel" sheet is spotwelded to the carbon steel wall. Built for Standard Oil Co., of N. J.; the complete order made up of 16 carloads in shipment. (Courtesy A. O. Smith Corp., Milwaukee, Wis.)

2,100–2,350°F, depending on the type of cladding, and rolled in a mill, reducing the thickness to the desired one and bonding permanently the cladding to the steel. The pack is then sheared or flame-cut just inside the weld edges, and separated into two clad steel plates, which are subsequently heat-treated, and descaled, by the sodium hydride process in at least one mill.* Thus to manufacture a 20 per cent clad steel, a 1-inch cladding material would be placed on a 4-inch slab of carbon steel, assembled with another similar pair, as explained, and rolled to ½ inch, a reduction of 10 to 1, for example. Of the 0.500-inch total thickness, 0.100 is cladding, 0.400 is steel.

Clad steels are manufactured with the corrosion-resistant layer 10, 15, and 20 per cent of the total thickness for all thicknesses, and also 5 per cent for plates over ½-inch in total thickness. The bond between the cladding and the steel is as strong as the steel itself; it results from the solid solution formed at the junction of the layers of unlike metals during the hot-rolling process.

The welding of clad steel in the course of fabrication of equipment is done with great care so as not to mix the two metals, for that would bring about a reduction of the stainless qualities of the cladding. The weld joining clad steel plates becomes a section of the corrosion-resistant surface. The plates are beveled and fitted up for welding. The steel is welded with steel electrodes, by arc welding. The cladding side is then back-chipped and otherwise prepared, and then arc-welded, using electrodes of the proper, recommended composition so that the weld metal will approximate or equal that of the cladding.†

Spot Lining. There are other methods of applying the corrosion-resistant alloy sheet, of which spot lining is the most prominent. The *spot-lined, corrosion-resistant liner* is securely attached to the steel plate by means of a vast number of small welds set close together, as for example on a pitch ranging from 1½ to 3 inches. Speaking specifically of the "Smithlined" pressure vessels, the procedure is as follows: A special automatic machine attaches the alloy sheets to the steel plates by resistance (electrical) spot welding. The uniform spacing of these spots is automatic and is determined in advance to suit the specified service conditions. The steel plates are lined while flat; after the lining operation, the plates are formed into shell sections, heads, and other details as required for the vessel. Special joint designs have been developed to prevent contamination of the alloy where lining sheets or carbon plates are welded together. Steel plates of any thickness from ½ inch up can be

---

* "Fabrication of Lukens Clad Steels," p. 9, Lukens Steel Company, Coatesville, Pa., 1949.

† "Fabrication of Lukens Clad Steels," p. 54. See also *Ind. Eng. Chem.*, **33**, 506 (1941).

Smithlined with alloy sheets in the range of $\frac{5}{64}$ to $\frac{9}{64}$ inches in thickness. Every spot weld is tested by means of nitrogen gas under pressures as high as 1,000 psi. A spot lining is shown in Figure 485.

Spot lining is very flexible, inasmuch as about fifteen different materials can be used, whereas only a few of them can be rolled on by the cladding process. Furthermore, spot welding is less expensive—so much so that only the relatively thinly clad plates can compete commercially.

FIGURE 486.—A spot-lined steel cylinder showing complete protection of the inner surface. Note the pattern of the spot welds. (Courtesy A. O. Smith Corp., Milwaukee, Wis.)

Plug welding is still another method of applying the lining. In this method, the sheet is provided with many perforations, within which the two metals are welded together with an alloy rod, and the holes then filled with corrosion-resistant metal.

SELECTION OF TYPE OF LINING

The wall thickness of a vessel gives a handy guide for the selection of the proper form of material, whether solid stainless, clad, lined, or other.

When the wall vessel thickness is $\frac{1}{4}$ inch or under, solid stainless steel is usually most economical.   From ¼ to ½ inch, solid material and clad material are competitive.   If consideration is given only to the higher allowable stresses permitted in the solid material, the latter is generally more economical in gauges from ¼ to ½ inch.   However, the majority of applications for clad steels under ⁵⁄₁₆ inch gauge in the past have been storage tanks, brewery tanks, and other types of vessels where stiffness and rigidity, more than tensile strength, are the governing factors in design.   There are additional factors, often overlooked, that apply to design of pressure vessels in gauges of ½ inch down to ³⁄₁₆ inch.   There are as follows:

(1) The use of higher tensile backing steels, such as A-212 or A-204, reduces the difference between the allowable stresses of the clad and of the solid materials.   However, high-temperature applications give the chrome-nickel stainless steels and "Inconel" in solid form a definite advantage over clad, while the straight chromium steels, "Monel," and nickel in solid form are at a disadvantage under these conditions.   This is due to the higher allowable stresses at elevated temperatures for the chrome-nickel steels and "Inconel."   If heat transfer only is considered, clad steel has a definite advantage over chrome-nickel steels, straight chromium steels, "Monel," and "Inconel" in the solid form, because of the better heat conductivity of these metals in clad form.

(2) The overweight tolerances for solid materials are somewhat in excess of the tolerances for clads.   This could be quite important if a large vessel were under consideration.

(3) Hot-forming costs are considerably higher for solid materials than for clad materials.   Moreover, annealing and pickling are not included in the base price for solid materials while they are included in the base price for clad materials.   Here again, this can be quite important if a large vessel is under consideration.

(4) It can readily be seen that in gauges under ½ inch, the fabricating cost of the two forms of material, solid or clad, will vary according to the design, and no definite advantage can be given to either form.   Each case must be considered individually.

From ½- to 1-inch wall thickness, clad and lined material are very competitive.   Above 1 inch, lined is usually most economical if operating conditions permit its use.   For many types of applications linings cannot be used because heat conductivity is a limiting factor.   Surface condition can be achieved with either method and will usually depend on the economical aspects.   Differential expansion of stainless linings has been found by experiment and service experience to be of little consequence at temperatures below 750°F with either clad or lined construction.   At temperatures in the creep range of 900 to 950°F, difficulties have been encountered with clad materials from the standpoint of stress rupture and graphitization because of variation in the cladding thickness at the weld seams requiring a heavier alloy weld deposit. This condition has not been encountered in spot-welded lined vessels operating at these temperatures because here the thickness of the alloy is uniform.

If severely corrosive conditions require a heavy gauge (⅝ inch and higher), a change in material is indicated. In general, heavy gauges of solid stainless steels and "Inconel" are used because of the higher allowable stress permitted at high temperatures and not because of severely corrosive conditions.

MULTILAYER CONSTRUCTION

Over the past twelve years there have been placed in successful operation a number of thick-walled vessels with multilayer construction, for uses in the chemical industries which involved pressures up to and some-

FIGURE 487.—View inside the multilayer vessel illustrated in Figure 492, showing the polished stainless alloy inner layer. (Courtesy A. O. Smith Corp., Milwaukee, Wis.)

what over 5,000 psi. The multilayer wall is made up of a number of layers of steel with surfaces cleaned and smooth. The layers are descaled only where heat transfer is necessary. The inner layer is usually thicker than ¼ inch. Each layer is progressively wrapped and tightened around the inner ones by mechanical means and then welded together at the edges (longitudinally). The innermost layer is started on heavy, removable guide rings. Each layer is perforated with small holes for venting; only the innermost layer need be leakproof. The inner layer may be an appropriate corrosion-resistant material, as shown in Figure 487. For multilayer vessels for highly corrosive service, the inner cylinder may be of solid corrosion-resistant material, or it may be a clad-lined or a Smith-lined cylinder depending on the demands of the service and the most economical method of producing a satisfactory vessel. Forged or cast carbon steel closures are alloy-lined with thin spot or plug welding where required.

FIGURE 488.—A closer view of the wall in a multilayer wall vessel. (Courtesy A. O. Smith Corp., Milwaukee, Wis.)

If the thickness of the plate is ¼ inch a 12-layer vessel would have a wall thickness of 3 inches, a medium value. The edges (lengthwise) of the outer cylindrical section are machined for the welding groove, and welded, finishing the wall along the side. The ends of the cylindrical sections are also machined, and several sections are assembled in the same way that solid sections would be, with a girth weld to join them together. In very heavy vessels, with 10- or 12-inch walls, additional layers are put on only after the girth welds are partially made, to avoid making the weld in very deep grooves.

The multilayer construction makes for safety. In tests to destruction it was shown that failure in the layer vessel occurs with a considerable amount of deformation, but without shattering or fragmentation. Solid-

FIGURE 489.—Multilayer vessel with special quick-opening door, to operate at 5,000 psi. The over-all length is 21 feet 8 inches. (Courtesy A. O. Smith Corp., Milwaukee, Wis.)

FIGURE 490.—Two air ballasted accumulator vessels, with multilayer construction, built for a working pressure of 5,000 psi. The walls are over 6 inches thick. (Courtesy A. O. Smith Corp., Milwaukee, Wis.)

walled vessels, on the other hand, tested at the same time, showed no deformation, and fragmented badly. The multilayer construction is being used for relatively thin-walled vessels as well as for thick-walled.

A commercial vessel built in 1931 has been in active operation since its installation at a pressure of 2,000 psi and is an example of early applications. A vessel 21 feet 8 inches in over-all length, with a quick-opening head (see Figure 489), operated in rapid heating and cooling cycles at a pressure of 5,000 psi, is a more recent one, as are also high-pressure separators for synthetic ammonia plant service. The large, air-ballasted accumulator vessel is still another example of multilayer construction; it has a 35-inch inside diameter and an over-all length of over 50 feet; it is built for a working pressure of 4,500 psi. Of late (1952), multilayer construction has been adopted for high-pressure gas and oil pipelines, as well as for penstocks. The highest pressures for which multi-layer vessels were built until lately were 10,000 and 11,000 psi. At the present time there is being built a vessel to withstand a pressure of 15,000 psi; it will have a wall thickness of 14¾ inches, and an average diameter $[(D_1 + D_2) \div 2]$ of 38¾ inches. Some other examples are

FIGURE 491.—A converter with multilayer construction for high-pressure synthesis, 4 feet I.D., with wall 8½ inches thick, and 45 feet long. The working pressure is 5,150 psi at 402°F. (Courtesy A. O. Smith Corp., Milwaukee, Wis.)

included in the list below; this also includes solid-walled vessels, which remain the more economical type for moderate service conditions.

The following are further examples of pressure vessels of various types:

A pressure vessel, 6 feet O.D., to operate at 1,200 psi.

A chrome-nickel Smithlined jacketed kettle, 7 feet 10 inches I.D., 1-inch wall thickness, and 11 feet 9⁷⁄₁₆ inches over-all length excluding motor and reducer mechanism, built to work at full vacuum and at 765°F.

A scrubber tower 5 feet 6 inches wide, 1⅞-inch wall thickness, and 84 feet 3⅞ inches over-all length, to operate at 450 psi.

A jacketed pressure vessel with solid wall, 5 feet 6 inches I.D., 2¾-inch wall thickness, 7 feet 2 inches over-all length, built for working pressure of 800 psi at 415°F.

A Multi-layer pressure vessel 48 inches I.D., 4⅛-inch wall thickness, 23 feet 10 inches over-all length, built for a working pressure of 2,000 psi at 480°F.

A Multi-layer converter, 48¼ inches I.D., 8½-inch wall thickness, 44 feet 6 inches over-all length, built to operate at 5,150 psi and at 402°F.

A coke drum of 12 feet inside diameter by 51 feet 5 inches long and 2⅝ inch thick, of carbon molybdenum steel. Weight 131 tons; operating pressure 435 psi at 870°F.

As may be seen from the foregoing list and from the illustrations, pressure vessels have a number of forms, including fractionating towers which work under pressure, and reaction chambers. Jacketed pressure vessels are not at all unusual; graphs which permit the ready determination of the thickness for jacketed, solid-walled kettles which are to withstand high internal pressures or external pressures will be found in Chapter 21.

FIGURE 492.—High-pressure multi-layer pressure vessel, equipped with agitator, built for chemical service; 48 inches I.D., 4⅛ inches wall thickness, 23 feet 10 inches over-all length; working pressure, 2,000 psi. (Courtesy A. O. Smith Corp., Milwaukee, Wis.)

FIGURE 493.—Vulcanizer roll for use in rubber processing, composed of two Luken-weld-steam platens, with inner steam labyrinth, formed into two halves of a shell and joined by welding. The shell face is Lukens Stainless-Clad Steel for high heat conductivity. Two separate steam fields are provided with inlets and outlets through the hubs. (Courtesy Lukenweld, Division of Lukens Steel Co.)

Balanced design has a bearing on the strength of the vessel, hence on safety, as well as the material of the walls and the welds. The effect of an elliptical head instead of an ordinary dished head and of reënforcement at manway openings is to raise the yield value by 30 and 70 per cent, respectively.

Figure 494.—Modern all-welded tank car for handling liquid sugar; built of 20 per cent Lukens Stainless-Clad Steel by General American Transportation Co., Sharon, Pa. (Courtesy Lukens Steel Co., Coatesville, Pa.)

Figure 495.—Shop view of one of the world's largest evaporators fabricated by Farrar and Trefts, Inc., Buffalo, N.Y. It is used for finishing glucose; the strike pan is made of Lukens Nickel-Clad Steel plates and heads, with solid nickel fittings. The pan is of the horizontal tube type with two banks of tubes, and an independent steam supply to each bank, to permit finishing batches up to 25,000 pounds. Engineered by Zaremba Co. (Courtesy Lukens Steel Co.)

Low Pressure and Medium Pressure Corrosion-lined Vessels

The lining for corrosion resistance is not limited, as already stated, to high-pressure vessels; on the contrary, it is equally applicable to low- and medium-pressure vessels and shapes of all kinds. Figure 493 exhibits a stainless-steel clad vulcanizer roll of special construction as to steam circulation; Figure 494 an all-welded tank car for handling liquid sugar built of 20 per cent "Lukens" stainless-clad steel; and Figure 495 an evaporator for finishing glucose, of "Lukens" nickel-clad steel plates and heads.

Spot lining similarly is used for low- and medium-pressure vessels, and the details of fabrication and testing which have been set forth in earlier sections apply here also.

Reading References

"Multi-layer construction of thick wall pressure vessels," by T. M. Jasper and C. M. Scudder, *Trans. Am. Inst. Chem. Eng.*, **37**, 885 (1941).

"Manual for the design of ferrous and non-ferrous pressure vessels and tanks," by K. Simon, Metuchen, N. J., published by the author, 1941.

"The design of high pressure plant and the properties of fluids at high pressure," by D. M. Newitt, Oxford University Press, 114 Fifth Avenue, New York, 1941.

"Factors in high-pressure design," by C. W. Seibel, *Ind. Eng. Chem.*, **29**, 414 (1937).

"Mechanical features of synthesis at high pressures," by R. V. Kleinschmidt, *Trans. Am. Inst. Chem. Eng.*, **29**, 88 (1933).

"Gaskets for pressure vessels and heat exchangers," by C. O. Sandstrom, *Chem. Met. Eng.*, **41**, 130 (1934).

"The design and construction of a high pressure plant," by H. Tongue, London, Chapman and Hall, 1934.

"Construction of welded pressure vessels for the petroleum industry," by R. K. Hopkins, *Trans. Am. Inst. Chem. Eng.*, **32**, 138 (1936).

"Metals and alloys used in chemical engineering plant construction," by J. A. Lee, *Trans. Am. Inst. Chem. Eng.*, **32**, 169 (1936).

"The design of vessels to withstand high internal pressures," by D. M. Newitt, *Trans. Inst. Chem. Eng.*, *(London)*, **14**, 85 (1936).

"The strength of steel at elevated temperatures, with particular reference to safety factors," by T. M. Jasper, Eighth annual meeting, American Petroleum Institute, Chicago, Dec. 5–8, 1927.

"Stainless-clad steels," by T. S. Fitch, *Ind. Eng. Chem.*, **33**, 502 (1941).

"Closures for high-pressure vessels," by Douglas Meigs, *Trans. Am. Inst. Chem. Eng.*, **39**, 769 (1943).

"Design of thick-walled pressure vessel shells," first in a series of three, by R. R. Maccary and R. F. Fey, *Chem. Eng.*, **56**, 124–127 (Aug. 1949); see also same vol., Sept., p. 105, and Oct., p. 120.

"High pressure; Chemical Engineering Report," *Chem. Eng.*, **56**, 107–123 (Aug. 1949).

"Survey of high pressure equipment designs in Germany," U. S. Field Information Agency Technical, FIAT Final Report 1067 (P. B. 8128P) (May 13, 1947).

"Interpretive report, fabrication division, pressure vessel research Committee," by H. C. Boardman, *Welding J.*, **29**, No. 9 422–S to 432–S (Sept. 1950).

"Welding of high-pressure air-vessel assemblies," by K. G. Lewis, *Metallurgia*, **20**, No. 236, 77–87 (June 1949).

"Factors influencing the economic design of pressure vessels," by G. E. Fratcher, American Society of Mechanical Engineers, Amarillo, Texas, meeting, October 3, 1948.

"Pressure vessels and boilers," Chapter 51, pp. 1157–1194, "Welding Handbook," 3rd Ed., American Welding Society, New York 18, N. Y., 1950.

Instrumentation is more than pressure gauges, potentiometers, and automatic valves. It is a tremendous force at work daily improving the economy of the process industries. Many integrated and complex processes would still be on the drafting boards were it not for the modern concepts of centralized instrumentation which make possible the almost instantaneous coordination of scores of variables. Today, we are on the threshold of the automatic factory which will become a reality because of the even newer concept of servomechanisms, computers, and final product analysis techniques.

25. INSTRUMENTATION. PART I: TEMPERATURE MEASUREMENT—PRESSURE-SPRING THERMOMETERS, THERMOCOUPLE PYROMETERS, RESISTANCE THERMOMETERS, TOTAL RADIATION PYROMETERS. PRESSURE MEASUREMENT. VACUUM MEASUREMENT*

Instrumentation is of paramount importance in regulating the course of a process, in insuring the proper product quality, and in effecting material savings; it contributes heavily to plant safety, to good cost accounting, to research projects, and to the success of pilot plants.

Temperature, pressure, flow, hydrogen-ion concentration, and gas composition are among the most important industrial process variables that have to be measured and controlled. For plant operation the most useful instruments are those which indicate and those which record. Often the same instrument does both. A pointer moves along a scale of temperature, for example, while at the same time a pen arm traces a record on a circular or strip chart. The indicating or recording instrument may be connected with other apparatus whereby the operation is controlled; e.g., when the temperature falls for any reason, more fuel oil or steam is admitted to the heating unit by the automatic opening of an electrically operated valve.

The flow meter is an example of an instrument which may be either indicating or recording, or both; here too, the recording instrument may be so connected to additional apparatus that any variation in flow is automatically corrected by altering the position of a master valve which governs the flow. Moreover, it may be important to summarize the flow for

* Prepared by Douglas M. Considine, Chemical Engineer and Manager of Market Extension, Industrial Division, Minneapolis-Honeywell Regulator Co., Philadelphia, Pa.

the day; this is done by connecting the flow meter to still another apparatus: the integrator or totalizer. Thus flow meters perform four functions: (1) indicating the flow, (2) recording it throughout the day, (3) restoring it to the desired value when for any reason there is a deviation (controlling), and (4) summarizing it for the day (or other period). The flow controller may be further extended to become a ratio controller by interconnecting two controllers so that the same relation between the two flows is maintained in spite of fluctuations in the absolute amounts; also either or both of these flows may be made to follow a specified time program of controlled values.

THE PROCESS VARIABLES

Underlying all instrumentation techniques are the *process variables.* Defined by the A.S.M.E., a process variable is "a quantity or condition

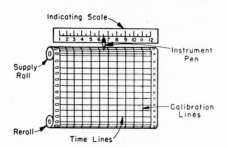

FIGURE 496.—Essential elements of a strip chart recorder.

associated with a process, the value of which is subject to change with time." If these quantities or conditions did not vary with time, there would be no need to measure, indicate, record, or control them—hence no need for instrumentation. The fact remains, however, that there is practically no process which is so self-stabilizing as to preclude the need for automatic control.

A number of process variables, though by no means all, are tabulated below.

        I. Energy Variables
           1. Temperature (heat or thermal energy)
           2. Pressure
           3. Radiation (radiant energy)
       II. Quantity and Rate Variables
           1. Flow
           2. Level of fluids and solids
           3. Weight, force, torque
           4. Thickness and caliper
           5. Position and displacement
           6. Velocity and acceleration

III. Material Property Variables
   1. Specific gravity (density)
   2. Humidity and dew point
   3. Moisture content
   4. Viscosity and consistency
   5. Calorific value
   6. Reflectance
   7. Color and opacity
   8. Turbidity; smoke and haze density
   9. Electrical conductivity
  10. pH (Hydrogen-ion conc.)
  11. Chemical composition
  12. Oxidation-reduction potential
IV. Electrical Variables
   1. Potential
   2. Current
   3. Power
   4. Resistance
 V. Time (as related to pressure, temperature, or other process variables.)

TEMPERATURE MEASUREMENT

The "variable" in chemical processes which nearly always receives first consideration is temperature. With a rise in temperature, the speed of a reaction increases rapidly; with a sufficiently large rise, it reverses or

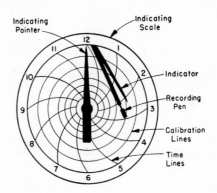

FIGURE 497.—Essential elements of a circular chart recorder.

gets out of control. With a rise in temperature, the pressure in a closed vessel rises, and solids become fluids. With a drop in temperature, the speed of a reaction slackens; materials do not melt or react, or if originally melted, they solidify, in part, and the expected reaction is not completed. A rise in temperature is not necessarily beneficial, even at or near room temperature; thus a temperature too far away from the ice point will spoil a diazotization in a dyestuff factory, and waste much valuable material. Temperature is the intensity factor for heat, the other factor of which is capacity, usually expressed as specific heat. The measurement and control of temperature constitutes the largest field of application for industrial instruments.

TABLE 87. CLASSIFICATION OF TEMPERATURE-MÉASURING ELEMENTS

Physical Manifestation of Temperature Change	Instruments Employing This Principle	Approximate, Practical. Temperature Range (°F)
Volumetric expansion or contraction of fluids	Liquid-in-glass thermometers	−250 to 1,000
	Pressure-type thermometers	
	(1) mercury filled system	−40 to 1,000
	(2) gas filled system	−40 to 1,000
	(3) liquid-and-vapor filled system	−10 to 600
Differential expansion of dissimilar metals	Bimetallic thermometers, thermostats	0 to 1,000
Generation of thermoelectric emf in circuit comprising two dissimilar metals	Thermocouple pyrometers	
	(1) Base-metal couples	−300 to 2,100
	(2) Noble-metal couples	0 to 2,900
	(3) Thermopiles (see radiation pyrometers)	
Change of electrical resistance	Resistance thermometers (metal wire)	−310 to 2,000
Monochromatic radiation from "hot" body	Optical pyrometer	1,200 to 6,500
Total radiation from "hot" body	Total radiation pyrometer (using the thermopile)	0 to 3,200
Fusion of solids	Seger cones (pyrometric cones)	1,100 to 3,700

Liquid-In-Glass Thermometers. The liquid-in-glass thermometers depend for their function on the expansion of a liquid in a bulb surmounted by a glass capillary on which the temperature scale has been etched. The best known thermometer is mercury in glass, made for use in a number of ranges, such as from a few degrees below zero centigrade to 360°C. By filling the capillary with nitrogen, the mercury thermometer will read temperatures as high as 450°C. By using special glass, temperatures as high as 600°C may be read. One such thermometer has pentane as the dilating fluid. For low temperatures, down to −70°C or so, alcohol-filled glass thermometers are useful; the alcohol is usually tinted red.

The use of glass thermometers is restricted by their fragility. An instrument rugged enough for industrial purposes is the stem thermometer; it may be alcohol filled, with the liquid tinted red, with a brass stem and an 18–8 stainless-steel bulb surmounted by a glass capillary. Portable industrial stem thermometers, straight type, are 3 or 4 feet long. Stem thermometers are available in 90° angle form and in 135° angle form. The ranges covered by these instruments are as wide as −40° to +100°F; 0° to 100°F; 200° to 1,000°F.

Liquid-in-glass thermometers are still useful in batch processes and pilot plant work, yet even here, the tendency is to utilize multiple-indicating potentiometers, employing thermocouples. By centralizing all important temperature measurements in one instrument, the gathering of data is much more convenient and efficient.

Pressure Thermometers. The pressure thermometer is a bulb-and-tubing instrument. The bulb contains the actuating agent, which may be a liquid, a vapor, or a gas. The tubing is a Bourdon tube, round or flattened, in the form of a spiral or helix. When the bulb is heated, the pressure developed is communicated through a capillary tubing to the helical tube, which is thereby slightly distorted. This distortion becomes the measure of the temperature. One end of the helix is fixed by the connecting capillary tubing; the other is free to move, and carries a pointer for indicating and a pen arm for recording. When pressure is developed, the helix tends to unwind.

The actuating agent may be either a liquid or a vapor. Mercury is the liquid most generally used, because of its uniform and high coefficient of expansion. It is suitable for the range −40 to 1,000°F. As the connecting capillary has a bore of 0.007 inch, the ratio of bulb volume to tubing volume is high; this practically eliminates any error due to changes in temperature along the connection. Bulb, capillary, and tube are all completely filled with liquid mercury. The helical or spiral tube must be of steel, as well as the capillary connection and bulb. Alcohol is sometimes used as a liquid filling medium, and serves over the range of −40 to 300°F.

Vapors used as indicating agents include ether, sulfur dioxide, or methyl chloride. The liquid partly fills the bulb; the connecting tube reaches to the bottom of the bulb and is filled with the liquid, as is also the helical or spiral tube. Vapor forms only in a part of the bulb. The vapor tension type instrument has a range of 250 and 320°, which may lie anywhere between −0 and 600°F.

The gas-filled tube is usually filled with very pure nitrogen. It responds more slowly than the mercury tube, and develops less power, but copper may be used for the helical tube, and the range is wide, from −40 to 1,000°F. The ratio of bulb volume to tube volume is 40:1 or better in order to reduce the error of compression in connecting tubing and helix, and the connecting tubing temperature error.

The pressure thermometer is a valuable indicating instrument, comparatively simple, and easily installed. Provided with a pen arm and suitable revolving round chart or traveling strip chart, it records as it measures.

Bimetallic Thermometers. "Bimetal" is a composite metal made up of two metals which differ in their coefficient of expansion when heated. More precisely, bimetal is a composite metal half of whose cross section is composed of a high temperature coefficient of expansion metal, and half of a low temperature coefficient of expansion metal. The two metals are permanently welded together throughout their entire surface of contact by a direct high-temperature, high-pressure process without any bonding material. When the bimetal is heated, a warping action is produced.

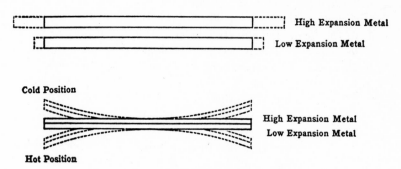

FIGURE 498.—Differential thermal expansion.

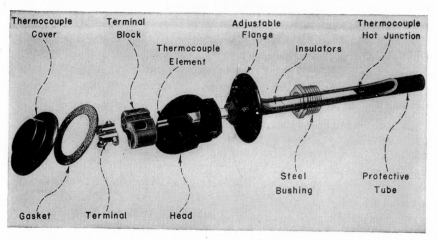

FIGURE 499.—Exploded view of typical industrial thermocouple with protective tube.

This change in curvature is the basis of the device. The differential thermal expansion is schematically illustrated in Figure 498.*

Thermocouple Pyrometers. An exploded view of a type of the thermocouple quite representative of those used in the processing industries is shown in Figure 499. A thermocouple consists of two dissimilar metal wires joined at one end, generally referred to as the *hot junction*. These wires are usually contained in a tube for protection against excessively

---

* From "Materials Engineering of Metal Products," by Norman E. Woldman, New York, Reinhold Publishing Corporation, 1949.

oxidizing or reducing furnace atmospheres and from other types of corrosion. When the hot junction of a thermocouple is subjected to a change in temperature, rising or falling, while the free ends (terminals) are maintained at a constant temperature, an electric potential is set up between the terminals which is definitely related to the hot junction temperature. This potential is measurable by a millivoltmeter or potentiometer.

Scores of thermocouple designs are available for specific purposes. Thus, the selection of a thermocouple best suited for a given application requires very serious consideration, since no pyrometric measurement can be better than the accuracy and reproducibility of temperature detection by the thermocouple.

While many combinations of metals have been used for thermocouples, there are four combinations most commonly used, namely: (1) copper and constantan wires, (2) iron and constantan wires, (3) chromel and alumel wires, and (4) platinum and platinum-plus-rhodium wires. The practical ranges of temperature over which these combinations are used are shown in Table 88. The first three combinations are commonly

TABLE 88. THERMOCOUPLE SELECTION GUIDE

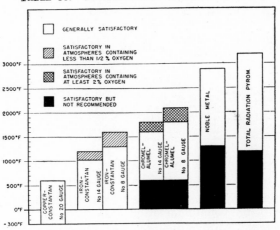

known as base metal couples, while the fourth combination is known as noble metal couples. Also shown are the effects of oxidizing and reducing conditions upon thermocouple wires. The range of the total radiation pyrometer is given for comparative purposes.

The superiority of copper-constantan for the measurement of relatively low temperatures, especially subzero temperatures, is well established. These couples are resistant to rust and corrosion, are reproducible to a high degree of precision, and are generally preferred for ranges between —300 and +600°F.

Iron-constantan couples are suitable for use where there is a deficiency of free oxygen.   Above 1,000°F, the rate of oxidation of the iron increases rapidly and the use of No. 8 gauge wire is required, the latter being satisfactory up to 1,600°F.

Chromel-alumel thermocouples were developed for use in atmospheres containing free oxygen.   Under these conditions, these couples generally will give better service than iron-constantan.   Complete absence of free oxygen has a tendency to alter the thermoelectric characteristics of the wires, with consequent loss of accuracy.   For this reason, vented thermocouple protection tubes are made available.

Platinum and platinum-plus-rhodium couples are expensive and generally are used only in those higher ranges in which other couples will deteriorate.   However, these couples are adversely affected by atmospheres containing no free oxygen and thus they should be protected by impervious tubes.   Where free hydrogen is present, a total radiation pyrometer will provide much better service than the noble metal couples.

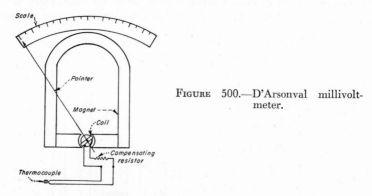

FIGURE   500.—D'Arsonval   millivoltmeter.

As mentioned above, the two basic types of instruments employed for measuring the millivoltages created by thermocouples are (1) deflectional type millivoltmeters, and (2) null-balance potentiometers.   Where precision is required, the potentiometer generally is used.

Millivoltmeters.   Millivoltmeters (see Figure 500) employ the D'Arsonval galvanometer.   Deflections are obtained by the reaction between an energized coil and the field of a permanent magnet.   The coil of fine wire is connected across the circuit to be measured, through spiral springs. It is supported by pivots and free to move in the annular space between a soft-iron core and the pole pieces of a permanent magnet.   Owing to the shape of the pole pieces and core, the strength of the magnetic field is uniform.   Hence, the deflections of the pointer are directly proportional to the current and the scale divisions are uniform.

Potentiometers.   Although it is possible to measure the temperature of a thermocouple directly by means of a millivoltmeter, this method introduces, as a possible variable, the resistance of the leads and connections. Consequently, a potentiometer is generally used as the measuring circuit in precision instruments since in this method resistance is ruled out as a variable, owing to the fact that the electrical potential applied is balanced against an equal and opposite potential produced by battery.

An elementary potentiometer circuit is shown in Figure 501. In the upper circuit, the battery produces a potential drop in the slidewire which may be adjusted by resistance R. In the lower circuits, an opposite potential is produced by a standard cell of definitely known voltage, and the drop in the slidewire can be made equal and opposite to that produced by the battery by an adjustment of the slider, this point being indicated by a zero reading of the galvanometer. A thermocouple can then be substituted for the standard cell, and the galvanometer again brought to zero by adjusting the slider. The relation between the first and second slider readings is a measure of the difference between the thermocouple and that of the standard cell, and the slidewire positions may be calibrated in terms

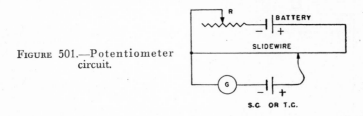

FIGURE 501.—Potentiometer circuit.

of temperature of the hot junction corresponding to the various potentials. The potentiometer just described is manually balanced. In industrial instruments, the balancing action is accomplished automatically and the thermocouple millivoltage (in terms of temperature) is indicated continuously by mechanical, electrical, or electronic means.

Space does not permit description of the many types of commercially available potentiometers. The detecting and rebalancing means used in one type of electronic potentiometer are illustrated in Figure 502. Briefly, the direct current millivoltage created by the thermocouple is changed to an alternating current voltage of proportional magnitude in a converter. The converter is essentially a flat metal reed oscillating between two contacts connected to the opposite ends of the primary winding of an input transformer. The unbalanced direct current voltage is impressed across the converter and the center tap of the primary winding on the input transformer. As the reed moves from one contact to the other, any unbalanced direct current voltage will cause direct current to flow first in one direction through one-half the primary winding—then in the opposite direction through the other half. This action generates an alternating flux in the input transformer core which, in turn, induces an alternating voltage on the transformer secondary.

The action of the converter is related to the alternating current supply voltage by the energizing coil which is excited by the latter through a stepdown transformer. The reed is polarized by a permanent magnet and, therefore, is actuated by the energizing coil to oscillate in synchronism with the alternating current supply voltage. The reed closes one contact to the transformer for one-half the supply voltage cycle and the other contact for the other half, making one complete oscillation for each cycle. The direct current flowing in each half of the transformer primary winding, therefore, will create an alternating voltage in the transformer secondary of the same frequency as the supply voltage. This alternating voltage is amplified in voltage and power to where it will actuate a two-phase balancing motor.

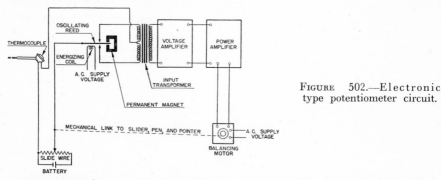

Figure 502.—Electronic type potentiometer circuit.

If there is an unbalance between the slidewire voltage and the thermocouple voltage, the balancing motor functions to rebalance the two voltages by moving the slider on the slidewire. The direction in which the motor turns is determined by a definite phase relationship between the alternating current supply voltage and the amplified alternating current thermocouple voltage. This relationship depends, of course, upon whether the measured variable (temperature in this case) is increasing or decreasing in magnitude.

Resistance Thermometers. The fact that metals increase in electrical resistance with increasing temperature provides a method of temperature measurement known as *resistance thermometry*. The detecting element takes the form of a wire-wound resistor commonly referred to as a *resistance thermometer bulb*. This bulb is connected to a measuring instrument incorporating a Wheatstone bridge. Simple indicating instruments employ a *deflectional* bridge, whereas recorders and controllers employ a *balanced* bridge. All of these instruments interpret changes in resistance at the thermometer bulb in terms of temperature.

Balanced Wheatstone Bridge. In the balanced type Wheatstone bridge resistance thermometer, a coil of pure nickel wire, which comprises the thermometer bulb, is connected into one branch of a direct current bridge circuit. Nickel is commonly used in the bulb because it has a high specific resistance as well as a high resistance change with temperature, and is relatively inexpensive. In another branch, there is a variable resistance in the form of a slidewire. The nickel wire coil, suitably protected, is placed in the medium to be measured. Variations in the temperature of the measured medium cause a change in the resistance of the nickel wire and a consequent unbalance of the bridge circuit.

A self-balancing Wheatstone bridge detects the condition of unbalance, determines its direction and magnitude, and positions the slidewire contactor to rebalance the bridge and to indicate the temperature on a suitable scale. With reference to the circuit diagram (Figure 503), operation of the system is as follows:

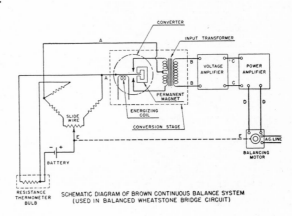

FIGURE 503.—Circuit of balanced Wheatstone bridge type resistance thermometer.

The direct current potential appearing at *AA* is converted to an alternating voltage appearing at *BB* and is multiplied by the voltage amplifier to a large value at *CC*. The potential is then used to control the power amplifier output *DD* which drives the balancing motor in the proper direction to balance the bridge. The mechanical connection between the balancing motor and the slidewire is shown by dotted line *EE*. As in the case of the potentiometer previously described, the polarity of the signal at *AA* determines the phase (or timing) of the alternating voltage at *BB* which, in turn, determines the direction of rotation of the balancing motor.

Deflectional Wheatstone Bridge. In the circuit (Figure 504) of the deflectional type indicator illustrated, points *A*, *B*, and *C* represent the terminals of the bulb located at the point of temperature measurement. *D* and *E* are ratio arms of equal resistance. *P* is a fixed resistance equal to the resistance of the bulb corresponding to the highest temperature reading on the indicator scale. *X* is a fixed resistance equal to the resistance of the bulb corresponding to the lowest temperature reading on the scale. A battery energizes the circuit and *RH* is the rheostat for adjusting the battery current to the standardized value. When standardizing the battery current, the switch is thrown to the side marked *Std* to include resistor *X* in the bridge circuit. The rheostat is then adjusted until the indicator deflects to the lowest temperature reading on the scale. After standardizing, the switch is thrown to the "bulb" position.

With the three-wire circuit illustrated for the two systems, it is not necessary to calibrate the equipment in the field or to equalize the resistance of the extension wire where the instrument is used with a number of bulbs. Three separate No. 16 gauge copper wires, or triple-conductor cable, are used for each bulb and can be used for distances up to 1,000 feet.

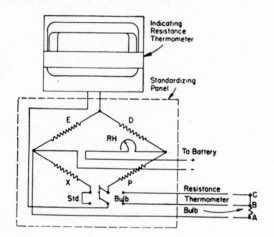

Figure 504.—Circuit of deflectional Wheatstone bridge type resistance thermometer.

The accuracy of resistance thermometers using the Wheatstone bridge circuits described is independent of any normal variation in the potential of the battery. Therefore, ordinary dry cells provide a perfectly satisfactory source of direct current, and standardization of the battery current is not required. In addition, the system requires no cold junction compensation.

Resistance Bulbs and Wells. The resistance bulb element for industrial temperature measurement is designed for use in protecting tube assemblies and measures $3\frac{1}{2}$ inches in length by approximately $\frac{1}{4}$ inch in diameter, with an active portion $1\frac{5}{8}$ inches in length. The Manganin coil in the element is used to adjust the temperature resistance characteristic so that all bulbs are identical and interchangeable.

Bulb assemblies with protecting tubes are available in numerous styles, some resembling the thermocouple assemblies previously described, others being supplied without a terminal head. Union connections and separable wells are available, such as with pressure type thermometers. In addition, a variety of wet and dry resistance bulb assemblies are supplied for relative humidity determinations.

As a result of the careful construction and selection of materials, the bulb assemblies afford high accuracy, sensitivity, and long life. Ruggedness is an in-built feature, safeguarding against short circuits, open circuits, and grounds. The element withstands severe vibration without mechanical failure or change in calibration.

Newer thin-walled bulb assemblies have recently been developed to provide exceptionally high measuring response.

Radiation Pyrometers. The industrial radiation pyrometer is a practical application of the Stefan-Boltzmann law of radiation energy which states that the intensity of radiant heat emitted from the surface of a body increases proportionately to the fourth power of its absolute temperature. As illustrated in Figure 505, energy from the object of measurement falling on the pyrometer lens is focused on a thermopile which generates an emf proportional to the amount of energy falling on it and hence propor-

FIGURE 505.—Principle of industrial type total radiation pyrometer.

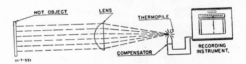

tional to the temperature of the body. The emf is fed to a potentiometer which indicates, records, and controls process temperatures in the same manner as the conventional thermocouple type potentiometer.

The radiation pyrometer possesses many advantages over the thermocouple pyrometer. The fact that it measures without coming into physical contact with the temperature source makes it ideally suited for a number of industrial temperature measuring problems, including cases where (1) very high temperatures are involved—temperatures definitely beyond the practical range for thermocouple measurements; (2) furnace atmospheres are detrimental to thermocouples and cause erratic measurement and short life, e.g., hydrogen atmospheres encountered in copper brazing, and bright annealing furnaces; (3) the surface temperature of hot objects within a furnace or of moving objects on mills is required, e.g., forgings, billets, ingots, steel plate, and substances in rotating kilns. The measuring unit can be sighted directly on an object considerably distant from the unit, or, where the lens and measuring unit must be protected from direct impingement of flames, a closed-end target tube can be employed.

Where ambient temperatures are quite high, the radiation pyrometer is available. It has an air-cooled fitting which prevents conduction of heat from the furnace walls and, where an open-end sighting tube is used, provides means for purging with compressed air to prevent dirt or smoke from obscuring the lens. A safety shutter can be included to protect the radiation measuring element from flame damage.

Thermopile and Compensator. The temperature-sensing element in one type of radiation pyrometer is a thermopile (Figure 506) which comprises a group of very small thermocouples connected in series much like the cells of a storage battery, so that the emf output of the couples is additive. The tiny thermocouple junctions, about pinpoint in size, are flattened and blackened so that they will absorb all of the energy reaching the thermopile. To compensate for the effects of varying ambient temperatures upon the thermopile, a nickel resistance spool provides a variable shunt across the emf produced. As the ambient temperature varies, the resistance of the nickel coil varies and adds to or subtracts from the

FIGURE 506.—Thermopile in industrial type total radiation pyrometer.

emf produced, resulting in accurate compensation over the entire measuring range of the instrument.

Radiation pyrometers are available in several types having different temperature limits or target size requirements. A low-range unit, suitable for measuring temperature from ambient to approximately 350°F, responds to 98 per cent of the temperature change in five seconds. In this unit, which differs somewhat from other models, a separate control box and heater coil maintain a constant reference junction temperature at the thermopile as a means of temperature compensation, in place of the resistor. The low-range unit requires a relatively large size target at close distance to the lens. The calibration is arbitrary and the measuring instrument uses a 0–100 evenly divided chart and scale.

Another series of three models covers temperature ranges of 200–1,200°F, 800–2,300°F, and 1,000–3,200°F. These units are factory calibrated for black body conditions and require a minimum target diameter $\frac{1}{20}$th of the distance from lens to target. Five models designed for extremely small target size requirements or very high ranges are available. Targets as small as $\frac{1}{4}$ inch can be sighted upon, while temperatures as high as 7,000°F can be measured, the unit responding to 98 per cent of the temperature change in two seconds. The models are calibrated in the field through use of a calibration adjustment in the measuring instrument.

Optical Pyrometer. A means of measuring radiant energy even more responsive than the radiation pyrometer is provided by the optical pyrometer, which responds to a full-scale change in temperature of hot materials in the range of 850°–3000°F in ⅗th of a second. The system utilizes a self-balancing optical pyrometer operating on the principle that the electrical resistance of a photocell varies with the intensity of the light to which the tube is exposed and that the intensity of the light given off by a hot body is related to the temperature of the body. The system is used, for example, to measure the metal temperature in rolling mills where the speed of the work requires highly responsive measurement.

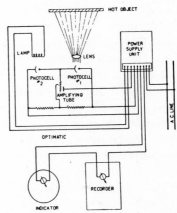

FIGURE 507.—Circuit of automatic optical type pyrometer.

The components of the system are shown schematically in the typical installation diagram (Figure 507), comprising: (1) the sensing unit with an over-all length of approximately 3 feet to the end of its sighting tube; (2) a power supply unit which contains electronic rectifying and amplifying equipment; (3) temperature indicator, which can be located near the process (optional); and (4) a deflectional type temperature recorder with calibrated chart width of only 4½ inches, especially suited for the almost instantaneous response of the unit. In addition, a selector switch can be used where it is desired to operate one recorder from several units.

Operation of the system is as follows. Two photocells, connected into an electronic bridge circuit, are employed, and an amplifying tube is substituted for the galvanometer usually found in such bridge circuits. When the sighting tube is "aimed" at a hot object, one of the cells is exposed to the illumination from that object, while the other cell is subjected to light from a balancing carbon filament lamp. As the brilliancy of the hot object varies with changes in temperature, the resistance of the measuring photocell changes, thus altering the current in the plate circuit of an amplifying tube. This instantaneously increases or decreases the current to the lamp which illuminates the second photocell, bringing it immediately into equilibrium with the photocell exposed to the hot object. The lamp current is measured by the instruments which are calibrated in terms of temperature.

The use of the second photocell gives the system stability, which is essential. Voltage fluctuations do not affect the accuracy of the temperature measurement. Likewise, normal variations in the photocell characteristics during continued service cause no error. A red filter narrows the spectrum used for temperature detection and minimizes the effect of gases or vapors in the sighting path.

PRESSURE MEASUREMENT

Under many conditions encountered in industrial processing, pressure and temperature are by nature interrelated, so that one variable is fixed by the other. Often the plant or instrumentation engineer will have to make a decision as to which variable should be selected as the basis of control for a piece of process equipment. Pressure, like temperature, markedly affects the boiling points of substances and, to a lesser degree, freezing points. Pressure also affects the rate of chemical reaction, especially where the products of reaction are gases. Where the reactants and products of reaction are solids or liquids, pressure may be relatively unimportant. Pressure control is extremely important to boiler operation, where the safety of personnel and equipment depends upon maintaining pressure within prescribed limits. Recent advances in both extremely high pressure and high vacuum techniques have accentuated the importance of pressure measurement and control.

An exceedingly wide range of pressures—from very high vacuums (pressures as low as one-thousandth of a millimeter) to positive pressures of 10,000 psi and greater—are encountered in the processing industries. Obviously, many types of pressure-measuring elements are required to cover this wide range. These elements vary from direct means, such as the Bourdon tube and spiral for high pressures, to inferential means, such as hot wire gauges used for measuring high vacuums.

In Table 89 are listed the principal methods used in industrial instruments for measuring pressure. The practical range of measurement for each type of instrument is also given.

Spiral Gauges. The spiral type actuating element, used widely in industrial pressure gauges, is basically a Bourdon tube wound in the form of a flat spiral. The spiral, as illustrated in Figure 508, provides a summation of the end movements of a number of Bourdon tubes, resulting in

TABLE 89. CLASSIFICATION OF PRESSURE MEASURING INSTRUMENTS*

Means for Sensing Pressure	Instruments Employing This Principle	Approximate, Practical Range
Heat loss from a hot filament surrounded by gas	Thermal gauges:	
	Pirani gauge	10^{-3} to 1.0 mm Hg
	Thermocouple gauge	10^{-3} to 0.5 mm Hg
Ionic current produced by electrodes which bombard molecules of residual gas	Ionization gauges:	
	Hot cathode ion gauge	10^{-6} to 10^{-3} mm Hg
	Alphatron gauge	10^{-3} to 10 mm Hg
Rise or fall of liquid in a manometer	McLeod gauge	10^{-6} to 1.0 mm Hg
	Conventional U-tube	1.0 mm to 20 cm Hg
Deformation of a shaped metal form	Bourdon tube gauges	5 to 100,000 psig
	Helix gauges	7 to 80,000 psig
	Spiral gauges	30 to 4,000 psig
	Diaphragm gauges	20 oz to 10 psig
Movement of spring-loaded bellows	Bellows gauges	10 to 760 mm Hg
Counterweight	Dead weight testers	0 to 10,000 psig
Conversion of pressure into mechanical displacement which is measurable by an electric strain gauge	Electric pressure and force transducers	0 to 50,000 psig

* Not including those devices designed principally for measuring differential pressure.

a much greater movement at the free end. This greater movement—a decided advantage in a recorder because the pen moves over a much wider arc—has led to the almost universal use of the spiral in instruments for measuring pressures in the range of from 10 to 4,000 psi. The spiral re-

FIGURE 508.—Typical spiral used in industrial pressure gauge.

quires no sector and pinion to obtain sufficient pointer travel, but is connected directly to the pen or pointer shaft by a single link. This direct linkage reduces friction to a minimum, eliminates inertia or lost motion, and increases the accuracy as well as the response of measurement.

Spirals of bronze, steel and stainless steel are usually available in ranges from 0–18 to 0–4,000 psi.

Spring and Bellows Gauges. Pressures in what are termed the "intermediate" and "low" ranges cannot be measured satisfactorily with the Bourdon tube or spiral in industrial type instruments.

The intermediate range unit, having either brass or stainless-steel bellows, is used to measure pressures with full-scale values between 100 inches of water and 40 psi gauge, or vacuums with full-scale values between 10 and 30 inches of mercury. It comprises a metallic bellows enclosed in a shell, the latter being connected to the pressure source. Pressure, acting on the outside of the bellows, tends to compress the bellows, moving its lower free end upward against the opposing force of the spring. A rod resting on the bottom of the bellows transmits the vertical motion through a suitable linkage into pen or pointer movement on a linear basis.

For lower pressures and vacuums, the second type of spring-opposed element is employed, being mounted on the back of the instrument case. In this unit, the pressure is connected to the inside of a larger bellows, which creates an appreciably greater force per unit area to act against an opposing spring force. For the measurement of vacuums or combinations of vacuum and pressure, this element is also equipped with a lower spring which opposes the collapsing bellows. This low-pressure element, using a brass bellows, is generally used for minimum full-scale pressures of 5 up to 90 inches of water and vacuums of 50 inches of water.

The spring-opposed bellows elements are very sensitive, the low-range type, for example, developing as much as 25 times the power of the spiral element for the same pressure change. Even on the lowest pressure range, there is no perceptible tapping error, as can occur with "weaker" gauges.

These elements also are characterized by an extremely long life, as proved by tests which indicate that the bellows and springs will withstand millions of cycles of flexing without rupture. Phosphor bronze is the material commonly used for the bellows while the springs are made from carefully heat-treated metal which, as such, is permanent in its gradient (change in force per unit of compression).

The bellows gradient is small in comparison to the spring gradient and does not enter into the calibration of the unit. The bellows, which does not generally have too linear a gradient in the first place, merely serves as a pressure enclosure. With such a construction, moreover, a change in range can often be made simply by replacement of the spring with one of a different gradient.

Absolute Pressure Gauge. The use of absolute pressure gauges is generally confined to the accurate measurement and control of pressure low enough to be seriously affected by variations in barometric pressure. Today, many industrial processes require such control in order to assure a uniform product or to attain the highest yields.

The importance of compensating for variations in barometric pressure is exemplified by the control of pressure in a distilling column which is to operate at 50 mm of mercury absolute. With the pressure controlled by a vacuum gauge, the control set point would be 710 mm of mercury with a barometric pressure of 760 mm of mercury (760 mm minus 50 mm). Should the barometer rise to 775 mm, the vacuum gauge would read 725 mm (775 mm minus 50 mm), and the control system would function so as to decrease the gauge pressure by 15 mm, which would actually *raise* the absolute pressure to 65 mm or 30 per cent over that desired.

This error, which is sufficient to impair seriously the effectiveness of the process, could be corrected by periodic readings of the barometer, but this would have to be done frequently and the main advantage of automatic control would be sacrificed. Absolute pressure measurement is, therefore, the ultimate answer to control problems of this type.

The absolute pressure gauge comprises a spring and bellows assembly, as illustrated in Figure 509, with an upper evacuated bellows which is sealed at very nearly a perfect vacuum, and an opposed lower actuating

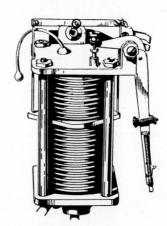

FIGURE 509.—Bellows arrangement in absolute pressure gauge.

bellows which is connected to the measured pressure. The adjacent end of each bellows is attached to a movable plate which transmits the bellows movement to the recording pen by means of a mechanical linkage.

The method of operation is identical to that of a conventional spring-opposed bellows element insofar as the actuating bellows is concerned. However, a difference in the resultant operation of the actuating bellows is obtained from the action of an evacuated bellows which expands and contracts in accordance with variations in barometric pressure. This action prevents any movement of the pen or pointer by the application of an equal but opposite force to the actuating bellows. The evacuated bellows functions like an aneroid barometer in its response to changes in atmospheric pressure.

VACUUM MEASUREMENT

High vacuums are widely used in the processing of foods, drugs, and chemicals. Efficient operation of such processes requires an indication and record of the vacuum during the pumping procedure rather than an estimate of the extent of the evacuation by the timing of the operation of the pump. In addition, a record of the evacuation process supplies a history of the process, so that a procedure can be set up which assures both good yield and quality of product.

Thermal Type and Resistance Type Vacuum Gauges. These operate on the principle that the heat loss from a hot coil of resistance wire or from a hot filament varies as the pressure changes. Below one millimeter of mercury down to one micron of mercury absolute, approximately, the variation in heat loss with respect to changes in pressure is relatively

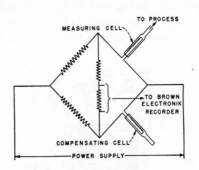

FIGURE 510.—Thermal type vacuum gauge employing resistance measuring circuit.

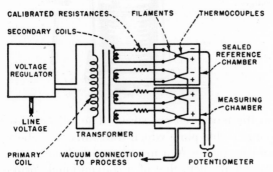

FIGURE 511.—Thermal type vacuum gauge employing thermocouple measuring circuit.

large. Thus, an accurate and reliable basis for the measurement of pressure is provided.

As shown in the two schematic wiring diagrams (Figures 510 and 511), there are two variations of the thermal type gauge. In the resistance type gauge, the heat lost by the coil of resistance wire which constitutes the sensing element is indicated directly by changes in the resistance of a leg in the bridge circuit of which it is an integral part. On the other hand, in the thermocouple type gauge, the heat lost by the filaments is measured by a thermocouple arrangement.

In the resistance gauge a tube with a resistance coil is sealed off at a pressure considerably below one micron to form a *compensating cell*.

The coil is so arranged that changes in its resistance will balance those changes in the *measuring cell* resistance which are due to temperature fluctuations rather than to pressure variations. The remaining two arms of the bridge circuit are equal fixed resistances. When power is supplied to the bridge circuit, the coil in the measuring cell is heated. The resistance of this coil varies with its temperature, which is governed by the heat lost from the filament. Since this heat loss is proportional to the vacuum existing in the measuring cell, the resistance of this coil is determined by the pressure.

In the thermocouple type gauge, four filaments are each continuously and uniformly heated. Two of these four filaments are in a *reference chamber* which is sealed off at a pressure of approximately one micron, while the other two filaments are in a *measuring chamber* exposed to the vacuum under measurement. A small sensitive thermocouple is situated on each of the four filaments and connected so that the two in the reference chamber are in series and the two in the measuring chamber are in series. In this way, sufficient emf is obtained. These two sets of thermocouples are connected so that their emf's oppose one another. The difference between the two opposing emf's is a measure of the difference in pressure between the reference chamber and the measuring chamber. From a pressure of one micron up to 500 microns, this emf varies from zero millivolts to about 19.2 millivolts and is accurately recorded by a potentiometer calibrated in terms of pressure.

Reading References

BOOKS

General

Eckman, D. P., "Industrial Process Control," New York, John Wiley & Sons, Inc., 1947.

Eckman, D. P., "Industrial Instrumentation," New York, John Wiley & Sons, Inc., 1950.

Miller, C. O., "Lectures on Instrumentation," Cleveland, Ohio, Case School of Applied Science, 1941.

Behar, M. F., "The Handbook of Measurement and Control," Pittsburgh, Pa., The Instruments Publishing Company, 1951.

Rhodes, T. J., "Industrial Instruments for Measurement and Control," New York, McGraw-Hill Book Co., Inc., 1941.

"The Instrument Manual," United Trade Press, Ltd., London, England, 1949.

Temperature

American Institute of Physics, Symposium, "Temperature, Its Measurement and Control in Science and Industry," New York, Reinhold Publishing Corporation, 1941.

Foote, P. D., Fairchild, C. O., and Harrison, T. R., "Pyrometric Practice," Technologic Paper No. 170, National Bureau of Standards, Washington, D. C., 1921.

Wood, W. P., and Cork, J. M., "Pyrometry," New York, McGraw-Hill Book Co., Inc., 1941.

PERIODICALS

Olive, T. R., "Measurement and control of process variables," *Chem. Met. Eng.*, **50**, No. 5, 97–144 (May 1943).

"Review of Scientific Instruments," American Institute of Physics.

"Instruments," Instruments Publishing Co.

"Instrumentation," Industrial Division of Minneapolis-Honeywell Regulator Co.

"Taylor Technology," Taylor Instrument Co.

"The Instrument Maker," Instruments Publishing Co.

Also: "Instrumentation" by Ralph H. Munch, monthly column in *Ind. Eng. Chem.*; and "Instrumentation" by R. H. Müller, monthly column in *Anal. Chem.*

The engineering world has its own hall of fame; its celebrities are unknown to the general public. One of them is Giovanni Batista Venturi, an early Italian physicist who experimented with the flow of gases and liquids through constrictions in pipes. Our most important flow-measuring device is based on his work.

26. INSTRUMENTATION. PART II: FLOW MEASUREMENT. LIQUID-LEVEL MEASUREMENT. MEASUREMENT OF CHEMICAL COMPOSITION. pH MEASUREMENT. MEASUREMENT OF ELECTROLYTIC CONDUCTIVITY*

FLOW MEASUREMENT

Flow measurement and control are important to chemical processes for several reasons: (1) *maintaining desired throughputs* in process equipment, as the feed rate to a fractionating column or drier; (2) *proportioning* two or more materials (a) to a reactor, (b) to maintain a desired reflux ratio in distillation or (c) to hold a correct fuel-air ratio in combustion; and (3) *gathering data* for cost accounting purposes. Since the *material balance* is so important to the design and operation of chemical processes and, since flow meters (for liquids) and scales (for solids) are the process engineer's principal tools for measuring materials, the importance of these instruments cannot be overstressed.

Flow metering devices can be classified into two broad categories: (1) *quantity* meters, in which the fluid is measured, in increments, by gravimetric or volumetric means, and (2) *rate-of-flow* meters, in which the quantity of fluid is inferred from some action of the flowing stream upon a primary element, such as an orifice. Meters in the latter category are used most widely for process control. For solid flow measurement, some adaptation of a weighing scale is generally used. A condensed classification of rate-of-flow meters is given in Table 90.

Head (Kinetic) Meters. Meters in this category operate on a principle which derives from Bernoulli's theorem. This theorem is a corollary of the law of conservation of energy; it states that the total energy of a unit weight of fluid passing through an isolated system remains constant from point to point along its flow, without regard to what may be done with the

* Prepared by Douglas M. Considine, Chemical Engineer and Manager of Market Extension, Industrial Division, Minneapolis-Honeywell Regulator Co., Philadelphia, Penna.

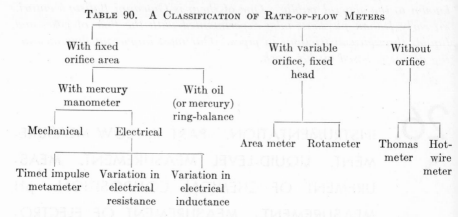

TABLE 90. A CLASSIFICATION OF RATE-OF-FLOW METERS

With fixed orifice area — With mercury manometer (Mechanical, Electrical — Timed impulse metameter, Variation in electrical resistance) — With oil (or mercury) ring-balance (Variation in electrical inductance)

With variable orifice, fixed head — Area meter, Rotameter

Without orifice — Thomsmeter, Hot-wire meter

fluid within the system. An isolated system precludes the addition of energy from the outside or the removal of energy to the outside. Thus, with exception of changes due to friction or volume variations which would alter the heat content of the system, the total mechanical energy of the fluid will remain constant from point to point. In the practical application of this principle to fluid metering, the above factors of heat removal or addition and of friction are reduced to an absolute minimum.

In head meters employing constrictions, commonly termed *differential pressure flow meters* in industry, the velocity of the fluid is changed momentarily as it passes through a constriction in the flow line. The resulting *change in static head* is taken as a measure of the velocity and hence the volume rate of flow. Constricting devices (known as primary elements) employed for causing this change in static head include: (1) thin-plate orifices, (2) flow nozzles, and (3) venturi tubes. A comparison of the advantages and disadvantages of each of these primary elements is given in Table 91.

Basically, the operation of differential pressure flow meters is shown by:

$$V = \sqrt{2gh}$$

where V = velocity in feet/sec/sec, g = gravitational force, and h = head in feet.

The fundamentals of this equation are illustrated in Figure 512. When a liquid is discharged through an opening in the side of a vessel, the jet of liquid issuing from that opening has a velocity approximately equal to $\sqrt{2gh}$, even though the flow does not actually fall through a vertical distance. Because of liquid friction at the discharge opening, the actual velocity is one or two per cent less than that shown by the above equation. Following the equation, the jet will issue in any direction and, if vertically, will rise to a height h above the opening. Where comparatively large

TABLE 91. RELATIVE ADVANTAGES AND DISADVANTAGES OF FLOW CONSTRICTING
DEVICES

Orifice Plate

   (1) Highest permanent pressure loss
   (2) Least expensive to install
   (3) Most commonly used
   (4) Easily reproduced
   (5) Requires periodic inspection

Flow Nozzle

   (1) Medium permanent pressure loss
   (2) More expensive than an orifice, but less expensive than a venturi tube
   (3) Very little maintenance
   (4) Offers a greater pressure differential than venturi tube
   (5) Passes 1.6 times more quantity than an orifice under similar conditions

Venturi Tube

   (1) Least permanent pressure loss
   (2) Most expensive
   (3) Very little maintenance
   (4) Most difficult to install
   (5) Passes 1.6 times more quantity than an orifice under similar conditions

heads are concerned, the height reached will be considerably less than h because of the friction imparted by the air and a natural breaking up of the jet.

From the equation given, it is obvious that the meter either will be calibrated in terms of the square root of the pressure differential produced by the constriction, or it will incorporate some means for extracting that square root to provide evenly divided graduations on its scale. Both

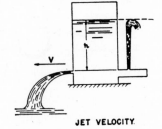

FIGURE 512.—Jet of liquid issuing from vessel opening has a velocity approximately equal to $\sqrt{2gh}$.

JET VELOCITY

types of meters are widely used. Square root calibration is satisfactory, sometimes preferred, when automatic flow control is concerned. For accounting purposes, the evenly divided scale is preferred.

Thin-Plate Orifice Meters. Three common types of orifices are used: (1) concentric, (2) eccentric, and (3) segmental (see Figure 513). The concentric orifice is installed with the center of the orifice concentric with the center of the pipe. In the eccentric type, the orifice is below the center of the pipe, the bottom opening usually being located approximately 0.10 inch above the bottom of the pipe. With the segmental orifice, flow is permitted only through a segment of the pipe area.

The concentric type is most commonly used. The orifice is most often a circular hole in a metal plate $\frac{1}{32}$ to $\frac{1}{16}$ inch in thickness. The eccentric and segmental orifices are useful where the fluid contains solids that

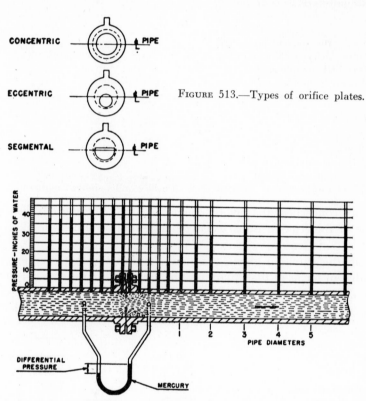

CONCENTRIC

ECCENTRIC

SEGMENTAL

FIGURE 513.—Types of orifice plates.

FIGURE 514.—Flow characteristics and differential pressures existing in proximity of orifice.

may deposit against the upstream side of a concentric orifice and thus change its characteristics.

The flow characteristics and differential pressures existing in the proximity of the orifice are illustrated in Figure 514. Increase in the velocity of the fluid passing through the orifice causes a decrease in the line pressure. This decrease in pressure attains a maximum value approximately one-half pipe diameter downstream from the upstream face of the orifice, a point known as the *vena contracta*. The line pressure is slowly restored in the downstream side until the restoration point, about four pipe diameters from the face of the orifice, is reached.   The pressure value at this point equals the original value, less the permanent pressure loss brought about by the orifice.   Location of high- and low-pressure taps is quite critical if maximum advantage is to be taken of the differential pressure produced.   Often, for convenience of installation, a small sacrifice in the differential pressure produced is made so as to include the pressure taps within the orifice flange casting.

Flow Nozzles.   For very high velocities, a thin-plate orifice may not be sufficiently accurate.   A flow nozzle is a rounded, funnel-like aperture, as illustrated in Figure 515.   Because the stream is constricted gradually, there is little or no contraction below the nozzle.   For maximum ac-

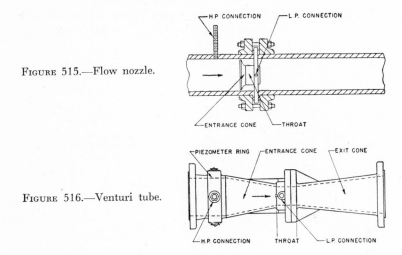

FIGURE 515.—Flow nozzle.

FIGURE 516.—Venturi tube.

curacy, each different design of flow nozzle must be individually calibrated.

Venturi Tubes.   This flow measuring device (see Figure 516) is inserted in a pipeline in much the same manner as any pipe section, but has a smaller diameter mid-section, termed the *throat.*

The venturi consists of a main barrel section of a diameter identical or closely corresponding to the internal diameter of the pipe to which it is connected.   The barrel leads into a cone of fixed angular convergence. This cone then connects a throat section accurately machined to calculated dimensions and of a smaller diameter than the barrel.   The throat connects to an exit cone of fixed angular divergence terminating at a diameter corresponding to the original pipe size (see also page 246).

The barrel is equipped with piezometer connections in an annular pressure ring for averaging the upstream pressure.   The high-pressure meter connection is made here.   The throat is similarly designed and the low-pressure meter connection is made to it. The difference in pressure between the barrel and the throat produces the differential pressure which is a function of rate of flow.

Methods for Measuring Differential Pressure. A mercury U-tube, with each leg tapped into either the high- or low-pressure side of the orifice, flow nozzle, or venturi tube, would comprise the simplest means for measuring the differential pressure. However, these U-tubes are fragile and are not easily adapted to industrial indicating, recording, or controlling instruments.

Mercury Manometers. In some industrial flow meters, a rugged adaptation of the simple U-tube (known as the meter body) is used. This type of instrument is illustrated diagrammatically in Figure 517. Just as in the glass U-tube, the mercury level in one leg rises and falls in the other with changes in differential pressure. A large, powerful float

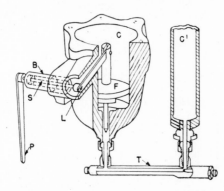

FIGURE 517.—Industrial type mercury manometer for flow measurement.

F of solid metal connects lever L to shaft S that passes outside the meter body through pressure-tight bearing B. The high-pressure tap from the flow line is connected to chamber C, while the low-pressure connection is made to chamber C'. The high- and low-pressure chambers are connected by a U-tube T. The float motion is translated through lever L and shaft T to arm P which mechanically actuates the indicating, recording, or controlling mechanisms in the instrument.

A meter body, equipped, with an electrical transmitter, for remote location, is illustrated in Figure 518. In this instrument, the float carries a nonmagnetic rod surmounted by a slender cylindrical armature which moves up and down, and is surrounded first by a pressure-tight, nonmagnetic tube, and the tube in turn by a divided inductance coil. When the position of the armature changes, the inductance of each section of its coil also changes, decreasing in one, increasing in the other. The change causes a current to flow in a common conductor. As shown in Figure 519, the current is transmitted to similar divided inductance coils in a receiving instrument, wherein the action is reversed. The current flowing through the receiving coils produces an inductance which acts upon an armature suspended within it, and moves it to a definite position. The indicating armature is suspended from counter-balanced rocker arms, which carry a pointer or a pen arm.

In another electrical type flow meter, a multirod resistance element, as shown in Figure 520, permits measurement of the mercury level without

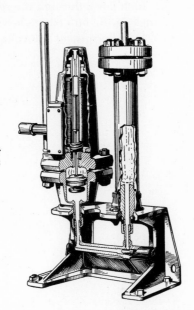

FIGURE 518.—Flow meter body equipped with electric transmitter.

FIGURE 519.—Principle of electric flow transmitter and receiver.

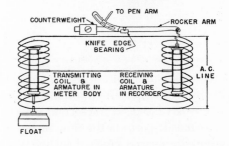

use of moving parts. The resistance element consists of a number of contact rods (vertical) and a continuous coil of resistance wire from which taps are taken off at *91* points; the sections of the coil between taps have gradually differing resistances in accordance with Ohm's law, to make the current proportional to the flow of liquid (flow proportional to I, where $I = E/R$). Each tap is connected to one end of a contact rod. The 91 contact rods are suspended above a mercury bath and the lower end of the rods are cut off so that they form a curve (a second power curve). The rods thus become gradually shorter, and as the mercury rises, one rod at a time, and one after another, makes contact. As each contact is made, one section of the resistance coil is by-passed: the total resistance of the scale decreases. Conversely, as the mercury falls, it restores to the circuit as many sections, in their proper sequence, in the resistance coil as equal the number of rods which lose contact: the resistance of the scale increases. The current which flows through the resistance is read on a current meter, and the readings on the latter become the measure of the flow of the liquid (see Figure 521). Because of the voltage compensation the current which

FIGURE 520.—The multirod resistance element, called "the scale," in the Republic electric-flow meter. The resistance coil is inside the cylinder.

flows is measured on an instrument which is really an ohmmeter, and the integrator is really an ohm hour meter, rather than a watt hour meter.

The advantage of the second power curve formed by the cut ends of the rod is that it permits the flow of liquid to be indicated by the penarm on an equally spaced chart, insuring the same accuracy and precision over any flow measured, large or small.

Meter bodies are of forged steel or built-up welded steel construction. Bolting, gasketing, and other constructional details conform to accepted pressure piping standards. Cast iron and cast steel are rarely used for meter body construction, even for low-pressure work, because the porosity of the casting tends to cause mercury absorption and results in material errors in reading.

Characterized Mercury Manometers. Flow meters with evenly divided scales and charts (as contrasted with square root calibration) are particularly desirable for accounting purposes and are used widely in power plants and in the water and sewage field. The Ledoux bell is one of the simplest methods for mechanically extracting the square root function and it has stood the test of time. The principle of the Ledoux bell can be explained best by reference to a schematic diagram (Figure 522).

The high-pressure connection is made to the upper part of the meter body housing. The low-pressure connection is made through a standpipe which extends up from the bottom of the housing. Mercury fills the bottom of the housing. The shaped bell is placed over the standpipe and floats freely with its open end in the mercury pool, so that the mercury acts as a seal between the two chambers. When the pressure increases

FIGURE 521.—Diagram of the simple-conductance meter circuit in the Republic electric-flow meter, showing the resistance element just touching the mercury, one electrical connection to top of element, the other to a ground screw on the body near the dust cap. *LP*, low-pressure side; *HP*, high-pressure or upstream side; *S*, solenoid of the indicating ammeter. The ammeter has a potential coil instead of the customary steel spring; the net effect of a voltage change in the supply line on the pointer motion will be nil.

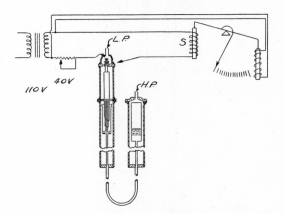

above the free-floating bell, the bell is pushed down into the mercury by a force depending upon the increased pressure and the effective top area of the bell. As it sinks, the *displacer* displaces mercury, which rises into the inside of the bell. The bell continues to move downward until the buoyant force of that mercury, against the interior of the bell surface, equals the force which is pushing the bell down. The pressure difference does not transfer any mercury from the outside to the inside, as it does in a U-tube—it merely sinks the bell.

In U-tube meters, the final difference in mercury level is the same as in the Ledoux bell, though it is differently produced. In U-tube meters, the mercury level is used to measure the flow, but its change is proportional to the square root of the flow. For low-flow values, the mercury rise is comparatively small and the per cent-of-scale lines are crowded at the low-flow end of the chart. The Ledoux bell is shaped so that in displacing the mercury for a given change in mercury level, it sinks by an amount which is proportional to the square root of the change in level.

The position of the bell, therefore, changes linearly with flow. The low-flow measures of the bell motion are spread out and, throughout the range of measurement, the chart is evenly divided.

Mercuryless Manometers (Pneumatic Balance Type). A comparatively recent development, the pneumatic balance unit, converts differential pressures produced by a primary flow device (such as an orifice) into a positive air pressure (range 3 to 15 psi), which is transmitted to an

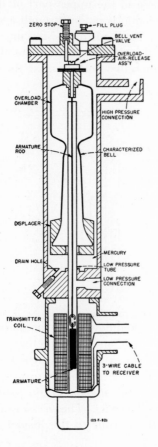

FIGURE 522.—Cross-section of Ledoux bell type flow meter.

indicating, recording, or controlling instrument. These units eliminate the need for a conventional mercury type manometer in flow measurement. The advantages which have led to their popularity are as follows: (1) the fast speed of response to flow changes permits better over-all automatic control; (2) the volume displacement is so small that seal pots (for corrosive fluids) and condensing chambers (for steam and condensable gases) can be eliminated in most instances; (3) their range is easily changed (10 to 1 change) with no change of parts; (4) since no mercury is used, there is no possibility of mercury contamination of product, nor mercury emulsification; and (5) their light weight and compactness makes for easy and quick installation.

Operation of one instrument of this type, known as the *Differential Converter*, can be clearly visualized by comparing its functioning to that of a conventional even-armed. balance. The meter body converts the difference between the low and high pressure connected to it into a force which acts on one end of a beam; this is analogous to the force of an unknown weight on one scale pan of a balance. Just as known calibrated weights are added to the other scale pan until the unknown weight is balanced and the scale arm is level, a pneumatic-balance system in the *Differential Converter* develops an opposing force due to air pressure

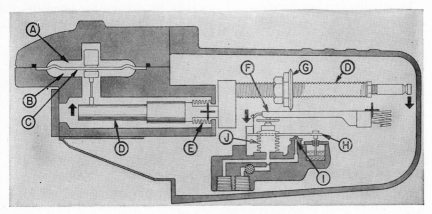

FIGURE 523.—Cross-section of pneumatic-balance (Honeywell) type mercuryless manometer. (For explanation see text).

which exactly balances the force due to the differential pressure in the meter body.

The basic operating principles can be gathered from schematic diagram (Figure 523). As shown, the low- and high-pressure chambers (*A* and *B*) are separated by a flexible diaphragm (*C*) which is connected to one end of a primary beam (*D*). The beam extends through a sealing bellows (*E*) which confines the measured fluid within the high-pressure chamber. Near the bellows is the fulcrum of the primary beam. Toward the opposite end of this beam is a bevel-edged rider (*G*), which is movable, to provide the range-changing feature, but which can be considered a fixed knife-edge in the operation of the unit.

Differential pressure in the meter body thus creates an upward force on the left-hand end of the primary beam. Because of the intermediate fulcrum on the beam, this force acts downward on a secondary beam (*F*) through the bevel-edged rider. As shown in the diagram, the right-hand end of the secondary beam is a fixed fulcrum point, while the other end is linked to a flapper (H). The downward force on the secondary beam thus moves the flapper toward a nozzle (I).

Air pressure from the supply is bled through a restriction into the pneumatic-balance system which comprises the flapper and nozzle and a balancing bellows (J), as illustrated. Thus, when the nozzle is covered, air pressure builds up in the balancing bellows and an upward force is created in opposition to the downward force due to the differential pressure. In this manner, output air pressure from the converter is directly proportional to the measured differential pressure and, by means of a pneumatic receiver bellows, can be translated directly into terms of flow or differential pressure readings.

Integration of Flow Readings. Especially for accounting purposes, the totalization of flow readings is very important. Integration must be

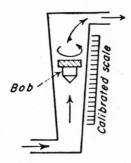

Figure 524.—Simple rotameter.

automatic, fast, and accurate. There are many mechanical, electrical, and electronic types of integration available, a few of which will be described below.

Area Flow Meters. Meters of this type operate on the principle that there is a different orifice area for each rate of flow and that consequently the differential pressure is constant. The most important area meter is the rotameter, schematically illustrated in Figure 524. As shown, a float, or bob, is supported in the flowing stream by the differential pressure. Flow area is the annular opening between the float and the flow chamber. As the flow increases, the float moves upward, thereby increasing the area of the opening until the differential pressure just balances the weight of the float. The float then assumes a position proportional to the flow rate. The type shown uses a rotating float or bob to produce the variable orifice, but rides at a level that varies with viscosity and, therefore, must be calibrated for the particular fluid handled. Rotameters are available, however, with special bob designs which automatically compensate for viscosity changes.

Other types of area meters are cylinder-and-piston meters, weirs, Parshall flumes, and Kennison nozzles.

Volumetric or Positive-Displacement Meters. Included among the positive-displacement meters are various arrangements of pistons, gears, diaphragms, rotating pistons, and rotating buckets. With this type of meter, total flow is an accumulation of measured increments which can be totalized with simple counters. Figure 525 is a diagrammatic sketch designed to illustrate the principle of *reciprocating-piston* meters. Under pressure of the fluid being metered, the piston shuttles back and forth, shifting the intake and discharge valve as it reaches the end of its stroke

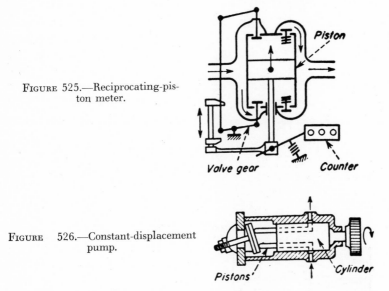

Figure 525.—Reciprocating-piston meter.

Figure 526.—Constant-displacement pump.

and operating a counter to add a fixed volume increment with each stroke. Another type of piston meter, a two-cylinder rayon-spinning pump, is shown in Figure 526. Although this device is used as a pump, it is also a constant-displacement meter. The cylinder rotates, causing reciprocation of the pistons which are secured to a swash plate of adjustable angle. By means of this adjustment, delivery of the pump per revolution can be adjusted precisely. A type of meter employing *rotating impellers* for positive displacement is illustrated in Figure 527. This type (Roots) may be considered the limit of a *gear pump* (Figure 528), which can also be used as a positive-displacement meter. The common *nutating-disk* meter used for domestic water metering (Figure 529), uses a form of rotating piston. The tilted disk is cut by a stationary vertical partition near the discharge, which causes the space above and below the disk to form separate chambers.   The pressure of water passing through then forces the disk to describe a continuous nutating action, causing rotation of a counter.

A number of elementary types of constant-volume meters in addition to those mentioned have been also used. The primitive *tilting-box* type

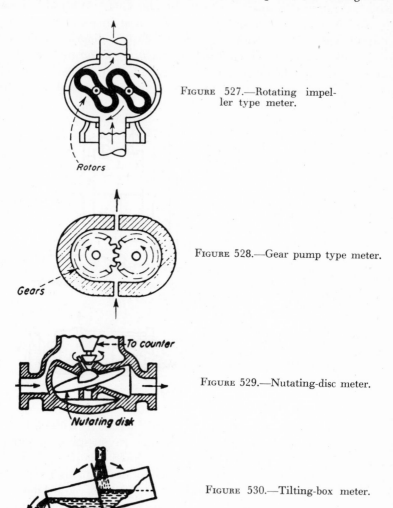

Figure 527.—Rotating impeller type meter.

Figure 528.—Gear pump type meter.

Figure 529.—Nutating-disc meter.

Figure 530.—Tilting-box meter.

shown (Figure 530) is probably not used today but has been important in the past.   The *condensate meter* (Figure 531) is, however, a modern development of this idea.   The vanes shown here in cross section are closed at the ends to form buckets which rotate at a rate directly proportional to the flow.   A similar principle is employed in the *water-sealed gas meter*, frequently used in gas plants. This meter, shown in Figure 532, uses water contained in the lower half of a casing as a sealing and valving agent to control the passage of gas into the various compartments which are caused to rotate by the pressure of the gas. A different, more complex principle is used in the ordinary domestic *diaphragm gas meter*. Figure

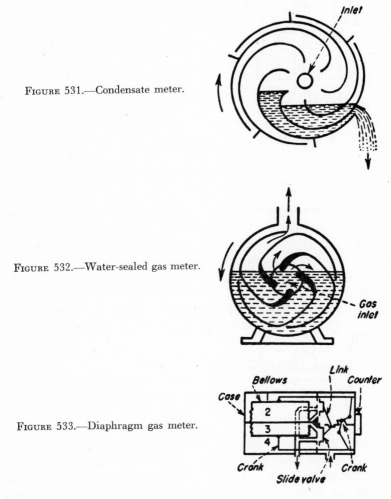

FIGURE 531.—Condensate meter.

FIGURE 532.—Water-sealed gas meter.

FIGURE 533.—Diaphragm gas meter.

533 attempts to illustrate the principle. This type of meter is difficult to portray in simple sketch, and the diagram is merely suggestive. Two partitions and two diaphragms form four chambers numbered 1, 2, 3, and 4. Reciprocation of the diaphragms operates cranks which in turn rotate a single crankshaft driving the counter and the slide valve, which alternately connect the chambers with the inlet end of the box and with the

discharge. Figure 534 illustrates the *meter prover*, which is merely a small water-sealed gas holder in which a known volume of gas at adjustable pressure can be stored. Since the amount of gas it discharges can

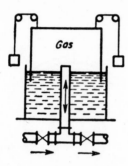

FIGURE 534.—Water-sealed gas holder.

be determined exactly, this device is often used for meter testing and calibration.

LIQUID-LEVEL MEASUREMENT

The measurement of liquid level in processing plants is important for several reasons, chiefly because it is often the basis for controlling part of a process. Many items of processing equipment, such as distillation columns, are designed for definite operating capacities. For example, if the bottoms level in a column rises or falls beyond certain limits, the entire operation of the column will be upset. Thus the level must be controlled.

Liquid level is measured both by direct and by inferential methods.

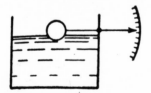

FIGURE 535.—Simple float and pointer.

The former include the gauge stick and gauge glass, floats, buoyancy-type displacers, and the method of weighing a small floating tank containing liquid at the same level as in the main tank. Among the inferential methods is that of measuring the hydrostatic head of the liquid above a suitable reference point. Float measurement often is the simplest for small or medium ranges of level fluctuation. For wide fluctuations, the hydrostatic method is usually most satisfactory.

Float-type methods are illustrated in Figures 535 and 536. In Figure 535 is shown a simple float and pointer; Figure 536 illustrates a simple float, rope, and pulley indicator. In Figure 537 is illustrated a means for interface level indication, with a float that floats on the heavier of two immiscible liquids and sinks in the lighter. Interface level also can be indicated by the buoyancy-type level indicator (Figure 538). In this method, a displacer counter-balanced by a spring rises not with the level, but by an amount proportional to level changes. Depending upon spring and displacer characteristics, any desired range of level variations can be handled with a small change in displacer position. Figure 539 illustrates

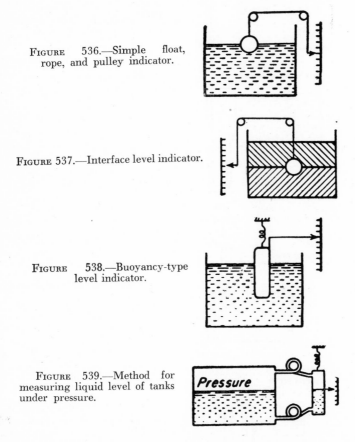

FIGURE 536.—Simple float, rope, and pulley indicator.

FIGURE 537.—Interface level indicator.

FIGURE 538.—Buoyancy-type level indicator.

FIGURE 539.—Method for measuring liquid level of tanks under pressure.

a method frequently used with vessels under pressure. A small spring-counterbalanced weigh tank connected flexibly to the main tank indicates by its level a quantity proportional to the main tank level.

Hydrostatic-pressure methods are illustrated in Figures 540 to 547. In Figure 540, the hydrostatic head is measured directly in terms of level in an open tank by means of a pressure gauge at the reference point. In a closed system under pressure, a differential-pressure manometer can be used to give a reading proportional to level. As shown in Figure 541,

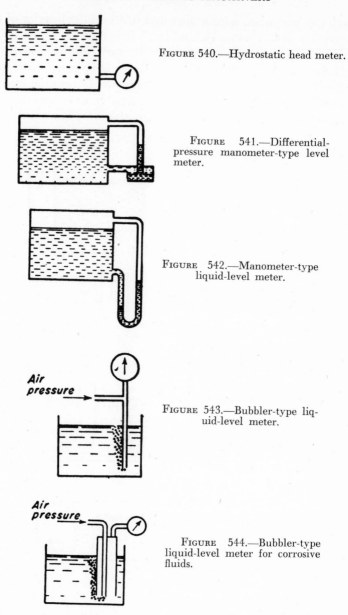

Figure 540.—Hydrostatic head meter.

Figure 541.—Differential-pressure manometer-type level meter.

Figure 542.—Manometer-type liquid-level meter.

Figure 543.—Bubbler-type liquid-level meter.

Figure 544.—Bubbler-type liquid-level meter for corrosive fluids.

the manometer is placed at the reference point. However, the manometer can be placed below the tank as in Figure 542, but the extra head thus introduced must be allowed for. Another method is shown in Figure 543. Here the pressure necessary to force air down a pipe until it bubbles from the bottom at the desired reference point is measured. A variation of this method often is used for corrosive liquids, as shown in Figure 544. Frequently, instead of bubbling air into the tank, a closed bell with a flexible diaphragm is used to apply pressure, equal to the hydrostatic pressure at the reference point, to the air inside a closed system (Figure 545). Figure 546 illustrates the same method applied to a pressure tank. If the diaphragm bell must be outside the tank, the arrangement of Figure 547

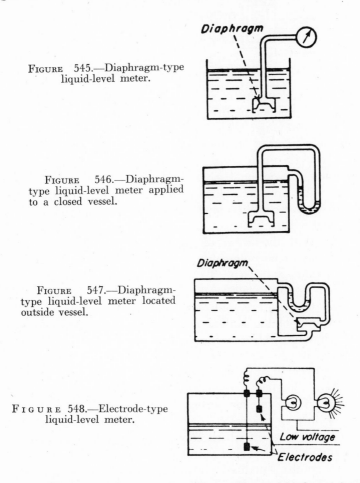

FIGURE 545.—Diaphragm-type liquid-level meter.

FIGURE 546.—Diaphragm-type liquid-level meter applied to a closed vessel.

FIGURE 547.—Diaphragm-type liquid-level meter located outside vessel.

FIGURE 548.—Electrode-type liquid-level meter.

can be used. Changes in density affect the readings of hydrostatic gauges. Therefore, where extreme accuracy is required, some means must be employed to compensate for the errors thus introduced.

Electrical methods of level measurement are also available, but are used chiefly for level control at one point or between two points without intermediate measurement. One method, shown in Figure 548, employs electrodes to detect the level in a conducting liquid. With an electronic amplifier the level of liquids of negligible conductivity can be detected. In another method (Figure 549) photocells and a light source are used.

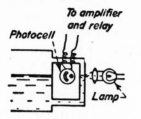

FIGURE 549.—Capacitance-type electronic liquid-level meter.

MEASUREMENT OF CHEMICAL COMPOSITION

With the development of so many instruments which are capable of analyzing final product quality, a new philosophy of process instrumentation is slowly evolving. More and more process engineers are considering the measurement of chemical and physical characteristics of the final product as criteria upon which to base automatic control, as contrasted with presently conventional schemes of basic control on such variables as temperature and pressure. For example, formerly, measurement of refractive index was confined to the laboratory and to manual determination by visual means. Hence, such methods were not conducive to process control. With the advent of a means for continuously measuring the refractive index, a possible solution to many difficult distillation control problems became manifest. To cite an example—in the separation of styrene from its parent material by fractional distillation, separation by conventional temperature control is difficult, and often unreliable owing to the proximity of the boiling points of parent and product materials. However, since the refractive indexes of the materials are widely separated, control by this means is exceedingly effective. In actual production, control is obtained by maintaining a constant steam pressure on the reboiler and automatically regulating the reflux rate by means of the refractometer. Thus, the measurement of chemical composition takes on large importance in process control. Space does not permit delineation of the scores of ways in which composition can be measured, including such devices as infrared and ultraviolet spectrometers, x-ray spectrometers, polarographs, automatic titrators, and emission and Raman spectrometers. The measurement and control of pH and electrical conductivity have been in use for many years and these methods have become well established as criteria for determining and controlling chemical composition.

pH MEASUREMENT

As a measure of the *effective* acidity or alkalinity of a process liquor, pH is of considerable importance to many of the chemical unit operations, including precipitation, coagulation, neutralization, and fermentation. Usually the pH of the final product is not nearly so important as the pH of the various liquors during production. For example, certain organic solvents and compounds are produced by the action of living enzymes or molds. These living organisms usually yield a maximum quantity of the desired substances at a definite pH value; therefore, close control of pH is important. On the other hand, the actual pH of the finished product is not usually of particular significance.

pH control is widely used in the sugar, paper, textile, and organic chemical industries. It also plays an important role in neutralizing industrial wastes before they are dumped into public streams.

Development of the glass electrode several years ago was the first real step toward industrial pH measuring and controlling applications. As a result of research during the past ten years, the following accomplish-

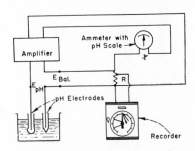

FIGURE 550.—Basic principles for electrometric method for measuring pH.

ments have been made: (1) continuous pH measurements can be made in boiling aqueous solutions; (2) accurate measurement in highly alkaline solutions containing sodium ion concentrations of two mols per liter and up to a pH of 12, is possible; (3) delicate handling of electrodes is no longer required; and (4) by improving the electronic measuring circuit and shielding the electrode leads, the effects of stray currents have been practically eliminated.

Electrometric Measurement of pH. The basic principles of the electrometric method of measuring pH can be gathered from Figure 550. An electrolytic cell, composed of two electrodes, is immersed in the solution being measured. This cell develops an emf in relation to the pH of the solution. A *glass electrode*, designated the *measuring electrode*, generates its own potential in accordance with the solution pH, while a *calomel electrode*, termed the *reference electrode*, has a constant potential. The reference electrode is used solely to complete the electrical circuit. The emf of the cell is the algebraic sum of the measuring and reference electrode potentials.

The Beckman glass electrode (see Figure 551) comprises a specially shaped glass tube about one-half inch in diameter with a small amount of buffer (constant pH) solution at the sealed end into which is inserted a silver-chloride-coated platinum wire which connects to the electrode lead. The glass tube has a thin but strong wall which forms a membrane, making the electrode sensitive to pH. Theories of why this arrangement develops a potential in accordance with the pH of the solution are quite complex and may be found in a number of texts.

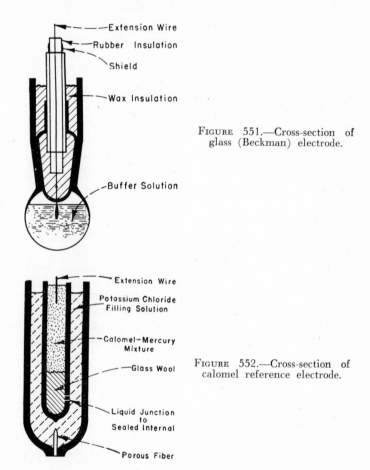

Extension Wire
Rubber Insulation
Shield
Wax Insulation

FIGURE 551.—Cross-section of glass (Beckman) electrode.

Buffer Solution

Extension Wire
Potassium Chloride Filling Solution
Calomel–Mercury Mixture
Glass Wool

FIGURE 552.—Cross-section of calomel reference electrode.

Liquid Junction to Sealed Internal
Porous Fiber

The calomel reference electrode (see Figure 552) comprises (1) an inner tube of calomel (mercurous chloride) and mercury which are mixed as a paste and connected to the electrode lead by a platinum wire; and (2) an outer tube containing a saturated solution of potassium chloride. The latter solution is used to provide a *liquid junction* between the calomel electrode and the process solution. In one common type of calomel electrode, this liquid junction is provided by a small hole in the outer tube which is covered by a ground glass sleeve so that a small amount of potassium chloride solution can flow from the tube into the solution. Another means of providing the liquid junction is the use of a porous fiber end on the outer tube through which the solution can flow. A second liquid junction is present in all calomel electrodes, namely, between the potassium chloride solution and the inner calomel-mercury paste, being provided by a tiny pinhole in the internal tube, as shown in Figure 552.

Electrode Assemblies. Electrode assemblies are obtainable in either an immersion type or a flow type. A flow assembly is illustrated in Figure 553. A resistance thermometer bulb is included in each of these assemblies to compensate for the effects of varying solution temperatures upon

F I G U R E 553.—Continuous flow type pH electrode assembly (Beckman).

the electrical characteristics of the glass electrode. The immersion assembly is used in both open and closed vessels of almost any design. The flow assembly is designed especially for pipelines. Both are available in numerous materials of construction to withstand corrosion. The immersion assembly is capable of withstanding pressures up to 30 psi.

Electrical Circuit. A conventional voltmeter cannot be used to measure the cell output because current must flow to actuate such an instrument and when an appreciable current flows, polarization effects at the electrodes cause changes in the cell voltage. Use of a null-balance potentiometer makes it possible to measure the cell voltage with no appreciable current flow.

The electrical circuit of the pH cell is characterized as one having a very low current flow (10^{-12} amperes) and a very high resistance (1,000 megohms or less at the thin membrane of the glass electrode). To cope with these electrical characteristics, a special amplifier is used between the cell and the standard potentiometer. Essentially, this amplifier is an electronic electrometer operating on a null-balance principle. Accuracy of such a system is better than 0.1 pH unit.

MEASUREMENT OF ELECTROLYTIC CONDUCTIVITY

Electrolytic conductivity is primarily a measure of chemical concentration in electrolytes, being equally applicable for concentrated solutions and very dilute solutions down to traces of a contaminant in water. Although instrumental means for its industrial measurement have developed rapidly in the last decade, the foundations for most of the present-day methods are not new. Operating principles involved have not changed appreciably since the pioneer work of Kohlrausch, first published in 1879.

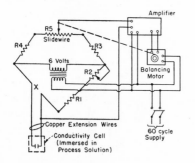

FIGURE 554.—Basic circuit for conductivity measurement.

Basic Principles of Conductivity. Electrolytic conductivity is basically the electrical conducting ability of ions present in solution when an emf is impressed across two electrodes immersed in the solution. In contrast to pH or Redox potential measurements, conductivity is affected by *all* ions dissociated in a solution because they all conduct current to some extent.

Because measurement of electrolytic conductivity is basically a measurement of resistance, the conventional potentiometer recorder with an alternating current Wheatstone bridge circuit is adapted simply to its measurement. In addition to this instrument, all that is required in the measuring circuit is a suitable primary element, termed the *conductivity cell*, which contains the two electrodes to establish the measured resistance.

Shown in Figure 554 is the basic measuring circuit. The conductivity cell is seen to form a variable resistance X in one leg of the Wheatstone bridge. Resistors $R1$, $R2$, $R3$, and $R4$ in the other legs of the bridge can all be considered fixed, $R5$ being the instrument slidewire used to rebalance the circuit. Upon a change in conductivity, resistance X changes and the electronic detecting system immediately reacts to move the slider on $R5$ to a new position of balance. With this rebalancing action, the instrument pen moves a corresponding amount to record the new conductivity value.

A prime consideration in the continuous measurement of conductivity is polarization of electrodes. This results with a d-c current when the ions attracted to an electrode become so concentrated that their collective electrical charge almost equals that of the electrodes. Because of the large measuring error which would be introduced by polarization, a-c current, usually 60 cycles, is employed in conductivity measurement.

The standard unit of measure for electrolytic conductivity is *specific conductance*. This unit is defined as the conductance in mhos of one cubic centimeter of solution, as measured between two electrodes one centimeter square located one centimeter apart. Practical considerations in the design and application of conductivity cells, however, dictate the use of electrodes which vary in size and spacing from these standards. This avoids measurement of extremely high or extremely low resistances encountered in practice, but requires a correction factor, termed the *cell constant*, to relate the actual measured value to the standard value.

Conductivity Electrodes.   There is a large variety of both the dip and screw-in type electrodes. The screw-in cells usually are preferred for permanent installation in vats or tanks. They are also used in pipelines of sufficiently large inside diameter to accommodate them. Cell constants vary from 0.10 to 100, enabling measurements to be made of practically all aqueous solutions without the need for special instruments to measure extremely high or low resistances.

Reading References

Annett, F. A., "Metering flow," *Power*, 86, 2, 69 (1942).

"Fluid Meters, Their Theory and Application," 4th Ed., New York, American Society of Mechanical Engineers, 1937.

MacLean, A. D., "The Orifice Meter," Pittsburgh Equitable Meter Co., Pittsburgh, 1938.

Gess, L., and Irwin, R. D., "Flow Meter Engineering Handbook," Industrial Division, Minneapolis-Honeywell Regulator Co., Philadelphia, Pa., 1946.

Measurement of Gases—Positive Displacement Meters, Handbook E-4, American Meter Company, Inc., Erie, Pa., 1936.

Richards, E. Curtiss, "Principles and Operation of Differential Fluid Meters," Industrial Division, Minneapolis-Honeywell Regulator Co., Philadelphia, Pa., 1947.

Spink, L. K., "Principles and Practice of Flow Meter Engineering," The Foxboro Company, Foxboro, Mass., 1937.

Principles and Significance of pH Measurement, *Chem. Met. Eng.*, 50, 108–124 (1943).

Automatic process control is used primarily for purposes of efficiency and economy. It reduces the human error and provides a continuous response in counteracting changes in the material and energy balance of the process. It soon pays for itself in savings of fuel, processing materials, and labor, as well as in increased value of product because of greater output or increased quality.

27. INSTRUMENTATION. PART III: AUTOMATIC CONTROL*

In the chemical and process industries, a large proportion of the measurements described in Chapters 25 and 26 are made in the interest of automatically controlling the process variables. The statement, "What can be measured can be controlled," is substantially true. In very infrequent cases, there are just causes why automatic control to some degree is not practical, but these instances are diminishing as new and better instrumentation techniques are developed.

Automatic Control Mechanisms

Three principal media are employed to obtain automatic control action: (1) pneumatic, (2) electric, and (3) hydraulic. Each has its own relative advantages and limitations, although the first two methods are used in the process industries much more than the latter.

Pneumatic-Operated Controllers

Pneumatic control units employ compressed air and are available in almost all types of industrial instruments, regardless of the type of primary element or process variable involved. The design of pneumatic control units differs principally with the mode of control desired. For example, two-position controllers are much simpler in design and construction than the more elaborate units for obtaining proportional-plus-reset-plus-rate action.†

---

* Prepared by Douglas M. Considine, Chemical Engineer and Manager of Market Extension, Industrial Division, Minneapolis-Honeywell Regulator Co., Philadelphia, Pa.

† Two-position single-point action is that in which a final control element is moved from one of two fixed positions to the other at a single value of the controlled variable.

Proportional-plus-reset-plus-rate action is that in which proportional-position action, proportional-speed floating action, and rate action are combined.

Proportional-plus-reset action is that in which proportional-position action and proportional-speed floating action are combined.

Rate action is that in which there is a continuous linear relation between rate of change of the controlled variable and position of a final control element.

Proportional-position action is that in which there is a continuous linear relation

Two-Position Control Units. Basically, any pneumatic-operated control system functions on the principle that air pressure to a diaphragm motor control valve determines the valve opening; it is this pressure which is governed by the control instrument in accordance with variations in the measured medium. The air-to-valve pressure depends upon a dynamic balance between the supply of air to the pneumatic system and the bleeding of air from the system. If the supply is greater than the bleed, as determined by the control action, the valve pressure approaches the supply pressure, and vice versa.

A two-position controller applies either full air pressure or zero pressure on the control valve when the controlled variable deviates a very small amount from the set point.* There is no intermediate positioning. As shown in Figure 555, the air supply comes from a compressor with a filter and pressure regulator to provide a clean, constant air pressure at about 17 psi. The bleed is a small nozzle, covered or uncovered by a flapper, which in turn is moved by the instrument pen mechanism to raise the air-to-valve pressure to a maximum or lower it to a minimum— in response to the pen movement over an extremely narrow neutral zone at the set point.

TABLE 92. UNITS OF MEASUREMENT OF BASIC PROCESS CHARACTERISTICS

Units of:	Thermal	Pressure	Liquid Level		Electrical	
Capacity	Btu	Cubic foot	Cubic foot-pounds		Coulomb	
Potential	Degree	Lb psi	Foot		Volt	
Capacitance	$\dfrac{\text{Btu}}{\text{Deg}}$	$\dfrac{\text{Cu ft}}{\text{Psi}}$	$\dfrac{\text{Cu ft}}{\text{Ft}}$ or	$\dfrac{\text{Lb}}{\text{Ft}}$	$\dfrac{\text{Coulomb}}{\text{Volt}} = \text{farad}$	
Resistance	Deg/Btu/sec	$\dfrac{\text{Psi}}{\text{Cu ft/sec}}$	$\dfrac{\text{Feet}}{\text{Cu ft/sec}}$ or	$\dfrac{\text{Feet}}{\text{Lb/sec}}$	$\dfrac{\text{Volt}}{\text{Coulomb/sec}} = \text{ohms}$	

Control action is effected through the use of a restriction in the supply line (Figure 555) of a diameter such that, when the nozzle is fully uncovered, no pressure exists between the restriction and the nozzle, but

---

between value of the controlled variable and position of a final control element.

Proportional-speed floating action is that in which there is a continuous linear relation between value of the controlled variable and rate of motion of a final control element.

The final control element is that portion of the controlling means which directly changes the value of the manipulated variable.

Automatic control terms have been prepared by the American Society of Mechanical Engineers. "Industrial Instruments and Regulators, Division, Committee on Terminology," published in *Mechanical Engineering*, February 1946.

* The set point of an automatic controller is the position of the control-point-setting mechanism translated into units of the controlled variable. Generally a set point scale is provided. The set point may be varied manually or by automatic means, such as in time-schedule or ratio control. The control point is the value of the controlled variable maintained by the controller.

when the nozzle is covered, air pressure between the restriction and nozzle can quickly build up.

If the air line shown connected to the *pilot valve* were directly connected to the control valve, all air required to change the pressure on the valve would have to pass in or out of the small restriction. Thus, with an appreciable volume in the line to the valve and in the diaphragm top, a serious lag in the pressure change to reposition the valve would occur. To eliminate this lag, many pneumatic controllers include a booster pilot, as shown in Figure 555. The pilot is simply a pneumatic relay which converts small changes in nozzle pressure into larger changes in the air-

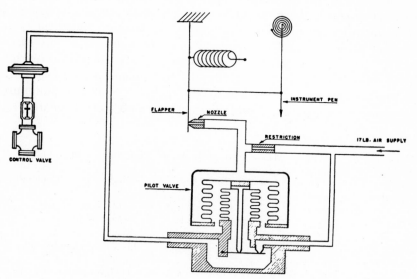

FIGURE 555.—Principle of operation of two-position pneumatic controller.

to-valve pressure through relatively large diameter inlet and exhaust nozzles.

Economy of operation is also a feature of non-bleed type pilot relays. They use air only when the air-to-valve pressure is increased, and then only at a rate of less than 0.1 cubic feet of free air per minute. Otherwise, the only air used is the nozzle bleed of approximately 0.01 cubic foot per minute. The actual total air consumption with a non-bleed pilot relay depends on the amount of control valve positioning required by the process. With a valve moving about 10 per cent of the time, the controller will consume approximately 0.05 cfm free air, or only about 72 cubic feet per 24-hour day.

Proportional Control Units. The fundamental difference between the two-position unit just described and the proportional unit, illustrated in

Figure 556, is the use of an auxiliary follow-up bellows which is acted upon instantaneously by the air-to-valve pressure.

Assume a small pen movement, such that the flapper moves toward the nozzle, causing an increase in the output pressure from the pilot relay. This increased pressure operates through the throttling bellows to move the flapper about its fulcrum (X) in a direction opposite from its first motion and to stabilize the output pressure at a slightly increased value. Manual adjustment of the proportional band causes a vertical shift of the flapper fulcrum point.

In operation, the unit responds as follows in a direct-acting controller: On a decrease in the controlled variable, the pen moves the flapper away from the nozzle, thereby decreasing the nozzle pressure and the air-to-valve pressure. Pressure decrease on the throttling bellows causes it to

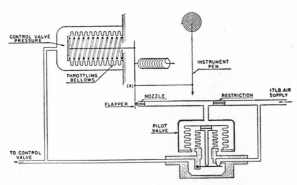

FIGURE 556.—Principle of operation of proportional type pneumatic controller.

move the flapper back toward the nozzle again by an amount depending upon the proportional band setting. The net movement of the flapper and the consequent change in air pressure decrease as the band setting is made wider. With an extremely wide band of 150 per cent, for example, a one per cent pen movement will position the flapper within $\frac{1}{150} \times 0.006$ inch or about 4/1,000,000ths of an inch.

With given controller adjustments, the proportional mode of control inherently provides a definite relationship between the pen position and the air-to-valve pressure. Thus, if an appreciable change in process load occurs and, for example, a greater normal valve opening is required to maintain the desired value, manual reset must be employed to shift the pen and air pressure relationship up or downscale. By this means, a a new air pressure can be obtained for the same pen position, but such an adjustment is, of course, practical only when the load changes are infrequent. Manual reset is provided by movement of a calibrated dial.

Proportional-Reset Control Units. To automatically obtain reset action, a unit of the type illustrated in Figure 557 can be employed. The bellows on the left provides the same function as just described for proportional control units. A similar bellows has been added on the right, and in addition, a set of small bellows has been installed within both of the larger ones. The space between the two bellows on either side is filled with a suitable liquid and these spaces are connected by a passage in which is installed a needle valve. The outside bellows on the right is open to atmosphere. The inner bellows are rigidly connected by a rod which provides a movable pivot for the flapper. With the pen at the set point, liquid pressures on both sides of the inner bellows are equal.

The proportional action of this unit is obtained in the same manner as in the proportional unit just described, except that, instead of the throttling bellows moving the flapper directly, the flapper is moved through

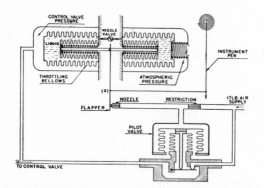

FIGURE 557.—Principle of operation of proportional-reset type pneumatic controller.

the inner bellows. If it is assumed that the liquid between the bellows is sealed, the proportional action takes place as follows: When the pen moves away from the set point in a direction to carry the flapper away from the nozzle, the control valve pressure is lowered. The throttling bellows then expands to the left, reducing the liquid pressure on that side, while the liquid pressure in the right remains momentarily the same as the atmospheric pressure on the outside. This unbalance of pressure causes the inner bellows to move to the left, returning the flapper toward the nozzle in accordance with the proportional band setting, as in the proportional type previously described.

The automatic reset action takes place as soon as the inner bellows has moved away from the central set-point position. The outer bellows, considered sealed thus far in the discussion, actually is connected when the needle valve is open; the valve opening is determined by the reset adjustment dial and permits liquid to flow from one bellows to the other. In the present case, the liquid flows from the high-pressure side on the right to the low-pressure side on the left, permitting the inner bellows assembly to move slowly to the right again toward its balanced position. This movement causes the flapper to move away from the nozzle and further decreases the control valve pressure at a *gradual rate*.

If the change in control valve opening does not reflect through the process being controlled and the pen continues to remain away from the set point, the inside bellows system continues to reduce the valve pressure until it becomes zero. It will be seen from a study of this action that the liquid pressures cannot equalize so long as the pen remains away from the set point. This unit, therefore, is capable of producing a full range of valve openings to maintain the controlled variable at the desired value regardless of load changes in the process.

Rate-Action Control Units. Rate action can be incorporated in the proportional or proportional-reset control units simply by interposing an additional bellows unit in the connecting line between the pilot relay and

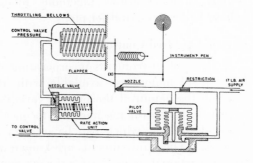

Figure 558.—Principle of operation of pneumatic controller with rate action.

the throttling bellows. Although rate action is more commonly used in conjunction with proportional-reset units, its operation can be described more simply by consideration of its combination in the proportional type, as shown in Figure 558.

Basically, the rate action bellows merely retards the follow-up pressure change on the throttling bellows, thereby permitting the control valve to travel *temporarily* further than it normally would for a departure of the pen from the set point. In more detail, the rate action takes place as follows: Assume that the pen departs a certain amount from the set point such as to cause the flapper to move toward the nozzle, thereby increasing the air-to-valve pressure from the pilot. This increased air pressure, instead of passing directly to the throttling bellows, acts on the inside of the rate action bellows which expands and compresses the air outside the bellows.

By the inherent design of the rate action bellows and the outer chamber, the resultant air pressure immediately impressed on the throttling bellows has a value one-tenth that of the increased air-to-valve pressure.

This reduced pressure moves the flapper away from the nozzle a relatively small amount, so that the immediate result of the pen departure is a relatively large increase in the air-to-valve pressure.

The remaining nine-tenths of the air pressure increase bleeds through the needle valve of the rate action unit to the throttling bellows, causing the flapper to move further away from the nozzle and the air-to-valve pressure to be reduced until the same pressure exists on both sides of the needle valve.   The valve loading pressure is thereby reduced to a stable value as called for by the proportional action of the controller.   Departure of the pen from the set point thus results in a temporary overcorrection of the control valve position, which tends to compensate for the large dead time or transfer lag of the controlled system.   It is to be stressed that the large majority of process applications do not require this type of controller action.

The flapper and nozzle is not the only principle used in pneumatic control units.   Various ingenious methods are used, including slide valves, ball valves, and jet pipes.

Electric-Operated Controllers

Industrial instruments incorporating means for the operation of electric control motors are available with a variety of measuring systems, running the gamut of the process variables.   Many instruments are furnished with control mechanisms to operate mercury switches or metal-to-metal contacts which can be used in two-position or floating control systems.   These instruments are known as *contact controllers*.   For electric proportional or proportional-reset control, the potentiometer type instrument generally is used.   Operating a sliding contact over a resistor, this type is known as a *resistor controller*.

Auxiliary electric contacts for alarm or limit functions are often added to electric or pneumatic-operated controllers, introducing a large variety of available combinations.

Electric Two-Position Controllers.   Contact controllers employ mechanical or electronic means of detecting the relative position of the pen with respect to the set point for the controlled variable.   Glass-enclosed mercury switches or metal-to-metal contacts are accordingly positioned to open or close electric circuits to the control or other electric final control elements.

Two-position control can be provided by a single contact controller with the contact closed below or above the set point.   Illustrated in Figure 559 is the use of such a controller for the operation of a solenoid valve. Here the valve is supplied as either *normally open* (energized to close) or *normally closed*, depending upon whether it is desired to have the valve remain open or closed by spring action in event of power failure.

The instrument contact action is, in turn, selected to close below or above the set point, depending upon the desired valve position in the respective zone.

Single-contact controllers can also provide *on-off* or *high-low* control of electrically heated furnaces through the operation of contractors (heavy-duty relays) or, where smaller currents are involved, directly through the instrument contact which can have ratings as high as 30 amperes at 115 volts a-c. These instruments find further usage as high limit controllers in conjunction with master controllers of process variables.

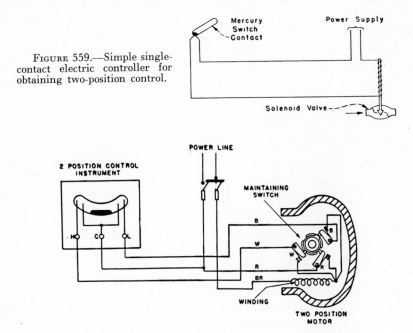

FIGURE 559.—Simple single-contact electric controller for obtaining two-position control.

FIGURE 560.—Two-position electric controller utilizing a unidirectional control motor.

Figure 560 illustrates a widely used circuit for two-position control utilizing a unidirectional control motor which provides more power for valve positioning and requires a *high* and a *low* contact. The width of the neutral zone between contact closure points is governed primarily by the process reaction rate, being wider for processes which react faster. Operation of such a control system can best be described by an example.

Assume that the control motor is positioning a fuel valve on a furnace in which the temperature is being regulated by the control instrument. A linkage or gear arrangement is used to convert circular motion of the motor crankshaft into valve position. Attached to the shaft are cams of a maintaining switch which rotate with the shaft.

Assume further that the diagram illustrates the conditions when the motor is in its closed or *low* position, with switch finger contact B closed, and that the temperature has dropped sufficiently to close the L contact, thereby calling for an open or *high* valve position. When this contact closes, current flows through the motor winding via contact B. The motor is thus energized to move the fuel valve toward the open position and also to rotate the maintaining switch cams.

When the motor shaft has rotated 30 degrees, the instrument low contact can be broken, because switch finger contact R is then closed and contact B opened; the current then feeds from the power source through R to the motor winding. The motor continues to run until the shaft has rotated one-half revolution, where contact R opens and contact W closes.

If the instrument low contact remains closed, the motor remains in the open position. When the temperature subsequently rises above the

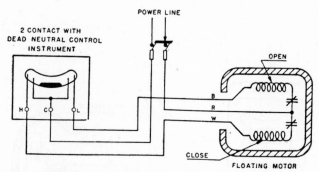

FIGURE 561.—Schematic wiring diagram of electric floating control circuit.

set point, the H contact is closed and current flows through switch finger contact W to cause rotation of the motor for the second one-half revolution, thereby moving the control valve to its closed position.

Electric Floating Control Units. Electric floating control requires a reversible control motor because the motor must be capable of reversing its direction of travel at any intermediate point. A high-low contact action with neutral zone is utilized in a circuit with the floating control motor, as shown in Figure 561.

In operation the system functions as follows: When the controlled variable drops below the neutral zone, the instrument *low* contact closes, thereby energizing the *open* winding of the motor and causing the motor to run toward the open position, so long as the contact remains closed. On the other hand, when the controlled variable rises above the neutral zone, the instrument *high* contact closes, thereby causing the motor to move in the closed direction. While the controlled variable is within the neutral zone, neither instrument contact is closed and the motor remains in its last position attained at the time the variable entered the neutral zone.

If the motor should run to the end of its travel in either direction, limit switches are arranged to open the circuit to the appropriate motor winding. These switches can be adjusted to limit the travel to less than normal full travel, if desired.

Electric Proportional Control. These systems utilize a null-balance Wheatstone bridge circuit to provide intermediate positioning of control motors over the proportional band of the controller. Any such system

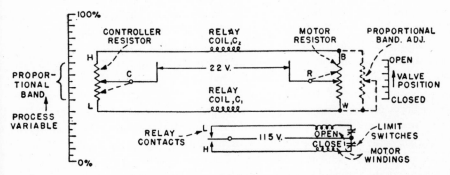

FIGURE 562.—Proportional type electric controller utilizing resistance balance system.

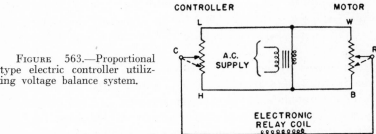

FIGURE 563.—Proportional type electric controller utilizing voltage balance system.

requires three basic elements: (1) a slidewire resistor in the controller over which a sliding contact moves in direct relation to the pen movement through proportional band; (2) a corresponding slidewire resistor in the control motor with a sliding contact moving in direct relation to rotation of the motor shaft through its travel; and (3) a balancing relay to detect an unbalance in the Wheatstone bridge circuit and to close contacts to the proper motor winding.

Two types of balancing circuits, illustrated in Figures 562 and 563, are in common use—the first being based upon a balance of *resistances*, the second upon a balance of *voltages*. The first system operates on an electromechanical principle which incorporates the less expensive components but is less sensitive in its control action. The voltage balance system is electronic in its balancing method and, in addition to being highly sensitive, more easily incorporates the necessary control adjustments.

Resistance Balance System. Referring to Figure 562, it is seen that when the instruments and motor sliders are in the center of their respective resistors, the upper and lower arms of the bridge circuit have equal resistances and no current flows. Motion of the instrument slider toward *L*, as caused by a decrease in the value of the controlled variable, places more resistance in the upper arm of the bridge, thereby permitting more current to flow in the lower arm through one coil (C_1) of the balancing relay and closing the relay contact to the *open* winding of the control motor.

Rotation of the motor moves the valve to the new position called for by the instrument, and at the same time moves the motor slider toward a new balance position. When the bridge balance is restored, the relay contact opens and motion of the motor is stopped. In this manner, a linear relation between the controlled variables and valve opening is provided.

Adjustment of the proportional band in this system can be provided by a rheostat wired in parallel with the motor slidewire, as shown dotted in Figure 562. The effect of this parallel resistance is to increase the movement of the motor slider necessary to balance a given movement of the instrument slider, or, in other words, to decrease the proportional band. Variation in the mechanical linkage between the pen and instrument slider, or use of a slidewire of different resistance value in the instrument, is also a method of changing the proportional band of electric controllers.

Voltage Balance System. The system illustrated in Figure 563 utilizes the same instrument and motor design, but incorporates an electronic relay to detect unbalance in the bridge circuit.

The desired function of the system is provided by electronic detection of a voltage unbalance between two opposing bridge circuits containing the instrument and motor slidewire, as shown. Any movement of the instrument slider causes an unbalance which constitutes the input to the electronic control circuit of the relay. This signal is amplified electronically and caused to operate mechanical contacts governing the power supply to the *open* or *close* drive windings of the motor.

Final Control Elements

The *final control element*, which effects changes in the control agent flow, and the *power unit*, which operates this element, are often treated as items of secondary importance—the main emphasis being placed upon the accuracy and sensitivity of the automatic control instrument. Equal attention, however, should be given to the proper selection of these critical components of the control system; the control instrument is entirely dependent upon them to carry out its commands. Sluggish response of the final control element can be as detrimental to close process regulation as are other lags present in the control loop.

Electric and pneumatic-operated power units designed for either two-position, floating, or proportional modes of control are available in combinations with the following common types of final control elements: (1) sliding stem valves, (2) adjustable orifice valves, and (3) butterfly valves and dampers. Also worthy of note are the various rheostat and similar arrangements which can be actuated by electric or pneumatic power units for such functions as regulation of electric heating elements, electric motor speeds, and variable speed drives.

Pneumatic Power Units

The most common type of pneumatic power unit is the *diaphragm motor* (Figure 564). This unit has a flexible diaphragm with a pressure-tight chamber on one side, to which air output from the pneumatic con-

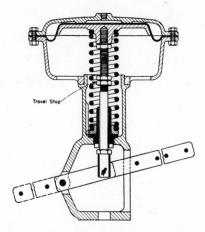

FIGURE 564.—Diaphragm motor operator.

troller is connected. On the other side of the diaphragm is placed a compression ring assembly. A rod rigidly fastened to the metal plate under the diaphragm is directly attached to the valve stem or lever.

Air pressure applied on the top of the diaphragm creates a downward force equal to the air pressure multiplied by the area of the diaphragm. As the diaphragm moves downward, the spring further compresses until it creates an equal, opposing upward force, resulting in a balanced position of the valve stem.

For proportional control, the diaphragm motor offers a sensitive means for intermediate positioning of the final control element in accordance with each value of controlled air pressure from the instrument. For two-position control, the same principle is used; in this case, however, controlled air pressure is either at a maximum or minimum value to position the final control element in one of two extremes of travel. Diaphragm motors for two-position control, therefore, are designed for a relatively small movement of the valve stem through its full travel. This is accomplished by suitable selection of the compression spring, and mechanical travel stops in the diaphragm head casting.

The compression springs in two-position as compared to proportional-control motors are selected to provide a markedly different relationship between the instrument-controlled air pressure and the stem travel. In two-position control, it is advantageous to reserve most of the force from the controlled air pressure for the end of the stem travel, where the valve plug or vane must be seated or unseated against the maximum force, because of fluid pressure of the control agent. In proportional control, the

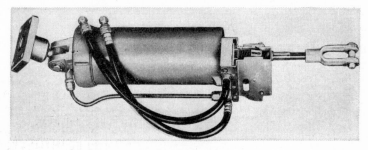

FIGURE 565.—Pneumatic power cylinder.

diaphragm motor must provide positioning of the stem over as much of the controlled air pressure range as possible.

In proportional control, the ability of the diaphragm motor to overcome friction and thrust on the stem, due to line pressures, determines the closeness of control obtainable. Because the motor inherently has only the force due to a *change* in controlled air pressure available for positioning, the proper size motor must be selected to suit the application. Where a large amount of friction or valve thrust appears likely or extra sensitive positioning is desired, the use of a *valve positioner* with a diaphragm motor is recommended.

Fundamentally, a valve positioner comprises an auxiliary air pilot system with separate air power supply (usually 15 or 30 psi) which either applies full air pressure on the motor diaphragm, or exhausts air from the diaphragm (completely if necessary) until the valve stem is positioned as called for by the controller output pressure. Small changes in controlled air pressure thereby cause maximum force for repositioning with a sensitivity expressed in thousandths of an inch of stem movement.

Power Cylinders. For the positioning of dampers or other final control elements which require more power and a longer stroke than are available with diaphragm motors, the power cylinder is used. This unit, shown in Figure 565, utilizes air power in both directions of travel and, for proportional control, incorporates a positioner similar in function to the valve positioner to insure that the piston will take a definite position for each intermediate value of controlled air pressure. Power cylinders are available with strokes up to 32 inches and diameters (internal) up to 12 inches. The latter, with an air supply of 100 psi, provides a force of over 11,000 pounds for positioning the final control element. Even with this large force, however, heavy dampers are counterbalanced with dead weights so that the cylinder need work only against the friction of the element.

Electric Power Units

Operating from electric contacts either directly connected to the control instrument, or through electric relays, electric power units are of two principal types: (1) electric motors, and (2) solenoid units.

FIGURE 566.—Electric motor operator.

Electric Motor Operators. Power units of this type, as shown in Figure 566, are designed specifically for industrial applications. The unit essentially comprises (1) an integral housing which contains the motor proper, and (2) a gear reduction unit to amplify the torque. For operation of rotary stem valves and dampers, one design has a horizontal shaft to which a lever arm is attached for connection to the damper arm or other actuating lever.

FIGURE 567.—Electric motorized sliding stem valve.

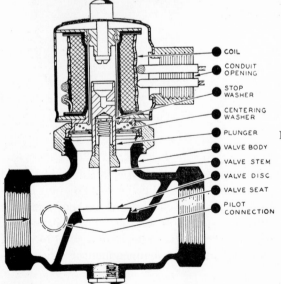

COIL

CONDUIT
OPENING

STOP
WASHER

CENTERING
WASHER

PLUNGER

VALVE BODY

VALVE STEM

VALVE DISC

VALVE SEAT

PILOT
CONNECTION

FIGURE 568.—Solenoid operated
control valve.

A second design (Figure 567) is equipped with an integral valve yoke for mounting on sliding stem valves; rotary motion of the gears is converted to linear motion by a suitable cam in the housing. Additionally, the latter motor has a horizontal shaft for simultaneous operation of a rotary valve. Both designs are supplied for two-position, floating, or proportional control and are available in several *timings* for full travel, such as 10, 15, 30, and 60 seconds. Wide face alloy gears, which are packed in grease and designed for long life, provide the required speed reduction. A dust splashproof housing totally encloses the motor and gears.

Solenoid Units. These units generally are confined to operation of sliding stem control valves (Figure 568). In this form, solenoid valves find wide application for all types of on-off control. The solenoid is positive in action and very fast, its chief limitation being that it is available only in small valve sizes, maximum about six inches.

Sliding Stem Control Valves

Sliding stem control valves for use either with electric or pneumatic power units are in most cases identical in design. The most common type incorporates the globe body, as shown in cross-section in Figure 569. There are three principal parts of the valve: (1) stuffing box, (2) inner port, and (3) inner valve or valve plug.

Stuffing Box. The stuffing box functions to seal the fluid flowing through the valve body, at the same time permitting the valve stem to pass through as freely as possible. The sealing gland around the stem, (5) in the diagram, is packed with composition rings and filled with a lubricant selected to suit the control agent being handled as well as the temperature encountered. A gland nut provides a means of tightening the seal, but must only be made hand-tight in order to prevent excessive friction on the valve stem.

Inner Port. The inner port is the opening within the valve body into which the valve plug seats as it throttles the control agent flow. Valve bodies are available in *single* or *double* seat construction, as shown in Figures 570 and 571. Single-seat bodies permit the thrust of fluid pressures to act over the entire bottom of the valve plug, thereby creating an upward force on the valve stem. The power unit, therefore, must overcome this force to move or hold the stem downward. The larger the valve size and the higher the fluid pressure, the more prohibitive this stem thrust becomes.

The double-seat construction is designed to minimize these undesirable effects. Inlet and outlet fluid pressures tend to balance themselves by acting both upward and downward on the two valve plugs, resulting in a *balanced* valve. One disadvantage of this construction is that with temperature variations, the stem portion between the two valve plugs contracts or expands linearly a different amount than the valve body. In the closed position, therefore, one valve disc seats first and prevents the second disc from seating completely. A small leakage flow results. For tight shut-off, therefore, a single port valve must be used.

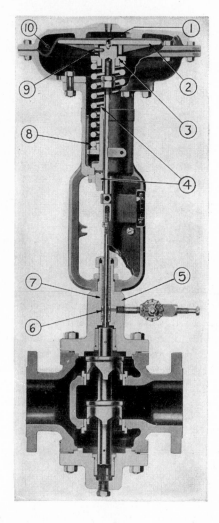

FIGURE 569.—Diaphragm motor operated sliding-stem control valve. Legend: (1) ball pivot; (2) pivoted inner plate; (3) cradle-mounted upper spring flange; (4) duplex stem guide; (5) forged bonnet; (6) grease lantern; (7) stuffing box; (8) coded spring; (9) anti-spin lock screw; (10) molded diaphragm.

Inner Valves. These fall into two classifications, according to their design for two-position or proportional control. Several features are common to both types: (1) provision for counter-acting the effects of horizontal thrust due to fluid pressure against the valve and plug, and (2) suitable design for connection between inner valve and valve stem.

Inner valves for two-position control usually are simply a flat disc, bevelled at the seating edge. This construction provides a maximum flow in the open position with a minimum of lift. The disc may have skirted or winged guides to offset stem thrust, or a removable composition disc on the seating surface. The latter has the advantage of providing tight seating, regardless of whether particles of dirt become lodged on the seat.

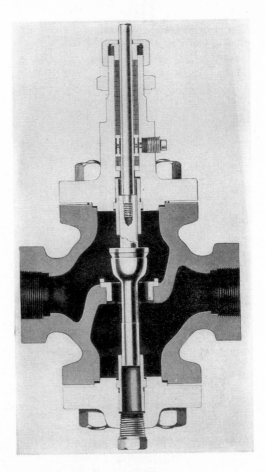

FIGURE 570.—Sliding-stem control valve body showing single-seat construction.

It is easily replaced and is suitable for air, steam, or water—provided these fluids do not contain corrosive materials.

Inner valves for proportional control are available in several designs. The design of the inner valve shape effects different relationships between flow and valve lift, known as valve characteristics.*

* For a detailed discussion of valve characteristics, the reader is referred to the following excellent reference: "Valve characteristics in automatic control," by S. D. Ross, *Ind. Eng. Chem.* (Sept. 1946).

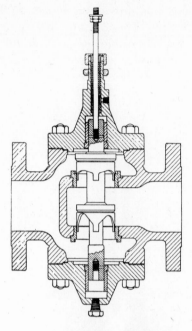

FIGURE 571.—Sliding-stem control valve showing double-seat construction.

RATIO CONTROL SYSTEMS

As illustrated in Figure 572, pneumatic transmission is used to advantage in two common arrangements for ratio-flow control, employing differential pressure-type flow meters. The basic principle involved is that changes in one flow, which is usually permitted to vary as determined

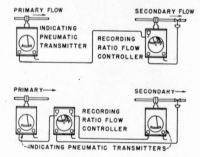

FIGURE 572.—Two common arrangements for ratio-flow control.

by the process, are caused to position the set point of a controller for the second flow in such a manner that the second flow is maintained at a fixed ratio to the first. The first flow is termed the *primary* and the ratio-controlled flow, the *secondary*.

In both arrangements, the primary flow is measured by an indicating pneumatic transmitter, the air pressure of which is connected to a ratio mechanism in the secondary controller. This device is essentially a pneumatic receiver for the primary flow with an adjustable linkage to the control index. As such, it performs three fundamental functions: (1) actuates a pen-recording of the primary flow, (2) positions the set point for the secondary flow at some fixed ratio of the primary pen position, and (3) provides a means for manual adjustment of the set ratio through adjustable linkage to the control index.

The secondary or ratio controller operates as any flow controller to measure and record the flow, and to control the flow in accordance with its continuously adjusted set point. To maintain the secondary flow at the shifting control point, this instrument is provided with proportional-reset controller action.

The approximate basic ratio of the two flows to be proportioned can be any desired value, being determined by the size and fluid pressure of the process lines, as well as the orifice design for the flow meters. This ratio is then maintained exactly by the ratio-control system, or set at some other value within the range of the ratio adjustments. For example, if the basic ratio of secondary to primary flow is to be 6:1, the piping system and orifices are designed to provide approximately this ratio. The ratio controller set at 100 per cent will maintain this relative proportion of flows. The 6:1 flow ratio, however, could be decreased to 3:1 by reducing the ratio setting to 50 per cent, or could be increased to 8.4:1 by a ratio setting of 140 per cent.

Use of Ratio-Flow Control Systems

At a chemical plant manufacturing a constant concentration of hydrochloric acid by the absorption of anhydrous hydrogen chloride gas with water in an absorption tower, ratio control was found to provide an excellent solution to the control problem. As shown in Figure 573, the ratio arrangement is seen to be one of the conventional type with hydrogen chloride gas as the uncontrolled primary flow and water as the related secondary flow. The water is introduced in the tower in the form of a spray and mixes intimately with the gas entering at top of tower.

Instrumentation of this process was first approached on the basis of measuring the density of the finished acid and accordingly controlling the water spray to maintain a constant concentration of acid. The plant chemists objected to this method, however, because they did not want any instrument parts in the finished acid line. Furthermore, the system did not appear practical because control action would lag too greatly behind the density measurement, conditions in the absorber possibly being proper, while the acid concentration in the discharge line might call for a change in water flow. Exact rationing of water to gas provided the desired answer.

At a petroleum refinery, it was desired to mix heavy and light gas-oil

feed stock to a catalytic cracking unit.   As shown in Figure 574, the ratio-
control arrangement differs from the conventional in that instead of light
gas-oil flow being metered as the primary to set the ratio of the secondary
heavy oil flow, the light oil flow and the total flow of the blend are measured, the heavy gas-oil flow being proportioned accordingly.   This was
done to avoid placing an orifice in the heavy gas-oil line, since this oil has

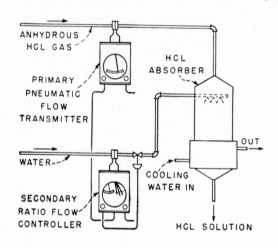

FIGURE   573.—Ratio-flow
control used in system where
hydrogen chloride gas is absorbed in water.

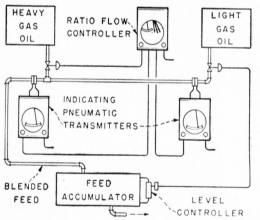

FIGURE   574.—Ratio-flow
control used in gas-oil blending
system.

an extremely high viscosity and tendency to plug small openings, such as
differential pressure connections.

In this application, it is also to be noted that the primary light gas-oil
is controlled from a liquid-level controller installed on the feed-accumu-
lator tank.   The ratio-control system then proportions the flow of the
heavy gas-oil to this varied flow to maintain a constant composition of
the blend.

Cascade Control Systems

The need for control systems of this type can best be explained by first describing the shortcomings of conventional control in a typical application requiring cascade control. It must be stressed, however, that the majority of applications do not require cascade control.

Assume that a pneumatic controller of the proportional-reset type is being used to position a diaphragm motor valve in the fuel line to a process, as shown in Figure 575. With changes in demand for fuel by the process, the controller positions the valve to provide any flow rate within its range in an attempt to maintain the temperature at the set point. If, however, variations in differential pressure across the valve occur, because of uncontrolled pressure changes up or downstream from the valve, the temperature controller is incapable of correcting for the resultant changes in heating effect until these changes are reflected in a temperature deviation. When the process characteristics are such that a large

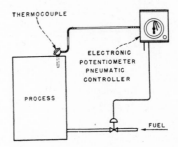

FIGURE 575.—Conventional temperature control application.

time lag exists between the change in flow of the fuel and its detection by a temperature measurement, serious deviation of the temperature from the set point can occur.

A flow control installed on the fuel line and operating the diaphragm motor valve would, of course, correct for changes in flow caused by varying pressure differentials; but it would necessarily need to have its set point changed in accordance with the temperature measurement in order to change the flow required by the process demand. Both the function of temperature control and flow control with adjusted set point can be accomplished by using the controlled air pressure from the temperature controller to adjust pneumatically the set point of the flow controller which, in turn, positions the diaphragm motor valve. Such an arrangement is illustrated in Figure 576 for a radiant tube furnace used in oil-cracking and is known as *cascade* control. With changes in heating requirements in the furnace, the master temperature controller functions to change the set point of the flow controller, such that the correct amount of fuel is supplied to meet the varied demand.   Otherwise, the flow controller functions to maintain the rate of flow at its set point, compensating for erratic variations due to pressure changes in the fuel line.

In cascade control, the master controller uses whatever mode of control is required by the process characteristics, just as if it were operating the control valve directly.   For applications where cascade control is desirable, the proportional-reset mode is usually necessary, or possibly this type plus rate action.   In contrast to ratio-flow control, it will be noted

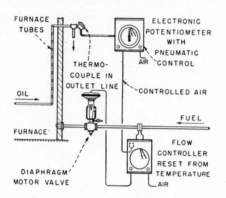

FIGURE 576.—Cascade control of flow from temperature on oil cracking furnace.

that cascade control involves no fixed relationship between the master variable and the secondary variable; the latter can be at any value required to maintain the master variable at its set point.

AUTOMATIC CONTROL SYSTEMS

A few of the numerous ways in which instruments and controls can be applied to a process are given below.

Figure 577 illustrates a simple *open-kettle temperature-control system.*   The measuring means comprises a pressure-type thermometer bulb located through the side of the vessel.   Internal pressure in the thermal system is transmitted to a measuring spiral within the instrument case by means of armored capillary tubing.   Automatic control is accomplished pneumatically by positioning a diaphragm motor valve on the steam-supply line to the heating coils.

In order to increase production, it may be desirable to heat the contents of the kettle as quickly as possible to a given temperature and then hold the kettle at that temperature.   The heating time is a controllable factor which should be reduced to a minimum because it is unproductive time.   This means that, during the heating time, a large heat input is required, and when the control temperature is reached, a much smaller heat input, sometimes only sufficient to supply radiation losses, is required. To meet the demands of such operations, two controlled valves, as illustrated in Figure 578, may be used in parallel—a large valve and a smaller valve. If the controlled output air pressure from the instrument varies from 0 to 15 psi with 7.5 psi at the control point, the large valve will be designed to throttle from an open to a closed position when the diaphragm air pressure is varied from 0 to 7.5 psi, and the smaller valve will be designed to proportion over the entire range from 0 to 15 psi. Thus, both valves will be open in the early stages of heating. The large valve will move toward a closed position and will be closed when the set point is reached, and the smaller valve will be throttling in mid-position at the set point.

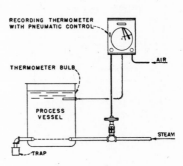

FIGURE 577.—Simple open-kettle temperature control system.

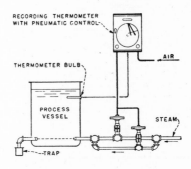

FIGURE 578.—Temperature control system designed for rapid heating.

In some operations, it is desirable to employ a *jacketed kettle* and circulate the heating or cooling medium through the jacket. Figure 579 is a schematic diagram of a temperature controller applied to such an installation. In this case, a three-way valve is used to direct any part or all the flow of the heating medium through the jacket. That which does not go through the jacket is by-passed around it. Three-way valves in such applications permit a large quantity to pass through the jacket for quick heating and a small quantity for holding the temperature at the set point similar to the two-valve application of Figure 578, and they do not materially restrict the total flow of heating medium being controlled.

Often it is desirable to bring an open kettle up to a given temperature, hold it at that temperature for a given length of time, and then shut off the heating medium and discharge the contents of the vessel. A process-control system to perform these operations is shown in Figure 580. A pressure switch in the air line to the steam valve closes when the temperature reaches the set point. The pressure switch starts a timer, and at the end of the period for which the timer is set, the three-way solenoid valves in the air lines to the steam valve and to the discharge valve are operated. Both the steam valve and the discharge valve are normally closed so that they will move to a closed position upon air failure. Therefore, at the

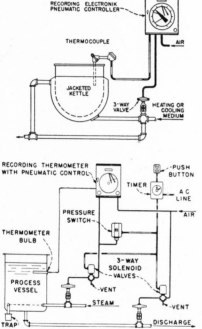

FIGURE 579.—System utilizing three-way diverting valve for temperature control.

FIGURE 580.—Electric-pneumatic time-temperature control system.

end of the timing period, the three-way solenoid valve in the air line to the steam valve closes and bleeds the air from the diaphragm, and the steam valve closes; also the three-way valve in the air line to the discharge valve closes its exhaust port and admits air to the diaphragm from the supply line to open the discharge valve. The steam valve remains closed, and the discharge valve remains open. When the vessel is recharged, the operator pushes the start button which momentarily opens the electric-current supply. This automatically resets the timer to its starting position and opens the steam valve and closes the discharge valve. In the meantime, while the vessel was being emptied, the temperature dropped below the set point, and the pressure switch opened.

The vessel now can be recharged to repeat the heating and holding cycle. In plants where a number of vessels are under the supervision of one operator, it may be desirable to incorporate signal lights with the automatic equipment to indicate when the vessels are being emptied.

In some operations, it is desirable that the *temperature follow a predetermined program*. Figure 581 is a schematic diagram of such an installation in which the control index of the recorder is moved by varying air pressure from the transmitter. The output air pressure from the transmitter varies in direct proportion to the radius of the cam mounted on it. Thus, the control instrument automatically conforms to the time-

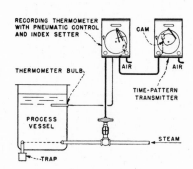

FIGURE 581.—Pneumatic time-temperature control system.

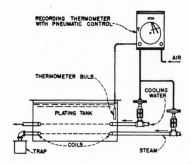

FIGURE 582.—Combined heating and cooling in one control system.

temperature pattern of the cam. The cams are usually constructed of aluminum or plastic sheets. Graduations are printed on the disk similar to the graduations printed on a paper chart. This makes it possible to keep transmitter disks on hand and to cut new cams from them as required. The index of the control instrument can be set manually for operations when an automatic time-temperature program is not required.

Where there is energy dissipation within a vessel, as with *exothermic reactions,* it is often necessary to remove heat from the process to prevent the temperature from becoming excessive. Chromium plating is an example of a process in which energy is dissipated in the bath owing to the passage of electric current. Figure 582 illustrates the application of temperature control to a plating tank. The bath contains both heating (steam) and cooling (water) coils. The valves in these lines are connected to the output air line from the control instrument. One valve opens with an increase in air pressure, and the other valve closes with an increase in air pressure. The valve springs are so adjusted that one valve is open to 0 psi and closed at 8 psi, while the other valve is open at 15 psi and closed at 9 psi. Thus, when the air pressure on the diaphragms is between 8 and 9 psi, both valves will be closed. The instrument-control mechanism is adjusted to a narrow proportioning band with an output air pressure of 8.5 psi at the set point. When the temperature rises above the set point, the steam valve is closed, and the water valve opens. When the temperature drops below the set point, the water valve is closed, and the steam valve opens.

Another method of obtaining both *heating and cooling* in a control system is shown in Figure 583. In this system, a tank of hot water is au-

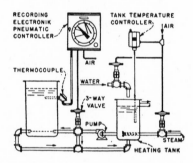

F I G U R E 583.—Combined heating and cooling control of process-control agent.

tomatically held at the set point by a separate controller which regulates the flow of steam and water to the tank. The tank is provided with an overflow. A pump circulates hot water from the tank through a closed-coil heater in the process vessel or through a jacket surrounding the vessel. The process temperature controller operates a three-way valve to regulate the flow of hot water to the process or by-pass it back to the auxiliary tank. With a high rate of circulation, very close control can be obtained with this method, and it has the advantage of limiting the temperature of heating medium where high temperatures would cause decomposition. The steam- and water-valve arrangement on the heating tank is similar to that shown in Figure 582.

Figure 584 illustrates an open vessel in which the liquid contents are *heated by means of an electric immersion element*. The power supply to the heating element is turned on and off automatically by means of a mercury switch in the control instrument. Mercury switches such as this are designed to break at about 30 amperes at 115 volts. For greater power requirements, an auxiliary contactor is necessary.

A number of other systems have been devised to regulate the power input to electrically heated processes, including the following:

(1) Automatic adjustment of resistances in series with the heating elements.

(2) Use of power input controllers which are a type of circuit interrupter in which the length of time that the power is supplied to the process is automatically varied in reference to departure from the set point.

(3) Automatically varying the voltage applied to the heating elements by means of multitap transformers or induction voltage regulators.

(4) Automatically varying the power supplied to the heating elements by means of a saturable reactor.

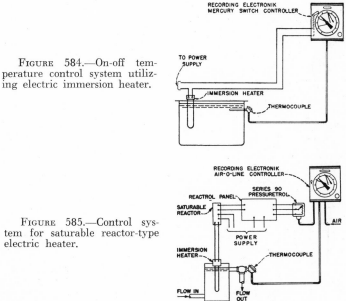

FIGURE 584.—On-off temperature control system utilizing electric immersion heater.

FIGURE 585.—Control system for saturable reactor-type electric heater.

Adjustable resistors, input controllers, multitap transformers, and induction regulators generally are operated by reversible motors from a single-pole, double-throw mercury switch operated by the automatic-control instrument. When the temperature is at the set point, the position of the switch is such that the circuits to the reversing motor are open so that the power input to the process remains at that value.

The saturable-reactor type of electric control system receives impulse from the change in position of the sliding contact on a resistor.

In Figure 585, a thermocouple is located in the discharge of an electrically heated continuous-fluid heater. The output air pressure of the pneumatic control instrument is applied to a small air-operated slidewire.   The purpose of using the pneumatic control instrument to operate the slider is to take advantage of the adjustable proportional band and reset rate incorporated in its control system.   These control characteristics are necessary for good control on continuous processes in which the throughput varies.

The potential unbalance caused by the change in position of the sliding contact is amplified electronically to regulate the amount of direct current in the saturating winding of a saturable-core reactor.   The power supply is connected to the primary of the saturable reactor, and the heating element is connected to the secondary.   As the direct current through

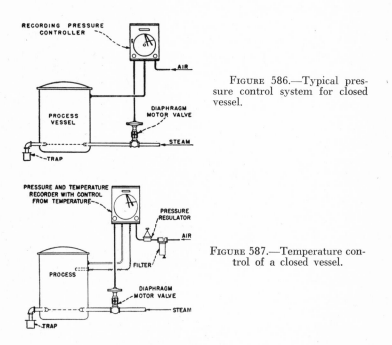

Figure 586.—Typical pressure control system for closed vessel.

Figure 587.—Temperature control of a closed vessel.

the saturating winding varies, more or less power is transmitted from the primary to the secondary to which the heating element is connected.

In most heating operations in *closed vessels*, such as autoclaves, the upper space in the vessel is filled with steam.   In such cases, a pressure controller may be used for regulating the flow of the heating medium. The steam pressure is an indirect measure of the temperature.   Thus, pressure controllers may be used in place of temperature controllers and have the advantages of lower cost, simplicity of operation and installation, and often better control because of less lag.   However, when pressure control is used, it is necessary to vent entrapped air or other gases released during the heating-up period.   Pressure control in lieu of temperature control may not be satisfactory for processes requiring the introduction of inert or other gases.

Figure 586 shows a pressure controller applied to a closed vessel. If direct temperature control is required, owing to the presence of inert gases or other reasons, the system illustrated in Figure 587 can be used. However, if either temperature or pressure is controlled, the uncontrolled temperature or pressure can be recorded on the same chart where desired.

Suppose that the upper space in a closed vessel is filled with steam and that a pressure recorder connected to it reads 100 psi. If a thermometer bulb partly filled with water is inserted in the same space and is connected to read on the same chart, it will also read 100 psi. This combination has been used to detect the presence of gases in closed vessels, such as paper digesters, by noting whether the pressure pen records the same value as the temperature pen. When other vapors are present, as in distillation columns, the thermometer bulb can be partly filled with the

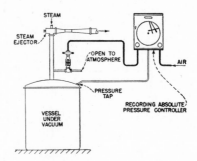

FIGURE 588.—Vacuum control of a steam-ejector system.

condensed vapors, and the difference between the temperature and pressure pens then will be a measure of the composition of the vapor in the column compared to the vapor in the thermometer bulb.

The pressure in closed vessels can be reduced *below atmospheric pressure* by means of a steam-jet ejector. As a rule, steam-jet ejectors will not operate satisfactorily over a wide range of steam flow. By setting the steam flow to the ejector at its optimum value, good control can be obtained by regulating a valve opening to atmosphere. Such an installation is illustrated in Figure 588. In low-pressure operations, it is often necessary to use absolute-pressure controllers to obtain consistent results. Absolute-pressure controllers compensate for variations in atmospheric pressure. When centrifugal pumps are used to reduce the pressure, control may be obtained by regulating a valve located in the suction line of the pump, as in Figure 589.

Pneumatic transmission of flow, temperature, pressure, and liquid-level measurements from process locations to a central control board was originally developed to avoid the use of electricity for this purpose in plant areas where explosive atmospheres are possible. A further advantage is the complete isolation from the control board of all process piping containing high pressures or hazardous fluids. A pressure-control system using pneumatic transmission is shown in Figure 590. The indicating-pressure transmitter is located near the high pressure line on the

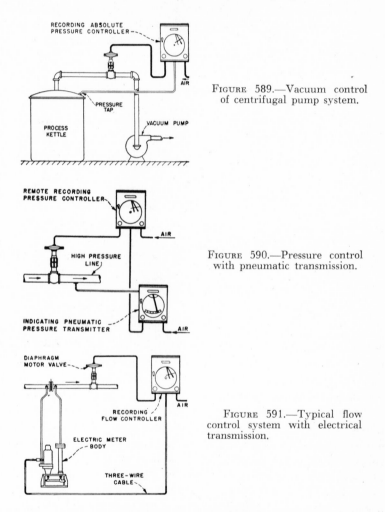

FIGURE 589.—Vacuum control of centrifugal pump system.

FIGURE 590.—Pressure control with pneumatic transmission.

FIGURE 591.—Typical flow control system with electrical transmission.

processing unit and transmits the pressure reading to the recording control instrument which operates the control valve in the pipeline. To reduce lag, a transmitter equipped with control often is used.

Automatic control of flow and liquid level represents the largest field of application for *differential-pressure controllers* in the process industries. Figure 591 is a schematic diagram of a typical flow-control installation in which the controlled valve is located in the flow line. A differential mercury manometer connected across the orifice transmits the movement of its mercury electrically to a recording control instrument which, in turn, operates the valve in the flow line to maintain a constant differential pressure across the orifice and consequently a uniform rate of flow in the pipe.

Figure 592 illustrates the application of a differential-pressure control

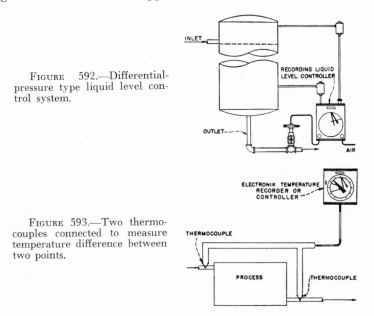

FIGURE 592.—Differential-pressure type liquid level control system.

FIGURE 593.—Two thermocouples connected to measure temperature difference between two points.

to maintain automatically the *level in a closed vessel under pressure.* Instruments of this type can be adjusted to hold the level within close limits, but this is not always desirable. For example, the level in an accumulator tank is not important until the tank is quite full or almost empty. For such applications, the controller can be adjusted to permit the level to change between wide limits, and where these limits are reached, the discharge valve will move to make large changes in the rate of discharge to prevent the tank from filling or becoming empty.

There are occasions when it is desirable to *record or control the difference in temperature between two points* in a process or to control one temperature at a fixed difference with respect to another. This can be accomplished by using two thermocouples connected differentially to a potentiometer. The temperature difference across heat exchangers, compressors, or centrifugal pumps, or between the heating jacket and column on adiabatic laboratory stills are but a few applications for this arrangement. A diagram of such an application is shown in Figure 593.

Heat exchangers are used to heat or cool, with heat conservation as a possible dividend. The temperature of the fluid being heated or cooled can be controlled automatically by regulating the rate of flow of the fluid through the exchanger by means of a temperature controller responsive to the outlet temperature. If it is not feasible to put a control valve in this line, it may be placed in the line of the heating or cooling fluid, but the control may not be so close with the valve in this location because of the increased time required for the effect of a change in flow rate to be felt by the control instrument.

Figure 594 shows a heat exchanger in which hot oil is being cooled to a constant lower temperature by water. For the purpose of water conservation and control stabilization, the outlet-water temperature is controlled by an inexpensive nonindicating controller which regulates the flow of water through the exchanger. The oil-temperature controller operates a three-way valve which divides the oil flow into two parts; one

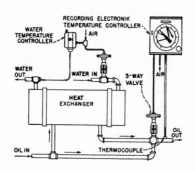

FIGURE 594.—Heat exchanger control system employing control of outlet oil temperature, with auxiliary control of cooling water.

part goes through the heat exchanger, and the other part by-passes the heat exchanger. The part that goes through the exchanger is cooled below the desired final temperature. Upon leaving the exchanger, the cooled oil is mixed with the hot oil by-passed around the exchanger. Thus, the temperature controller blends hot oil and cold oil to obtain oil at the desired temperature. In this system, a change in valve position is felt very quickly by the temperature controller, and only a controller that will respond quickly should be used.

In some cases, a liquid is heated by steam in a heat exchanger. If the exchanger has excess capacity, a pressure controller can be used to regulate the flow of steam, and the final temperature of the liquid also can be recorded on the same chart.

Dowtherm vapor is used as a high-temperature heating medium in many of the process industries. Figure 595 is a diagram of an automatic-control system applied to an oil-fired Dowtherm vaporizer. A pressure controller responsive to the outlet pressure of the vaporizer regulates the flow of oil and air to the burner. A photo-electric flame detector and pressure switches in the air and oil lines are safety devices which open the circuit of the solenoid valve to shut off the oil supply and sound an alarm when the air pressure is too low, when the oil pressure is too low, or if the flame goes out. On electrically heated Dowtherm vaporizers, the pressure controller can be used to operate a switch to open and close the circuit to the heating elements or to operate the slider on a potential divider, as shown previously for the control of electric heating elements by means of saturable reactors.

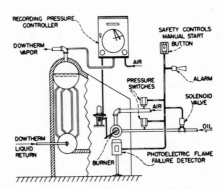

FIGURE 595.—Control system for oil-fired Dowtherm vaporizer.

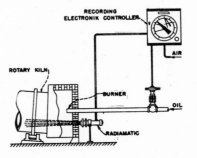

FIGURE 596.—Temperature control system for oil-fired rotary kiln.

Kilns used for drying may be automatically controlled in response to the temperature of the exit material. The material dried in kilns is usually in the form of small particles so that a stationary thermocouple can be placed in the stream of material leaving the kiln. Care should be taken so that the thermocouple will respond to changes in temperature of the material and not be affected by air currents.

Figure 596 is a *kiln-control system* in which the oil burner is regulated from an instrument connected to a radiation pyrometer sighted on the material in the kiln or leaving the kiln.

Dust is a problem around most kilns, and the air-cooled fitting not only cools the radiation heat, but prevents dust from depositing on the lens. The location of the radiation pyrometer should be selected so that the line of sight does not include any part of the flame.

When the *rate of drying* is to be controlled, wet- and dry-bulb measurements of the air prior to its contact with the material are desirable. If the wet and dry bulbs are located in the air stream leaving the materials, a measure of the moisture from the material is obtained. The rate of drying may be accelerated by introduction of fresh air and retarded by introduction of water vapor. It should be borne in mind that, when applying control equipment to driers, moisture removed is carried away in the exit air; the distribution of air in the drier is important from the standpoint of uniform drying. The air velocity across the wet bulb should be at least 10 feet per sec to ensure sufficient evaporation.

Use of hair elements for direct measurement of relative humidity is restricted to temperatures below 40°C; also, they should be used only in

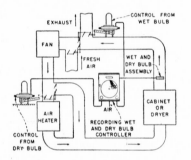

FIGURE 597.—Humidity control system for recirculating drier.

clean atmospheres because grease and dust close the pores of the hair, making it slow to respond to moisture changes.

Thermocouples, particularly pencil-type couples, can be used satisfactorily for wet-bulb measurements. The wet bulb should be sufficiently long to preclude erroneous readings due to heat conduction to the hot junction of the thermocouple. When relative humidities above 90 per cent are involved, careful consideration should be given to the sensitivity and accuracy of the instruments because the wet- and dry-bulb temperatures approach the same value at 100 per cent.

Figure 597 shows a wet- and dry-bulb-control installation on a *recirculating drier*. The sensitive elements are located in the air leaving the drier. The dry bulb controls dampers either to direct air through the heater or to by-pass it around the heater. The wet bulb controls admission of fresh and release of moisture-laden air by means of a three-way damper.

Reading References

See Chapters 25 and 26.

APPENDIX

1 meter = 39.37 inches.

1 foot = 304.80 millimeters.

1 inch = 25.40 millimeters.

1 pound avoirdupois = 453.6 grams = 7000 grains.

1 gram = 15.438 grains a.d.p. and Troy

1 cubic foot = 28.315 liters; 1 cubic foot of water at 62°F weighs 62.321 pounds.

1 cubic foot contains 7.48 gallons (U. S.); 1 cubic meter = 35.3166 cu. ft.

1 gallon (U. S.) of water weighs 8.33 pounds.

1 gallon (U. S.) = 3.78 liters

1 gallon (English) of water weighs 10.0 pounds

1 kilometer = 0.6214 mile.

1 gross ton = 1 long ton = 2200 pounds.

1 short ton = 1 net ton = 2000 pounds.

1 metric ton = 1000 kilograms = 2205 pounds.

1 square meter = 10.7631 square feet.

1 ounce avoirdupois = 28.35 grams.

= 437.5 grains.

1 gram mole of gas at S.T.P.

= 22.4 liters = 0.791 cubic foot

$1 \mu = 10^{-6}$ meter = 10^{-4} centimeter.

= 10^{-3} millimeter.

$1 \, m\mu = 10^{-6}$ millimeter = 10 A.U.

Pressure on air, produced by fan and blower action.

1 ounce = 0.1276 inch mercury at 62°F = 1.732 inches water at 62°F.

16 ounces pressure = 1 pound pressure = 27.71 inches water at 62°F.

1 atmosphere (standard) = 14.7 psi = 30 inches mercury at 62°F = 29.92 inches mercury at 32°F = 33.947 feet water at 62°F.

Inch of mercury (at 32°F) × 1.133 gives feet of water (60°F).

Inch of mercury (at 32°F) × 0.4912 gives pounds per square inch.

Foot of water (at 60°F) × 0.4331 gives pounds per square inch.

Pound per square inch × 2.309 gives feet of water (at 60°F).

To change centigrade degrees to Fahrenheit degrees, multiply by ⅘ and add 32.

The British Thermal Unit (Btu.) is the quantity of heat necessary to raise 1 pound of water 1°F from 60 to 61°; it also equals 777.52 foot-pounds.

The large Calorie, also called the kilogram calorie (Cal), is the amount of heat necessary to raise 1 kilogram of water 1°C from 17 to 18°.

1 Cal = 3.968 Btu. 970 Btu. are required to vaporize 1 pound of water at 212°F to steam at 212°F.

The specific heat of water is 1.

Latent heat of ice = 144 Btu. per pound.

1 ton refrigeration = 200 Btu. per minute, also 288,000 Btu. per 24 hours.

---

1 cubic foot of dry air at standard barometric pressure and at 60°F weighs 0.07640 pound; at 100°F, 0.07093 pound.

In a cubic foot of saturated air, at standard atm. pressure, at 60°F, the dry air it contains weighs 0.07506 pound, the water vapor it contains weighs 0.000829 pound.

54.00 cubic feet of saturated air (at S.T. and P.) are warmed 1°F per Btu. absorbed; 1 cubic foot of saturated air absorbs 0.01852 Btu. per °F.

---

1 horsepower = 0.7457 kilowatt.

1 kilowatt = 1.341 horsepower.

Horsepower and kilowatts require a time factor to mean a quantity of power.

1 horsepower-hour = 0.7457 kilowatt-hour.
1 horsepower-second = 550 foot-pounds.

---

1 volt times 1 ampere equals 1 watt.
1000 watts equal 1 kilowatt.
1 ampere-second deposits 0.001118 gram of silver.

The number called pH is a negative exponent of 10; 10 with that exponent, times 1, gives the amount of hydrogen ions, in grams, in 1 liter of the solution. The range is from 0 to 14.0, 7.0 being the neutral point.

TABLE OF THE MORE IMPORTANT CHEMICAL ELEMENTS WITH THEIR SYMBOLS AND
ATOMIC WEIGHTS

From the International Table of Atomic Weights (1950)

Aluminum	Al	26.97	Manganese	Mn	54.93
Antimony	Sb	121.76	Mercury	Hg	200.61
Argon	A	39.944	Molybdenum	Mo	95.95
Arsenic	As	74.91	Neon	Ne	20.183
Barium	Ba	137.36	Nickel	Ni	58.69
Beryllium	Be	9.02	Nitrogen	N	14.008
Bismuth	Bi	209.0	Osmium	Os	190.2
Boron	B	10.82	Oxygen	O	16.000
Bromine	Br	79.916	Palladium	Pd	106.7
Cadmium	Cd	112.41	Phosphorus	P	30.98
Calcium	Ca	40.08	Platinum	Pt	195.23
Carbon	C	12.01	Plutonium	Pu	239.
Cerium	Ce	140.13	Potassium	K	39.096
Cesium	Cs	132.91	Radium	Ra	226.05
Chlorine	Cl	35.457	Radon	Rn	222.
Chromium	Cr	52.01	Rhodium	Rh	102.91
Cobalt	Co	58.94	Rubidium	Rb	85.48
Columbium	Cb	92.91	Selenium	Se	78.96
Copper	Cu	63.57	Silicon	Si	28.06
Fluorine	F	19.0	Silver	Ag	107.880
Gallium	Ga	69.72	Sodium	Na	22.997
Germanium	Ge	72.60	Strontium	Sr	87.63
Gold	Au	197.2	Sulfur	S	32.06
Helium	He	4.003	Tellurium	Te	127.61
Hydrogen	H	1.008	Thorium	Th	232.12
Iodine	I	126.92	Tin	Sn	118.70
Iridium	Ir	193.1	Titanium	Ti	47.90
Iron	Fe	55.85	Tungsten	W	183.92
Krypton	Kr	83.7	Uranium	U	238.07
Lanthanum	La	138.92	Vanadium	V	50.95
Lead	Pb	207.21	Zinc	Zn	65.38
Lithium	Li	6.940	Zirconium	Zr	91.22
Magnesium	Mg	24.32			

STEAM TEMPERATURES (BOILING POINTS) AT LOW PRESSURES; SATURATED STEAM; ASSUMING THE ATMOSPHERIC PRESSURE TO SUPPORT A COLUMN OF 29.922 INCHES OF MERCURY (AT 60°F)

*Vacuum Reading (in Hg)	Boiling Point Temperature of the Steam (°F)	Absolute Pressure (psi)
29.7417	32	0.08854
29.6543	42	0.13150
29.5314	52	0.19182
29.4002	60	0.2563
29.1928	70	0.3631
28.8899	80	0.5069
28.5005	90	0.6982
27.9895	100	0.9492
27.1826	112	1.3504
26.4762	120	1.6924
26.0745	124	1.8897
25.7333	128	2.1064
25.1495	132	2.3440
24.6198	136	2.6042
24.0408	140	2.8886
23.4188	144	3.1990
22.720	148	3.537
21.970	152	3.906
21.155	156	4.306
20.270	160	4.741
17.150	172	6.273
14.631	180	7.510
10.079	192	9.746
6.455	200	11.526
0	212	14.696

* Vacuum reading, as a column of mercury, equal to the differential between the two legs of a U tube, pulled up on one side by the reduced pressure in the vessel, other side under atmospheric pressure.

INDEX

723